Grant$ for Libraries and Information Services

Covers grants in the U.S. and abroad to public, academic, and special libraries, and to archives and information centers for construction, operations, acquisitions, computerization, and education.

The Foundation Center...2001/2002

Cover design: Greg Apicella

ISBN 0-87954-984-X

INTRODUCTION

Grants for Libraries & Information Services lists 2,736 grants of $10,000 or more with a total value of $507,801,886 made by 624 foundations, mostly in 1999 or 2000. It covers grants to public, academic, research, school, and special libraries, and to archives and information centers for construction, operations, equipment, acquisitions, computerization, and library science education. Also included are grants for citizen information and philanthropy information centers.

Grants for Libraries & Information Services is one of 15 topic-oriented publications included in the Foundation Center's *Grant Guide* series (see page xvii for a list of titles in the series). The *Grant Guides* are derived from the Center's grants database, which covers most of the 1,000 largest U.S. foundations. Many of these foundations report their grants directly to the Center by way of paper grant reporting forms, electronic files, newsletters, annual reports, or other grants lists. The *Grant Guides* provide a general overview of foundation giving in a particular field of nonprofit activity.

The grants in the *Grant Guide* series are also listed in *The Foundation Grants Index on CD-ROM*, published this year in its second edition. They will also appear in the November, 2001 monthly update of *The Foundation Directory Online Plus, The Foundation Directory Online Premium,* and *The Foundation Directory Online Platinum.* Research using these products will help the grantseeker determine the overall giving interests of a particular foundation and decide on appropriate foundations to apply to for funding.

BUT REMEMBER: IF YOU DO NOT QUALIFY, DO NOT APPLY.

It is essential to remember that many foundations place limitations on their giving, including subject areas, recipient types, and geographic locations. Finding out about those limitations before submitting proposals will save you time, decrease the number of rejections you receive, and demonstrate to the foundations you target that you know your field. The restrictions to giving under which some foundations operate appear in two places: in the "Grant Listings" section following the foundation name, as well as under their names and addresses in the "List of Foundations" section. If you do not fall within their limitations, do not apply to these foundations. For all foundations, however, it is vitally important that you do further research before applying for funding.

After developing a list of foundations with a funding history in your field, it is imperative that you learn more about each one by consulting additional reference sources. These sources include the annual reports published by over 1,000 foundations; IRS information returns, which are available for all private foundations; entries in the Center's *Foundation Directory* (available in print and on CD-ROM) and *Foundation 1000,* on *FC Search: The Foundation Center's Database on CD-ROM* and on *The Foundation Directory Online, Online Plus, Online Premium,* and *Online Platinum;* the Foundation Center's Web site (http://www.fdncenter.org), which among other features has direct and annotated links to the Web sites of 2,040 grantmakers and 627 nonprofit and government agencies; as well as local directories and resources. These publications plus additional resources are available for free public use at the Center's library reference collections nationwide. A list of such collections is provided in this publication under "The Foundation Center Cooperating Collections," or you can call 1-800-424-9836 for the collection nearest you.

Arrangements and Contents

Within this volume, grants are arranged alphabetically by state, then by foundation name and recipient name within each foundation listing. For each grant you will find the following information: the name, city, and state location (or foreign country location) of the recipient organization; the amount awarded; the fiscal year of grant authorization (or payment); and a description of the activity funded.

Access to the grants is available through three indexes: an index of recipient names; a geographic index (arranged by recipient state, or foreign country location, then recipient name); and an index of subject words. These indexes can be found following the list of grants. References are to grant identification numbers, NOT page numbers.

Statistical tables analyzing overall giving follow this introduction. These tables provide information on the dollar amount and number of grants according to the following breakdowns: foundation name; recipient state (or foreign country); primary subject; type of support (capital, general, research, etc.); recipient type; and population group served. Additionally, a list of the top 15 recipients by highest grant dollar amount and a list of the top 25 foundations awarding grants in this subject area are included with the statistics.

A list of foundation addresses and geographic limitations can be found at the back of this volume.

Research Using *Grants for Libraries & Information Services*

In developing your basic list of potential funding sources, you should scan the grant listings in the category or categories closest to your field. Depending on the nature of your search, you will add to your list of possibilities the names of those foundations whose recent grants seem to indicate a potential interest in your organization or project. You should be looking for foundations that have funded an organization or project like yours, that are located or seem to award grants in your geographic area, and/or that have made grants in dollar amounts similar to the amount you are seeking. If you are new to grantseeking research, read the Center's *Foundation Fundamentals,* and *The Foundation Center's Guide to Grantseeking on the Web.* You can also visit the Learning Lab area of our Web site at fdncenter.org/learn/.

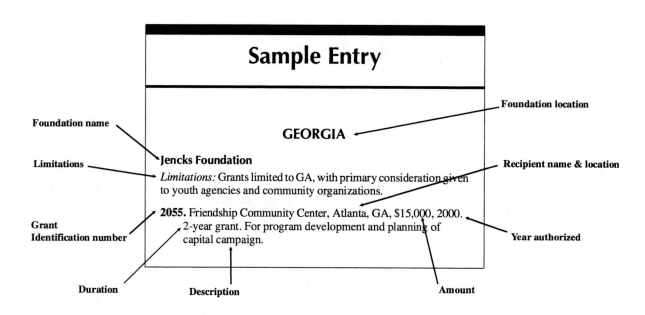

TABLE 1. Grants for libraries & information services by foundation

Foundation	Amount	No.
Abbott Laboratories Fund	$20,000	2
ABC, Inc. Foundation	225,000	2
Abell Foundation, Inc., The	134,615	2
Abell-Hanger Foundation	545,960	12
Abrons Foundation, Inc., Louis and Anne	30,000	1
Achelis Foundation, The	220,000	4
AEGON Transamerica Foundation	10,000	1
Aetna Foundation, Inc.	10,000	1
Ahmanson Foundation, The	2,090,000	21
Alabama Power Foundation, Inc.	20,000	2
Albertson Foundation, Inc., J. A. & Kathryn	184,388	3
Alcoa Foundation	149,733	7
Alden Trust, George I., The	600,000	2
Alkek Foundation, Albert and Margaret	200,000	1
Allstate Foundation, The	25,000	1
Altman Foundation	2,705,000	7
Amado Foundation, Maurice	10,000	1
Amarillo Area Foundation, Inc.	40,357	1
American Express Foundation	230,000	3
Andersen Foundation	83,500	2
Andersen Foundation, Hugh J.	160,000	5
Anderson Foundation, John W.	125,000	1
Anderson Foundation, M. D.	50,000	1
Anheuser-Busch Foundation	345,000	3
Annenberg Foundation, The	6,374,000	13
Aon Foundation	10,000	1
Archer Daniels Midland Foundation	110,000	2
Arison Foundation, Inc.	37,900	1
Arizona Community Foundation	121,876	6
Assisi Foundation of Memphis, Inc., The	310,000	3
AT&T Foundation	846,000	13
Atlantic Foundation of New York, The	7,983,250	3
AXA Foundation, Inc.	175,000	6
Babcock Foundation, Inc., Mary Reynolds	71,000	1
Bader Foundation, Inc., Helen	140,000	3
Baker Foundation, Inc., Pat and Jay	50,000	1
Baker Trust, George F., The	260,000	2
Balfour Foundation, L. G.	113,000	2
Ball Brothers Foundation	60,000	2
Ball Foundation, George and Frances	100,000	1
Bank of America Foundation, Inc.	552,500	22
BANK ONE Foundation	57,500	2
Banyan Tree Foundation	50,000	1
Barker Welfare Foundation, The	87,400	3
Barr Foundation	120,000	2
Barra Foundation, Inc.	632,500	5
Battle Creek Community Foundation	25,000	2
Bayport Foundation, Inc.	95,000	1
Bechtel, Jr. Foundation, Elizabeth and Stephen	100,000	3
Beckman Foundation, Arnold and Mabel	100,000	1
Bedsole Foundation, J. L., The	295,000	4
Benedum Foundation, Claude Worthington	1,133,900	6
Benwood Foundation, Inc.	100,000	1
Berger Foundation, H. N. & Frances C.	250,000	3
Berkshire Taconic Community Foundation	20,000	1
Bettingen Corporation, Burton G.	50,000	1
Beveridge Foundation, Inc., Frank Stanley, The	55,000	1
Bielfeldt Foundation, The	19,601	1
Bigelow Foundation, F. R.	100,000	1
Bishop Foundation, E. K. and Lillian F.	50,000	1
Blandin Foundation, The	50,000	2
Blank Family Foundation, Arthur M., The	363,000	4
Blaustein Foundation, Inc., Jacob and Hilda, The	50,000	1
Blum-Kovler Foundation	22,000	2
Bodman Foundation, The	185,000	4
Boettcher Foundation	165,000	4
Booth Ferris Foundation	140,000	1
Boston Foundation, Inc.	883,086	11
Bovaird Foundation, Mervin, The	347,500	3
BP Amoco Foundation, Inc.	2,760,000	3
Brach Foundation, Helen	20,000	1
Bradley Foundation, Inc., Lynde and Harry, The	807,506	12
Bremer Foundation, Otto	175,000	9
Bridgestone/Firestone Trust Fund	250,000	1
Bristol-Myers Squibb Foundation, Inc., The	20,000	2

TABLE 1. (continued)

Foundation	Amount	No.
Britton Fund	25,000	1
Bronfman Foundation, Inc., Samuel, The	375,000	2
Brown Foundation, Inc., The	4,604,479	14
Bruening Foundation, Eva L. and Joseph M.	175,000	2
Buchanan Family Foundation, The	30,000	2
Buell Foundation, Temple Hoyne	103,000	5
Buffett Foundation, The	25,000	2
Buhl Foundation, The	470,725	6
Bullitt Foundation, The	60,000	2
Burns Foundation, Fritz B.	10,000	1
Burroughs Wellcome Fund	50,000	1
Bush Foundation, The	1,401,355	8
Cabell Foundation, Robert G. Cabell III and Maude Morgan, The	550,000	2
Cafritz Foundation, Morris and Gwendolyn, The	197,500	6
Calder Foundation, Louis, The	887,000	11
California Endowment, The	12,614,405	28
California Wellness Foundation, The	520,000	4
Callaway Family Foundation, Cindy and Ely	10,000	1
Camp Younts Foundation	25,000	1
Cannon Foundation, Inc., The	125,000	4
Capital Group Companies Charitable Foundation, The	193,300	4
Carls Foundation, The	22,200	1
Carnegie Corporation of New York	7,438,700	21
Carolyn Foundation	16,500	1
Carpenter Foundation, E. Rhodes & Leona B.	1,599,311	8
Carter Foundation, Amon G.	77,500	2
Casey Foundation, Annie E., The	3,528,541	23
Castle Foundation, Harold K. L.	50,000	1
Castle Foundation, Samuel N. and Mary	40,000	2
Caterpillar Foundation	12,500	1
CH Foundation, The	48,257	1
Challenge Foundation, The	221,982	9
Champlin Foundations, The	6,671,118	45
Chapman Charitable Trust, H. A. and Mary K.	65,000	2
Chartwell Charitable Foundation	20,000	2
Chatlos Foundation, Inc., The	131,370	5
Cheney Foundation, Ben B.	215,000	6
Chicago Community Trust and Affiliates, The	1,288,980	13
Chicago Tribune Foundation	23,300	2
Chichester duPont Foundation, Inc.	100,000	1
China Medical Board of New York, Inc.	180,000	1
Cincinnati Foundation, Greater, The	10,000	1
Cisco Systems Foundation	25,000	1
Citigroup Foundation	1,321,600	38
Claiborne & Art Ortenberg Foundation, Liz	227,000	1
Claiborne Foundation, Liz	10,120	1
Clark Foundation, The	223,000	3
Clark Foundation, Edna McConnell, The	270,000	3
Clark Foundation, Inc., Robert Sterling	385,000	7
Cleveland Foundation, The	1,835,796	5
Clorox Company Foundation, The	45,000	3
Clowes Fund, Inc., The	25,000	1
Coca-Cola Foundation, Inc., The	165,000	5
Cohen Foundation, Naomi and Nehemiah	535,000	2
Collins Foundation, The	35,000	1
Columbia Foundation	115,000	2
Columbus Foundation and Affiliated Organizations, The	295,000	11
Comer Foundation, The	50,000	1
Commonwealth Fund, The	817,364	7
Communities Foundation of Texas, Inc.	117,961	5
Community Foundation, The	27,200	2
Community Foundation for Greater Atlanta	25,000	2
Community Foundation for Greater Buffalo	18,275	1
Community Foundation for Southeastern Michigan	64,200	1
Community Foundation for the National Capital Region, The	171,637	6
Community Foundation of Greater Birmingham, The	110,200	4
Community Foundation of Greater Lorain County, The	34,000	1
Community Foundation of Greater Memphis	80,000	5
Community Foundation of South Alabama, The	34,150	1

Foundation	Amount	No.
Community Foundation of Western Massachusetts	30,000	1
Community Foundation Serving Richmond & Central Virginia, The	205,000	4
Compton Foundation, Inc.	55,000	3
Connelly Foundation	1,651,235	9
Coors Foundation, Adolph	30,000	3
Cord Foundation, The	87,000	2
Corning Incorporated Foundation	10,000	1
Cowell Foundation, S. H.	85,000	2
Cowles Foundation, Inc., Gardner and Florence Call	150,000	1
Crowell Trust, Henry P. Crowell and Susan C.	165,000	3
Crown Memorial, Arie and Ida	93,333	3
Crystal Trust	190,000	2
Cullman Foundation, Inc., Lewis B. & Dorothy	1,020,000	2
Cummings Foundation, Inc., Nathan, The	75,000	4
Dade Community Foundation, Inc.	11,500	1
DaimlerChrysler Corporation Fund	700,000	4
Dallas Foundation, The	85,940	4
Dana Charitable Trust, Eleanor Naylor	40,000	2
Danforth Foundation, The	108,500	4
Daniel Foundation of Alabama, The	75,000	2
Dater Foundation, Inc., Charles H.	45,000	2
Davis Foundation, Irene E. and George A.	65,000	2
Davis Foundation, Joe C.	525,000	1
Davis Foundations, Arthur Vining, The	648,000	4
DeCamp Foundation, Ira W., The	200,000	2
Deere Foundation, John	125,000	2
Dekko Foundation, Inc.	218,217	7
Delany Charitable Trust, Beatrice P.	50,000	1
Delmas Foundation, Gladys Krieble, The	421,797	14
Denver Foundation, The	70,500	5
Deutsche Bank Americas Foundation	443,000	3
Diamond Fund, Irene	500,000	2
Dibner Fund, Inc., The	1,657,159	4
Dickenson Foundation, Harriet Ford	1,041,000	1
Dillon Foundation	22,857	1
Dillon Fund, The	101,000	4
Disney Company Foundation, Walt, The	50,000	1
Dodge Foundation, Inc., Geraldine R.	350,000	5
Dodge Jones Foundation	128,000	3
Doheny Foundation, Carrie Estelle	30,000	2
Donner Foundation, Inc., William H., The	100,000	1
Dorot Foundation	950,000	3
Dow Chemical Company Foundation	203,902	2
Dow Foundation, Herbert H. and Grace A., The	40,000	1
Drown Foundation, Joseph	110,000	2
Duke Charitable Foundation, Doris	4,215,000	4
Duke Endowment, The	12,693,941	10
Duke Energy Foundation	30,000	2
Durham Foundation	1,000,000	1
Dyson Foundation	2,062,188	4
Earhart Foundation	10,000	1
Eastman Kodak Charitable Trust	200,000	1
Eberly Foundation, The	97,000	2
Eccles Foundation, George S. and Dolores Dore, The	840,000	6
Eden Hall Foundation	175,000	2
Educational Foundation of America, The	130,000	2
El Pomar Foundation	132,000	2
Emerson Charitable Trust	65,000	3
Emerson Foundation, Inc., Fred L.	350,000	3
Energy Foundation	150,000	2
Engelhard Foundation, Charles, The	247,000	3
English-Bonter-Mitchell Foundation	20,000	1
ExxonMobil Foundation	80,000	5
Fairchild Foundation, Inc., Sherman, The	75,000	2
Fannie Mae Foundation	839,200	24
Fidelity Foundation	110,000	4
Fikes Foundation, Inc., Leland	50,000	1
First Union Foundation, The	55,000	3
Firstar Foundation, Inc.	75,000	4
FirstEnergy Foundation	35,000	1
Fleck Foundation	10,000	1
FleetBoston Financial Foundation	127,200	6

TABLE 1. (continued)

Foundation	Amount	No.
Fluor Foundation, The	25,000	1
Fondren Foundation, The	1,550,000	3
Ford Family Foundation, The	242,500	4
Ford Foundation, The	14,217,079	97
Ford Motor Company Fund	215,000	5
Foundation for Child Development	240,000	5
Foundation for Deep Ecology	30,000	2
Foundation For The Carolinas	337,691	4
France-Merrick Foundation	127,000	3
Freddie Mac Foundation	2,964,808	11
Freedom Forum, Inc.	252,500	5
Freeman Foundation, The	6,331,460	5
Fremont Area Community Foundation, The	1,295,972	14
Frey Foundation	370,770	4
Frist Foundation, The	475,000	3
Frueauff Foundation, Inc., Charles A.	90,000	3
Fry Foundation, Lloyd A.	35,000	2
Fuller Foundation, George F. and Sybil H.	300,000	2
Fund for New Jersey, The	115,000	2
Gannett Foundation, Inc.	36,000	2
Garland Foundation, John Jewett & H. Chandler	1,055,000	5
Gates Family Foundation	84,300	3
Gates Foundation, Bill & Melinda	75,692,257	54
GE Fund	45,000	3
Gebbie Foundation, Inc.	210,137	6
Geffen Foundation, David, The	410,000	3
General Mills Foundation	99,800	7
General Service Foundation	115,000	4
Getty Foundation, Ann and Gordon, The	10,000	1
Getty Trust, J. Paul	1,922,860	22
Gheens Foundation, Inc., The	17,000	1
Gilder Foundation, Inc.	5,284,671	3
Gill Foundation, The	72,000	4
Gilmore Foundation, Irving S.	60,000	2
Goergen Foundation, Inc., The	28,825	2
Goldman Fund, Richard & Rhoda	964,000	14
Goldseker Foundation of Maryland, Inc., Morris	326,000	4
Goldsmith Foundation, Horace W.	3,205,000	13
Gottesman Fund, The	122,000	3
Gould Foundation, Florence, The	589,800	6
Grable Foundation	200,000	2
Graham Fund, Philip L.	40,000	2
Grand Rapids Community Foundation	15,000	1
Grant Foundation, William T.	865,460	5
Graustein Memorial Fund, William Caspar	241,750	4
Green Fund, Inc., The	12,500	1
Greenwall Foundation, The	40,000	3
Grousbeck Family Foundation, The	180,000	3
Guenther Foundation, Henry L.	25,000	1
Gund Foundation, Agnes, The	75,000	3
Gund Foundation, George, The	444,000	5
H & R Block Foundation, The	33,750	2
Haas Fund, Walter and Elise	95,000	3
Haas, Jr. Fund, Evelyn and Walter	291,000	9
Hagedorn Fund	25,000	1
Hall Family Foundation	3,020,000	2
Hallmark Corporate Foundation	40,000	1
Halsell Foundation, Ewing, The	110,000	2
Harden Foundation	30,000	3
Harland Charitable Foundation, Inc., John H. and Wilhelmina D.	12,500	1
Harriman Foundation, Gladys and Roland	50,000	2
Hartford Foundation, Inc., John A., The	606,054	1
Hartford Foundation for Public Giving	885,000	6
Hayden Foundation, Charles	160,000	2
Haynes Foundation, John Randolph Haynes and Dora, The	57,950	2
Healthcare Foundation of New Jersey, The	45,500	2
Hearst Foundation, Inc., The	290,000	5
Hearst Foundation, William Randolph	2,525,000	6
Hedco Foundation	56,016	1
Heinz Endowment, Howard	1,225,000	4
Heinz Endowment, Vira I.	480,000	7
Heinz Family Foundation	80,250	3
Heinz Trust, Drue	86,333	4
Helmerich Foundation, The	120,000	3
Heron Foundation, F. B., The	60,000	1

TABLE 1. (continued)

Foundation	Amount	No.
Herrick Foundation	1,200,000	3
Hewlett Foundation, William and Flora, The	2,260,000	8
Highland Street Connection, The	10,000	1
Hillcrest Foundation	320,000	6
Hillman Foundation, Inc., The	2,550,000	2
Hobby Family Foundation	100,000	1
Hoblitzelle Foundation	500,000	1
Hollis Foundation, Inc., William M. & Nina B.	10,000	1
Honeywell Foundation	50,000	1
Honeywell International Foundation	10,000	1
Hoover Foundation, The	815,000	3
Houston Endowment Inc.	5,935,000	7
HRK Foundation	30,650	1
Hubbard Foundation, The	53,000	1
Hudson-Webber Foundation	84,000	1
Humana Foundation, Inc., The	30,000	2
Hume Foundation, Jaquelin	35,000	2
Huntsman Foundation, Jon and Karen, The	1,100,000	2
Hyams Foundation, Inc., The	37,500	2
Hyde and Watson Foundation, The	45,000	3
Illinois Tool Works Foundation	60,000	2
Independence Foundation	150,000	4
Institute for Aegean Prehistory, The	173,594	2
Intel Foundation	69,230	1
International Paper Company Foundation	35,000	2
Iowa West Foundation	55,000	2
Irvine Foundation, James, The	5,965,000	11
Janirve Foundation	460,000	2
Jeld-Wen Foundation, The	102,000	3
Jennings Foundation, Mary Hillman, The	45,000	2
Jerome Foundation	25,000	1
Jesselson Foundation	39,375	3
JM Foundation, The	15,000	1
Johnson Controls Foundation	20,000	1
Johnson Endeavor Foundation, Christian A.	125,000	2
Johnson Foundation, Helen K. and Arthur E.	70,000	3
Johnson Foundation, Robert Wood, The	17,838,003	15
Johnston Trust for Charitable and Educational Purposes, James M., The	25,000	1
Jones Foundation, Fletcher, The	1,425,000	5
Jones Foundation, Inc., W. Alton	790,000	7
Joukowsky Family Foundation	10,000	1
Joyce Foundation, The	2,119,060	8
Kaiser Family Foundation, Henry J., The	45,000	1
Kansas City Community Foundation and Affiliated Trusts, Greater, The	328,810	5
Kansas Health Foundation	929,224	7
Kaplan Fund, Inc., J. M., The	1,090,000	7
Kauffman Foundation, Ewing Marion	904,179	12
Kauffman Foundation, Muriel McBrien	50,000	1
Kellogg Foundation, W. K.	1,608,582	9
Kellogg's Corporate Citizenship Fund	10,000	1
Kemper Foundation, William T.	92,500	3
Kenan, Jr. Charitable Trust, William R.	124,000	2
Kendall Foundation, Henry P., The	10,000	1
Kiewit Foundation, Peter	273,000	4
Kimmel Foundation, Sidney, The	275,000	2
King Foundation, Inc., Stephen and Tabitha	312,000	7
Kirby Foundation, Inc., F. M.	107,500	4
Klingenstein Fund, Inc., Esther A. & Joseph, The	533,350	3
Kluge Foundation, John W., The	2,400,000	2
Knight Foundation, John S. and James L.	2,306,000	22
Koch Charitable Foundation, David H.	15,000	1
Koch Foundation, Inc.	31,000	2
Koret Foundation	284,455	3
Kresge Foundation, The	5,300,000	8
Kress Foundation, Samuel H.	133,000	7
Kronkosky Charitable Foundation, Albert & Bessie Mae	1,899,616	17
Lannan Foundation	51,710	2
Lattner Foundation, Inc., Forrest C.	71,000	2
Laurel Foundation	70,000	2
Lebensfeld Foundation, The	92,000	5
Lee Foundation, Sara	157,500	5
Libra Foundation	185,000	7
Lied Foundation Trust	5,000,000	1
Lilly Endowment Inc.	9,290,320	8

TABLE 1. (continued)

Foundation	Amount	No.
Lincy Foundation, The	10,000	1
Link, Jr. Foundation, Inc., George	25,000	1
List Foundation, Inc., Albert A.	75,000	4
Littauer Foundation, Inc., Lucius N., The	31,000	3
Lockheed Martin Corporation Foundation	10,000	1
Longwood Foundation, Inc.	1,520,000	5
Lounsbery Foundation, Inc., Richard	235,000	2
Lowenstein Foundation, Inc., Leon	260,000	1
Luce Foundation, Inc., Henry, The	2,970,000	8
Lucent Technologies Foundation	10,000	1
Lyndhurst Foundation	15,000	1
MacArthur Foundation, John D. and Catherine T.	1,901,000	8
Macy, Jr. Foundation, Josiah	86,000	3
M&T Charitable Foundation	10,000	1
Mardag Foundation	15,000	1
Marin Community Foundation	630,422	11
Markle Foundation, John and Mary R., The	10,000	1
Mathers Charitable Foundation, G. Harold & Leila Y.	20,000	1
Mattel Children's Foundation	53,000	1
May Department Stores Company Foundation, Inc., The	1,298,745	2
Maytag Corporation Foundation	43,000	2
McBeath Foundation, Faye	40,000	2
McCabe Foundation, B. C.	62,500	1
McCasland Foundation	10,000	1
McCormick Tribune Foundation, Robert R.	1,172,500	16
McCune Charitable Foundation	67,000	5
McCune Charitable Trust, John R.	30,000	1
McCune Foundation	375,000	3
McDermott Foundation, Eugene, The	1,625,000	3
McElroy Trust, R. J.	260,000	4
McGovern Foundation, John P.	640,000	12
McGovern Fund	770,000	5
McGowan Charitable Fund, William G.	250,000	1
McGregor Fund	120,000	3
McKnight Foundation, The	199,000	4
McNair Foundation, Robert and Janice, The	259,179	3
Meadows Foundation, Inc., The	1,110,075	11
Medtronic Foundation, The	175,000	4
Mellon Foundation, Andrew W., The	34,291,400	76
Mellon Foundation, Richard King	3,025,000	5
Merck Company Foundation, The	90,000	4
Merck Fund, John, The	215,000	6
Merrill Lynch & Co. Foundation, Inc.	25,000	1
Mertz-Gilmore Foundation, Joyce	125,000	3
Metropolitan Life Foundation	297,500	3
Meyer Foundation, Eugene and Agnes E.	84,500	3
Meyer Memorial Trust	1,890,668	11
Milstein Foundation, Paul and Irma	3,000,000	1
Milwaukee Foundation, Greater	322,000	3
Minneapolis Foundation, The	217,275	3
Monell Foundation, Ambrose, The	510,000	7
Moore Family Foundation	125,000	2
Morgan Chase Foundation, J. P., The	340,000	9
Moriah Fund	265,000	11
Motorola Foundation	20,000	1
Mott Foundation, Charles Stewart	5,193,583	48
Murdock Charitable Trust, M. J.	2,350,000	3
Murphy Foundation, John P.	30,000	2
Murphy Foundation, Katherine John	25,000	1
Nationwide Foundation	12,713	1
NCC Charitable Foundation II	70,500	5
New York Community Trust, The	340,000	8
New York Foundation	60,000	2
New York Times Company Foundation, Inc., The	215,000	9
Newhouse Foundation, Inc., Samuel I.	469,500	5
Noble Foundation, Inc., Samuel Roberts, The	30,000	1
Nord Family Foundation, The	171,071	3
Nordson Corporation Foundation, The	10,000	1
Norfolk Foundation, The	66,744	1
Norris Foundation, Kenneth T. and Eileen L., The	470,000	6
Northern Trust Company Charitable Trust, The	25,000	1
Northwest Area Foundation	15,000	1
Northwestern Mutual Foundation	30,000	1

Foundation	Amount	No.
Noyes Foundation, Inc., Jessie Smith	315,000	9
Oakleaf Foundation	15,000	1
Offield Family Foundation, The	60,000	2
Ohrstrom Foundation, Inc., The	311,000	1
Olin Foundation, Inc., F. W.	318,463	1
Olin Foundation, Inc., John M.	50,000	1
Olive Bridge Fund, Inc.	17,000	1
Omaha Community Foundation	54,351	3
ONDEO Nalco Foundation, The	10,000	1
Open Society Institute	2,094,961	28
Oregon Community Foundation, The	1,051,242	11
Osher Foundation, Bernard	100,000	1
Overbrook Foundation, The	500,000	1
Packard Foundation, David and Lucile, The	10,315,532	37
Park Foundation, Inc.	310,000	4
Parsons Foundation, Mary Morton, The	250,000	3
Parsons Foundation, Ralph M., The	583,600	6
Pasadena Foundation	12,000	1
Payne Foundation, Frank E. Payne and Seba B.	88,000	1
Peabody Charitable Fund, Amelia	850,800	4
Peabody Foundation, Amelia	200,000	2
Peninsula Community Foundation	369,980	12
Penn Foundation, William, The	2,945,814	12
PepsiCo Foundation, Inc., The	142,750	3
Peterson Foundation, Hal & Charlie	155,326	2
Pettit Foundation, Jane Bradley	20,000	1
Pew Charitable Trusts, The	11,923,000	36
Pforzheimer Foundation, Inc., Carl and Lily, The	88,361	1
Pharmacia Foundation, Inc.	10,000	1
Philadelphia Foundation, The	99,000	5
Phillips Family Foundation, Jay and Rose, The	81,000	3
Phipps Foundation, Howard	35,000	2
Picower Foundation, The	10,000	1
Pincus Family Fund, The	100,000	1
Pinkerton Foundation, The	132,400	3
Pittsburgh Foundation, The	544,773	8
Plough Foundation	230,000	2
PNC Foundation, The	50,000	2
Polk Bros. Foundation, Inc.	75,000	4
PPG Industries Foundation	50,000	3
Pritzker Foundation	2,275,000	3
Procter & Gamble Fund, The	50,000	1
Prospect Hill Foundation, Inc., The	105,000	4
Prudential Foundation, The	1,000,000	1
Public Welfare Foundation, Inc.	368,500	10
Publix Super Markets Charities	50,000	1
Qwest Foundation	85,500	6
Ralphs-Food 4 Less Foundation, The	10,000	1
Rapoport Foundation, Bernard and Audre	64,714	3
Raskob Foundation for Catholic Activities, Inc.	12,000	1
Reader's Digest Foundation	756,000	3
Reiman Charitable Foundation, Inc.	43,000	3
Reliant Energy Foundation	11,265	1
Retirement Research Foundation, The	94,820	4
Reynolds Charitable Trust, Kate B.	16,570	1
Reynolds Foundation, Donald W.	7,839,294	12
Reynolds Foundation, Inc., Z. Smith	195,000	8
Rhode Island Foundation, The	210,346	6
Richardson Foundation, Sid W.	116,400	2
Richardson Foundation, Inc., Smith	80,000	2
Righteous Persons Foundation	172,000	3
Rippel Foundation, Fannie E.	32,000	1
Robins Foundation	25,000	1
Rockefeller Brothers Fund, Inc.	235,000	4
Rockefeller Foundation, The	3,190,807	37
Rockefeller Foundation, Winthrop, The	63,707	3
Rockwell Fund, Inc.	80,000	4
Rockwell International Corporation Trust	10,000	1
Rogers Foundation, Mary Stuart	1,000,000	1
Rose Foundation, Frederick P. & Sandra P.	3,062,040	4
Rose Fund, Inc., Daniel and Joanna S.	35,000	2
Rosenberg Foundation	18,000	1
Ross Family Charitable Foundation	100,000	2
Rubinstein Foundation, Inc., Helena	80,000	3

TABLE 1.   (continued)

Foundation	Amount	No.
Rudin Family Foundation, Inc., May and Samuel	160,000	5
Saint Paul Foundation, Inc., The	443,000	10
Samuels Foundation, Inc., Fan Fox and Leslie R., The	344,700	7
San Diego Foundation, The	534,145	3
San Francisco Foundation, The	217,100	11
Santa Barbara Foundation	55,000	3
Sarkeys Foundation	275,000	2
SBC Foundation	2,505,000	26
Scaife Foundation, Inc., Sarah	100,000	1
Scherman Foundation, Inc., The	415,000	3
Scheuer Family Foundation, Inc., S. H. and Helen R.	30,000	2
Schmidlapp Trust No. 1 and No. 2, Jacob G.	50,000	1
Schmidt Family Foundation	15,000	1
Scholl Foundation, Dr.	140,000	5
Schumann Fund for New Jersey, Inc., The	19,500	1
Schusterman Family Foundation, Charles and Lynn	35,000	3
Schwab Corporation Foundation, Charles, The	37,000	3
Schwab Foundation, Charles and Helen	29,000	1
Scripps Howard Foundation	20,000	2
Seattle Foundation, The	508,019	12
Selby Foundation, William G. Selby and Marie	14,650	1
Self Family Foundation, The	10,000	1
Sharp Foundation, Peter Jay, The	600,000	1
Sheldon Foundation, Inc., Ralph C.	91,580	3
Shell Oil Company Foundation	190,000	6
Shubert Foundation, Inc., The	40,000	2
Siebert Lutheran Foundation, Inc.	25,000	1
Sierra Health Foundation	25,000	1
Simmons Family Foundation, R. P.	150,000	1
Skillman Foundation, The	5,380,000	3
Skirball Foundation	200,000	1
Sloan Foundation, Alfred P.	1,760,000	10
Smart Family Foundation	370,000	2
Smith Foundation, Kelvin and Eleanor, The	2,195,000	1
Spangler Foundation, Inc., C. D.	25,000	1
Spencer Foundation, The	102,820	4
St. Paul Companies, Inc. Foundation, The	146,036	5
Stanley Foundation, Theodore & Vada	50,000	1
Stark Community Foundation, Inc.	448,934	5
Starr Foundation, The	4,991,000	17
State Farm Companies Foundation	10,000	1
State Street Foundation	45,000	2
Steelcase Foundation	75,000	2
Steele Foundation, Inc., The	10,000	1
Steinberg Charitable Trust, Harold & Mimi, The	10,000	1
Steinhardt Foundation, Judy and Michael, The	45,000	3
Stewardship Foundation, The	165,000	4
Stewart Education Foundation	25,000	1
Stiftung Trust, Silva Casa	193,280	2
Straus Foundation, Inc., Philip A. and Lynn, The	1,510,000	2
Strauss Foundation, Levi	775,000	8
Stuart Foundation	770,702	4
Sturgis Charitable and Educational Trust, Roy and Christine	50,000	2
Surdna Foundation, Inc.	820,000	7
Taper Foundation, S. Mark	90,000	1
Target Foundation	140,000	4
Teagle Foundation, Inc., The	275,000	2
Temple Foundation, T. L. L.	895,256	10
Temple-Inland Foundation	29,620	1
Templeton Foundation, John	269,155	3
Tenet Healthcare Foundation	100,000	6
Thaw Charitable Trust, Eugene V. & Clare E.	5,100,000	6
Times Mirror Foundation, The	25,000	2
Timken Foundation of Canton	75,000	3
Tinker Foundation Inc., The	142,500	2
Tisch Foundation, Inc.	1,085,000	4
Town Creek Foundation, Inc.	40,000	2
Tremaine Foundation, Inc., Emily Hall	158,000	1
Trexler Trust, Harry C.	221,000	2
Trust for Mutual Understanding, The	125,000	6
TRW Foundation	25,000	1

TABLE 1. (continued)

Foundation	Amount	No.
Turner Foundation, Inc.	615,000	8
Turrell Fund	401,500	10
Union Pacific Foundation	69,000	4
United States-Japan Foundation	132,000	1
UPS Foundation, The	60,000	2
USAA Foundation, A Charitable Trust	135,000	2
USX Foundation, Inc.	20,000	1
Valley Foundation, The	85,000	3
Valley Foundation, Wayne & Gladys	1,197,085	5
van Ameringen Foundation, H.	25,000	1
Verizon Foundation	184,425	11
Victoria Foundation, Inc.	237,500	3
Wachovia Foundation, Inc., The	75,000	2
Wal-Mart Foundation	35,000	2
Wallace Genetic Foundation, Inc.	105,000	4
Wallace-Readers Digest Funds	700,000	3
Wallis Foundation	10,000	1
Washington Mutual Foundation	260,000	2
Wasserman Foundation	310,000	4
Watson Foundation, Thomas J., The	30,000	2
Wean Foundation, Raymond John, The	260,000	3
Weinberg Foundation, Inc., Harry and Jeanette, The	35,000	2
Weingart Foundation	335,000	6
Welfare Foundation, Inc.	395,000	4
Wells Fargo Foundation, The	70,454	4
WEM Foundation	600,000	1
Wendt Foundation, Margaret L., The	326,700	2
Weyerhaeuser Company Foundation	38,000	1
Whirlpool Foundation	10,000	1
Whitaker Foundation, The	30,000	3
Whitaker Fund, Helen F., The	96,871	2
Whitehead Foundation, The	195,000	6
Wiegand Foundation, E. L.	281,945	3
Wilson Fund, Matilda R.	25,000	1
Winston Foundation, Inc., Norman and Rosita, The	85,000	4
Wisconsin Energy Corporation Foundation, Inc.	25,000	1
Wolfe Associates, Inc.	90,000	3
Wood-Claeyssens Foundation	10,000	1
Woodruff Foundation, Inc., Robert W.	3,100,000	4
WPWR-TV Channel 50 Foundation	27,500	2
Zellerbach Family Fund, The	78,000	4
Total	**$507,801,886**	**2,736**

TABLE 2. Grants for libraries & information services by recipient location

Recipient location	Amount	No.
Alabama	$504,350	11
Arizona	3,149,897	21
Arkansas	8,749,001	11
Austria	117,637	1
Azerbaijan	29,646	2
Belarus	40,000	1
Belgium	104,536	4
Botswana	67,000	1
Brazil	180,000	1
Bulgaria	118,154	2
California	55,584,599	366
Canada	8,018,385	17
Chile	7,856,000	3
China	301,107	5
Colorado	2,435,400	40
Connecticut	3,095,250	30
Costa Rica	40,000	1
Czech Republic	135,000	2
Delaware	2,110,000	11
Denmark	45,000	1
District of Columbia	34,831,952	181
Egypt	40,000	1
England	10,801,412	56
Estonia	25,000	1
Finland	1,050,000	2
Florida	1,410,436	29
France	1,153,947	8
Georgia	14,438,605	25
Germany	323,000	2
Ghana	395,077	3
Greece	173,594	2
Hawaii	50,000	3
Honduras	95,000	1
Hong Kong	100,000	1
Hungary	100,000	1
Idaho	1,269,286	4
Illinois	12,414,548	100
India	231,000	2
Indiana	1,603,146	24
Indonesia	628,300	4
Iowa	703,422	16
Israel	180,000	3
Italy	151,267	5
Jamaica	10,000	1
Japan	130,000	2
Kansas	2,409,582	20
Kentucky	112,500	5
Kenya	1,253,422	8
Latvia	60,000	3
Lebanon	150,000	1
Louisiana	64,296	4
Maine	812,000	22
Maryland	2,041,777	32

TABLE 2.   (continued)

Recipient location	Amount	No.
Massachusetts	26,731,839	105
Mexico	1,298,522	11
Michigan	16,640,252	58
Minnesota	8,206,384	62
Mississippi	48,000	2
Missouri	7,311,032	45
Moldova	25,000	1
Montana	977,190	4
Mozambique	450,000	2
Myanmar (Burma)	180,000	1
Namibia	47,000	1
Nebraska	477,550	10
Nevada	5,477,650	10
New Hampshire	10,000	1
New Jersey	5,130,911	42
New Mexico	1,257,690	23
New York	110,252,775	472
New Zealand	40,000	1
Nigeria	145,000	2
North Carolina	18,204,282	37
North Dakota	100,000	2
Ohio	7,681,196	63
Oklahoma	1,062,500	18
Oregon	5,567,644	41
Papua New Guinea	12,000	1
Pennsylvania	26,333,270	154
Peru	26,733	1
Philippines	1,496,400	4
Poland	219,700	2
Puerto Rico	12,713	1
Rhode Island	7,438,464	58
Romania	57,250	1
Russia	2,495,695	21
Senegal	12,119	1
Slovakia	40,000	1
South Africa	3,929,950	13
South Carolina	5,600,000	12
South Dakota	50,000	1
Switzerland	293,280	3
Tennessee	3,234,950	21
Texas	26,457,370	165
Thailand	270,700	2
Utah	3,175,900	14
Uzbekistan	13,648	1
Vermont	5,191,000	6
Vietnam	257,000	2
Virginia	13,408,552	55
Washington	5,594,394	36
West Virginia	229,900	8
Wisconsin	2,560,950	31
Wyoming	29,000	1
Yugoslavia	70,000	1
Zimbabwe	75,000	2
Total	**$507,801,886**	**2,736**

TABLE 3.   Grants for libraries & information services by primary subject

Subject	Amount	%	No.
Animals & wildlife	$524,500	0.1	5
Arts & culture	48,088,594	9.5	253
Civil rights & social action	2,647,500	0.5	29
Community improvement & development	7,726,718	1.5	86
Crime, justice & public protection	6,127,682	1.2	28
Education	312,123,245	61.5	1,330
Employment	1,988,479	0.4	31
Environmental protection	8,348,049	1.6	81
Food, nutrition & agriculture	1,130,000	0.2	11
Health—general & rehabilitative	34,887,383	6.9	159
Health—specific diseases	5,285,807	1.0	38
Housing & shelter	2,019,022	0.4	46
Human services—multipurpose	15,365,202	3.0	193
International affairs, development & peace	9,061,315	1.8	84
Medical research	1,005,000	0.2	6
Membership benefit activities	13,000	0.0	1
Mental health	8,581,870	1.7	28
Philanthropy & voluntarism	17,363,341	3.4	190
Public affairs & government	7,588,959	1.5	53
Recreation & sports	900,000	0.2	2
Religion	2,127,612	0.4	16
Safety & disaster relief	55,000	0.0	2
Science	4,612,959	0.9	11
Social sciences	9,122,649	1.8	36
Youth development	1,108,000	0.2	17
Total	**$507,801,886**	**100.0**	**2,736**

TABLE 4.   Grants for libraries & information services by type of support*

Type of support	Amount	No.
Annual campaigns	$40,940	2
Awards/prizes/competitions	1,280,835	5
Building/renovation	85,812,681	299
Capital campaigns	31,633,253	49
Collections acquisition	19,448,250	78
Collections management/preservation	30,329,006	118
Commissioning new works	20,000	1
Computer systems/equipment	79,298,947	181
Conferences/seminars	4,052,670	57
Continuing support	84,180,070	526
Curriculum development	2,155,554	13
Debt reduction	266,000	3
Electronic media/online services	74,912,295	243
Endowments	22,342,439	36
Equipment	8,296,915	97
Exhibitions	1,116,697	18
Faculty/staff development	70,154,240	88
Fellowships	3,119,600	20
Film/video/radio	3,824,268	19
General support	29,799,870	321
Internships	625,193	12
Land acquisition	210,000	4
Management development	3,160,530	32
Matching or challenge grants	19,150,763	58
Performance/productions	256,710	4
Professorships	2,595,000	4
Program development	121,655,212	865
Program evaluation	2,365,614	14
Publication	19,601,404	92
Research	32,502,247	118
Scholarships	2,862,902	11
Seed money	2,810,022	34
Student aid	795,000	3
Technical assistance	14,688,141	37
Not specified	29,866,297	301

* Grants may be for multiple types of support, and would thereby be counted twice.

TABLE 5. Grants for libraries & information services by recipient type*

Recipient Type	Amount	No.
Animal/Wildlife Agencies	$83,090	2
Arts/Humanities Organizations	44,421,799	198
Churches/Temples	6,209,476	30
Civil Rights Groups	3,548,900	31
Colleges & Universities	100,343,126	264
Community Improvement Organizations	13,891,483	122
Disease-Specific Health Associations	2,013,993	31
Educational Support Agencies	58,365,534	417
Environmental Agencies	7,857,949	76
Ethics Organizations	876,000	3
Government Agencies	63,036,268	76
Graduate Schools	15,288,886	33
Hospitals/Medical Care Facilities	15,206,650	84
Human Service Agencies	34,968,282	360
Information/Public Education Centers	64,614,051	673
International Organizations	10,985,087	82
Junior/Community Colleges	450,000	7
Libraries	155,493,876	1,083
Media Organizations	7,949,335	35
Medical Research Organizations	1,199,408	5
Mental Health Agencies/Hospitals	2,148,816	19
Museums/Historical Societies	37,186,922	180
Performing Arts Groups	4,512,927	17
Philanthropy Organizations	21,078,841	253
Professional Societies & Associations	27,108,799	164
Public Administration Agencies	61,680,419	122
Public/General Health Organizations	30,554,672	144
Public Policy Institutes	3,747,470	32
Recreation Organizations	311,000	1
Reform Organizations	131,000	2
Research Institutes	8,143,933	28
Schools	17,483,435	98
Science Organizations	4,223,574	15
Single Organization Support	33,101,259	267
Social Science Organizations	6,406,878	25
Technical Assistance Centers	22,756,019	103
Volunteer Bureaus	309,420	7
Youth Development Organizations	1,215,000	12

* Grants may support multiple recipient types, and would thereby be counted twice.

TABLE 6. Grants for libraries & information services by population group served*

Population group	Amount	No.
Aging	$5,094,652	41
Alcohol or drug abusers	7,560,400	8
Asians & Pacific Islanders	353,842	7
Blacks	13,105,794	31
Children & youth	50,395,282	355
Crime/abuse victims	2,369,459	18
Disabled	3,384,462	54
Economically disadvantaged	103,813,325	294
Gays or lesbians	282,000	11
Hispanics	1,634,257	19
Homeless	2,167,042	29
Immigrants & refugees	4,316,194	45
Men & boys	2,844,235	10
Migrant workers	190,257	2
Military & veterans	60,000	2
Minorities, general	18,312,935	109
Native Americans	1,229,822	16
Offenders or ex-offenders	1,357,999	8
People with AIDS	2,314,000	26
Single parents	70,000	2
Women & girls	15,395,697	94
Not specified	330,650,583	1,970

* Grants may support multiple population groups, and would thereby be counted twice.

TABLE 7. Top 15 recipients in libraries & information services by single highest grant amount

	Recipient name	Donor	Grant amount	Entry
1.	Duke University	The Duke Endowment, NC	$9,200,000	1989
2.	Union Theological Seminary	Lilly Endowment Inc., IN	8,000,000	738
3.	New York Public Library	The Atlantic Foundation of New York, NY	7,900,000	1224
4.	Philander Smith College	Donald W. Reynolds Foundation, NV	7,839,294	1113
5.	New York, State of	Bill & Melinda Gates Foundation, WA	7,603,773	2663
6.	Biblioteca Nacional de Chile, Direccion de Bibliotecas, Archivos y Museos (DIBAM)	Bill & Melinda Gates Foundation, WA	7,387,000	2633
7.	Texas, State of	Bill & Melinda Gates Foundation, WA	7,108,836	2674
8.	Boston University, School of Public Health	The Robert Wood Johnson Foundation, NJ	6,000,000	1131
9.	North Carolina, State of	Bill & Melinda Gates Foundation, WA	5,801,080	2664
10.	Michigan, State of	Bill & Melinda Gates Foundation, WA	5,508,626	2655
11.	Ministere de la Culture et des Communications du Quebec	Bill & Melinda Gates Foundation, WA	5,471,562	2657
12.	Gilder Lehrman Institute of American History	Gilder Foundation, Inc., NY	5,141,371	1504
13.	Vermont Department of Libraries	The Freeman Foundation, NY	5,000,000	1497
14.	University of Houston-University Park	Houston Endowment Inc., TX	5,000,000	2462
15.	Task Force for Child Survival and Development	The Robert Wood Johnson Foundation, NJ	5,000,000	1142

TABLE 8. Top 25 foundations in libraries & information services

	Foundation	State	Amount	No.
1.	Bill & Melinda Gates Foundation	WA	$75,692,257	54
2.	The Andrew W. Mellon Foundation	NY	34,291,400	76
3.	The Robert Wood Johnson Foundation	NJ	17,838,003	15
4.	The Ford Foundation	NY	14,217,079	97
5.	The Duke Endowment	NC	12,693,941	10
6.	The California Endowment	CA	12,614,405	28
7.	The Pew Charitable Trusts	PA	11,923,000	36
8.	The David and Lucile Packard Foundation	CA	10,315,532	37
9.	Lilly Endowment Inc.	IN	9,290,320	8
10.	The Atlantic Foundation of New York	NY	7,983,250	3
11.	Donald W. Reynolds Foundation	NV	7,839,294	1
12.	Carnegie Corporation of New York	NY	7,438,700	21
13.	The Champlin Foundations	RI	6,671,118	45
14.	The Annenberg Foundation	PA	6,374,000	13
15.	The Freeman Foundation	NY	6,331,460	5
16.	The James Irvine Foundation	CA	5,965,000	11
17.	Houston Endowment Inc.	TX	5,935,000	7
18.	The Skillman Foundation	MI	5,380,000	3
19.	The Kresge Foundation	MI	5,300,000	8
20.	Gilder Foundation, Inc.	NY	5,284,671	3
21.	Charles Stewart Mott Foundation	MI	5,193,583	48
22.	Eugene V. & Clare E. Thaw Charitable Trust	NM	5,100,000	6
23.	Lied Foundation Trust	NV	5,000,000	1
24.	The Starr Foundation	NY	4,991,000	17
25.	The Brown Foundation, Inc.	TX	4,604,479	14
	Total		**$294,267,492**	**567**

FOUNDATION CENTER COOPERATING COLLECTIONS   FREE FUNDING INFORMATION CENTERS

The Foundation Center is an independent national service organization established by foundations to provide an authoritative source of information on foundation and corporate giving. The New York, Washington D.C., Atlanta, Cleveland, and San Francisco reference collections operated by the Foundation Center offer a wide variety of services and comprehensive resources on foundations and grants. Cooperating Collections are libraries, community foundations, and other nonprofit agencies that make accessible a collection of Foundation Center print and electronic publications, as well as a variety of supplementary materials and education programs in areas useful to grantseekers. The collection includes:

FC SEARCH: THE FOUNDATION CENTER'S DATABASE ON CD-ROM
THE FOUNDATION DIRECTORY 1 AND 2, AND SUPPLEMENT
FOUNDATION FUNDAMENTALS
THE FOUNDATION 1000

FOUNDATIONS TODAY SERIES
FOUNDATION GRANTS TO INDIVIDUALS
THE FOUNDATION CENTER'S GUIDE TO GRANTSEEKING ON THE WEB
THE FOUNDATION CENTER'S GUIDE TO PROPOSAL WRITING

GUIDE TO U.S. FOUNDATIONS, THEIR TRUSTEES, OFFICERS, AND DONORS
NATIONAL DIRECTORY OF CORPORATE GIVING
NATIONAL GUIDE TO FUNDING IN. . . . (SERIES)
SECURING YOUR ORGANIZATION'S FUTURE

All five Foundation Center libraries and most Cooperating Collections have *FC: Search: The Foundation Center's Database on CD-ROM* available for public use and all provide Internet access. Increasingly, those seeking information on fundraising and nonprofit management are referring to our Web site (http://www.fdncenter.org) for a wealth of data and advice on grantseeking, including links to foundation IRS information returns (990-PFs). Because the Cooperating Collections vary in their hours, it is recommended that you call the collection in advance of a visit. To check on new locations or current holdings, call toll-free 1-800-424-9836, or visit our site at http://fdncenter.org/collections/index.html.

THE FOUNDATION CENTER	THE FOUNDATION CENTER	THE FOUNDATION CENTER	THE FOUNDATION CENTER	THE FOUNDATION CENTER
2nd Floor	312 Sutter St., Suite 606	1627 K St., NW, 3rd floor	Kent H. Smith Library	Suite 150, Grand Lobby
79 Fifth Ave.	San Francisco, CA 94108	Washington, DC 20006	1422 Euclid Ave., Suite 1600	Hurt Bldg., 50 Hurt Plaza
New York, NY 10003	(415) 397-0902	(202) 331-1400	Cleveland, OH 44115	Atlanta, GA 30303
(212) 620-4230			(216) 861-1933	(404) 880-0094

REFERENCE COLLECTIONS OPERATED BY THE FOUNDATION CENTER

ALABAMA

BIRMINGHAM PUBLIC LIBRARY
Government Documents
2100 Park Place
Birmingham 35203
(205) 226-3620

HUNTSVILLE PUBLIC LIBRARY
915 Monroe St.
Huntsville 35801
(256) 532-5940

AUBURN UNIVERSITY AT MONTGOMERY LIBRARY
74-40 East Dr.
Montgomery 36117-3596
(334) 244-3200

ALASKA

CONSORTIUM LIBRARY
3211 Providence Dr.
Anchorage 99508
(907) 786-1848

JUNEAU PUBLIC LIBRARY
292 Marine Way
Juneau 99801
(907) 586-5267

ARIZONA

FLAGSTAFF CITY-COCONINO COUNTY PUBLIC LIBRARY
300 W. Aspen Ave.
Flagstaff 86001
(520) 779-7670

PHOENIX PUBLIC LIBRARY
Information Services Department
1221 N. Central Ave.
Phoenix 85004
(602) 262-4636

TUCSON PIMA PUBLIC LIBRARY
101 N. Stone Ave.
Tucson 87501
(520) 791-4393

ARKANSAS

WESTARK COLLEGE— BOREHAM LIBRARY
5210 Grand Ave.
Ft. Smith 72913
(501) 788-7200

CENTRAL ARKANSAS LIBRARY SYSTEM
100 Rock St.
Little Rock 72201
(501) 918-3000

CALIFORNIA

KERN COUNTY LIBRARY
Beale Memorial Library
701 Truxtun Avenue
Bakersfield 93301

HUMBOLDT AREA FOUNDATION
Rooney Resource Center
373 Indianola
Bayside 95524
(707) 442-2993

VENTURA COUNTY COMMUNITY FOUNDATION
Resource Center for Nonprofit Organizations
1317 Del Norte Rd., Suite 150
Camarillo 93010-8504
(805) 988-0196

FRESNO REGIONAL FOUNDATION
Nonprofit Advancement Center
3425 N. First St., Suite 101
Fresno 93726
(559) 226-0216

CENTER FOR NONPROFIT MANAGEMENT IN SOUTHERN CALIFORNIA
Nonprofit Resource Library
606 South Olive St. #2450
Los Angeles 90014
(213) 623-7080

PHILANTHROPY RESOURCE CENTER
Flintridge Foundation
1040 Lincoln Ave, Suite 100
Pasadena 91103
(626) 449-0839

GRANT & RESOURCE CENTER OF NORTHERN CALIFORNIA
Bldg. C, Suite A
2280 Benton Dr.
Redding 96003
(530) 244-1219

LOS ANGELES PUBLIC LIBRARY
West Valley Regional Branch Library
19036 Van Owen St.
Reseda 91335
(818) 345-4393

RICHMOND PUBLIC LIBRARY
325 Civic Center Plaza
Richmond 94804
(510) 620-6555

RIVERSIDE PUBLIC LIBRARY
3581 Mission Inn Ave.
Riverside 92501
(909) 826-5201

SACRAMENTO PUBLIC LIBRARY
328 I St., 2nd Floor
Sacramento 95814
(916) 264-2772

SAN DIEGO FOUNDATION
Funding Information Center
1420 Kettner Blvd., Suite 500
San Diego 92101
(619) 235-2300

NONPROFIT DEVELOPMENT LIBRARY
1922 The Alameda, Suite 212
San Jose 95126
(408) 248-9505

PENINSULA COMMUNITY FOUNDATION
Peninsula Nonprofit Center
1700 S. El Camino Real, #R201
San Mateo 94402-3049
(650) 358-9392

LOS ANGELES PUBLIC LIBRARY
San Pedro Regional Branch
931 S. Gaffey St.
San Pedro 90731
(310) 548-7779

VOLUNTEER CENTER OF GREATER ORANGE COUNTY
Nonprofit Resource Center
1901 E. 4th St., Suite 100
Santa Ana 92705
(714) 953-5757

SANTA BARBARA PUBLIC LIBRARY
40 E. Anapamu St.
Santa Barbara 93101-1019
(805) 962-7653

SANTA MONICA PUBLIC LIBRARY
1343 6th St.
Santa Monica 90401-1603
(310) 458-8600

SONOMA COUNTY LIBRARY
3rd & E Sts.
Santa Rosa 95404
(707) 545-0831

SEASIDE BRANCH LIBRARY
550 Harcourt Ave.
Seaside 93955
(831) 899-8131

SONORA AREA FOUNDATION
20100 Cedar Rd., N.
Sonora 95370
(209) 533-2596

COLORADO

PENROSE LIBRARY
20 N. Cascade Ave.
Colorado Springs 80903
(719) 531-6333

DENVER PUBLIC LIBRARY
10 W. 14th Ave. Pkwy.
Denver 80204
(303) 640-6200

CONNECTICUT

DANBURY PUBLIC LIBRARY
170 Main St.
Danbury 06810
(203) 797-4527

GREENWICH LIBRARY
101 W. Putnam Ave.
Greenwich 06830
(203) 622-7900

HARTFORD PUBLIC LIBRARY
500 Main St.
Hartford 06103
(860) 543-8656

NEW HAVEN FREE PUBLIC LIBRARY
133 Elm St.
New Haven 06510-2057
(203) 946-7091

DELAWARE

UNIVERSITY OF DELAWARE
Hugh Morris Library
Newark 19717-5267
(302) 831-2432

FLORIDA

VOLUSIA COUNTY LIBRARY CENTER
City Island
105 E. Magnolia Ave.
Daytona Beach 32114-4484
(386) 257-6036

NOVA SOUTHEASTERN UNIVERSITY
Einstein Library
3301 College Ave.
Fort Lauderdale 33314
(954) 262-4601

INDIAN RIVER COMMUNITY COLLEGE
Learning Resources Center
3209 Virginia Ave.
Fort Pierce 34981-5596
(561) 462-4757

JACKSONVILLE PUBLIC LIBRARIES
Grants Resource Center
122 N. Ocean St.
Jacksonville 32202
(904) 630-2665

MIAMI-DADE PUBLIC LIBRARY
Humanities/Social Science
101 W. Flagler St.
Miami 33130
(305) 375-5575

ORANGE COUNTY LIBRARY SYSTEM
Social Sciences Department
101 E. Central Blvd.
Orlando 32801
(407) 425-4694

SELBY PUBLIC LIBRARY
Reference
1331 1st St.
Sarasota 34236
(941) 316-1181

TAMPA-HILLSBOROUGH COUNTY
PUBLIC LIBRARY
900 N. Ashley Dr.
Tampa 33602
(813) 273-3652

COMMUNITY FOUNDATION OF PALM
BEACH & MARTIN COUNTIES
324 Datura St., Suite 340
West Palm Beach 33401
(561) 659-6800

GEORGIA

ATLANTA-FULTON PUBLIC LIBRARY
Foundation Collection—Ivan Allen
  Department
1 Margaret Mitchell Square
Atlanta 30303-1089
(404) 730-1909

HALL COUNTY LIBRARY SYSTEM
127 Main Street NW
Gainesville 30501
(770) 532-3311

UNITED WAY OF CENTRAL GEORGIA
Community Resource Center
277 Martin Luther King Jr. Blvd.,
  Suite 301
Macon 31201
(478) 745-4732

SAVANNAH STATE UNIVERSITY
Asa Gordon Library
Thompkins Rd.
Savannah 31404
(912) 356-2185

THOMAS COUNTY PUBLIC LIBRARY
201 N. Madison St.
Thomasville 31792
(912) 225-5252

HAWAII

UNIVERSITY OF HAWAII
Hamilton Library
2550 The Mall
Honolulu 96822
(808) 956-7214

HAWAII COMMUNITY FOUNDATION
Funding Resource Library
900 Fort St., Suite 1300
Honolulu 96813
(808) 537-6333

IDAHO

BOISE PUBLIC LIBRARY
Funding Information Center
715 S. Capitol Blvd.
Boise 83702
(208) 384-4024

CALDWELL PUBLIC LIBRARY
1010 Dearborn St.
Caldwell 83605
(208) 459-3242

ILLINOIS

DONORS FORUM OF CHICAGO
208 S. LaSalle, Suite 735
Chicago 60604
(312) 578-0175

EVANSTON PUBLIC LIBRARY
1703 Orrington Ave.
Evanston 60201
(847) 866-0300

ROCK ISLAND PUBLIC LIBRARY
401 19th St.
Rock Island 61201-8143
(309) 732-7323

UNIVERSITY OF ILLINOIS
AT SPRINGFIELD, LIB 23
Brookens Library
Springfield 62794-9243
(217) 206-6633

INDIANA

EVANSVILLE–VANDERBURGH
PUBLIC LIBRARY
22 SE 5th St.
Evansville 47708
(812) 428-8200

ALLEN COUNTY PUBLIC LIBRARY
900 Webster St.
Ft. Wayne 46802
(219) 421-1200

INDIANAPOLIS–MARION COUNTY
PUBLIC LIBRARY
Social Sciences
40 E. St. Clair
Indianapolis 46206
(317) 269-1733

VIGO COUNTY PUBLIC LIBRARY
1 Library Square
Terre Haute 47807
(812) 232-1113

IOWA

CEDAR RAPIDS PUBLIC LIBRARY
500 1st St., SE
Cedar Rapids 52401
(319) 398-5123

SOUTHWESTERN COMMUNITY
COLLEGE
Learning Resource Center
1501 W. Townline Rd.
Creston 50801
(515) 782-7081

PUBLIC LIBRARY OF DES MOINES
100 Locust
Des Moines 50309-1791
(515) 283-4957

SIOUX CITY PUBLIC LIBRARY
Siouxland Funding Research Center
529 Pierce St.
Sioux City 51101-1203
(712) 255-2933

KANSAS

PIONEER MEMORIAL LIBRARY
375 West 4th St.
Colby 67701
(785) 462-4470

DODGE CITY PUBLIC LIBRARY
1001 2nd Ave.
Dodge City 67801
(316) 225-0248

KEARNY COUNTY LIBRARY
101 East Prairie
Lakin 67860
(316) 355-6674

TOPEKA AND SHAWNEE COUNTY
PUBLIC LIBRARY
1515 SW 10th Ave.
Topeka 66604
(785) 580-4400

WICHITA PUBLIC LIBRARY
223 S. Main St.
Wichita 67202
(316) 261-8500

KENTUCKY

WESTERN KENTUCKY UNIVERSITY
Helm-Cravens Library
Bowling Green 42101-3576
(270) 745-6163

LEXINGTON PUBLIC LIBRARY
140 E. Main St.
Lexington 40507-1376
(859) 231-5520

LOUISVILLE FREE PUBLIC LIBRARY
301 York St.
Louisville 40203
(502) 574-1617

LOUISIANA

EAST BATON ROUGE PARISH LIBRARY
Centroplex Branch Grants Collection
120 St. Louis St.
Baton Rouge 70802
(225) 389-4967

BEAUREGARD PARISH LIBRARY
205 S. Washington Ave.
De Ridder 70634
(318) 463-6217

OUACHITA PARISH PUBLIC LIBRARY
1800 Stubbs Ave.
Monroe 71201
(318) 327-1490

NEW ORLEANS PUBLIC LIBRARY
Business & Science Division
219 Loyola Ave.
New Orleans 70112
(504) 596-2580

SHREVE MEMORIAL LIBRARY
424 Texas St.
Shreveport 71120-1523
(318) 226-5894

MAINE

UNIVERSITY OF SOUTHERN
MAINE LIBRARY
Maine Philanthropy Center
314 Forrest Ave.
Portland 04104-9301
(207) 780-5029

MARYLAND

ENOCH PRATT FREE LIBRARY
Social Science & History Dept.
400 Cathedral St.
Baltimore 21201
(410) 396-5430

MASSACHUSETTS

ASSOCIATED GRANT MAKERS OF
MASSACHUSETTS
55 Court St.
Room 520
Boston 02108
(617) 426-2606

BOSTON PUBLIC LIBRARY
Soc. Sci. Reference
700 Boylston St.
Boston 02116
(617) 536-5400

WESTERN MASSACHUSETTS FUNDING
RESOURCE CENTER
65 Elliot St.
Springfield 01101-1730
(413) 452-0697

WORCESTER PUBLIC LIBRARY
Grants Resource Center
160 Fremont St.
Worcester 01603
(508) 799-1655

MICHIGAN

ALPENA COUNTY LIBRARY
211 N. 1st St.
Alpena 49707
(517) 356-6188

UNIVERSITY OF
MICHIGAN–ANN ARBOR
Graduate Library

Reference & Research Services
  Department
Ann Arbor 48109-1205
(734) 763-1539

WILLARD PUBLIC LIBRARY
Nonprofit & Funding Resource
  Collections
7 W. Van Buren St.
Battle Creek 49017
(616) 968-8166

HENRY FORD CENTENNIAL LIBRARY
16301 Michigan Ave.
Dearborn 48124
(313) 943-2330

WAYNE STATE UNIVERSITY
Purdy/Kresge Library
5265 Cass Ave.
Detroit 48202
(313) 577-6423

MICHIGAN STATE UNIVERSITY
LIBRARIES
Main Library
Funding Center
100 Library
East Lansing 48824-1049
(517) 353-8700

FARMINGTON COMMUNITY LIBRARY
32737 W. 12 Mile Rd.
Farmington Hills 48334
(248) 553-0300

UNIVERSITY OF MICHIGAN—FLINT
Frances Willson Thompson Library
Flint 48502-1950
(810) 762-3413

GRAND RAPIDS PUBLIC LIBRARY
60 Library Plaza NE
Grand Rapids 49503-3093
(616) 456-3600

MICHIGAN TECHNOLOGICAL
UNIVERSITY
Van Pelt Library
1400 Townsend Dr.
Houghton 49931
(906) 487-2507

NORTHWESTERN MICHIGAN COLLEGE
Mark & Helen Osterlin Library
1701 E. Front St.
Traverse City 49686
(231) 995-1060

MINNESOTA

DULUTH PUBLIC LIBRARY
520 W. Superior St.
Duluth 55802
(218) 723-3802

SOUTHWEST STATE UNIVERSITY
University Library
N. Hwy. 23
Marshall 56253
(507) 537-6108

MINNEAPOLIS PUBLIC LIBRARY
Sociology Department
300 Nicollet Mall
Minneapolis 55401
(612) 630-6300

ROCHESTER PUBLIC LIBRARY
101 2nd St. SE
Rochester 55904-3777
(507) 285-8002

ST. PAUL PUBLIC LIBRARY
90 W. 4th St.
St. Paul 55102
(651) 266-7000

MISSISSIPPI

LIBRARY OF HATTIESBURG, PETAL
AND FORREST COUNTY
329 Hardy Street
Hattiesburg 39401-3824
(601) 582-4461 '

JACKSON/HINDS LIBRARY SYSTEM
300 N. State St.
Jackson 39201
(601) 968-5803

MISSOURI

CLEARINGHOUSE FOR
MIDCONTINENT FOUNDATIONS
University of Missouri—Kansas City
Center for Business Innovation
4747 Troost
Kansas City 64113-0680
(816) 235-1176

KANSAS CITY PUBLIC LIBRARY
311 E. 12th St.
Kansas City 64106
(816) 701-3541

METROPOLITAN ASSOCIATION FOR
PHILANTHROPY, INC.
211 N. Broadway, Suite 1200
St. Louis 63102
(314) 621-6220

SPRINGFIELD-GREENE
COUNTY LIBRARY
The Library Center
4653 S. Campbell
Springfield 65810
(417) 874-8110

MONTANA

MONTANA STATE UNIVERSITY—
BILLINGS
Library—Special Collections
1500 N. 30th St.
Billings 59101-0245
(406) 657-1687

BOZEMAN PUBLIC LIBRARY
220 E. Lamme
Bozeman 59715
(406) 582-2402

MONTANA STATE LIBRARY
Library Services
1515 E. 6th Ave.
Helena 59620-1800
(406) 444-3115

UNIVERSITY OF MONTANA
Mansfield Library
32 Campus Dr. #9936
Missoula 59812-9936
(406) 243-6800

NEBRASKA

UNIVERSITY OF NEBRASKA—
LINCOLN
Love Library
14th & R Sts.
Lincoln 68588-2848
(402) 472-2848

OMAHA PUBLIC LIBRARY
W. Dale Clark Library
Social Sciences Dept.
215 S. 15th St.
Omaha 68102
(402) 444-4826

NEVADA

CLARK COUNTY LIBRARY
1401 E. Flamingo
Las Vegas 89119
(702) 733-3642

WASHOE COUNTY LIBRARY
301 S. Center St.
Reno 89501
(775) 327-8312

NEW HAMPSHIRE

CONCORD PUBLIC LIBRARY
45 Green St.
Concord 03301
(603) 225-8670

PLYMOUTH STATE COLLEGE
Herbert H. Lamson Library
Plymouth 03264
(603) 535-2258

NEW JERSEY

CUMBERLAND COUNTY LIBRARY
800 E. Commerce St.
Bridgeton 08302
(856) 453-2210

FREE PUBLIC LIBRARY OF ELIZABETH
11 S. Broad St.
Elizabeth 07202
(908) 354-6060

NEWARK ENTERPRISE COMMUNITY
RESOURCE DEVELOPMENT CENTER
303-309 Washington St.
Newark 07102
(973) 624-8300

COUNTY COLLEGE OF MORRIS
Learning Resource Center
214 Center Grove Rd.
Randolph 07869
(973) 328-5296

NEW JERSEY STATE LIBRARY
185 W. State St.
Trenton 08625-0520
(609) 292-6220

NEW MEXICO

JEMEZ PUEBLO COMMUNITY LIBRARY
020 Mission Road
Jemez Pueblo 87024
(505) 834-9171

NEW MEXICO STATE LIBRARY
Information Services
1209 Camino Carlos Rey
Santa Fe 87505-9860
(505) 476-9702

NEW YORK

NEW YORK STATE LIBRARY
Humanities Reference
Cultural Education Center, 6th Fl.
Empire State Plaza
Albany 12230
(518) 474-5355

SUFFOLK COOPERATIVE
LIBRARY SYSTEM
627 N. Sunrise Service Rd.
Bellport 11713
(516) 286-1600

BROOKLYN PUBLIC LIBRARY
Social Sciences/Philosophy Division
Grand Army Plaza
Brooklyn 11238
(718) 230-2122

BUFFALO & ERIE COUNTY
PUBLIC LIBRARY
Business, Science & Technology Dept.
1 Lafayette Square
Buffalo 14203-1887
(716) 858-7097

HUNTINGTON PUBLIC LIBRARY
338 Main St.
Huntington 11743
(631) 427-5165

QUEENS BOROUGH PUBLIC LIBRARY
Social Sciences Division
89-11 Merrick Blvd.
Jamaica 11432
(718) 990-0700

LEVITTOWN PUBLIC LIBRARY
1 Bluegrass Ln.
Levittown 11756
(516) 731-5728

ADRIANCE MEMORIAL LIBRARY
Special Services Department
93 Market St.
Poughkeepsie 12601
(914) 485-3445

ROCHESTER PUBLIC LIBRARY
Social Sciences
115 South Ave.
Rochester 14604
(716) 428-8120

ONONDAGA COUNTY PUBLIC LIBRARY
447 S. Salina St.
Syracuse 13202-2494
(315) 435-1900

UTICA PUBLIC LIBRARY
303 Genesee St.
Utica 13501
(315) 735-2279

WHITE PLAINS PUBLIC LIBRARY
100 Martine Ave.
White Plains 10601
(914) 422-1480

YONKERS PUBLIC LIBRARY
Reference Department, Getty
Square Branch
7 Main St.
Yonkers 10701
(914) 476-1255

NORTH CAROLINA

PACK MEMORIAL LIBRARY
Community Foundation of Western North
Carolina
67 Haywood St.
Asheville 28802
(704) 254-4960

THE DUKE ENDOWMENT
100 N. Tryon St., Suite 3500
Charlotte 28202-4012
(704) 376-0291

DURHAM COUNTY PUBLIC LIBRARY
300 N. Roxboro St.
Durham 27702
(919) 560-0100

FORSYTH COUNTY PUBLIC LIBRARY
660 W. 5th St.
Winston-Salem 27408
(336) 727-2264

NORTH DAKOTA

BISMARCK PUBLIC LIBRARY
515 N. 5th St.
Bismarck 58501-4081
(701) 222-6410

FARGO PUBLIC LIBRARY
102 N. 3rd St.
Fargo 58102
(701) 241-1491

MINOT PUBLIC LIBRARY
516 Second Avenue SW
Minot 58701-3792
(701) 852-1045

OHIO

STARK COUNTY DISTRICT LIBRARY
715 Market Ave. N.
Canton 44702
(330) 452-0665

PUBLIC LIBRARY OF CINCINNATI &
HAMILTON COUNTY
Grants Resource Center
800 Vine St.—Library Square
Cincinnati 45202-2071
(513) 369-6000

COLUMBUS METROPOLITAN LIBRARY
Business and Technology
96 S. Grant Ave.
Columbus 43215
(614) 645-2590

DAYTON & MONTGOMERY COUNTY
PUBLIC LIBRARY
Grants Information Center
215 E. Third St.
Dayton 45402
(937) 227-9500

MANSFIELD/RICHLAND COUNTY
PUBLIC LIBRARY
42 W. 3rd St.
Mansfield 44902
(419) 521-3100

TOLEDO–LUCAS COUNTY
PUBLIC LIBRARY
325 Michigan St.
Toledo 43612
(419) 259-5209

PUBLIC LIBRARY OF YOUNGSTOWN &
MAHONING COUNTY
305 Wick Ave.
Youngstown 44503
(330) 744-8636

OKLAHOMA

OKLAHOMA CITY UNIVERSITY
Dulaney Browne Library
2501 N. Blackwelder
Oklahoma City 73106
(405) 521-5822

TULSA CITY–COUNTY LIBRARY
400 Civic Center
Tulsa 74103
(918) 596-7977

OREGON

OREGON INSTITUTE OF TECHNOLOGY
Library
3201 Campus Dr.
Klamath Falls 97601-8801
(541) 885-1770

PACIFIC NON-PROFIT NETWORK
Southern Oregon University
1600 N. Riverside #1094
Medford 97501
(541) 779-6044

MULTNOMAH COUNTY LIBRARY
801 SW 10th Ave.
Portland 97205
(503) 248-5123

OREGON STATE LIBRARY
State Library Bldg.
250 Winter St. NE
Salem 97301-3950
(503) 378-4277

PENNSYLVANIA

NORTHAMPTON COMMUNITY
COLLEGE
Learning Resource Center
3835 Green Pond Rd.
Bethlehem 18017
(610) 861-5360

ERIE COUNTY LIBRARY SYSTEM
160 E. Front St.
Erie 16507
(814) 451-6927

DAUPHIN COUNTY LIBRARY SYSTEM
Central Library
101 Walnut St.
Harrisburg 17101
(717) 234-4976

LANCASTER COUNTY PUBLIC LIBRARY
125 N. Duke St.
Lancaster 17602
(717) 394-2651

FREE LIBRARY OF PHILADELPHIA
Regional Foundation Center
1901 Vine St.
Philadelphia 19103-1189
(215) 686-5423

CARNEGIE LIBRARY OF PITTSBURGH
Foundation Collection
4400 Forbes Ave.
Pittsburgh 15213-4080
(412) 622-1917

POCONO NORTHEAST
DEVELOPMENT FUND
James Pettinger Memorial Library
1151 Oak St.
Pittston 18640-3795
(570) 655-5581

READING PUBLIC LIBRARY
100 S. 5th St.
Reading 19602
(610) 655-6355

JAMES V. BROWN LIBRARY
19 East Fourth Street
Williamsport 17701
(570) 326-0536

MARTIN LIBRARY
159 E. Market St.
York 17401
(717) 846-5300

RHODE ISLAND

PROVIDENCE PUBLIC
LIBRARY
225 Washington St.
Providence 02906
(401) 455-8088

SOUTH CAROLINA

ANDERSON COUNTY LIBRARY
300 N. McDuffie St.
Anderson 29622
(864) 260-4500

CHARLESTON COUNTY LIBRARY
68 Calhoun St.
Charleston 29401
(843) 805-6930

SOUTH CAROLINA STATE LIBRARY
1500 Senate St.
Columbia 29211-1469
(803) 734-8666

COMMUNITY FOUNDATION OF
GREATER GREENVILLE
27 Cleveland St., Suite 101
Greenville 29601
(864) 233-5925

SOUTH DAKOTA

SINTE GLESKA UNIVERSITY LIBRARY
Rosebud Sioux Reservation
Mission 57555-0107
(605) 856-2355

SOUTH DAKOTA STATE LIBRARY
800 Governors Dr.
Pierre 57501-2294
(605) 773-3131
(800) 592-1841 (SD residents)

DAKOTA STATE LIBRARY
Nonprofit Grants Assistance
2505 Career Ave.
Sioux Falls 57108
(605) 367-5380

SIOUXLAND LIBRARIES
201 N. Main Ave.
Sioux Falls 57104
(605) 367-8720

TENNESSEE

UNITED WAY OF GREATER
CHATTANOOGA
Center for Nonprofits
406 Frazier Ave.
Chattanooga 37405
(423) 265-0514

KNOX COUNTY PUBLIC LIBRARY
500 W. Church Ave.
Knoxville 37902
(865) 215-8751

NASHVILLE PUBLIC LIBRARY
615 Church St.
Nashville 37219
(615) 862-5842

TEXAS

NONPROFIT RESOURCE CENTER
Funding Information Library
500 S. Chestnut, Suite 1634
Abilene 79604
(915) 677-8166

AMARILLO AREA FOUNDATION
Grants Center
801 S. Filmore, Suite 700
Amarillo 79101
(806) 376-4521

HOGG FOUNDATION FOR
MENTAL HEALTH
Regional Foundation Library
3001 Lake Austin Blvd., Suite 400
Austin 78703
(512) 471-5041

BEAUMONT PUBLIC LIBRARY
801 Pearl St.
Beaumont 77704-3827
(409) 838-6606

CORPUS CHRISTI PUBLIC LIBRARY
Funding Information Center
805 Comanche St.
Reference Dept.
Corpus Christi 78401
(361) 880-7000

DALLAS PUBLIC LIBRARY
Urban Information
1515 Young St.
Dallas 75201
(214) 670-1487

SOUTHWEST BORDER NONPROFIT
RESOURCE CENTER
1201 W. University Dr.
Edinburgh 78539
(956) 384-5920

FUNDING INFORMATION CENTER
OF FORT WORTH
329 S. Henderson
Ft. Worth 76104
(817) 334-0228

HOUSTON PUBLIC LIBRARY
Bibliographic Information Center
500 McKinney
Houston 77002
(713) 236-1313

NONPROFIT MANAGEMENT AND
VOLUNTEER CENTER
Laredo Public Library
1120 E. Calton Rd.
Laredo 78041
(956) 795-2400

LONGVIEW PUBLIC LIBRARY
222 W. Cotton St.
Longview 75601
(903) 237-1350

LUBBOCK AREA FOUNDATION, INC.
1655 Main St., Suite 209
Lubbock 79401
(806) 762-8061

NONPROFIT RESOURCE CENTER
OF TEXAS
7404 Hwy. 90 W.
San Antonio 78212-8270
(210) 227-4333

WACO-MCLENNAN COUNTY LIBRARY
1717 Austin Ave.
Waco 76701
(254) 750-5941

NONPROFIT MANAGEMENT
CENTER OF WICHITA FALLS
1105 Holliday
Wichita Falls 76301
(940) 322-4961

UTAH

SALT LAKE CITY PUBLIC LIBRARY
209 E. 500 S.
Salt Lake City 84111
(801) 524-8200

VERMONT

VERMONT DEPT. OF LIBRARIES
Reference & Law Info. Services
109 State St.
Montpelier 05609
(802) 828-3261

VIRGINIA

WASHINGTON COUNTY
PUBLIC LIBRARY
205 Oak Hill St.
Abingdon 24210
(540) 676-6222

HAMPTON PUBLIC LIBRARY
4207 Victoria Blvd.
Hampton 23669
(757) 727-1312

RICHMOND PUBLIC LIBRARY
Business, Science & Technology Dept.
101 E. Franklin St.
Richmond 23219
(804) 646-7223

ROANOKE CITY PUBLIC
LIBRARY SYSTEM
Main Library
706 S. Jefferson
Roanoke 24016
(540) 853-2471

WASHINGTON

MID-COLUMBIA LIBRARY
1620 South Union St.
Kennewick 99338
(509) 783-7878

REDMOND REGIONAL LIBRARY
15990 NE 85th
Redmond 98052
(425) 885-1861

SEATTLE PUBLIC LIBRARY
Fundraising Resource Center
800 Pike St.
Seattle 98101
(206) 386-4645

SPOKANE PUBLIC LIBRARY
Funding Information Center
901 W. Main Ave.
Spokane 99201
(509) 444-5300

UNIVERSITY OF WASHINGTON
TACOMA LIBRARY
1900 Commerce St.
Tacoma 98402-3100
(253) 692-4440

GREATER WENATCHEE COMMUNITY
FOUNDATION AT THE WENATCHEE
PUBLIC LIBRARY
310 Douglas St.
Wenatchee 98807
(509) 662-5021

WEST VIRGINIA

KANAWHA COUNTY PUBLIC LIBRARY
123 Capitol St.
Charleston 25301
(304) 343-4646

WISCONSIN

UNIVERSITY OF WISCONSIN–MADISON
Memorial Library, Grants Information
Center
728 State St.
Madison 53706
(608) 262-3242

MARQUETTE UNIVERSITY
MEMORIAL LIBRARY
Funding Information Center
1415 W. Wisconsin Ave.
Milwaukee 53201-3141
(414) 288-1515

UNIVERSITY OF WISCONSIN—
STEVENS POINT
Library—Foundation Collection
900 Reserve St.
Stevens Point 54481-3897
(715) 346-2540

WYOMING

CASPER COLLEGE
Goodstein Foundation Library
125 College Dr.
Casper 82601
(307) 268-2269

LARAMIE COUNTY COMMUNITY
COLLEGE
Instructional Resource Center
1400 E. College Dr.
Cheyenne 82007-3299
(307) 778-1206

CAMPBELL COUNTY PUBLIC LIBRARY
2101 4-J Rd.
Gillette 82718
(307) 687-0115

TETON COUNTY LIBRARY
125 Virginian Ln.
Jackson 83001
(307) 733-2164

ROCK SPRINGS LIBRARY
Grantwriting Collection
400 C St.
Rock Springs 82901
(307) 352-6667

PUERTO RICO

UNIVERSIDAD DEL SAGRADO
CORAZON
M.M.T. Guevara Library
Santurce 00914
(787) 728-1515

Participants in the Foundation Center's Cooperating Collections network are libraries or nonprofit information centers that provide fundraising information and other funding-related technical assistance in their communities. Cooperating Collections agree to provide free public access to a basic collection of Foundation Center publications during a regular schedule of hours, offering free funding research guidance to all visitors. Many also provide a variety of services for local nonprofit organizations, using staff or volunteers to prepare special materials, organize workshops, or conduct orientations.

The Foundation Center welcomes inquiries from libraries or information centers in the U.S. interested in providing this type of public information service, particularly for communities with special need for this information. If you are interested in establishing a funding information library for the use of nonprofit organizations in your area or in learning more about the program, please contact the coordinator of Cooperating Collections: Erika Wittlieb, The Foundation Center, 79 Fifth Avenue, New York, NY 10003 (e-mail: eaw@fdncenter.org).

The Foundation Center's *Grant Guide* series includes the following titles:

Arts, Culture & the Humanities (#1)
Children & Youth (#2)
Elementary & Secondary Education (#3)
Environmental Protection & Animal Welfare (#4)
Film, Media & Communications (#5)
Foreign & International Programs (#6)
Higher Education (#7)
Libraries & Information Services (#8)
Mental Health, Addictions & Crisis Services (#9)
Minorities (#10)
Physically & Mentally Disabled (#11)
Religion, Religious Welfare & Religious Education (#12)
Scholarships, Student Aid & Loans (#13)
Social Services (#14)
Women & Girls (#15)

The *Grant Guides* use the following two-letter state and U.S. territory abbreviations:

AL = Alabama	HI = Hawaii	MO = Missouri	PR = Puerto Rico
AK = Alaska	ID = Idaho	MT = Montana	RI = Rhode Island
AS = American Samoa	IL = Illinois	NE = Nebraska	SC = South Carolina
AZ = Arizona	IN = Indiana	NV = Nevada	SD = South Dakota
AR = Arkansas	IA = Iowa	NH = New Hampshire	TN = Tennessee
CA = California	KS = Kansas	NJ = New Jersey	TX = Texas
CM = Marianas	KY = Kentucky	NM = New Mexico	UT = Utah
CO = Colorado	LA = Louisiana	NY = New York	VT = Vermont
CT = Connecticut	ME = Maine	NC = Noth Carolina	VA = Virginia
DE = Delaware	MD = Maryland	ND = North Dakota	VI = Virgin Islands
DC = District of Columbia	MA = Massachusetts	OH = Ohio	WA = Washington
FL = Florida	MI = Michigan	OK = Oklahoma	WV = West Virginia
GA = Georgia	MN = Minnesota	OR = Oregon	WI = Wisconsin
GU = Guam	MS = Mississippi	PA = Pennsylvania	WY = Wyoming

Section 1—Grant Listings

ALABAMA

Alabama Power Foundation, Inc.
Limitations: Giving limited to AL. No support for religious organizations or fraternal, athletic, or veterans' programs. No grants to individuals (except for employee-related scholarships), or for fundraisers or operating funds that duplicate United Way support.

1. Center for Democratic Renewal and Education, Atlanta, GA. $10,000, 1999. For general operating support.
2. Union Springs Library, Union Springs, AL. $10,000, 1999. For capital support.

The J. L. Bedsole Foundation
Limitations: Giving limited to AL, with emphasis on the southwestern region. No grants to individuals, except for J.L. Bedsole Scholars Program.

3. Grove Hill Public Library, Grove Hill, AL. $10,000, 1999. For operating support.
4. Ina Pullen Smallwood Memorial Library, Chickasaw, AL. $25,000, 1999. For capital support.
5. Mobile Public Library, Mobile, AL. $250,000, 1999. For capital support.
6. Monroe County Public Library, Monroeville, AL. $10,000, 1999. For operating support.

The Community Foundation of Greater Birmingham
Limitations: Giving limited to the Birmingham, AL, area, including five counties: Jefferson, Shelby, Blount, St. Clair and Walker. No support for religious or political purposes from unrestricted and field of interest funds. No grants to individuals or for scholarships, endowment funds, operating budgets, deficit reduction, national fundraising drives, conference or seminar expenses, benefits tickets, or replacement of government funding cuts.

7. Mountain Brook Library Foundation, Mountain Brook, AL. $65,200, 1999.
8. Nonprofit Resource Center of Alabama, Birmingham, AL. $15,000, 1999. For continued development and implementation of education and training programs, and for member services.
9. Parnell Memorial Library Foundation, Montevallo, AL. $10,000, 1999. For renovation and new construction of Montevallo City Library.
10. Ronald Reagan Presidential Foundation, Simi Valley, CA. $20,000, 1999.

The Community Foundation of South Alabama
Limitations: Giving primarily in southern AL, south of Montgomery County (Mobile and Baldwin counties). No support for political organizations. No grants to individuals, or for research, films, conferences, workshops, or fundraising events.

11. Mobile Public Library, Mobile, AL. $34,150, 2000.

The Daniel Foundation of Alabama
Limitations: Giving primarily in the southeastern U.S., with emphasis on AL.

12. Greenville Butler County Public Library, Greenville, AL. $50,000, 1999.
13. Parnell Memorial Library Foundation, Montevallo, AL. $25,000, 1999.

ARIZONA

Arizona Community Foundation
Limitations: Giving limited to AZ. No support for sectarian religious purposes. No grants to individuals, or for deficit financing, annual campaigns, land acquisition, endowment funds, travel to or support of conferences, consulting services, or capital grants; generally, no loans.

14. Desert Foothills Library, Cave Creek, AZ. $20,000, 1999. For grant made through Ingebritson Family Foundation.
15. Library Friends of Payson, Payson, AZ. $10,000, 1999.
16. Scottsdale, City of, Library Department, Scottsdale, AZ. $20,614, 1999. For Community Services program.
17. Yuma County Library District, Yuma, AZ. $31,262, 1999.
18. Yuma Library Foundation, Yuma, AZ. $30,000, 1999.
19. Yuma Library Foundation, Yuma, AZ. $10,000, 1999.

The Steele Foundation, Inc.
Limitations: Giving only in AZ. No grants to individuals.

20. Phoenix Public Library, Phoenix, AZ. $10,000, 1999.

ARKANSAS

Charles A. Frueauff Foundation, Inc.
Limitations: Giving limited to the U.S. with emphasis on east of the Rockies, the South, and Northeast. No grants to individuals, primary or secondary schools, state colleges and universities, or for research; no loans.

21. Kansas University Endowment Association, Lawrence, KS. $30,000, 1999. For technology equipment for Law library.
22. Project Connect, Jackson, MS. $10,000, 1999. For HIV/AIDS program support.
23. Westminster College, Salt Lake City, UT. $50,000, 1999. For library reference software.

The Winthrop Rockefeller Foundation
Limitations: Giving limited to AR, or for projects that benefit AR. No grants to individuals, or for capital expenditures, endowments, building funds, equipment, annual fund drives, deficit financing, general support, emergency funds, most types of research, travel, scholarships, or fellowships.

24. Arkansas River Valley Library, Dardanelle, AR. $28,757, 1999. For Libraries for Literacy Program.
25. Arkansas River Valley Regional Library System, Dardanelle, AR. $20,000, 1999.
26. Arkansas River Valley Regional Library System, Dardanelle, AR. $14,950, 1999. For Bookmobile.

Wal-Mart Foundation
Limitations: Giving primarily in areas of company operations. No support for cultural performances or film and video projects. No grants to individuals (except for scholarship programs), or for research, endowments, capital campaigns, conferences, travel, or fundraising dinners or galas.

27. National First Ladies Library, Canton, OH. $25,000, 2000.
28. North Country Community Development Center, Bethlehem, PA. $10,000, 2000. For Environmental School Grant.

CALIFORNIA

The Ahmanson Foundation

Limitations: Giving primarily in southern CA, with emphasis on the Los Angeles area. No grants to individuals, or for continuing support, annual campaigns, deficit financing, professorships, internships, fellowships, film production, media projects, seminars, general research and development, underwriting, or exchange programs; no loans.

29. American Antiquarian Society, Worcester, MA. $50,000, 2000. Toward endowment fund for collections and acquisition.
30. Biola University, La Mirada, CA. $150,000, 2000. Toward construction of Library Resource Center.
31. Damien High School, La Verne, CA. $25,000, 2000. Toward upgrading technology for instructional classrooms and library.
32. Foundation Center, NYC, NY. $30,000, 2000. For general support and technology for Online program.
33. Harvard University, Cambridge, MA. $12,500, 2000. Toward book acquisition fund for Biblioteca Berenson at Villa I Tatti.
34. Harvard University, Cambridge, MA. $12,500, 2000. For additional support toward book acquisition fund for Biblioteca Berenson at Villa I Tatti.
35. Healthcare and Elder Law Programs Corporation, Torrance, CA. $15,000, 2000. For printing and distribution of personalized healthcare workbook.
36. Huntington Library, Art Collections and Botanical Gardens, San Marino, CA. $500,000, 2000. 2-year grant. Toward book acquisitions.
37. Huntington Library, Art Collections and Botanical Gardens, San Marino, CA. $50,000, 2000. Toward acquisitions for Sanford and Helen Berger William Morris Collection.
38. Huntington Library, Art Collections and Botanical Gardens, San Marino, CA. $40,000, 2000. For acquisition of Prince Roland Bonaparte's photographs of Omaha Indians.
39. Huntington Library, Art Collections and Botanical Gardens, San Marino, CA. $10,000, 2000. Toward exhibit, Religion and the Founding of the American Republic.
40. Library Foundation of Los Angeles, Los Angeles, CA. $300,000, 2000. Toward Building Essential Skills in Young Adults initiative.
41. Los Angeles County Public Library Foundation, Downey, CA. $30,000, 2000. Toward Family Multi-ethnic Dramatic Storytelling Festival.
42. Museum Associates, Los Angeles, CA. $50,000, 2000. Toward book acquisition fund for Art Research Library.
43. Omaha Botanical Center, Omaha, NE. $25,000, 2000. Toward Horticulture Resource Library.
44. Pasadena Christian School, Pasadena, CA. $250,000, 2000. Toward construction of Library/Media Center.
45. Saint James Episcopal Church, Saint James School, Wilshire, Los Angeles, CA. $450,000, 2000. Toward construction of Ahmanson Library.
46. University of California at Los Angeles Foundation, William Andrews Clark Memorial Library, Los Angeles, CA. $50,000, 2000. Toward book acquisitions.
47. University of California at Los Angeles Foundation, William Andrews Clark Memorial Library, Los Angeles, CA. $20,000, 2000. For Post-doctoral Fellowship.
48. University of California at Los Angeles Foundation, William Andrews Clark Memorial Library, Los Angeles, CA. $10,000, 2000. For Undergraduate Fellowships.
49. University of Richmond, Richmond, VA. $10,000, 2000. For library materials to support Baroque Festival and to enrich Baroque Art and Music Courses.

Maurice Amado Foundation

Limitations: Giving on a national basis, with some emphasis on Los Angeles, CA and New York, NY.

50. American Jewish Historical Society, NYC, NY. $10,000, 1999.

Elizabeth and Stephen Bechtel, Jr. Foundation

Limitations: Giving primarily in the San Francisco Bay Area and northern CA. No grants to individuals, or for tenured or contract positions, or endowment activities.

51. Berkeley Public Library Foundation, Berkeley, CA. $50,000, 2000. For capital support.
52. Oakland Public Library Foundation, Oakland, CA. $35,000, 2000. For program support.
53. SocialTech, Burlingame, CA. $15,000, 2000. For capital support for TRAK, Technology to Recover Abducted Kids, computer software system designed to help law enforcement agencies locate and recover abducted children.

Arnold and Mabel Beckman Foundation

Limitations: Giving primarily in the U.S.. No support for political or religious purposes, or for research that does not fall within areas of interest. No grants to individuals (except for Beckman Young Investigator's Program), or for dinners, mass mailings, or fundraising campaigns; no loans.

54. Richard Nixon Library and Birthplace Foundation, Yorba Linda, CA. $100,000, 1999.

H. N. & Frances C. Berger Foundation

Limitations: Giving primarily in CA. No grants to individuals.

55. Huntington Library, Friends of the, San Marino, CA. $150,000, 1999. For construction of Botanical Teaching Center.
56. Methodist Hospital of Southern California Foundation, Arcadia, CA. $50,000, 1999. For library.
57. Women at Work, Pasadena, CA. $50,000, 1999. For continued support for Free Job Information Services.

Burton G. Bettingen Corporation

Limitations: Giving primarily in southern CA. No grants to individuals, or for general fundraising events, conferences, seminars, dinners, or mass mailings.

58. Family Helpline, Los Angeles, CA. $50,000, 2000. For general support.

Fritz B. Burns Foundation

Limitations: Giving primarily in the Los Angeles, CA, area. No support for private foundations. No grants to individuals.

59. Library Foundation of Los Angeles, Los Angeles, CA. $10,000, 2000.

The California Endowment

Limitations: Giving limited to CA. No grants to individuals.

60. Boys and Girls Club of Los Angeles, Watts/Willowbrook, Los Angeles, CA. $700,000, 2000. 2-year grant. To develop youth center and health and fitness program to provide health information, referrals and services for medically underserved community in South Central Los Angeles.
61. California Association of Food Banks, Sacramento, CA. $25,000, 2000. To develop library of food bank resources, identify sources of expertise and implement system by which this expertise will be shared with area food banks.
62. California Health Foundation and Trust, Sacramento, CA. $4,250,000, 2000. 2-year grant. To augment resources of California Tele-health and Tele-medicine Center to continue re-granting program to fund and evaluate targeted tele-health and tele-medicine projects in medically underserved regions throughout state.
63. California Health Foundation and Trust, Sacramento, CA. $210,000, 2000. To increase use and quality of tele-health and tele-medicine statewide.
64. California Primary Care Association, Sacramento, CA. $500,000, 2000. To provide technical assistance to member clinics to enhance their information systems capacity.
65. California Primary Care Association, Sacramento, CA. $150,000, 2000. 2-year grant. For continued support for toll-free, multilingual referral service to increase perinatal care awareness, access and use, improve pregnancy outcomes and raise awareness of perinatal care for medically indigent women.
66. California State Foster Parents Association, Anaheim, CA. $15,000, 2000. For activities of information and resource center at Straight

from the Heart which provides resources and information to foster parents.

67. Center for Governmental Studies, Los Angeles, CA. $436,567, 2000. 2-year grant. To develop interactive, electronic community resource center linking low-income individuals to community-building information.

68. Center for Health Care Rights (CHCR), Los Angeles, CA. $1,700,000, 2000. 3-year grant. For joint Health Rights Hotline Project of Center for Health Care Rights and Legal Services of Northern California which will allow continuation of services that provide information and solutions to consumers concerning health and health policy.

69. Central California Blood Bank, Fresno, CA. $100,000, 2000. To promote bone marrow registration program to sponsor individual marrow registrants who do not have financial means to pay registration fees.

70. Community Health Councils, Los Angeles, CA. $500,000, 2000. To provide stakeholders with current information on increased access to health insurance coverage for California children and families.

71. Community Service Education and Research Fund of the Sacramento-El Dorado Medical Society, Sacramento, CA. $144,670, 2000. 1.50-year grant. To establish centralized referral system and clearinghouse for volunteer physicians throughout Sacramento region.

72. Disability Rights Advocates, Oakland, CA. $920,000, 2000. 3-year grant. To decrease health system barriers for people with disabilities in California and to complement information and referral projects such as Disability Wellness Guide.

73. Dominican Santa Cruz Hospital, Santa Cruz, CA. $249,771, 2000. 2-year grant. For start-up support for new cancer resource center which will provide single point of access to information and referral services, train volunteers to advocate for cancer patients and encourage physician interdisciplinary treatment planning.

74. Familia Unida Living with Multiple Sclerosis, Los Angeles, CA. $25,000, 2000. Toward program for individuals with Multiple Sclerosis and their families which provides information, referrals, resources, counseling, and crisis intervention in Spanish and English through telephone, in-home visits, hospital visits, office visits and the Internet.

75. Homeless Prenatal Program, San Francisco, CA. $480,000, 2000. 3-year grant. To enhance parenting skills and promote healthy births, optimal child development and positive health outcomes through home visits, case management, and prenatal and parenting classes for homeless and low-income expectant mothers.

76. Human Response Network, Weaverville, CA. $420,454, 2000. 2-year grant. To support work of health care coordinators in communities who provide children and families access to health care information and transportation to health and social services.

77. Lavender Youth Recreation and Information Center (LYRIC), San Francisco, CA. $55,000, 2000. For statewide expansion of Talkline/Infoline which provides peer support, health information and service referrals to lesbian, gay, bisexual and transgender youth.

78. Narika, Berkeley, CA. $23,492, 2000. To develop guide to health and social service resources for South Asian community in Alameda and Santa Clara counties, and to develop plan and proposal to conduct community-sensitive, scientifically rigorous research survey to assess health and social needs of local South Asian community.

79. Open Door Community Health Centers, Arcata, CA. $130,257, 2000. For start-up support for primary medical service and referral center serving Hispanic migrant workers in Del Norte County.

80. QueensCare Medical Groups, Los Angeles, CA. $304,194, 2000. For purchase, installation, and first year personnel costs of new information system for clinics and managed care program that will provide access to comprehensive, coordinated and affordable health programs to low-income, uninsured and underserved high-risk residents of greater Hollywood area.

81. Reach L.A., Los Angeles, CA. $250,000, 2000. 3-year grant. To reduce incidence of HIV/AIDS among at-risk teens by developing and implementing Computer Active, youth-driven, web-based health education resource library and tracking system.

82. Sacramento Surplus Book Room, Sacramento, CA. $25,000, 2000. To promote and encourage full participation in Census to avoid undercount of Caribbean community in order to ensure community receives appropriate health-related government funding.

83. SeniorNet, San Francisco, CA. $25,000, 2000. To provide health-related information to older Californians via television programs and Web site.

84. Tides Center, San Francisco, CA. $25,000, 2000. To build and supply data to web site that will serve needs of low-income, seriously ill children and their families.

85. United Way of Tulare County, Tulare, CA. $50,000, 2000. To expand information and referral service to link residents with services in community.

86. University of California, Los Angeles, CA. $750,000, 2000. To provide information and analysis regarding access to health care coverage for California's uninsured children and families.

87. Urban League of San Diego, San Diego, CA. $150,000, 2000. For Health Information Project which provides San Diego injection drug users and their partners with health education and intervention services.

The California Wellness Foundation

Limitations: Giving limited to CA; national organizations providing services in CA are also considered. No support for religious or sectarian organizations. No grants to individuals (except for research fellowships and awards), or for annual fund drives, building campaigns, major equipment, or biomedical research.

88. Homeless Prenatal Program, San Francisco, CA. $120,000, 2001. 2-year grant. For core operating support to strengthen organizational capacity and begin implementation of five-year strategic plan.

89. National Health Foundation, Los Angeles, CA. $100,000, 2001. 2-year grant. To expand HealthQuery, health data analysis Web site, to become statewide resource.

90. Nonprofit Resource Center, California Management Assistance Partnership, Sacramento, CA. $100,000, 2001. 2-year grant. For core operating support to strengthen California Management Assistance Partnerships network of management support centers that serve primarily health and social service nonprofit organizations statewide.

91. Resource Center for Nonprofit Management, Riverside, CA. $200,000, 2001. 2-year grant. To build organizational capacity of nonprofit health orgranizations in Riverside and San Bernardino Counties.

Cindy and Ely Callaway Family Foundation

Limitations: Giving on a national basis.

92. Survivors of the Shoah Visual History Foundation, Los Angeles, CA. $10,000, 1999.

The Capital Group Companies Charitable Foundation

Limitations: Giving primarily in CA, with emphasis on Los Angeles. No grants to individuals.

93. Charities Aid Foundation America, Alexandria, VA. $40,000, 2000. For general support.

94. Huntington Library, Art Collections and Botanical Gardens, San Marino, CA. $73,500, 2000. For general support.

95. Huntington Library, Art Collections and Botanical Gardens, San Marino, CA. $36,650, 2000. For general support.

96. Library Foundation of Los Angeles, Los Angeles, CA. $43,150, 2000. For general support.

Chartwell Charitable Foundation

Limitations: Giving primarily in CA and NY.

97. Library Foundation of Los Angeles, Los Angeles, CA. $10,000, 2000.

98. Ronald Reagan Presidential Foundation, Simi Valley, CA. $10,000, 2000.

Cisco Systems Foundation

Limitations: Giving primarily in CA. No support for religious or sectarian organizations. No grants to individuals, or for capital building funds, start-up programs, fundraising events, conferences, or seminars.

99. AIDS Resources Information and Services of Santa Clara County, San Jose, CA. $25,000, 1999. For residential care facility.

The Clorox Company Foundation

Limitations: Giving primarily in Oakland, CA, and other areas of company operations. No support for sectarian religious purposes, or for veterans', political, fraternal, or labor organizations. No grants to individuals, or for goodwill advertising, deficit funding, raffles, benefits, conferences, athletic events or leagues, field trips, tours, travel expenses, media productions, fundraising events, or travel.

100. Houston Public Library, Friends of the, Houston, TX. $10,000, 2000.
101. UniTEQ/PipeVine, San Francisco, CA. $25,000, 2000. For GIFT campaign services.
102. UniTEQ/PipeVine, San Francisco, CA. $10,000, 2000. For GIFT campaign services.

Columbia Foundation

Limitations: Giving primarily in the San Francisco Bay Area, CA and London, England for arts. No support for private foundations, institutions supported by federated campaigns or heavily subsidized by government funds, or projects in medicine or religion. No grants to individuals, or for scholarships, fellowships, ongoing programs, or operating budgets of established agencies.

103. Environmental Protection Information Center (EPIC), Garberville, CA. $100,000, 2000. For general program support for advocacy, litigation, and public education/outreach to conserve forest watershed and endangered species in the Redwood region of Northern California.
104. Foundation Center, San Francisco, CA. $15,000, 2000. For renovating and expanding Foundation Center Library.

Compton Foundation, Inc.

Limitations: Giving on an international basis to U.S.-based organizations for projects in Mexico, Central America, and Sub-Saharan Africa and on a national basis for programs in peace and population and the environment. Other funding limited to areas where board members reside: primarily San Francisco, Marin, and Santa Clara counties, CA. No grants to individuals, or for capital or building funds, no loans (except for program-related investments).

105. Environmental Protection Information Center (EPIC), Garberville, CA. $25,000, 1999.
106. National Security Archive Fund, Center for National Security Studies, DC. $15,000, 1999.
107. Sexuality Information and Education Council of the U.S. (SIECUS), NYC, NY. $15,000, 1999.

S. H. Cowell Foundation

Limitations: Giving limited to CA, excluding southern CA. No support for political or sectarian religious purposes, or hospitals. No grants to individuals, or for operating budgets, endowments, media programs, continuing support, annual campaigns, routine program administration, workshops, symposia, deficit financing, fellowships, academic or other research, medical research or treatment, publications, or conferences.

108. Berkeley Public Library, Berkeley, CA. $75,000, 1999.
109. Bolinas-Stinson Beach Library Improvement Society, Bolinas, CA. $10,000, 1999.

The Walt Disney Company Foundation

Limitations: Giving primarily in areas of company operations, including Los Angeles and Orange County, CA, and Orange and Osceola counties, FL. No support for public agencies, educational institutions, nonprofit organizations supported predominantly by tax dollars, agencies receiving funds from consolidated giving programs supported by the foundation, or sectarian organizations. No grants to individuals (except for employee-related scholarships), or for endowment funds, building campaigns, seed money, or medical research.

110. Library Foundation of Los Angeles, Los Angeles, CA. $50,000, 1999.

Carrie Estelle Doheny Foundation

Limitations: Giving primarily in the Los Angeles, CA, area. No support for tax-supported organizations, radio or television programs, or for political purposes. No grants to individuals, or for endowment funds, publications, travel, advertising, or scholarships.

111. Harbor Pregnancy Help Center, Wilmington, CA. $20,000, 1999. For services for pregnant women with crisis pregnancies.
112. Library Foundation of Los Angeles, Los Angeles, CA. $10,000, 1999. For Grandparents and Books program.

Joseph Drown Foundation

Limitations: Giving primarily in CA. No support for religious purposes. No grants to individuals, or for endowments, capital campaigns, building funds, or seminars or conferences.

113. Jonsson Cancer Center Foundation, Rhonda Fleming Mann Resource Center for Women with Cancer, Los Angeles, CA. $85,000, 2000. To develop Web site.
114. University of California at Los Angeles Foundation, Film and Television Archive, Los Angeles, CA. $25,000, 2000. For preservation of Hearst-Metrotone Newsreel Collection.

Energy Foundation

Limitations: Giving limited to the U.S. and China. No support for sectarian or religious purposes or political organizations. No grants to individuals, or for endowment funds, debt reduction, planning, renovation, maintenance, retrofit, or purchase of buildings, equipment purchases, land acquisition, annual fundraising campaigns, research and development of technology, demonstration projects or capital construction.

115. Clean Air Task Force, Boston, MA. $50,000, 2000. To maintain centralized database designed to help advocates working to clean up or repower nation's dirtiest power plants.
116. National Consumer Law Center, Boston, MA. $100,000, 2000. For continued support of Low-Income Energy Project, which provides high-quality and effective advocacy and informational services to advance energy efficiency and affordability programs available to low-income households.

The Fluor Foundation

Limitations: Giving primarily in areas where the corporation has permanent offices, with some emphasis on Orange County, CA, Greenville, SC, and Fort Bend and Harris County, TX. No support for guilds and sports organizations, veterans', fraternal, labor or religious organizations, or political organizations or campaigns. No grants to individuals (except for employee-related scholarships), or for medical research, film productions, or publishing activities.

117. Columbia Basin College Foundation, Pasco, WA. $25,000, 1999. To upgrade computer resources in student library.

Foundation for Deep Ecology

Limitations: Giving on a national and international basis. No support for curriculum development or K-12 educational projects, or for businesses or debt. No grants for television, video, photography (visual arts) or film productions, research, or individual academic pursuits (including graduate work or scholarships).

118. Environmental Protection Information Center (EPIC), Garberville, CA. $10,000, 2000. For general support.
119. Southwest Center for Biological Diversity, Tucson, AZ. $20,000, 2000. For endangered species listing campaign.

John Jewett & H. Chandler Garland Foundation

Limitations: Giving primarily in CA, with emphasis on southern CA. No grants to individuals, or for seed money.

120. Huntington Library, Art Collections and Botanical Gardens, San Marino, CA. $1,000,000, 1999. For maintenance of botanical gardens.
121. Huntington Library, Friends of the, San Marino, CA. $25,000, 1999. For general support.
122. Los Angeles Public Library, Los Angeles, CA. $10,000, 1999. For adult reading program.

123. Los Angeles Public Library, Los Angeles, CA. $10,000, 1999. For Service to Shut-ins Program.
124. Pasadena Public Library, Pasadena, CA. $10,000, 1999. For adult and family literacy program.

The David Geffen Foundation

Limitations: Giving primarily in Los Angeles, CA, and New York, NY. No grants to individuals or for documentaries or other types of audio-visual programming, including publication of books or magazines.

125. Jewish Community Library of Los Angeles, Los Angeles, CA. $10,000, 1999.
126. Survivors of the Shoah Visual History Foundation, Los Angeles, CA. $200,000, 1999. For general support.
127. William J. Clinton Presidential Foundation, Little Rock, AR. $200,000, 1999. For general support.

The Ann and Gordon Getty Foundation

Limitations: Giving primarily in CA, with emphasis on the San Francisco Bay Area. No grants to individuals.

128. Library Foundation of San Francisco, San Francisco, CA. $10,000, 1999.

J. Paul Getty Trust

Limitations: Giving on an international basis. No grants for operating or endowment purposes, construction or maintenance of buildings, or acquisition of works of art.

129. Antelope Valley Indian Museum Interpretive Association, Friends of the, Lancaster, CA. $19,909, 1999. For electronic cataloguing initiative.
130. Art Museum Image Consortium, Pittsburgh, PA. $20,000, 1999. For special initiative.
131. Center for the Study of Political Graphics, Los Angeles, CA. $250,000, 1999. For electronic cataloguing initiative.
132. Ente Raccolta Vinciana, Milan, Italy. $59,011, 1999. For publications.
133. Finnish Committee for the Restoration of the Viipuri Library, Helsinki, Finland. $50,000, 1999. For architectural conservation.
134. Fondation Le Corbusier, Paris, France. $228,947, 1999. For archival projects.
135. Huntington Library, Art Collections and Botanical Gardens, San Marino, CA. $20,000, 1999. For local libraries.
136. Huntington Library, Art Collections and Botanical Gardens, San Marino, CA. $20,000, 1999. For matching grant.
137. Huntington Library, Art Collections and Botanical Gardens, San Marino, CA. $10,200, 1999. For multicultural internships.
138. Istituto di Studi Rinascimentali, Ferrara, Italy. $25,256, 1999. For Museum Interpretive projects.
139. Metropolitan Museum of Art, NYC, NY. $95,000, 1999. For archival projects.
140. Museum Associates, Los Angeles, CA. $350,000, 1999. For electronic cataloguing initiative.
141. Museum of Modern Art, NYC, NY. $78,000, 1999. For archival projects.
142. National Library of New Zealand, Wellington, New Zealand. $40,000, 1999. For conservation trainings.
143. Natural History Museum of Los Angeles County Foundation, Los Angeles, CA. $34,000, 1999. For electronic cataloguing initiative.
144. Northeast Document Conservation Center, Andover, MA. $150,000, 1999. For conservation training.
145. Norton Simon Museum, Pasadena, CA. $30,000, 1999. For electronic cataloguing initiative.
146. Occidental College, Los Angeles, CA. $137,000, 1999. For electronic cataloguing initiative.
147. Osterreichische Akademie der Wissenschaften, Vienna, Austria. $117,637, 1999. For cataloguing of collections.
148. Scripps College, Claremont, CA. $120,000, 1999. For electronic cataloguing initiative.
149. University of Southern California, Los Angeles, CA. $37,900, 1999. For electronic cataloguing initiative.
150. 18th Street Arts Complex, Santa Monica, CA. $30,000, 1999. For electronic cataloguing initiative.

Richard & Rhoda Goldman Fund

Limitations: Giving primarily in the San Francisco Bay Area, CA. No support for unsolicited proposals from arts organizations, or from primary, secondary, or higher educational institutions. No grants to individuals, (except for Goldman Environmental Prize) or for deficit budgets, endowment funds, documentary films, conferences, research, scholarships, fellowships, matching gifts, or general operating budgets of established organizations; no loans.

151. Alameda County Library Foundation, Fremont, CA. $144,000, 1999. For Jail Tutoring Program, services for low-literacy-level inmates in Alameda County jail system.
152. California Pacific Medical Center Foundation, San Francisco, CA. $25,000, 1999. For Community Health Resource Center, which provides counseling and education to individuals seeking to make difficult lifestyle changes critical to their health.
153. Catholic Charities of Santa Clara County, San Jose, CA. $35,000, 1999. For Grandparent Caregiver Resource Center.
154. Center for Jewish History, NYC, NY. $25,000, 1999. For capital campaign.
155. Childrens Hospital Medical Center of Northern California, Oakland, CA. $40,000, 1999. For Children's Hospital Oakland to create Northern California Pediatric Tuberculosis Resource and Research Center.
156. EarthRights International, DC. $200,000, 1999. For EarthRights Resource Center to support coordination of coalition between human rights and environmental organizations.
157. Foundation Center, San Francisco, CA. $20,000, 1999.
158. Friends and Foundation of the San Francisco Public Library, San Francisco, CA. $10,000, 1999. For Project Read.
159. Homeless Prenatal Program, San Francisco, CA. $25,000, 1999.
160. Intergroup Clearinghouse, San Francisco, CA. $15,000, 1999.
161. Lavender Youth Recreation and Information Center (LYRIC), San Francisco, CA. $20,000, 1999. For general support.
162. National Abortion and Reproductive Rights Action League (NARAL) Foundation, DC. $350,000, 1999. For Choice for America, public-education and grassroots organizing campaign.
163. National Womens Health Network, DC. $40,000, 1999. For program promoting expansion of contraceptive options available to women.
164. Oakland Public Library Foundation, Oakland, CA. $15,000, 1999.

The Grousbeck Family Foundation

Limitations: No grants to individuals.

165. Institute for Multiracial Justice, San Francisco, CA. $60,000, 1999. For general support.
166. Institute for Multiracial Justice, San Francisco, CA. $60,000, 1999. For general support.
167. Women of Color Resource Center, Berkeley, CA. $60,000, 1999. For general support.

Henry L. Guenther Foundation

Limitations: Giving primarily in Los Angeles, CA. Generally no support for government agencies, or religious organizations for religious purposes. No grants to individuals, including scholarships; or for operating deficits.

168. Library Foundation of Los Angeles, Los Angeles, CA. $25,000, 1999.

Walter and Elise Haas Fund

Limitations: Giving primarily in San Francisco, CA; activities of unusual merit in the counties of Alameda, Marin and San Mateo, CA, are also supported. Professional ethics grants are awarded nationally. No grants to individuals, or for deficit financing, general fundraising, or for video or film production or distribution.

169. Greater Bay Area Family Resource Network, San Francisco, CA. $50,000, 1999. For Family Support California.
170. Lavender Youth Recreation and Information Center (LYRIC), San Francisco, CA. $35,000, 1999.
171. Oakland Public Library Foundation, Oakland, CA. $10,000, 1999. For Partners in Achieving School Success (PASS).

Evelyn and Walter Haas, Jr. Fund

Limitations: Giving primarily in San Francisco and Alameda counties, CA. No support for private foundations, consumer or professional groups, labor or trade associations, research centers, or religious organizations. No grants to individuals, or for deficit or emergency financing, workshops, major equipment, scholarships, direct mail campaigns, fundraising events, annual appeals, conferences, publications, capital or endowment campaigns, films or videos, or basic research.

172. California Advocates for Nursing Home Reform, San Francisco, CA. $15,000, 1999. For Residential Care Consumer Information Project.
173. Childrens Council of San Francisco, San Francisco, CA. $50,000, 1999. For Childcare Switchboard.
174. Foundation Center, NYC, NY. $26,000, 1999.
175. Friends and Foundation of the San Francisco Public Library, San Francisco, CA. $20,000, 1999. For Ocean View Library Project.
176. Homeless Prenatal Program, San Francisco, CA. $25,000, 1999. For Homeless Families Project.
177. Homeless Prenatal Program, San Francisco, CA. $20,000, 1999. For Case Management Services Program.
178. Lavender Youth Recreation and Information Center (LYRIC), San Francisco, CA. $25,000, 1999.
179. National Center for Family Philanthropy, DC. $100,000, 1999.
180. Oakland Public Library Foundation, Oakland, CA. $10,000, 1999.

Harden Foundation

Limitations: Giving limited to Monterey County, with emphasis on the Salinas Valley, CA, area. No support for sectarian religious programs, nonagricultural related educational programs, operating foundations, or associations established for the benefit of organizations receiving substantial tax support. No grants for endowments, annual campaigns, conferences, or fundraising events.

181. Marina Larger Library Committee, Marina, CA. $10,000, 2000. For library site in Marina.
182. Monterey County Free Libraries, Foundation for, Salinas, CA. $10,000, 2000. For Electronic Information Access program.
183. Monterey County Free Libraries, Foundation for, Salinas, CA. $10,000, 2000. For Electronic Information Access program.

The John Randolph Haynes and Dora Haynes Foundation

Limitations: Giving limited to the greater Los Angeles, CA, area. No grants to individuals, or for building or endowment funds or operating budgets.

184. Huntington Library, Art Collections and Botanical Gardens, San Marino, CA. $21,600, 2000. For fellowships in History Division.
185. Museum of Chinese-American History, Los Angeles, CA. $36,350, 2000. For Archive Project.

Hedco Foundation

Limitations: Giving primarily in CA. No grants to individuals, or for general support, operating budgets, endowment funds, scholarships, fellowships, special projects, research, publications, or conferences; no loans.

186. Oakland Public Library, Oakland, CA. $56,016, 1999. For capital expenses.

The William and Flora Hewlett Foundation

Limitations: Giving limited to the San Francisco Bay Area, CA, for family and community development program; performing arts primarily limited to the Bay Area; environment programs limited to North American West. No support for medicine and health-related projects, law, criminal justice, and related fields, juvenile, delinquency or drug and alcohol addiction, prevention or treatment programs, problems of the elderly and the handicapped, or television or radio projects. No grants to individuals, or for building funds or capital construction funds, basic research, equipment, seminars, conferences, festivals, touring costs, fundraising drives, scholarships, or fellowships; no loans.

187. Allied Fellowship Service, Oakland, CA. $50,000, 2000. For Family Resource Network project.
188. American Music Center, NYC, NY. $280,000, 2000. 3-year grant. For general support and for new Web site project.

189. EdSource, Menlo Park, CA. $480,000, 2000. 3-year grant. For general support.
190. Library of Congress, DC. $200,000, 2000. For I Hear America Singing concert series.
191. Library of Congress, DC. $50,000, 2000. For conference entitled Democracy and the Rule of Law in a Changing World Order.
192. Link Services, San Francisco, CA. $50,000, 2000. For general support.
193. National Housing Institute, Orange, NJ. $150,000, 2000. 3-year grant. For Shelterforce, journal used by nonprofit, community-based organizations active in affordable housing, economic development and related services.
194. Sexuality Information and Education Council of the U.S. (SIECUS), NYC, NY. $1,000,000, 2000. 3-year grant. For general support.

Jaquelin Hume Foundation

Limitations: Giving primarily in the San Francisco Bay Area, CA, and to organizations with a national impact. No support for organizations outside the U.S.. No grants to individuals.

195. Foundation Center, NYC, NY. $10,000, 1999.
196. Friends and Foundation of the San Francisco Public Library, San Francisco, CA. $25,000, 1999.

The James Irvine Foundation

Limitations: Giving limited to CA. No support for agencies receiving substantial government support. No grants to individuals.

197. Art Resources and Technical Services (Arts Inc.), Los Angeles, CA. $50,000, 2000. 1.50-year grant. For business planning and online publication of 5th edition of Greater Los Angeles Arts Resource Directory.
198. Catholic Charities of Santa Clara County, San Jose, CA. $545,000, 2000. For planning phase of Communities Organizing Resources to Advance Learning (CORAL) Initiative in San Jose.
199. Catholic Charities of Santa Clara County, San Jose, CA. $75,000, 2000. For preplanning phase of Communities Organizing Resources to Advance Learning (CORAL) Initiative in San Jose.
200. EdSource, Menlo Park, CA. $400,000, 2000. 2-year grant. For core support.
201. Foundation Center, NYC, NY. $105,000, 2000. 3-year grant. For core support and expansion of programs and services for grantseekers and grantmakers at San Francisco office.
202. HandsNet, San Jose, CA. $40,000, 2000. For Youth Media Assessment Project, to document current capacities of youth media organizations in California and provide recommendations for shared learning and collaboration opportunities.
203. Link Services, San Francisco, CA. $50,000, 2000. For strategic planning to build organizational capacity to scale its product, Internet-based matching system that connects nonprofits with research needs and university-based researchers.
204. National Center for Family Philanthropy, DC. $100,000, 2000. 2-year grant. For assistance, education, and information on philanthropic giving to donors, potential donors, and philanthropic advisors in California.
205. New Vision Partners, Pasadena, CA. $4,000,000, 2000. 2-year grant. For implementation of Communities Organizing Resources to Advance Learning (CORAL) Initiative in Pasadena.
206. United Way of Fresno County, Fresno, CA. $75,000, 2000. For preplanning phase of Communities Organizing Resources to Advance Learning (CORAL) Initiative in Fresno.
207. YMCA of Greater Long Beach, Long Beach, CA. $525,000, 2000. For planning phase of Communities Organizing Resources to Advance Learning (CORAL) Initiative in Long Beach.

The Fletcher Jones Foundation

Limitations: Giving primarily in CA. No support for K-12 schools; political campaigns or organizations. No grants to individuals, or for operating funds, deficit financing, conferences, seminars, workshops, travel exhibits, surveys, or projects supported by government agencies; no loans.

208. Biola University, La Mirada, CA. $400,000, 1999. For equipment for library.

209. Huntington Library, Art Collections and Botanical Gardens, San Marino, CA. $25,000, 1999. For Botanical Library.
210. Library Foundation of Los Angeles, Los Angeles, CA. $250,000, 1999. To enlarge database.
211. Loyola Marymount University, Law School, Los Angeles, CA. $500,000, 1999. To upgrade library.
212. Mount Saint Marys College, Los Angeles, CA. $250,000, 1999. For construction of library.

The Henry J. Kaiser Family Foundation

Limitations: Giving limited to CA for the California Grants Program only; and South Africa for the international grants program; other grants nationwide. No support for political organizations. No grants to individuals (except for Media Fellows and consultants), or for construction, equipment, capital funds, annual appeals, fundraising events, ongoing general operating expenses, or indirect costs; generally no funding for direct service type projects.

213. National Health Law Program, Los Angeles, CA. $45,000, 1999. For resource guides and workshops on immigration and health.

Koret Foundation

Limitations: Giving limited to the Bay Area counties of San Francisco, Alameda, Contra Costa, Marin, Santa Clara, and San Mateo, CA; giving also in Israel. No support for private foundations, or veterans', fraternal, military, religious, or sectarian organizations whose principal activity is for the benefit of their own membership. No grants to individuals (except for the Koret Israel Prize), or for general fundraising campaigns, scholarships, endowment funds, equipment funds, deficit financing, or emergency funds; no loans.

214. Berkeley Public Library Foundation, Berkeley, CA. $100,000, 2000.
215. SocialTech, Burlingame, CA. $100,000, 2000.
216. SocialTech, Burlingame, CA. $84,455, 2000.

The Lincy Foundation

Limitations: Giving primarily in CA. No grants to individuals.

217. Help of Southern Nevada, Las Vegas, NV. $10,000, 2000.

Marin Community Foundation

Limitations: Giving from Buck Trust limited to Marin County, CA; other giving on a national and international basis with emphasis on the San Francisco Bay Area. No grants for planning initiatives, research, or generally for capital projects (except those meeting criteria specified in the funding guidelines). Other limitations specific to each program area are outlined in the funding guidelines.

218. Foundation Center, NYC, NY. $19,000, 2000. To expand information, programs, and services to grantmakers and grantseekers in the Bay Area.
219. Impact Project, Arlington, MA. $12,000, 2000. To publish More Than Money journal.
220. Marin County Housing Authority, San Rafael, CA. $318,922, 2000. For continued operating support for Housing Assistline.
221. Marin County Housing Authority, San Rafael, CA. $75,000, 2000. For Shelter Plus Care program, which provides services to disabled households.
222. marin.org, Novato, CA. $120,000, 2000. To upgrade network, server, and software capacity of MIDAS, which serves educational, nonprofit, government, and public service organizations.
223. Marin, County of, San Rafael, CA. $15,000, 2000. For collaborative process to develop workbook for creating housing elements addressing need for affordable housing.
224. Marin, County of, San Rafael, CA. $15,000, 2000. For collaborative process to develop workbook for creating housing elements addressing the need for affordable housing.
225. Marin, County of, San Rafael, CA. $10,000, 2000. For planning of Health and Human Services Information Fair.
226. Peninsula Library Foundation, Belvedere, CA. $10,500, 2000.
227. Small Press Distribution, Berkeley, CA. $10,000, 2000. For Get Lit Program and Library Outreach Project to increase availability of books by Marin County writers and small literary publishers in bookstores and libraries.
228. United Negro College Fund, Fairfax, VA. $25,000, 2000. For College Fair for Marin high school students.

Mattel Children's Foundation

Limitations: Giving on a national and international basis, with emphasis in Los Angeles, CA, Mount Laurel, NJ, Buffalo, NY, and Madison, WI. No support for religious, fraternal, athletic, social, veterans', or labor organizations. No grants to individuals, or for research or courtesy advertising; no loans.

229. Alliance for Technology Access, San Rafael, CA. $53,000, 1999. For continued support for Family Learning Centers project.

B. C. McCabe Foundation

Limitations: Giving primarily in CA.

230. Social Services Referral Center, Whittier, CA. $62,500, 1999.

Moore Family Foundation

Limitations: Giving primarily in CA. No grants to individuals.

231. Ecotrust, Portland, OR. $75,000, 1999. For Bioregional Information System, Bioregional Profile Project, mapping support, conservation based development planning and Coastal Cities and the Salmon Initiative.
232. Ecotrust, Portland, OR. $50,000, 1999. For ShoreBank Pacific Bank and Interrain Pacific Programs.

The Kenneth T. and Eileen L. Norris Foundation

Limitations: Giving limited to southern CA. No support for political organizations or campaigns. No grants to individuals; no loans.

233. Huntington Library, Art Collections and Botanical Gardens, San Marino, CA. $400,000, 2000. For general support.
234. Huntington Library, Art Collections and Botanical Gardens, San Marino, CA. $10,000, 2000. For general support.
235. Library Foundation of Los Angeles, Los Angeles, CA. $30,000, 2000. For general support.
236. Rancho Santa Fe Library Guild, Rancho Santa Fe, CA. $10,000, 2000. For general support.
237. Rancho Santa Fe Library Guild, Rancho Santa Fe, CA. $10,000, 2000. For general support.
238. Ronald Reagan Presidential Foundation, Simi Valley, CA. $10,000, 2000. For general support.

Bernard Osher Foundation

Limitations: Giving limited to Alameda and San Francisco counties, CA. No grants to individuals.

239. Berkeley Public Library, Berkeley, CA. $100,000, 1999.

The David and Lucile Packard Foundation

Limitations: Giving for the arts and community development primarily in Santa Clara, San Mateo, Santa Cruz, and Monterey counties, CA, with some support also in the Pueblo, CO, area; national giving for child health and development; national and international giving for population and the environment. No support for religious purposes. No grants to individuals.

240. Alameda, County of, San Leandro, CA. $20,000, 2000. To develop Operational Database for Children and Families Commission.
241. Americans for the Arts, DC. $585,000, 2000. For National Arts Policy Center and Clearinghouse.
242. Americans for the Arts, DC. $100,000, 2000. For general operating support.
243. Americans for the Arts, DC. $50,000, 2000. For Nonprofit Arts and Entertainment Initiative.
244. California History Center Foundation, De Anza College, Cupertino, CA. $20,000, 2000. For strategic planning.
245. Community Health Partnership of Santa Clara County, San Jose, CA. $267,500, 2000. 2-year grant. For Member Services Network.
246. Conservation Fund, Arlington, VA. $32,000, 2000. For Integrated Knowledge Database.

247. Essential Information, DC. $40,000, 2000. For Sprawl Watch Clearinghouse.
248. Family Voices, Algodones, NM. $391,182, 2000. For report, From Data to Action: Putting Information from Families to Work.
249. Family Voices, Algodones, NM. $47,805, 2000. For assessment and planning, board development, and leadership transition.
250. Finance Project, Welfare Information Network, DC. $45,000, 2000. For California Welfare Information Clearinghouse Web Site.
251. Foundation Center, NYC, NY. $100,000, 2000. For new facility in Washington D.C.
252. Future Families, Aptos, CA. $36,831, 2000. For Adoptive Family Therapeutic and Educational Resources (AFTER) Project, single point of access for post adoption services for Aptos region, including information and referral, real-time library, help for families experiencing problems with Adoption Assistance Program, advocacy, behavioral, emotional and other family issues, crisis resolution, access to network of adoptive parent, and child, support groups.
253. HandsNet, San Jose, CA. $200,000, 2000. 2-year grant. For Technology Learning Community Initiative.
254. Intensive Family Preservation Services National Network, Laurel, MD. $45,000, 2000. For Strategic Planning and Fund Development Initiative.
255. Johns Hopkins University, International Society for Third-Sector Research, Baltimore, MD. $100,000, 2000. For Regional Network meetings.
256. Joint Venture: Silicon Valley, San Jose, CA. $900,000, 2000. 2-year grant. For Silicon Valley Civic Action Network.
257. Kelola, Sulawesi, Indonesia. $40,000, 2000. For Grassroots Coastal Zone Village Network.
258. Kern County Superintendent of Schools, Department of Child Development and Family Services, Bakersfield, CA. $39,882, 2000. For Local Investment in Child Care (LINCC) Community Connection for Child Care.
259. Linangan Ng Kababaihan, Quezon City, Philippines. $790,000, 2000. 4-year grant. To expand access to reproductive health care information and services.
260. Link Services, San Francisco, CA. $100,000, 2000. For Planning and Pilot Phase for Link.
261. London Family Court Clinic, London, Canada. $249,136, 2000. To publish handbook for educators, youth agency workers, juvenile probation officers, and law enforcement about childhood exposure to domestic violence.
262. Los Altos, City of, Los Altos, CA. $10,000, 2000. To survey Los Altos Library service area.
263. Monterey County Free Libraries, Foundation for, Salinas, CA. $82,856, 2000. 2-year grant. For Homework Center Program.
264. National Center for Family Philanthropy, DC. $150,000, 2000. To publish The Guide to Starting a Family Foundation.
265. Population Services International, DC. $800,000, 2000. For Green Star Clinic Network in Pakistan.
266. Remedios AIDS Foundation, Manila, Philippines. $556,000, 2000. 3-year grant. For Youthzone, shopping mall-based center for Filipino youth.
267. Resources for Human Development, Future Search Network, Philadelphia, PA. $50,000, 2000. For Future Search Conference in Nigeria.
268. San Jose State University Foundation, San Jose, CA. $77,340, 2000. For Beethoven Bibliography Database.
269. Santa Clara, County of, San Jose, CA. $50,000, 2000. To implement Santa Clara County Green Book project.
270. Scenic America, DC. $40,000, 2000. To develop strategies for Affiliate Network.
271. Sexuality Information and Education Council of the U.S. (SIECUS), NYC, NY. $1,000,000, 2000. 3-year grant. For Media Outreach Initiative.
272. Sexuality Information and Education Council of the U.S. (SIECUS), NYC, NY. $50,000, 2000. For Executive Search.
273. SocialTech, Burlingame, CA. $3,000,000, 2000. 2-year grant. For national launch of redesigned Technology to Recover Abducted Kids (TRAK) Project software. TRAK is an investigative tool usable by any police officer to quickly and easily create photo bulletins and share them electronically with other law enforcement jurisdictions, the media, and the community.
274. Virginia Tech Foundation, Blacksburg, VA. $50,000, 2000. For Community Arts Network.
275. Volunteer Consulting Group, NYC, NY. $50,000, 2000. To develop boardnetUSA, Internet resource for connecting board candidates and nonprofit organizations.
276. World Conservation Monitoring Centre, Cambridge, England. $150,000, 2000. 2-year grant. For Marine Ornamentals Information Service.

The Ralph M. Parsons Foundation

Limitations: Giving limited to Los Angeles County, CA, with the exception of some grants for higher education. No support for sectarian, religious, or fraternal purposes, or for programs for which substantial support from government or other sources is readily available. No grants to individuals, or for continuing support, annual campaigns, federated fundraising appeals, emergency or endowment funds, land acquisition, workshops, exhibits, surveys, or conferences.

277. Aviva Family and Childrens Services, Aviva Center, Los Angeles, CA. $50,000, 1999. For management information system at residential facility serving severely emotionally disturbed adolescent girls.
278. Boys and Girls Club, Variety, Los Angeles, CA. $40,000, 1999. For computer learning center and library.
279. California Heritage Museum, Santa Monica, CA. $25,000, 1999. For community outreach programs and to computerize photography archives.
280. Shelter Partnership, Los Angeles, CA. $65,000, 1999. For Shelter Resource Bank, which provides basic goods to frontline homeless service agencies.
281. South Pasadena Educational Foundation, South Pasadena, CA. $53,600, 1999. For computer equipment for Libraries Without Walls.
282. Venice Family Clinic, Venice, CA. $350,000, 1999. For Phase I of computerized management information system.

Pasadena Foundation

Limitations: Giving limited to the Pasadena, CA, area. No support for private foundations, organizations seeking to influence legislation, or for educational institutions or sectarian organizations (except for programs sponsored by educational institutions or sectarian organizations). No grants to individuals, or for continuing support, scholarships, general or operating support, expenses incurred in performance of program services, or elections.

283. Altadena Library, Friends of the, Altadena, CA. $12,000, 1999. For computers with Internet and multimedia.

Peninsula Community Foundation

Limitations: Giving limited to San Mateo County and northern Santa Clara County, CA. No support for fraternal organizations, religious organizations for religious purposes, or political activities. No grants for endowment funds, annual campaigns, building funds, deficit financing, land acquisition, research or fundraising events.

284. AIDS Resources Information and Services of Santa Clara County, San Jose, CA. $30,000, 2000. For support to continue and expand programs.
285. Bancroft Library, Friends of the, Berkeley, CA. $10,000, 2000. For processing recently acquired collection of personal and professional writings and photographs of Bill Mott, Sr..
286. Franklin-McKinley School District, San Jose, CA. $15,000, 2000. For Kennedy School Library Restoration Project.
287. Homework Central, San Mateo, CA. $42,500, 2000. For continuing support for capacity-building for school year, including support for associate director, volunteer coordinator, and fund development consultant.
288. Las Lomitas School District, Menlo Park, CA. $25,000, 2000. For New Library Building Fund.
289. Lavender Youth Recreation and Information Center (LYRIC), San Francisco, CA. $10,000, 2000. For continued support for Talkline/Infoline which provides peer support and referrals to underserved lesbian, gay, bisexual, transgender, and questioning young people in San Mateo and Santa Clara counties.

290. Redwood City Library Foundation, Redwood City, CA. $101,505, 2000. 1.50-year grant. For librarian to coordinate School Readiness Program and related materials.
291. San Mateo County Office of Education, Redwood City, CA. $35,000, 2000. For printing and distribution of Parent's Guide to Kindergarten to Peninsula Partnership collaborative sites and to school districts and various community agencies that serve children in San Mateo County.
292. San Mateo Public Library Foundation, San Mateo, CA. $25,700, 2000. For continued support for Project Read's Computer Lab, specifically salary support for half-time computer lab coordinator.
293. San Mateo-Foster City Education Foundation, San Mateo, CA. $10,000, 2000. For Books for School Libraries.
294. South San Francisco Library, South San Francisco, CA. $40,275, 2000. For Project Read's Family Learning Lab.
295. Volunteer Center of San Mateo County, San Mateo, CA. $25,000, 2000. For Organizational Capacity Grants Initiative (OCGI) to complete Information Technology Project that will streamline day-to-day operations and communicate information about Volunteer Center's initiatives and services.

The Ralphs-Food 4 Less Foundation

Limitations: Giving primarily in southern CA. No support for political activities or fund programs that are discriminatory. Generally, no grants to individuals, or for memorial campaigns or endowments.

296. Labor Community Services Food and Emergency Program, Los Angeles, CA. $10,000, 1999. To provide increase of food delivery to unemployed, seniors, disabled and homeless families and individuals.

Righteous Persons Foundation

Limitations: Giving on a national basis. No support for individual schools or synagogues. No grants to individuals or for research, publications, or projects related to the Middle East.

297. Javne Fund, NYC, NY. $32,000, 1999.
298. Jewish Womens Archives, Brookline, MA. $40,000, 1999.
299. National Yiddish Book Center, Amherst, MA. $100,000, 1999.

Mary Stuart Rogers Foundation

Limitations: Giving primarily in CA.

300. Provo City Library, Provo, UT. $1,000,000, 1999. For general support.

Rosenberg Foundation

Limitations: Giving limited to CA, except for national grants related to the promotion of philanthropy and for projects likely to benefit CA. No grants to individuals, or for endowment, building, or capital funds, operating expenses of established agencies, scholarships, fellowships, continuing support, annual campaigns, emergency funds, deficit financing, matching funds, land acquisition, renovation projects, or conferences and seminars; generally no grants for equipment, films, or publications (except when a necessary part of larger project).

301. Foundation Center, NYC, NY. $18,000, 2000. For national and Bay Area programs.

The San Diego Foundation

Limitations: Giving primarily in the greater San Diego, CA, region. No support for political or religious organizations. No grants to individuals, or for annual or capital fund campaigns, endowment funds, conferences, travel, or to underwrite fundraising events and performances.

302. Athenaeum Music and Arts Library, La Jolla, CA. $12,249, 1999.
303. San Diego Public Library, San Diego, CA. $31,896, 1999.
304. Solana Beach Library, Friends of, Solana Beach, CA. $490,000, 1999.

The San Francisco Foundation

Limitations: Giving limited to the San Francisco Bay Area, CA, counties of Alameda, Contra Costa, Marin, San Francisco, and San Mateo. No support for religious purposes. No grants for annual campaigns, general fundraising campaigns, emergency or endowment funds, deficit financing, matching funds, or for scholarships or fellowships, except when so designated by donor.

305. Berkeley Public Library Foundation, Berkeley, CA. $10,000, 2000.
306. EdSource, Menlo Park, CA. $10,000, 2000.
307. Foundation Center, San Francisco, CA. $55,000, 2000. 3-year grant. Toward move into larger space and computerized research capabilities.
308. Friends and Foundation of the San Francisco Public Library, San Francisco, CA. $15,350, 2000.
309. Homeless Prenatal Program, San Francisco, CA. $16,000, 2000.
310. Jewish Womens Archives, Brookline, MA. $35,000, 2000.
311. Project Inform, San Francisco, CA. $21,000, 2000.
312. San Francisco Network of Mental Health Clients, San Francisco, CA. $15,000, 2000. For continued support to enhance quality of life for homeless and mentally ill.
313. San Francisco Network of Mental Health Clients, San Francisco, CA. $10,000, 2000.
314. University of California, Bancroft Library, Berkeley, CA. $14,750, 2000.
315. University of California, Water Resources Center Archives, Berkeley, CA. $15,000, 2000. To develop inventory and interactive information system for all San Francisco Bay Fund projects, with links to other systems.

Santa Barbara Foundation

Limitations: Giving limited to Santa Barbara County, CA. No support for religious organizations or schools, colleges, or universities. No grants to individuals (except for scholarship and student loan programs for Santa Barbara County secondary school graduates), annual campaigns, deficit financing, endowment funds, scholarships, fellowships, or research.

316. Lompoc Public Library, Friends of, Lompoc, CA. $20,000, 1999. For books and materials for three branches; shelving, tables and chairs for Vandenberg Village.
317. Santa Barbara Public Library, Friends of the, Santa Barbara, CA. $25,000, 1999. For books and materials for bookmobile and seven branches.
318. Solvang Heritage Associates, Solvang, CA. $10,000, 1999. For Archival Video Project.

The Charles Schwab Corporation Foundation

Limitations: Giving primarily in the San Francisco Bay Area, CA; limited giving where company has branch locations (350 cities nationwide); state or national organizations are considered only if they serve branch communities; grants are mostly to local organizations. No support for religious purposes, athletic organizations, or single-disease organizations. No grants for advertising, scholarship funds, colleges, universities, or medical research; no challeage grants.

319. Foundation Center, San Francisco, CA. $14,500, 2000.
320. Oakland Public Library Foundation, Oakland, CA. $10,000, 2000.
321. Project Inform, San Francisco, CA. $12,500, 2000.

Charles and Helen Schwab Foundation

Limitations: Giving limited to San Francisco and San Mateo counties, CA.

322. Friends and Foundation of the San Francisco Public Library, San Francisco, CA. $29,000, 2000. For Center for Learning Differences.

Sierra Health Foundation

Limitations: Giving limited to the following CA counties: Alpine, Amador, Butte, Calaveras, Colusa, El Dorado, Glenn, Lassen, Modoc, Mono, Nevada, Placer, Plumas, Sacramento, San Joaquin, Shasta, Sierra, Siski-you, Solano (eastern), Stanislaus, Sutter, Tehama, Trinity, Tuolumne, Yolo, and Yuba. No support for programs, activities, or organizations that are not health-related. No grants to individuals, or for endowments.

323. Nonprofit Resource Center, Sacramento, CA. $25,000, 1999. For challenge grant to expand training of health personnel.

Levi Strauss Foundation

Limitations: Giving generally limited to areas of company operations in AR, CA, FL, GA, KY, NV, TN, and TX. No support for sectarian or religious purposes. No grants to individuals, or for sponsorships, tickets to special events, or courtesy advertising; endowments, capital campaigns, research, conferences, films, videos, or publications are considered only if they are an integral part of a larger effort being supported.

324. Body Positive Resource Center, Miami, FL. $20,000, 1999. To expand HIV/AIDS educational and wellness center with multipurpose library and full gym facility.

325. Center for Democratic Renewal and Education, Atlanta, GA. $50,000, 1999. To develop climate reports in targeted states across country to help citizens understand immediate threat and implications of hate activity, hate crimes, and hate groups.

326. Center for Entrepreneurship and Economic Development, Edinburg, TX. $70,000, 1999. For continued support for funding information library and technical assistance center for nonprofits in Rio Grande Valley.

327. Charities Aid Foundation, West Malling, England. $330,000, 1999. To establish Advised Fund to support grants in areas of HIV/AIDS, economic empowerment, social justice and youth empowerment in England and Scotland.

328. Charities Aid Foundation, West Malling, England. $220,000, 1999. To establish Advised Fund to support programs in areas of HIV/AIDS, economic empowerment, social justice and youth empowerment in Germany.

329. Community AIDS Treatment Information Exchange (CATIE), Toronto, Canada. $40,000, 1999. To develop national membership base of nonprofits, health care providers and people with HIV/AIDS in order to strengthen treatment information services.

330. El Paso Community College, El Paso, TX. $30,000, 1999. To improve bilingual vocational training programs for limited English-speaking, dislocated workers by providing information about available resources as well as assistance with finding jobs.

331. Foundation Center, NYC, NY. $15,000, 1999. To provide information to grantmakers and grantseekers to expand San Francisco field office library.

Stuart Foundation

Limitations: Giving primarily in CA and WA. No grants to individuals, or generally for endowments, building funds, or annual campaigns.

332. Foundation Center, San Francisco, CA. $10,000, 1999. Toward building new facility.

333. Greatschools.net, San Francisco, CA. $200,000, 1999. To further develop and expand School Profiles on the Web for all California schools.

334. New Beginnings, San Diego, CA. $75,000, 1999. To support planning for information technology assistance program.

335. University of California, Graduate School of Education, Berkeley, CA. $485,702, 1999. To develop network of career academies in Seattle.

S. Mark Taper Foundation

Limitations: Giving primarily in CA. No grants to individuals.

336. Los Angeles County Public Library Foundation, Downey, CA. $90,000, 1999.

Tenet Healthcare Foundation

Limitations: Giving on a nationwide basis, with emphasis on communities where Tenet employees live and work.

337. Cancer Association of Greater New Orleans, New Orleans, LA. $10,000, 2000. To help print resource book for breast cancer patients.

338. Community Health Library of Los Gatos, Los Gatos, CA. $35,000, 2000. For general operating support.

339. Educational and Research Trust of the Missouri Hospital Association, Jefferson City, MO. $10,000, 2000. To assess and develop repository/lending library of health care related materials translated into common languages of Saint Louis community.

340. Educational and Research Trust of the Missouri Hospital Association, Jefferson City, MO. $10,000, 2000. To perform needs assessment of culture- and language-specific health education materials and develop inventory of these materials to be made available to health care providers treating patients with limited English proficiency.

341. Health Promotion Council of Southeastern Pennsylvania, Philadelphia, PA. $25,000, 2000. For development and printing of easy-to-read guide explaining available healthcare options for medically uninsured or underinsured.

342. Senior Adult Services, Carrollton, TX. $10,000, 2000. For case management, information and referral, mobile meals, home repairs, and transportation for senior population.

The Times Mirror Foundation

Limitations: Giving primarily in communities served by the company's subsidiaries, with emphasis on southern CA. No support for religious, political, fraternal, veterans', or labor organizations. No grants to individuals, or for publications, conferences, or films; no loans.

343. Long Beach Public Library Foundation, Long Beach, CA. $15,000, 1999.

344. Los Feliz Library, Friends of, Los Angeles, CA. $10,000, 1999.

The Valley Foundation

Limitations: Giving limited to Santa Clara County, CA. No support for religious purposes. No grants to individuals.

345. Community Health Library of Los Gatos, Los Gatos, CA. $50,000, 1999. For equipment, books and videos, administrative support and assistant librarian.

346. Community Health Partnership of Santa Clara County, San Jose, CA. $20,000, 1999. To update and reprint Women's Health Resource Directories into Chinese, English, Spanish and Vietnamese.

347. Saint Vincent de Paul Society of Santa Clara County, San Jose, CA. $15,000, 1999. For salary of Emergency Services Coordinator for Gilroy Help Desk.

Wayne & Gladys Valley Foundation

Limitations: Giving primarily in Alameda and Contra Costa counties, CA.

348. Eden Information and Referral Service, Hayward, CA. $15,000, 2000. For budget support.

349. John F. Kennedy University, Orinda, CA. $1,000,000, 2000. For construction of library at new site in Concord.

350. National Association for Visually Handicapped, San Francisco, CA. $20,793, 2000. To establish Low Vision Aids Library at Mercy Retirement and Care Center.

351. Saint Annes Catholic Church, Walnut Creek, CA. $36,292, 2000. For expansion of hall and library, and facility upgrades.

352. San Leandro Public Library Foundation, San Leandro, CA. $125,000, 2000. For computer equipment, educational materials and furnishings for newly renovated library.

Wallis Foundation

Limitations: Giving primarily in CA. No grants to individuals.

353. Friends and Foundation of the San Francisco Public Library, San Francisco, CA. $10,000, 2000.

Wasserman Foundation

Limitations: Giving primarily in CA. No grants to individuals.

354. John F. Kennedy Library Foundation, Boston, MA. $50,000, 1999.

355. John F. Kennedy Library Foundation, Boston, MA. $10,000, 1999.

356. Lyndon Baines Johnson Foundation, Austin, TX. $50,000, 1999.

357. Survivors of the Shoah Visual History Foundation, Los Angeles, CA. $200,000, 1999.

Weingart Foundation

Limitations: Giving limited to 7 southern CA counties; Los Angeles, Kern, Orange, Santa Barbara, Riverside, San Bernadino, and Ventura. No support for environmental or religious programs, political refugee or international concerns, federated fundraising groups, or national organizations. No grants to individuals, or for endowment funds, normal operating expenses, annual campaigns, emergency funds, deficit financing, and acquisition, scholarships, fellowships, seminars, conferences, publications, workshops, travel, surveys, films, medical research, or publishing activities.

358. Congregation Beth Israel, San Diego, CA. $250,000, 2000. 2-year grant. To build library.
359. Foundation Center, NYC, NY. $25,000, 2000. For program serving foundations and other grantmakers.
360. Huntington Library, Art Collections and Botanical Gardens, San Marino, CA. $10,000, 2000. For lecture series.
361. Oaks School, Los Angeles, CA. $30,000, 2000. For library relocation and expansion project.
362. Resource Center for Nonprofit Management, Riverside, CA. $10,000, 2000. Toward library equipment.
363. University of California, Los Angeles, CA. $10,000, 2000. For Clark Library.

The Wells Fargo Foundation

Limitations: Giving primarily in areas of company operations, including AZ, CO, IA, IL, IN, MN, MT, ND, NE, NM, NV, OH, SD, TX, WI, and WY. No support for religious organizations for religious purposes, or for fraternal organizations. No grants to individuals, or for conferences, tickets, or travel; no loans.

364. Minneapolis Neighborhood Employment Network, Minneapolis, MN. $12,000, 1999.
365. Saint Paul Public Library, Friends of the, Saint Paul, MN. $38,454, 1999.
366. University of New Mexico, University General Libraries, Albuquerque, NM. $10,000, 1999.
367. W. H. Johnston Foundation, Fort Dodge, IA. $10,000, 1999.

Wood-Claeyssens Foundation

Limitations: Giving limited to Santa Barbara and Ventura counties, CA. No support for tax-supported educational institutions, government-funded organizations, religious organizations or political organizations. No grants to individuals or for medical research.

368. Lompoc District Libraries Foundation, Lompoc, CA. $10,000, 2000.

The Zellerbach Family Fund

Limitations: Giving primarily in the San Francisco Bay Area, CA. No grants to individuals, or for capital or endowment funds, research, scholarships, or fellowships; no loans.

369. Alameda County Network of Mental Health Clients, Berkeley, CA. $10,000, 1999. For Bay Area Network of Mental Health Clients, coordination and organizational development and training program for mental health client self-help agencies in Bay Area.
370. Alameda County Network of Mental Health Clients, Berkeley, CA. $10,000, 1999. For Mental Health Technical Assistance Program, coordination and organizational development and training program for mental health client self-help agencies in Bay area.
371. Community Housing Development Corporation of North Richmond, Richmond, CA. $25,000, 1999. To upgrade technology and information systems.
372. Foundation Center, San Francisco, CA. $33,000, 1999. 2-year grant. Toward relocation, expansion and general support of office and library.

COLORADO

Boettcher Foundation

Limitations: Giving limited to CO. No grants to individuals (except for scholarship program), or for endowment funds.

373. Columbine High School, Littleton, CO. $50,000, 2000. Toward construction of new library.
374. Cortez Public Library, Cortez, CO. $15,000, 2000. Toward expansion.
375. Hotchkiss Public Library, Hotchkiss, CO. $40,000, 2000. Toward library expansion.
376. Mountain Resource Center, Conifer, CO. $60,000, 2000. Toward new headquarters and service center.

Temple Hoyne Buell Foundation

Limitations: Giving primarily in CO. No support for political organizations, sectarian programs, or promoting religion. No grants to individuals,

or for past operating deficit, retirement of debt, testimonial dinners, membership drives, conferences or endowments; no loans.

377. Colorado Office of Resource and Referral Agencies, Englewood, CO. $15,000, 1999. For general operating support.
378. Denver Public Library, Denver, CO. $33,000, 1999. For processing and cataloging of Temple Hoyne Buell's architectural record collection.
379. Denver Public Library Friends Foundation, Denver, CO. $20,000, 1999. For After School is Cool program.
380. Glendale Family Resource Center, Denver, CO. $20,000, 1999. For Parents as Teachers Program.
381. Moffat Consolidated School District No. 2, Moffat, CO. $15,000, 1999. For matching grant for library upgrades.

Adolph Coors Foundation

Limitations: Giving primarily in CO. No support for preschools, day care centers, nursing homes or other extended care facilities, churches or tax-supported organizations. Generally, no grants to individuals, or for endowment funds, research, production of films or other media-related projects, capital or program needs of churches, conduit funding, deficits, debt retirement, special benefit programs, or purchase of blocks of tickets.

382. Globeville Community Resource Center, Denver, CO. $10,000, 2000. For general operating support to provide education, recreation, emergency services and referrals for low-income community residents.
383. Inter-Faith Task Force for Community Services, Littleton, CO. $10,000, 2000. To provide resource guidance to low-income and indigent families in South Metro Denver.
384. Providers Resource Clearinghouse, Denver, CO. $10,000, 2000. For general operating support.

Henry P. Crowell and Susan C. Crowell Trust

Limitations: No support for churches. No grants to individuals, or for endowment funds or research; no loans.

385. Biola University, La Mirada, CA. $100,000, 1999. For Library Resource Center.
386. Christian Heritage College, El Cajon, CA. $25,000, 1999. For library resources.
387. Interdev, Seattle, WA. $40,000, 1999. For Strategic Evangelism Partnership Development.

The Denver Foundation

Limitations: Giving limited to Adams, Arapahoe, Boulder, Denver, Douglas, and Jefferson counties, CO. No support for religious, political or sectarian programs, or projects supported largely by public funds. No grants to individuals, or for scholarships, debt liquidation, endowment funds, research, publications, films, travel, or conferences, symposiums, workshops, or individual healthcare procedures.

388. Denver Public Library Friends Foundation, Denver, CO. $15,000, 1999. For After School is Cool program.
389. Jefferson County Public Schools, Foster Elementary School, Golden, CO. $10,000, 1999. For general operating support for FOSTERing Better Communities Resource Center.
390. League of Women Voters of Denver Education Fund, Denver, CO. $10,500, 1999. For Voter Hotline program.
391. Mountain Resource Center, Conifer, CO. $15,000, 1999. For general operating support.
392. Parent Education and Assistance for Kids, Colorado Springs, CO. $20,000, 1999. To establish Denver office.

El Pomar Foundation

Limitations: Giving limited to CO. No support for organizations that distribute funds to other grantees, religious or political organizations, primary or secondary education, or for camps or seasonal facilities. No grants to individuals, or for annual campaigns, travel, film or other media projects, conferences, deficit financing, endowment funds, research, matching gifts, seed money, or publications.

393. Penrose-Saint Francis Health Care System, Colorado Springs, CO. $122,000, 1999. For operating support and Webb Library.
394. Pikes Peak Library District, Colorado Springs, CO. $10,000, 1999. For Imagination Celebration.

Gates Family Foundation

Limitations: Giving limited to CO, with emphasis on the Denver area, except for foundation-initiated grants. No support for private foundations, medical facilities, or individual public schools of public school districts. No grants to individuals, or for operating budgets, medical research, annual campaigns, emergency funds, deficit financing, purchase of tickets for fundraising dinners, parties, balls, or other social fundraising events, purchase of vehicles or office equipment, conferences, meetings, research, or scholarships; no loans.

395. Cortez Public Library, Cortez, CO. $10,000, 2000. For challenge grant toward expansion of library.
396. Grover Regional Library Association, Grover, CO. $49,300, 2000. To complete renovation of Grover Opera House building for use as library.
397. Mountain Resource Center, Conifer, CO. $25,000, 2000. Toward construction of new facility.

General Service Foundation

Limitations: Giving limited to the U.S., Mexico, Central America and the Caribbean.

398. Bank Information Center, DC. $40,000, 1999. To empower civil society in Latin America to effectively participate in development decision making so that development lending furthers principles of democracy, social justice, ecological sustainability and peace.
399. Center for Constitutional Rights, NYC, NY. $30,000, 1999. For Cuba Travel Project that serves as clearinghouse for information and representation in connection with Cuba travel regulations.
400. National Womens Health Network, DC. $15,000, 1999. For technological infrastructure upgrade.
401. Sexuality Information and Education Council of the U.S. (SIECUS), NYC, NY. $30,000, 1999. For general support.

The Gill Foundation

Limitations: Giving primarily in non-metropolitan areas with populations of 1.5 million or less. No support for clinical HIV/AIDS research, direct client services to community based HIV/AIDS organizations outside CO, or art programs for or about HIV.

402. Colorado State University Foundation, Fort Collins, CO. $15,000, 1999. 3-year grant. For seed money for Gay, Lesbian, Bisexual, Transgender Resource Center.
403. Lavender Youth Recreation and Information Center (LYRIC), San Francisco, CA. $20,000, 1999. For program support for Youth Talkline/Infoline for non-urban California Communities.
404. Project Inform, San Francisco, CA. $25,000, 1999. For continued general support.
405. University of Colorado, Gay, Lesbian, Bisexual, Transgender Resource Center, Boulder, CO. $12,000, 1999. For general operating support.

Helen K. and Arthur E. Johnson Foundation

Limitations: Giving limited to CO. No support for political organizations. No grants to individuals, or for endowment funds, conferences, or purchase of blocks of tickets; no loans.

406. Denver Public Library, Denver, CO. $40,000, 1999. For reading proficiency project.
407. Mountain Resource Center, Conifer, CO. $20,000, 1999. For capital campaign.
408. Providers Resource Clearinghouse, Denver, CO. $10,000, 1999. For continued program support.

Qwest Foundation

Limitations: Giving limited to the states served by Qwest, including AZ, CO, IA, ID, MN, MT, ND, NE, NM, OR, SD, UT, WA, and WY. No support for international organizations, or national health organizations. No grants to individuals (except for awards programs), or for endowment funds, general operating budgets, building funds, renovations, capital campaigns, trips, or tours.

409. Edwin A. Bemis Public Library, Littleton, CO. $16,000, 1999. For equipment and/or services in lieu of cash.
410. Edwin A. Bemis Public Library, Littleton, CO. $12,500, 1999.

411. Moriarty Community Library, Moriarty, NM. $16,000, 1999. For equipment and/or services in lieu of cash.
412. Moriarty Community Library, Moriarty, NM. $12,500, 1999.
413. Schuyler Public Library, Schuyler, NE. $16,000, 1999. For equipment and/or services in lieu of cash.
414. Schuyler Public Library, Schuyler, NE. $12,500, 1999.

CONNECTICUT

Aetna Foundation, Inc.

Limitations: Giving primarily to organizations in the U.S. No support for non-501(c)(3) organizations, religious organizations for religious purposes, private secondary or elementary schools, or political activities. No grants to individuals, or for endowment funds, debt reduction drives, scholarships, capital or building funds, renovation projects, advertising, fundraising dinners or similar special events, sporting events, computer hardware or annual operating funds for colleges, universities, or social service agencies; no loans.

415. Hartford Public Library, Hartford, CT. $10,000, 2000. For Capital Improvement Project.

The Dibner Fund, Inc.

Limitations: Giving primarily in CT, MA, and NY. No support for religious sects or institutions, or political parties or programs. No grants to individuals, or generally for building or endowment funds, scholarships, fellowships (except through universities, educational agencies and/or specific academic programs) capital expenditures, or matching gifts; no loans.

416. Dibner Institute for the History of Science and Technology, Burndy Library, Cambridge, MA. $1,612,959, 1999.
417. Putnam Valley Library, Putnam Valley, NY. $10,000, 1999.
418. Smithsonian Institution, DC. $24,200, 1999. For Libraries.
419. YIVO Institute for Jewish Research, NYC, NY. $10,000, 1999.

The Educational Foundation of America

Limitations: Giving limited to the U.S.. No grants to individuals, annual fund-raising campaigns, or for capital or endowment funds; no loans.

420. Sexuality Information and Education Council of the U.S. (SIECUS), NYC, NY. $50,000, 1999. For New York State Public Policy Initiative.
421. Sprawl Watch Clearinghouse, DC. $80,000, 1999. For public outreach program.

GE Fund

Limitations: Giving on a national and international basis; grants mainly to areas where the company has a significant presence. No support for religious or sectarian groups. No grants to individuals, including scholarships and research grants, or for capital or endowment funds, or other special purpose campaigns; no loans or equipment donations.

422. Council for Basic Education, DC. $10,000, 1999.
423. Foundation Center, NYC, NY. $10,000, 1999.
424. North American Center of Environmental Information and Communication, Mexico City, Mexico. $25,000, 1999.

The Goergen Foundation, Inc.

Limitations: Giving primarily in CT, NY, and PA. No grants to individuals.

425. Quogue Free Library, Quogue, NY. $18,825, 1999. For general support. Grant made in form of stock.
426. Quogue Free Library, Quogue, NY. $10,000, 1999. For general support.

William Caspar Graustein Memorial Fund

Limitations: Giving primarily in CT. No grants to individuals.

427. Connecticut Policy and Economic Council, Hartford, CT. $48,000, 1999. To pilot Date-Driven Civic Engagement Model that brings community members together to create public school guide in Hartford.
428. Connecticut State Library, Hartford, CT. $67,750, 1999. For Connecticut Information Connection about Children project, creation of Web site providing access to information responsive to

needs of parents, caregivers, health care professionals of young children.

429. National Funding Collaborative on Violence Prevention, DC. $50,000, 1999. To develop and implement national communications component for national violence prevention movement through advocacy and public information.

430. Southern Connecticut Library Council, Hamden, CT. $76,000, 1999. To create regional network of Family Place Libraries in towns in greater New Haven area, transforming library into community hub for early childhood information and parent support.

Hartford Foundation for Public Giving

Limitations: Giving limited to the greater Hartford, CT, area. No support for sectarian purposes or tax-supported agencies. No grants to individuals, or for operating budgets, continuing support, annual campaigns, deficit financing, endowment funds, research, publications, or conferences.

431. Connecticut Historical Society, Hartford, CT. $50,000, 2000. For acquisition of Automated Library Management System.

432. Connecticut Humanities Council, Hartford, CT. $150,000, 2000. To expand Book Voyagers, series of youth and family reading programs to public libraries throughout Greater Hartford.

433. Hartford Public Library, Hartford, CT. $500,000, 2000. Toward Central Library renovations and expansion capital campaign.

434. Hartford Public Library, Hartford, CT. $150,000, 2000. For furniture and equipment.

435. Hartford Public Library, Hartford, CT. $25,000, 2000. For general support.

436. Stowe-Day Foundation, Harriet Beecher Stowe Center, Hartford, CT. $10,000, 2000. For technical assistance.

Smith Richardson Foundation, Inc.

Limitations: Giving limited to U.S.-based organizations only. No support for programs in the arts and humanities, direct service programs, charities, advocacy organizations, historic restoration, or regional or community programs concerning employment, recreation, or regional or community health and welfare. No grants to individuals, or for deficit financing, documentaries, building or endowment funds, scholarships, fellowships, operating budgets, or research in the physical sciences; no loans.

437. George C. Marshall Research Foundation, Lexington, VA. $15,000, 1999.

438. Richard Nixon Presidential Archives Foundation, Yorba Linda, CA. $65,000, 1999.

Smart Family Foundation

Limitations: No grants to individuals.

439. Center for Jewish History, NYC, NY. $200,000, 1999.

440. Newberry Library, Chicago, IL. $170,000, 1999.

Theodore & Vada Stanley Foundation

Limitations: No grants to individuals.

441. Ronald Reagan Presidential Foundation, Simi Valley, CA. $50,000, 2000.

Emily Hall Tremaine Foundation, Inc.

Limitations: No grants to individuals or for building funds, research projects, or experimental demonstrations.

442. American Library Association, Chicago, IL. $158,000, 1999.

DELAWARE

Chichester duPont Foundation, Inc.

Limitations: Giving primarily in DE and MD. No grants to individuals.

443. William A. Farnsworth Library and Art Museum, Rockland, ME. $100,000, 1999. For art initiative for Maine schools.

Crystal Trust

Limitations: Giving primarily in DE, with emphasis on Wilmington. No grants to individuals, or for endowment funds, research, scholarships, fellowships, or matching gifts.

444. Family and Workplace Connection, Wilmington, DE. $40,000, 1999. For computers.

445. Wilmington Library Foundation, Wilmington, DE. $150,000, 1999. For capital improvements.

Longwood Foundation, Inc.

Limitations: Giving limited to DE, with emphasis on the greater Wilmington area. No grants to individuals, or for special projects.

446. Arden Archives and Museum, Arden, DE. $125,000, 2000.

447. Concord Pike Library, Friends of the, Wilmington, DE. $1,250,000, 2000. For capital campaign for construction of new facilities.

448. Downingtown Good Neighbor Center, Downingtown, PA. $100,000, 2000.

449. Family and Workplace Connection, Wilmington, DE. $25,000, 2000.

450. University of Delaware, Center for Community Development and Family Policy, Newark, DE. $20,000, 2000. For Housing Capacity Building Program.

Raskob Foundation for Catholic Activities, Inc.

Limitations: Giving to domestic and international programs affiliated with the Catholic church. No grants to individuals, or for continuing support, annual campaigns, deficit financing (except missions), endowment funds, tuition, scholarships, fellowships, individual research, capital campaigns, building projects prior to the start or after the completion of construction, continuing subsidies, or requests that are after-the-fact by the time of the spring and fall trustee meetings.

451. Missionary Franciscan Sisters of the Immaculate Conception, Aitape, Papua New Guinea. $12,000, 1999. To build chapel-library for Formation House.

Welfare Foundation, Inc.

Limitations: Giving limited to DE, with emphasis on the greater Wilmington area. No grants to individuals.

452. Catalyst Project, Wilmington, DE. $20,000, 1999. For computer hardware.

453. Family and Workplace Connection, Wilmington, DE. $25,000, 1999. For technology upgrades.

454. Hagley Museum and Library, Wilmington, DE. $100,000, 1999. For endowment.

455. Wilmington Institute Free Library, Wilmington, DE. $250,000, 1999. For technolgoy upgrades.

DISTRICT OF COLUMBIA

Banyan Tree Foundation

Limitations: Giving on an international basis. No support for organizations with religious affiliations. No grants to individuals.

456. International Monitor Institute, Los Angeles, CA. $50,000, 1999.

The Morris and Gwendolyn Cafritz Foundation

Limitations: Giving limited to the greater metropolitan Washington, DC, area. No grants to individuals, or for emergency funds, deficit financing, capital, endowment, or building funds, demonstration projects, or conferences; no loans (except for program related investments).

457. Council for Basic Education, DC. $50,000, 2000. For general support to implement study of Student Academic Work program in Arlington, VA and Washington, DC Public Schools.

458. Folger Shakespeare Library, DC. $80,000, 2000. For general support and precollege Shakespeare education programs.

459. Foundation Center, NYC, NY. $17,500, 2000. For general support for resources, outreach, and programs integral to foster public understanding of private grantmaking.

460. Metropolitan Washington Council of Governments, DC. $20,000, 2000. To develop comprehensive affordable rental housing database for DC metropolitan region.

461. Partners for Livable Communities, DC. $10,000, 2000. To disseminate research of Shirley Bruce Heath of Carnegie

Foundation for Advancement of Teaching and Stanford University, and to develop network to apply that research.

462. Washington Child Development Council, DC. $20,000, 2000. For Maximizing Resources to Expand Licensed Family Child Care project.

Naomi and Nehemiah Cohen Foundation

Limitations: Giving primarily in Washington, DC and Israel. No grants to individuals.

463. Boston Public Library Foundation, Boston, MA. $10,000, 2000.
464. Library of Congress, Hebraic Section, DC. $525,000, 2000.

The Community Foundation for the National Capital Region

Limitations: Giving limited to the metropolitan Washington, DC, area. No grants to individuals (except for scholarships and fellowships), or from discretionary funds for annual campaigns, endowment funds, equipment, land acquisition, renovation projects, operating budgets, or matching gifts.

465. Library of Virginia Foundation, Richmond, VA. $33,900, 2000.
466. Prince Georges Child Resource Center, Largo, MD. $53,275, 2000.
467. Prince Georges County Hotline and Suicide Prevention Center, Homeless Hotline, Hyattsville, MD. $27,362, 2000.
468. Upper Montgomery Volunteer Network, Gaithersburg, MD. $26,336, 2000.
469. Washington Child Development Council, DC. $10,767, 2000.
470. Weslaco Public Library, Weslaco, TX. $19,997, 2000.

Fannie Mae Foundation

Limitations: Giving within the United States only. No support for sectarian organizations. No grants to individuals (except for housing-related research grants and fellowships), or for general or scholarship support of institutions of higher learning or secondary education.

471. Center for Nonprofit Management, Dallas, TX. $10,200, 1999. To publish and distribute African-American Nonprofit Directory in Dallas.
472. Clark County Legal Services Program, Las Vegas, NV. $50,000, 1999. To create self-help legal clinics that use law students to train Nevada residents about their housing rights and responsibilities.
473. Cleveland Housing Network, Cleveland, OH. $70,000, 1999. For Phase II of Technology Link 2000, on-line sales and leasing center for individuals interested in homeownership and rental information in Cleveland.
474. Community Home Ownership Center, Seattle, WA. $100,000, 1999. 2-year grant. To expand homeownership outreach, counseling and referral services to potential home buyers in Seattle.
475. Council for Advancement and Support of Education, DC. $10,000, 1999. For National Clearinghouse for Corporate Matching Gifts.
476. Donors Forum of Chicago, Chicago, IL. $25,000, 1999. For Fund for Immigrants and Refugees, which provides grants to local organizations that focus on immigration policy and research, advocacy and education in Chicagoland area.
477. Donors Forum of Chicago, Chicago, IL. $25,000, 1999. For conference, Building an Agenda to Strengthen Refugee and Immigrant Families in the 21st Century.
478. Home Buyer Assistance and Information Center (HBAIC), Oakland, CA. $50,000, 1999. To expand homeownership education and counseling services to residents of Bay Area in California.
479. HOPE Worldwide DC, McLean, VA. $15,000, 1999. For HOPE for Kids Day, which will inform families of health care resources for inner-city children in Washington, DC area.
480. Iowa Coalition for Housing and the Homeless, Des Moines, IA. $40,000, 1999. For start-up and development support for Affordable Housing Co-op of Iowa, statewide network of nonprofit housing providers.
481. King County Housing Authority, Seattle, WA. $50,000, 1999. 2-year grant. To create county-wide network of affordable housing opportunities for people with disabilities and special needs.
482. Little Dixie Community Action Agency, Hugo, OK. $25,000, 1999. For Homeownership Center, which will provide home-buyer education and counseling to low- and moderate-income residents in Southeast Oklahoma.
483. Massachusetts Affordable Housing Alliance, Boston, MA. $25,000, 1999. For general operating support.

484. National First Ladies Library, Canton, OH. $10,000, 1999. For First Ladies Salute First Women Awards Dinner to benefit operations.
485. National Low Income Housing Coalition and Low Income Housing Information Service, DC. $100,000, 1999. For general operating support.
486. New York Academy of Medicine, NYC, NY. $10,000, 1999. For Annual Gala Dinner and Dance to benefit operations.
487. New York Mortgage Coalition, NYC, NY. $50,000, 1999. For Homeownership Counseling Collaborative, which provides operating support and training to counseling providers in New York area.
488. North Carolina Community Development Initiative, Raleigh, NC. $25,000, 1999. For housing counseling and relief services for families whose homes were damaged by Hurricane Floyd in North Carolina.
489. Peoples Homesteading Group, Baltimore, MD. $16,500, 1999. For capacity building through information and technological upgrades for affordable housing developer in Baltimore.
490. Reston Interfaith, Reston, VA. $17,500, 1999. For Employment Resource Center which helps homeless individuals and families obtain living wage jobs, affordable housing, child and health care through help in Fairfax County, VA as part of Help the Homeless Initiative.
491. Restore Orlando, Orlando, FL. $25,000, 1999. For housing counseling program serving low-income families in Orlando.
492. Saint Louis Public Library, Saint Louis, MO. $25,000, 1999. For programs involving homeownership education, credit counseling and affordable lending for residents of Saint Louis.
493. Seattle Master Builders Association, Bellevue, WA. $25,000, 1999. For Green Building Program, education and outreach program on environmentally beneficial development practices for building industry in Seattle metropolitan area.
494. Union of Pan Asian Communities of San Diego County, San Diego, CA. $40,000, 1999. For Homeownership Outreach and Education Project, which provides outreach, educational and counseling services to raise awareness of benefits of homeownership among Pan Asian immigrant and refugee populations in San Diego.

The Gottesman Fund

Limitations: Giving primarily in NY. No grants to individuals.

495. American Jewish Historical Society, Waltham, MA. $10,000, 2000. For general support.
496. Center for Jewish History, NYC, NY. $100,000, 2000. For general support.
497. Cornwall Library Associates, Cornwall, CT. $12,000, 2000. For general support.

Philip L. Graham Fund

Limitations: Giving primarily in the metropolitan Washington, DC, area. No support for national or international organizations, religious organizations for religious purposes, or for political activities. No grants to individuals, or for medical services, research, annual campaigns, fundraising events, conferences, publications, tickets, films, travel expenses, courtesy advertising, advocacy, or litigation.

498. Consortium of Universities of the Washington Metropolitan Area, DC. $25,000, 1999. For Greater Washington College Information Center.
499. Folger Shakespeare Library, DC. $15,000, 1999. For Student Shakespeare Festivals.

William G. McGowan Charitable Fund

Limitations: Giving limited to northern CA, the Washington, DC, area, IL, the metropolitan Kansas City, KS, area, western NY, northeastern PA, central TX, and northern VA.

500. College Misericordia, Dallas, PA. $250,000, 2000. For McGowan Center in new library.

Eugene and Agnes E. Meyer Foundation

Limitations: Giving limited to the metropolitan Washington, DC, area, including suburban MD and northern VA. No support for sectarian purposes, or for programs that are national or international in scope. No grants to individuals, or for annual campaigns, deficit financing, endowment funds, equipment, scholarships, fellowships, scientific or medical research, publications, special events or conferences.

501. Foundation Center, NYC, NY. $62,500, 2000. For continued general operating support and capital campaign for DC field office and library.
502. Greater D.C. Cares, DC. $10,000, 2000. For Greater Washington Nonprofit Summit and development of post-Summit report.
503. Washington Council of Agencies, DC. $12,000, 2000. For development of Winning Ways, book and initial web-based resource of nonprofit management ideas from Washington Post Award for Excellence in Nonprofit Management.

Moriah Fund

Limitations: Giving nationally and internationally, including Israel and Latin America; giving primarily in Washington, DC for poverty program. No support for lobbying or political campaigns, private foundations, or arts organizations. No grants to individuals, or for medical research.

504. Bank Information Center, DC. $25,000, 2000. For Global Legislators Organization for a Balanced Environment (GLOBE) to work to conserve biodiversity by educating legislators about need to reform export credit agencies; to maintain pressure on World Bank to adhere to own environmental standards; and to continue efforts to foster dialogue with World Trade Organization (WRO) Secretariat on role of legislators in WRO oversight.
505. Bank Information Center, DC. $20,000, 2000. For continued support of Early Warning System, information service and empowerment project for developing country civil society organizations working to address negative impacts of multilateral development bank projects.
506. Bank Information Center, DC. $15,000, 2000. For Trasparencia, to reform practices and policies of Multilateral Development Banks (MDBs) in Mexico, and to focus on consolidating vertical linkages between grassroots groups, NGOs, government, and MDBs.
507. Calvary Bilingual Multicultural Learning Center, DC. $40,000, 2000. For Family Institute, which provides wide variety of family support services, such as parenting workshops, social service referrals, and health screening.
508. Jewish Theological Seminary of America, NYC, NY. $30,000, 2000. For matching grant for Project Judaica, Jewish Studies and Archives Program offered at secular Russian State Humanities University in the former Soviet Union, in conjunction with YIVO Institute for Jewish Research.
509. Marie Stopes International, DC. $30,000, 2000. To provide family planning information and supplies, education and communication services to Guatemalans who have returned home from refuge in Mexico after the civil war.
510. National Womens Health Network, DC. $25,000, 2000. For efforts to inform and improve debate on emerging contraceptive technology issues.
511. National Womens Law Center, DC. $20,000, 2000. For D.C. Child and Family Support Project, which provides information and assistance to low-income single parents on child support and range of related issues.
512. Sexuality Information and Education Council of the U.S. (SIECUS), NYC, NY. $25,000, 2000. For general support to promote sexuality education, develop and disseminate information about sexuality to the public and policymakers, and advocate for rights of individuals to make responsible sexual choices.
513. South Wings, Chattanooga, TN. $15,000, 2000. For general support to provide environmental community with overflights as tool to document and dramatize need for preservation and restoration of forest ecosystems of Southeast.
514. Workers Hotline, Israel. $20,000, 2000. To ensure equal rights for Palestinian and foreign workers in Israel by providing legal and practical assistance to those whose rights have been violated in course of employment, and to devote increased efforts to problems of female workers. Grant made through New Israel Fund.

Public Welfare Foundation, Inc.

Limitations: Giving is generally limited to the U.S. (more than 90 percent). No grants to individuals, or for building funds, capital improvements,

endowments, scholarships, graduate work, foreign study, conferences, seminars, publications, research, workshops, or annual campaigns; no loans.

515. Bank Information Center, DC. $80,000, 2000. 2-year grant. For Indigenous Peoples Project.
516. Center for Democratic Renewal and Education, Atlanta, GA. $50,000, 2000. For continued general support.
517. DataCenter, Oakland, CA. $35,000, 2000. For continued support for Environmental Research Project providing information and research services to grassroots organizations especially those working with low-income groups.
518. Environmental Justice Resource Center, Atlanta, GA. $40,000, 2000. For continued general support.
519. Foundation Center, NYC, NY. $50,000, 2000. For general support for office relocation project.
520. Foundation Center, NYC, NY. $13,500, 2000. For annual support.
521. Miami Workers Center, Miami, FL. $25,000, 2000. For general support for work with Minority Families Fighting Against WAGES.
522. Recovery Network of Northern Kentucky, Covington, KY. $20,000, 2000. For general support.
523. Southwest Research and Information Center, Albuquerque, NM. $25,000, 2000. For Uranium Impact Assessment Project.
524. Unemployment Information Center, Philadelphia, PA. $30,000, 2000. For general support.

Wallace Genetic Foundation, Inc.

Limitations: No grants to individuals, or for scholarships, endowments, or university overhead expenses; no loans.

525. American Public Information on the Environment, South Glastonbury, CT. $20,000, 1999.
526. Genetic Resources Communications Systems, DC. $50,000, 1999.
527. New York Farms, Auburn, NY. $15,000, 1999.
528. Vetiver Network, Leesburg, VA. $20,000, 1999.

FLORIDA

Arison Foundation, Inc.

Limitations: Giving primarily in NY.

529. New Israel Fund, DC. $37,900, 1999. To install library and purchase books.

The Frank Stanley Beveridge Foundation, Inc.

Limitations: Giving only in Orange County, CA, Boca Raton, FL, Kauai County, HI, Hampden and Hampshire counties, MA, NH, and RI. No grants to individuals, or for endowment or operating funds, scholarships, or fellowships; no loans.

530. Redwood Library and Athenaeum, Newport, RI. $55,000, 1999.

The Chatlos Foundation, Inc.

Limitations: No support for individual church congregations, secondary schools or for the arts. No grants to individuals, or for seed money, deficit financing, endowment funds, medical research, conferences, bricks and mortar, or multi-year grants; no loans.

531. Christar, Reading, PA. $25,000, 2000. For library needs at Jordan Evangelical Theological Seminary in Amman, Jordan.
532. Florida College, Temple Terrace, FL. $50,000, 2000. For matching grant to complete wing of William F. Chatlos Library.
533. Lancaster Theological Seminary, Lancaster, PA. $20,000, 2000. To update technology in Philip Schaff Library.
534. Nyack College, Nyack, NY. $26,370, 2000. To add computer workstations to library and for computer projector for classroom instruction.
535. Phoenix Seminary, Scottsdale, AZ. $10,000, 2000. For technology advancement of library services.

The Community Foundation

Limitations: Giving primarily in northeastern FL, including Baker, Clay, Duval, Nassau and St. Johns counties; and southeastern GA. No grants for general operating support, construction or renovation, equipment, or tickets for fundraising activities.

536. Lutheran Social Services of Northeast Florida, Jacksonville, FL. $15,200, 1999. To design public awareness campaign in cooperation with Catholic Charities and Jewish Family and Community Services to increase community understanding of major faith-based social ministries and ways to access their resources.

537. Yulee Elementary School, Yulee, FL. $12,000, 1999. To establish SAY YES to Reading Success program, designed to encourage families to come together for planned reading and storytelling activities and give parents information and provide resources to enable them to help their children succeed in school.

Dade Community Foundation, Inc.

Limitations: Giving limited to Dade County, FL. No grants to individuals (except through scholarship funds), or for memberships, fundraising, memorials, deficit financing, or conferences.

538. Miami-Dade Public Library, Friends of, Miami, FL. $11,500, 1999. To work with local theater organizations to present theatrical performances in libraries county-wide, as part of Community Partners for Arts and Culture Initiative.

The Arthur Vining Davis Foundations

Limitations: Giving limited to the U.S. and its possessions and territories. No support for community chests, institutions primarily supported by government funds, or projects incurring obligations extending over many years. No grants to individuals; no loans.

539. Bethany Theological Seminary, Richmond, IN. $148,000, 2000. To automate library.

540. Flagler College, Saint Augustine, FL. $200,000, 2000. For endowment for library collections.

541. Saint Patricks Seminary, Menlo Park, CA. $150,000, 2000. To expand library.

542. Yale University, Yale Divinity School, New Haven, CT. $150,000, 2000. To construct new space for special library collections.

William M. & Nina B. Hollis Foundation, Inc.

Limitations: Giving primarily in Lakeland, FL.

543. Free Library of Philadelphia, Philadelphia, PA. $10,000, 1999. For educational programs.

John S. and James L. Knight Foundation

Limitations: Giving limited to projects serving the 26 communities where the Knight brothers published newspapers for Community Initiatives Program and local grants: Long Beach and San Jose, CA, Boulder, CO, Boca Raton, Bradenton, Miami, and Tallahassee, FL, Columbus, Macon, and Milledgeville, GA, Fort Wayne and Gary, IN, Wichita, KS, Lexington, KY, Detroit, MI, Duluth and St. Paul, MN, Biloxi, MS, Charlotte, NC, Grand Forks, ND, Akron, OH, Philadelphia and State College, PA, Columbia and Myrtle Beach, SC, and Aberdeen, SD; international for Journalism. No support for organizations whose mission is to prevent, eradicate and/or alleviate the effects of a specific disease; hospitals, unless for community-wide capital campaigns; activities to propagate a religious faith or restricted to one religion or denomination; political candidates; international programs, except in support of a free press around the world; charities operated by service clubs; or activities that are the responsibility of government. No grants to individuals, or generally for fundraising events; second requests for previously funded capital campaigns; operating deficits; films, videos, or television programs; commercial television or radio time; honoraria; writing or publication of books; group travel; memorials; medical research; or conferences.

544. Altru Health Foundation, Grand Forks, ND. $75,000, 2000. For Patient and Family Education Library, state-of-the-art resource center.

545. American Library Association, Chicago, IL. $250,000, 2000. 2-year grant. For LIVE at Library 2000, national project providing support for libraries to present theme-based cultural programming.

546. American Newspaper Repository, South Berwick, ME. $100,000, 2000. To house temporarily and catalogue collection of rare bound volumes of New York World, New York Herald-Tribune and Chicago Tribune.

547. Arts and Scraps, Detroit, MI. $20,000, 2000. For program enhancements and capital improvements.

548. Bass Museum, Friends of, Miami Beach, FL. $125,000, 2000. 3-year grant. Toward challenge grant for New Information Workshop, comprehensive program using technology to build relationships between museum and audiences.

549. Black Archives, History and Research Foundation of South Florida, Miami, FL. $100,000, 2000. To complete restoration of historic Lyric Theater and build addition to improve staging and public areas and add new spaces for education and training programs.

550. California State University at Long Beach Foundation, Long Beach, CA. $60,000, 2000. To organize and conduct statewide meeting to share effective strategies for K-16 reform developed in Long Beach and other California communities.

551. Commission on Presidential Debates, DC. $200,000, 2000. To develop and distribute Presidential Debates: A Teacher's Guide, and to update and distribute Inside Debates: A Practical Guide to Sponsorship and Production.

552. Community Technology Alliance, San Jose, CA. $35,000, 2000. To develop website containing information on subsidized housing for the homeless.

553. Council for Basic Education, DC. $225,000, 2000. 3-year grant. To continue and expand participation by Horry County, SC, teachers in Schools Around the World: An International Study of Student Academic Work.

554. Donors Forum of Miami, Miami, FL. $60,000, 2000. For continued support for Promotion of Philanthropy: A South Florida Collaboration project.

555. Foundation Center, NYC, NY. $30,000, 2000. For continued general operating support.

556. Friends of the Campbell Library, East Grand Forks, MN. $52,500, 2000. For new shelving.

557. Indiana Institute of Technology, Fort Wayne, IN. $100,000, 2000. 3-year grant. For renovation of McMillan Library and Dana Engineering Center.

558. Long Beach Public Library Foundation, Long Beach, CA. $25,000, 2000. To establish family learning center at Dana Branch Library for elementary and middle-grades children and their families.

559. Northern State University, Aberdeen, SD. $50,000, 2000. To expand activities of Volunteer Service Clearinghouse and hire full-time coordinator.

560. Public Library of Charlotte and Mecklenburg County, Charlotte, NC. $50,000, 2000. For exhibition highlighting African-American soldiers and their role in U.S. Army from 1866-1912.

561. Robert C. Maynard Institute for Journalism Education, Oakland, CA. $200,000, 2000. 2-year grant. To create and disseminate oral/visual archive of pioneering journalists of color who served in predominantly white newsrooms.

562. Rosenbach Museum and Library, Philadelphia, PA. $100,000, 2000. For renovations of historic buildings to expand public outreach and research services and to upgrade exhibition and collection storage space.

563. Syracuse University, Syracuse, NY. $250,000, 2000. 3-year grant. To expand Transactional Records Access Clearinghouse as information service for news organizations.

564. Tallahassee-Leon County Cultural Resources Commission, Tallahassee, FL. $18,500, 2000. To create central arts and culture community information center.

565. United Way of the Chattahoochee Valley, Columbus, GA. $180,000, 2000. 3-year grant. Toward challenge grant for start-up support to establish Nonprofit Community Resource Center.

Koch Foundation, Inc.

Limitations: No grants to individuals, or for endowment funds, deficit financing, emergency funds, or scholarships or fellowships; no loans.

566. National Religious Vocation Conference, Chicago, IL. $11,000, 2000. To increase awareness of religious vocation in elementary school children through National Coalition for Church Vocations (NCCV).

567. United States Catholic Conference, Department of Education, DC. $20,000, 2000. For production of video materials to supplement directory on catechesis.

Forrest C. Lattner Foundation, Inc.

Limitations: Giving primarily in Palm Beach County, FL, Wichita, KS, St. Louis, MO, and Westerly, RI.

568. Delray Beach Library, Delray Beach, FL. $20,000, 1999.
569. Wichita Public Library Foundation, Wichita, KS. $51,000, 1999.

The Picower Foundation

Limitations: Giving primarily in southeast FL and the Northeast. No grants to individuals.

570. New York Public Library, NYC, NY. $10,000, 1999.

Publix Super Markets Charities

Limitations: Giving primarily in FL. No grants to individuals.

571. Broward Public Library Foundation, Fort Lauderdale, FL. $50,000, 1999.

Schmidt Family Foundation

Limitations: Giving primarily in southern FL. No grants to individuals.

572. Child Care Resource and Referral, Delray Beach, FL. $15,000, 1999.

William G. Selby and Marie Selby Foundation

Limitations: Giving limited to Charlotte, DeSoto, Manatee, and Sarasota counties, FL. No support for grantmaking foundations or for non-501(c)(3) organizations. No grants to individuals (except through Selby Scholars Program), or for general purposes, continuing support, annual campaigns, deficit financing, seed money, emergency funds, operating budgets, endowment funds, special projects, surveys, program advertising, research, graduate study, publications, seminars, workshops, travel, fundraising, or conferences; no loans.

573. Selby Public Library, Friends of the, Sarasota, FL. $14,650, 2000.

GEORGIA

The Arthur M. Blank Family Foundation

Limitations: Giving primarily in Los Angeles, CA, Atlanta, GA, Boston, MA, and New York City.

574. Georgia School-Age Care Association, Decatur, GA. $63,000, 2000. For metro-Atlanta directory of school age programs and mapping component.
575. Higher Education Resource Center, Boston, MA. $25,000, 2000. For access to tools to overcome barriers to higher education.
576. Nonprofit Resource Center, Atlanta, GA. $200,000, 2000.
577. YouthBuild USA, Somerville, MA. $75,000, 2000. For alumni project to give graduates access to one another and community resources in Boston, New York, Phoenix and Los Angeles.

Camp Younts Foundation

Limitations: Giving primarily in FL, GA, NC, and VA. No grants to individuals.

578. George C. Marshall Research Foundation, Lexington, VA. $25,000, 1999. For continued operating support.

The Coca-Cola Foundation, Inc.

Limitations: No support for religious organizations or religious endeavors, political, fraternal or veterans' organizations, hospitals, or local chapters of national organizations. No grants to individuals, or for workshops, travel costs, conferences or seminars, and related advertising publications, equipment, or land acquisition; generally, no loans.

579. Atlanta University Center, Atlanta, GA. $50,000, 2000. Toward strengthening of the Robert W. Woodruff Library.
580. Free Library of Philadelphia, Philadelphia, PA. $25,000, 2000. For technology expansion as part of urban library renovation project.
581. Integrated Care Society, Cairo, Egypt. $40,000, 2000. For children's educational programs in public libraries throughout Egypt.

582. John F. Kennedy Library Foundation, Boston, MA. $25,000, 2000. For after-school program for local high school students.
583. Los Angeles County Public Library Foundation, Downey, CA. $25,000, 2000. To develop homework center for local Los Angeles schools.

Community Foundation for Greater Atlanta

Limitations: Giving limited to the 22-county metropolitan area of Atlanta, GA. No support for religious organizations (except through donor-advised funds). No grants to individuals, or for endowment funds, continuing support, annual campaigns, deficit financing, long-term research, films, conferences, scholarships (except for George & Pearl Strickland Scholarship Fund, which is limited to Atlanta University Center schools), or fellowships; a limited number of grants for operating budgets.

584. Cherokee Garden Club Library, Atlanta, GA. $13,000, 2000.
585. Metro Fair Housing Services, East Point, GA. $12,000, 2000.

John H. and Wilhelmina D. Harland Charitable Foundation, Inc.

Limitations: Giving limited to GA, with emphasis on metropolitan Atlanta. No support for private, primary, or secondary schools, except for those serving the handicapped. No grants to individuals; or for annual campaigns or special events; no loans.

586. Quality Care for Children, Atlanta, GA. $12,500, 1999. For child care referral program.

Katherine John Murphy Foundation

Limitations: Giving primarily in Atlanta, GA. No grants to individuals, or for research, or matching gifts; no loans.

587. Cherokee Garden Club Library, Atlanta, GA. $25,000, 1999. For capital support.

Turner Foundation, Inc.

Limitations: Giving primarily in AK, CO, FL, GA, MT, NE, NM, SC, Argentina, Mexico, and Russia. No grants to individuals, or for buildings, land acquisition, endowments, start-up funds, books, magazines, and other specific media projects.

588. Bank Information Center, DC. $25,000, 1999. To advocate for democratic reforms in Multilateral Development Bank (MDB) and to support non-governmental organizations in efforts to influence local MDB lending.
589. Clark Atlanta University, Atlanta, GA. $325,000, 1999. To empower grassroots community groups of color on transportation decision-making in Atlanta region, and serve as information clearinghouse on transportation policies and practices; to facilitate inclusion of grassroots community leaders into mainstream of environmental decision-making and coalition building.
590. Communication Works, San Francisco, CA. $15,000, 1999. For Western Environmental Media Center project, which provides environmental reporters with information, educates public about environmental issues and organizations and offers western environmental organizations access to media.
591. Foundation Center, NYC, NY. $15,000, 1999. For general support.
592. Montana Environmental Information Center, Helena, MT. $135,000, 1999. For campaigns to halt cyanide heap leach mining, to oppose Blackfoot River gold mine, and to oppose mine expansion near Fort Belknap Indian Reservation.
593. Pinchot Institute for Conservation, DC. $20,000, 1999. For Options for Forest Sustainability Using Non-Wood Forest Products, designed to organize and disseminate information via the Internet and make policy analysis and recommendations about native non-wood forest products.
594. Sexuality Information and Education Council of the U.S. (SIECUS), NYC, NY. $50,000, 1999. To disseminate information about sexuality education and advocate for adolescent sexual health in United States through variety of programs.
595. Southwest Research and Information Center, Albuquerque, NM. $30,000, 1999. To oppose construction and operation of proposed uranium mines in northwestern New Mexico.

The UPS Foundation

Limitations: Giving limited to the U.S., Mexico, and Canada. No support for religious organizations or theological functions, or church-sponsored programs limited to church members. No grants to individuals (except for employee-related scholarships), or for building or endowment funds, operating funds, annual campaigns, emergency funds, deficit financing, land acquisition, or publications; no loans.

596. Louisville Free Public Library Foundation, Louisville, KY. $10,000, 1999.
597. Resource Center for Community Development, Bronx, NY. $50,000, 1999.

Robert W. Woodruff Foundation, Inc.

Limitations: Giving primarily in GA. No grants to individuals, or for endowment funds, research, publications, conferences, or seminars; no loans.

598. Agnes Scott College, Decatur, GA. $2,500,000, 2000. For capital campaign, including renovation and expansion of Lettie Pate Evans Dining Hall and McCain Library.
599. Council on Library and Information Resources, DC. $300,000, 2000. For establishment of Digital Leadership Institute at Emory University.
600. Foundation Center, NYC, NY. $250,000, 2000. For program support for Atlanta office.
601. National Charities Information Bureau (NCIB), NYC, NY. $50,000, 2000. For program support.

HAWAII

Harold K. L. Castle Foundation

Limitations: Giving limited to HI; priority to Windward Oahu. No grants to individuals, or for ongoing program or operating support, sponsorships, special events, or annual fund drives.

602. Saint John Vianney School, Rancho Cordova, CA. $50,000, 1999. Toward Phase II of capital campaign for expansion improvements and furniture and fixtures for library.

Samuel N. and Mary Castle Foundation

Limitations: Giving generally limited to HI. Generally, no support for publicly funded organizations or lobbying organizations. No grants to individuals, or for continuing support; generally, no support for general operating budgets, endowment funds, annual campaigns, scholarships, or research; no loans.

603. Saint John Vianney School, Kailua, HI. $20,000, 1999. For improvements for school library.
604. Saint Joseph School, Waipahu, HI. $20,000, 1999. For library renovation and computer lab.

IDAHO

J. A. & Kathryn Albertson Foundation, Inc.

Limitations: Giving limited to ID. No grants to individuals.

605. Boise State University, College of Health Sciences, Department of Nursing, Boise, ID. $25,000, 1999. For Nursing Library.
606. Idaho State Library, Boise, ID. $124,388, 1999. For Read to Me program.
607. Information and Referral - Volunteer Connection, Coeur d Alene, ID. $35,000, 1999. To produce Early Childhood Education Professional Development web site.

ILLINOIS

Abbott Laboratories Fund

Limitations: Giving primarily in areas of company operations. No support for purely social or religious organizations, political parties or candidates. No grants to individuals, or for symposiums, conferences, social events, ticket purchases, memberships, business-related purposes, or for advertising journals or booklets; no loans.

608. Body Positive, Houston, TX. $10,000, 1999.

609. National Library of Medicine, Friends of the, DC. $10,000, 1999.

The Allstate Foundation

Limitations: Giving limited to the U.S. No support for fraternal or religious organizations or for bands and choirs. No grants to individuals (except for employee-related scholarships), or for annual campaigns, deficit financing, building funds, capital campaigns, endowment funds, fundraising events, conferences, films, videotapes or audio productions, travel funds, athletic events or teams, memorial grants, or medical research.

610. Donors Forum of Chicago, Chicago, IL. $25,000, 1999.

Aon Foundation

Limitations: Giving on a national basis. No support for the operation of secondary educational institutions or vocational schools.

611. Survivors of the Shoah Visual History Foundation, Los Angeles, CA. $10,000, 1999. For Last Days Premier in Chicago.

Archer Daniels Midland Foundation

612. Decatur Public Library, Decatur, TX. $60,000, 2000.
613. George Bush Presidential Library Foundation, College Station, TX. $50,000, 2000.

BANK ONE Foundation

Limitations: Giving limited to the metropolitan Chicago, IL, area. No support for fraternal or religious organizations, preschool, elementary, or secondary education, public agencies, or United Way/Crusade of Mercy-supported agencies. No grants to individuals, or for emergency funds, deficit financing, land acquisition, research, publications, conferences, or multi-year operating pledges; no loans (except for program-related investments).

614. Chicago Public Library Foundation, Chicago, IL. $25,000, 1999.
615. Newberry Library, Chicago, IL. $32,500, 1999.

The Bielfeldt Foundation

Limitations: Giving primarily in Peoria, IL. No grants to individuals.

616. Peoria Heights Public Library, Peoria Heights, IL. $19,601, 1999.

Blum-Kovler Foundation

Limitations: Giving primarily in the Chicago, IL, area.

617. American Jewish Historical Society, Waltham, MA. $10,000, 1999.
618. Richard Nixon Presidential Archives Foundation, Yorba Linda, CA. $12,000, 1999.

BP Amoco Foundation, Inc.

Limitations: Giving nationally in areas of company representation to assist communities, including the areas of Denver, CO, Washington, DC, Atlanta, GA, Chicago and Warrenville, IL, northwest IN, New Orleans, LA, Towson, MD, Minneapolis, MN, Lima, OH, Tulsa, OK, SC, Houston and Texas City, TX, Salt Lake City, UT, VA, and Casper, WY; international giving in areas where BP Amoco operates. No support for religious, fraternal, political, social, or athletic organizations; generally, no support for organizations already receiving operating support through the United Way. No grants to individuals (except for employee-related scholarships), or for endowment funds, medical research, publications, or conferences.

619. Charities Aid Foundation, West Malling, England. $2,000,000, 1999.
620. Charities Aid Foundation, West Malling, England. $750,000, 1999.
621. National First Ladies Library, Canton, OH. $10,000, 1999.

Helen Brach Foundation

Limitations: Giving primarily in the Midwest, and CA, MA, OH, PA and SC, No grants outside continental U.S.. No support for political organizations. No grants to individuals, or to organizations with less than one year of budget history.

622. Genesis Center for Health and Empowerment, Des Plaines, IL. $20,000, 2000. For unrestricted support.

The Buchanan Family Foundation

Limitations: Giving primarily in Chicago, IL. No grants to individuals.

623. Lake Forest Library, Lake Forest, IL. $15,000, 1999. For general operating support.
624. Newberry Library, Chicago, IL. $15,000, 1999. For general operating support.

Caterpillar Foundation

Limitations: Giving primarily in areas of company operations. No support for fraternal organizations, religious organizations whose services are limited to one sectarian group, or political activities. No grants to individuals, or for general operations, or agency programs funded by the United Way, or for tickets or advertising for fundraising benefits.

625. Everett McKinley Dirksen Endowment Fund, Pekin, IL. $12,500, 1999.

The Chicago Community Trust and Affiliates

Limitations: Giving primarily in Cook County, IL. No support for religious purposes. No grants to individuals (except for limited fellowship programs), or for annual campaigns, deficit financing, endowment funds, publications, conferences, or scholarships; no support for the purchase of computer hardware; no general operating support for agencies or institutions whose program activities substantially duplicate those already undertaken by others.

626. Chicago Public Library Foundation, Chicago, IL. $85,000, 2000. For Chicago Matters project.
627. Chicago Reporter, Chicago, IL. $70,000, 2000. For Chicago Matters project.
628. Connection Resource Services, Libertyville, IL. $15,000, 2000. For general operating support.
629. Coordinated Advice and Referral Program for Legal Services, Chicago, IL. $60,000, 2000. 2-year grant. For hiring of additional attorneys.
630. Donors Forum of Chicago, Chicago, IL. $25,000, 2000. For Greater Chicago Philanthropy Initiative.
631. Donors Forum of Chicago, Chicago, IL. $18,480, 2000. For general operating support.
632. Foundation Center, NYC, NY. $10,000, 2000. For general operating support.
633. Metropolitan Chicago Information Center, Chicago, IL. $180,000, 2000. 2-year grant. For Metro Survey program.
634. Newberry Library, Chicago, IL. $80,000, 2000. 2-year grant. For general operating support.
635. Northwestern University, School of Law/Legal Clinic, Evanston, IL. $100,000, 2000. 2-year grant. For establishment of Police and Community Data Collection and Information Project.
636. South Austin Job Referral Service, Chicago, IL. $10,000, 2000. For partial salary support of administrative assistant.
637. W B E Z, Chicago, IL. $210,500, 2000. For Chicago Matters series.
638. W T T W Chicago Public Television, Chicago, IL. $425,000, 2000. For Chicago Matters series.

Chicago Tribune Foundation

Limitations: Giving primarily in the metropolitan Chicago, IL, area. No grants to individuals, or for building or endowment funds, fundraising functions, free advertising, or fellowships; no loans.

639. Donors Forum of Chicago, Chicago, IL. $13,300, 1999. For membership support to promote effective philanthropy and for CD-ROM for Illinois Directory of Foundations.
640. North Suburban Library System Foundation, Wheeling, IL. $10,000, 1999. For author lecture series.

The Comer Foundation

Limitations: Giving primarily in Chicago, IL. No grants to individuals.

641. Newberry Library, Chicago, IL. $50,000, 2000. For general support.

Arie and Ida Crown Memorial

Limitations: Giving primarily in metropolitan Chicago, IL. No support for government-sponsored programs. No grants to individuals, or for consulting services, conferences, or film or documentary projects; no loans.

642. National Yiddish Book Center, Amherst, MA. $33,333, 1999.
643. Newberry Library, Chicago, IL. $50,000, 1999.
644. Survivors of the Shoah Visual History Foundation, Los Angeles, CA. $10,000, 1999.

John Deere Foundation

Limitations: Giving limited to areas where company employees live and work. No grants to individuals, or for endowment funds; no loans.

645. Harry S. Truman Library Institute for National and International Affairs, Independence, MO. $100,000, 1999.
646. Rock Island Public Library, Rock Island, IL. $25,000, 1999.

Dillon Foundation

Limitations: Giving primarily in the Sterling, IL, area. No grants to individuals; no loans.

647. Sterling Public Library, Sterling, IL. $22,857, 2000.

Lloyd A. Fry Foundation

Limitations: Giving primarily in Chicago, IL. No support for governmental bodies or tax-supported educational institutions for services that fall within their responsibilities. No grants to individuals, or for annual campaigns, emergency funds, deficit financing, building funds, fundraising benefits, land acquisition, renovation projects, or endowment funds; no loans.

648. Legal Assistance Foundation of Chicago, Chicago, IL. $25,000, 2000. For Public Benefits Hotline.
649. Northwestern University, Evanston, IL. $10,000, 2000. For library.

Illinois Tool Works Foundation

Limitations: Giving primarily in areas of company operations, with emphasis on Chicago, IL. No grants to individuals (except for employee-related scholarships), or for endowment funds or research; no loans.

650. Newberry Library, Chicago, IL. $50,000, 2000. For capital campaign.
651. Newberry Library, Chicago, IL. $10,000, 2000. For continued operating support.

The Joyce Foundation

Limitations: Giving primarily in the Great Lakes region, including IA, IL, IN, MI, MN, OH, and WI; limited number of environment grants made in Canada; culture grants restricted to the metropolitan Chicago, IL, area. No support for religious activities. No grants for endowment campaigns, scholarships, direct service programs, or capital proposals.

652. Donors Forum of Chicago, Chicago, IL. $17,820, 2000. For membership.
653. Edmund S. Muskie Foundation, National Caucus of Environmental Legislators, DC. $75,000, 2000. To organize workshops, information exchange, and technical support for state legislators interested in environmental programs.
654. Education Commission of the States, Denver, CO. $585,700, 2000. 3-year grant. To create National Center for Innovation in Governing American Education, clearinghouse of information on innovative governance issues from preschool through post-secondary education.
655. Federation for Community Planning, Cleveland, OH. $56,700, 2000. To develop health and human services case management system and service provider database for Cleveland Municipal School District.
656. Land Information Access Association, Traverse City, MI. $173,000, 2000. 2-year grant. To disseminate Geographic Information System (GIS) model developed under previous grant.
657. National Conference of State Legislatures, Denver, CO. $353,400, 2000. 2-year grant. To establish and manage National Clearinghouse on School Finance.
658. New York Academy of Medicine, NYC, NY. $750,000, 2000. 3-year grant. For Doctors Against Handgun Injury (DAHI),

coalition of medical organizations dedicated to mobilizing influence, authority, and clinical expertise of physicians to reduce handgun injury.

659. Women in Government (WIG), DC. $107,440, 2000. To conduct policy sessions on Education, Gun Violence and Campaign Reform.

Sara Lee Foundation

Limitations: Giving primarily in the Chicago, IL, area. No support for elementary or secondary schools, religious organizations, disease-specific health organizations, fraternal, political, or veterans' organizations, or national or international organizations with limited relationships to local company operations. No grants to individuals, or for fundraising events, goodwill advertising, endowments, or capital campaigns.

660. Chicago Public Library Foundation, Chicago, IL. $15,000, 1999.
661. Donors Forum of Chicago, Chicago, IL. $15,000, 1999.
662. Donors Forum of Chicago, Chicago, IL. $12,500, 1999.
663. Newberry Library, Chicago, IL. $15,000, 1999.
664. Survivors of the Shoah Visual History Foundation, Los Angeles, CA. $100,000, 1999.

John D. and Catherine T. MacArthur Foundation

Limitations: Giving on a national and international basis, with emphasis on Palm Beach County, FL, and Chicago, IL. No support for churches or religious programs, political activities or campaigns. No grants for capital or endowment funds, equipment purchases, plant construction, conferences, publications, media productions, debt retirement, development campaigns, fundraising appeals, scholarships, or fellowships (other than those sponsored by the foundation).

665. American Library Association, DC. $100,000, 2000. 2-year grant. For Office for Information Technology Policy.
666. Amigos Contra el SIDA, Friends Against AIDS, Mexico. $30,000, 2000. 2-year grant. For web page on AIDS in Mexico.
667. Coletivo Feminista Sexualidade e Saude, Sao Paulo, Brazil. $180,000, 2000. 3-year grant. For hotline and web site to improve communication with clients and other providers of reproductive health services.
668. Journal Storage Project (JSTOR), NYC, NY. $300,000, 2000. 3-year grant. For project to provide electronic access to archived journals in sciences, social sciences, and humanities for selected universities in Russia and Belarus.
669. Metropolitan Chicago Information Center, Chicago, IL. $50,000, 2000. For completion of survey to measure community capacity.
670. Mexican Center for Philanthropy, Centro Mexicano para la Filantropia, Mexico City, Mexico. $225,000, 2000. 3-year grant. For communications activities and provision of training and technical assistance.
671. National Security Archive Fund, DC. $900,000, 2000. 3-year grant. To foster greater transparency in U.S. foreign policy and intelligence operations and for special projects in Mexico and Cuba.
672. Saratov Legal Reform Project, Saratov, Russia. $116,000, 2000. 2-year grant. To improve understanding of human rights laws and legal practices among judges, legal experts, and courtroom lawyers in Russia.

Robert R. McCormick Tribune Foundation

Limitations: Giving primarily in the metropolitan Chicago, IL, area; except for Journalism Program which gives on a national basis and in Latin America; and communities program which operates in: Phoenix, AZ, Anaheim, Escondido, Los Angeles, Sacramento and San Diego, CA, Denver, CO, Fort Lauderdale and Orlando, FL, Atlanta, GA, Chicago, IL, Indianapolis, IN, Manhattan, KS, New Orleans, LA, Boston and Lowell, MA, New York, NY, Cleveland, OH, Philadelphia and York, PA, Dallas, Houston, and El Paso, TX, and Newport News, VA. No grants to individuals, or for endowment funds, scholarships, or single events.

673. Broward Public Library Foundation, Fort Lauderdale, FL. $50,000, 1999.
674. Chicago Public Library Foundation, Chicago, IL. $35,000, 1999.
675. Child Care Resource and Referral, Delray Beach, FL. $10,000, 1999.
676. Community Information and Referral Services, Phoenix, AZ. $35,000, 1999.

677. Connection Resource Services, Libertyville, IL. $25,000, 1999.
678. Denver Public Library Friends Foundation, Denver, CO. $344,000, 1999.
679. Denver Public Library Friends Foundation, Denver, CO. $40,000, 1999.
680. Denver Public Library Friends Foundation, Denver, CO. $12,000, 1999.
681. Donors Forum of Chicago, Chicago, IL. $25,000, 1999.
682. First Call for Help of Broward, Fort Lauderdale, FL. $11,500, 1999.
683. Illinois Network of Child Care Resource and Referral Agencies, Bloomington, IL. $50,000, 1999.
684. Los Angeles County Public Library Foundation, Downey, CA. $50,000, 1999.
685. Metropolitan Chicago Information Center, Chicago, IL. $45,000, 1999.
686. Phoenix Public Library Foundation, Phoenix, AZ. $400,000, 1999.
687. Phoenix Public Library, Friends of the, Phoenix, AZ. $25,000, 1999.
688. South Austin Job Referral Service, Chicago, IL. $15,000, 1999.

Motorola Foundation

Limitations: Giving primarily in communities where the company has major facilities, with emphasis on Huntsville, AL, Phoenix, AZ, Boyton Beach and Fort Lauderdale, FL, IL, Austin and Sequin, TX; and internationally, where company has a significant presence. No support for strictly sectarian or denominational religious organizations, national health organizations or their local chapters, trade schools, or state institutions (except through the employee matching gift program). No grants to individuals, or for university endowment funds, research, courtesy advertising, operating expenses of organizations receiving United Way funding, benefits, or capital fund drives.

689. Broward Alliance, Fort Lauderdale, FL. $20,000, 1999.

The Northern Trust Company Charitable Trust

Limitations: Giving limited to Cook County, IL, with focus on the Chicago area. No support for national organizations, health organizations concentrating efforts in one area of human disease (except through matching gift program), religious organizations whose services are limited to any one sectarian group, fraternal or political groups, or operating support for United Way agencies. No grants to individuals, or for fellowships, advertising for fundraising benefits, or research; no loans.

690. Newberry Library, Chicago, IL. $25,000, 1999. For capital support.

The Offield Family Foundation

Limitations: Giving primarily in AZ, CA, the Chicago, IL, area and MI. No grants to individuals.

691. Harbor Springs Library, Harbor Springs, MI. $10,000, 2000.
692. Sedona Public Library, Sedona, AZ. $50,000, 2000.

The ONDEO Nalco Foundation

Limitations: Giving primarily in areas where company has major offices, labs, or manufacturing operations: metropolitan and the western suburbs of Chicago, IL, Carson, CA, Garyville, LA, Paulsboro, NJ, Chagrin Falls, OH, and Sugar Land and Freeport, TX. No support for public colleges or universities, secondary or elementary schools, churches or religious education, or political activities or lobbying. No grants to individuals, or for endowment funds, ads in charitable publications, purchase of special event tickets or matching gifts; no loans.

693. Little Company of Mary Hospital Foundation, Evergreen Park, IL. $10,000, 2000. For Cancer Center Community Resource Library.

Frank E. Payne and Seba B. Payne Foundation

Limitations: Giving primarily in the metropolitan Chicago, IL, area and PA. No grants to individuals, or for fellowships; generally no support for endowments; no loans.

694. Bethlehem Area Public Library, Bethlehem, PA. $88,000, 2000. For carpeting and general support.

Polk Bros. Foundation, Inc.

Limitations: Giving primarily in Chicago, IL. No support for political organizations or religious institutions seeking support for programs whose participants are restricted by religious affiliation, or tax-generating entities (municipalities and school districts) for services within their normal responsibilities. No grants to individuals, or for medical, scientific or academic research, or purchase of dinner or raffle tickets.

695. Citizens Information Service of Illinois, Chicago, IL. $10,000, 2000.
696. Coordinated Advice and Referral Program for Legal Services, Chicago, IL. $20,000, 2000.
697. Donors Forum of Chicago, Chicago, IL. $20,000, 2000.
698. Newberry Library, Chicago, IL. $25,000, 2000.

Pritzker Foundation

Limitations: Giving on a national basis, with some emphasis on Chicago, IL. No grants to individuals.

699. Chicago Public Library Foundation, Chicago, IL. $200,000, 1999. For general operating support.
700. Chicago Public Library Foundation, Chicago, IL. $75,000, 1999. For general operating support.
701. Northwestern University, Evanston, IL. $2,000,000, 1999. For general operating support for Pritzker Library.

The Retirement Research Foundation

Limitations: Giving limited to the Midwest (IA, IL, IN, KY, MI, MO, WI) and FL for direct service projects not having the potential of national impact. No grants to individuals, or for computers, construction, general operating expenses of established organizations, endowment or developmental campaigns, emergency funds, deficit financing, land acquisition, publications, conferences, scholarships, media productions, dissertation research, annual campaigns, or renovation projects.

702. Clifton Heights Senior Center, Saint Louis, MO. $32,000, 2000. For Healthy Choices Resource Guide.
703. Donors Forum of Chicago, Chicago, IL. $30,000, 2000. For Fund for Immigrants and Refugees.
704. Donors Forum of Chicago, Chicago, IL. $17,820, 2000. For Annual Dues.
705. Foundation Center, NYC, NY. $15,000, 2000. For Foundation and Philanthropic Information Dissemination.

Dr. Scholl Foundation

Limitations: Giving in the U.S., with emphasis on IL. No support for public education. No grants to individuals, or for general support, continuing support, operating budgets, deficit financing, or unrestricted purposes.

706. Alzheimers Disease and Related Disorders Association, Skokie, IL. $15,000, 1999. Toward Helpline.
707. Chicago Public Library Foundation, Chicago, IL. $45,000, 1999. Toward tutoring and homework assistance program.
708. Newberry Library, Chicago, IL. $50,000, 1999. For center's endowment.
709. Woodstock Theological Center, DC. $20,000, 1999. For computer conversion.
710. YWCA of Greater Toronto, Toronto, Canada. $10,000, 1999. For Stop 86 In-Shelter/After-Shelter programs.

The Spencer Foundation

Limitations: Giving on a national and international basis. No grants to individuals (except those working under the auspices of an institution), or for capital funds, general purposes, operating or continuing support, sabbatical supplements, work in instructional or curriculum development, any kind of training or service program, scholarships, travel fellowships, endowment funds, pre-doctoral research, or matching gifts; no loans.

711. Council for Basic Education, DC. $25,000, 2000. For conference, Beyond the Standards Horse Race: Implementation, Assessment, and Accountability-The Keys to Improving Student Achievement.
712. Donors Forum of Chicago, Chicago, IL. $17,820, 2000. For membership dues.
713. Foundation for International Arts and Education, Bethesda, MD. $25,000, 2000. Toward research project to assess feasibility of distance learning among academic institutions in Newly

Independent States and for support of the development of other archival material to strengthen higher education system in Russia.
714. University of Wisconsin, Madison, WI. $35,000, 2000. For research project, The History of the American Public School Library.

State Farm Companies Foundation

Limitations: Giving in Bloomington, IL, and 27 U.S. regional office sites. No support for fraternal, political, labor, or religious organizations. No grants to individuals (except for doctoral award and fellowship programs), or for dinners, sponsorships of events, special events, exhibitions, performances, or goodwill advertising, fundraising events, conferences, tours, related travel or seminars.

715. Council for Basic Education, DC. $10,000, 2000. For insurance education.

WPWR-TV Channel 50 Foundation

Limitations: Giving primarily in the metropolitan Chicago, IL, area and northwestern IN. No support for religious or fraternal purposes, or for political campaigns. No grants to individuals, or for scholarships, underwriting or tables for events, or special projects or productions.

716. Donors Forum of Chicago, Chicago, IL. $17,500, 2000.
717. Gerber-Hart Gay and Lesbian Archives and Library, Chicago, IL. $10,000, 2000.

INDIANA

John W. Anderson Foundation

Limitations: Giving primarily in Lake and Porter counties in northwest IN. No grants to individuals, or for endowment funds, seed money, deficit financing, or scholarship funds; no loans.

718. Valparaiso University, Library Center, Valparaiso, IN. $125,000, 2000. For operating support.

Ball Brothers Foundation

Limitations: Giving limited to IN. No grants to individuals.

719. Muncie Public Library, Muncie, IN. $50,000, 2000. For capital campaign.
720. Remnant Trust, Hagerstown, IN. $10,000, 2000. For general operating support.

George and Frances Ball Foundation

Limitations: Giving primarily in Muncie and Delaware County, IN. No grants to individuals.

721. Muncie Public Library, Muncie, IN. $100,000, 2000. For capital campaign.

The Clowes Fund, Inc.

Limitations: Giving primarily in Indianapolis, IN, Boston, MA, and Seattle, WA. No support for foreign organizations or programs promoting specific religious doctrine. No grants to individuals, or for videos, publications, conferences, or seminars; no loans.

722. Indianapolis-Marion County Public Library Foundation, Indianapolis, IN. $25,000, 2000. For computer equipment.

Dekko Foundation, Inc.

Limitations: Giving primarily in Limestone County, AL; Clarke, Decatur, Lucas, Ringgold, and Union counties, IA; Noble, DeKalb, Whitley, Steuben, LaGrange, and Kosciousko counties, IN; and Lincoln and Giles counties, TN. No grants to individuals.

723. Kendallville Public Library, Kendallville, IN. $28,000, 2000.
724. Lamoni Public Library, Lamoni, IA. $100,000, 2000.
725. Ligonier Public Library, Ligonier, IN. $19,700, 2000.
726. Murray Public Library, Murray, IA. $13,571, 2000.
727. Noble County Public Library, Albion, IN. $20,000, 2000.
728. Noble County Public Library, Albion, IN. $20,000, 2000.
729. Syracuse-Turkey Creek Township Public Library, Syracuse, IN. $16,946, 2000.

English-Bonter-Mitchell Foundation

Limitations: Giving primarily in Fort Wayne, IN. No grants to individuals.

730. Allen County Public Library Foundation, Fort Wayne, IN. $20,000, 1999.

Lilly Endowment Inc.

Limitations: Giving limited to IN, with emphasis on Indianapolis, for community development projects (including the arts, preservation, capital building funds, operating funds, and social services). Education funding focused principally on Indiana under invitational grant programs. National giving in religion, philanthropic studies, leadership education, and selected higher education initiatives. Generally, no support for health care programs, or mass media projects. No grants to individuals, (except for fellowships awarded under special programs), or for endowed chairs.; grants for endowments limited generally to community foundations in Indiana.

731. American Theological Library Association, Evanston, IL. $150,000, 2000. For fund for Interactive conference facility at theological school.
732. Foundation Center, NYC, NY. $75,000, 2000. For General operating support.
733. Indiana Cooperative Library Services Authority, Indianapolis, IN. $297,100, 2000. For Access to electronic database of scholarly journals in academic libraries in Indiana.
734. International Center of Indianapolis, Indianapolis, IN. $300,000, 2000. For general operating support of international cultural exchange programs.
735. International Center of Indianapolis, Indianapolis, IN. $15,000, 2000. For Roots of Brazil project.
736. National Center for Family Philanthropy, DC. $50,000, 2000. For Publication on faith and family philanthropy.
737. Pennsylvania State University, University Park, PA. $403,220, 2000. For The American Religion Data Archive project.
738. Union Theological Seminary, NYC, NY. $8,000,000, 2000. For renewed support for collections at Burke Library.

IOWA

AEGON Transamerica Foundation

Limitations: No grants to individuals.

739. National Czech and Slovak Museum and Library, Cedar Rapids, IA. $10,000, 1999.

Gardner and Florence Call Cowles Foundation, Inc.

Limitations: Giving limited to IA, with emphasis on Des Moines. No grants to individuals, or for scholarships or fellowships; no loans.

740. Wartburg College, Waverly, IA. $150,000, 1999. For library expansion.

Iowa West Foundation

Limitations: Giving primarily in southwest IA and the Council Bluffs, Omaha, NE, area. No support for nonoperating foundations or religious organizations. No grants to individuals, or for scholarships, general operating funds, deficit budgets, debt financing, salaries, ticket/table purchases, advertising, and discriminatory activities.

741. Dunlap Public Library, Dunlap, IA. $25,000, 1999.
742. Woodbine Carnegie Public Library, Woodbine, IA. $30,000, 1999.

Maytag Corporation Foundation

Limitations: Giving limited to areas of company operations, particularly Searcy, AR, Anana and Newton, IA, Galesburg and Herrin, IL, North Canton, OH, Florence and Williston, SC, Cleveland and Jackson, TN. No support for health agencies, churches, religious causes, fraternal organizations, or international relations. No grants to individuals (except for employee-related scholarships), or for benefit dinners, complimentary advertising, or sponsorship of charity events.

743. Cleveland Public Library, Cleveland, OH. $10,000, 2000.
744. National First Ladies Library, Canton, OH. $33,000, 2000. For Founding Sponsorship.

R. J. McElroy Trust

Limitations: Giving primarily in the KWWL viewing area, 22 counties in northeast IA. No grants to individuals (except for fellowship program).

745. Barlow Memorial Library, Iowa Falls, IA. $20,000, 2000. For building project.
746. Matthias M. Hoffman Public Library, Dyersville, IA. $15,000, 2000. For building project.
747. Northeast Iowa Regional Library System, Waterloo, IA. $25,000, 2000. For library computer grants program.
748. Wartburg College, Waverly, IA. $200,000, 2000. For Wartburg Learner's Library.

KANSAS

Kansas Health Foundation

Limitations: Giving limited to KS. No grants to individuals.

749. CDC Foundation, Atlanta, GA. $109,894, 1999. To expand Kansas Integrated Public Health System to become statewide clearinghouse for public health data and to partner with Foundation to provide informatics specialist.
750. Kansas Action for Children, Topeka, KS. $287,786, 1999. To plan and implement statewide report card reflecting health status of Kansas children through partnership with Greater Kansas City Community Foundation.
751. Kansas Advocates for Better Care, Lawrence, KS. $15,000, 1999. For updated database that ensures consumers and their families have adequate information when selecting adult-care facility.
752. Kansas Health Institute, Topeka, KS. $389,000, 1999. To expand Kansas Integrated Public Health System to become statewide clearinghouse for public health data.
753. Kansas University Endowment Association, Lawrence, KS. $14,496, 1999. For public radio in Kansas to provide information that will benefit health and lives of Kansas communities.
754. Ottawa County Health Planning Commission, Minneapolis, KS. $89,705, 1999. To expand Foundation's Integrated Community Health Development (ICHD) project to more rural communities so they are able to design integrated rural health delivery systems that provide local access to care while focusing on health promotion and disease prevention activities.
755. Wichita State University Endowment Association, Wichita, KS. $23,343, 1999. To develop resource listing of health related non-profit organizations in Kansas.

David H. Koch Charitable Foundation

Limitations: Giving on a national basis, with emphasis on KS for education, social science, and public affairs; New York, NY, for arts and culture. No grants to individuals (except for scholarships), or for deficit financing, exchange programs, land acquisition, or professorships; no loans.

756. Library of Congress, DC. $15,000, 1999. For Madison Council Fund.

KENTUCKY

The Gheens Foundation, Inc.

Limitations: Giving primarily in KY, with emphasis on Louisville.

757. Volunteer and Information Agency, New Orleans, LA. $17,000, 2000.

The Humana Foundation, Inc.

758. Claremont University Center and Graduate School, Graduate School of Management, Claremont, CA. $10,000, 2000. For Peter F. Drucker archive.
759. Louisville Free Public Library Foundation, Louisville, KY. $20,000, 2000. For Youth Summer Reading program and for Gutenberg exhibit.

MAINE

Libra Foundation

Limitations: Giving limited to ME. No grants to individuals.

760. Belfast Free Library, Belfast, ME. $10,000, 1999. For capital campaign.
761. Blue Hill Library, Blue Hill, ME. $20,000, 1999. For computers/technology upgrade.
762. Guilford Memorial Library, Guilford, ME. $10,000, 1999. For expansion and renovation.
763. Norway Memorial Library, Norway, ME. $10,000, 1999. For renovation and addition to building.
764. Rangeley Library Association, Rangeley, ME. $10,000, 1999. To build addition to library.
765. Rockland Public Library Endowment Association, Rockland, ME. $25,000, 1999. To enlarge and renovate library.
766. York Public Library Association, York, ME. $100,000, 1999. To construct new modern library facility.

MARYLAND

The Abell Foundation, Inc.

Limitations: Giving limited to MD, with emphasis on Baltimore. Generally no support for housing or medical facilities. No grants to individuals, or for operating budgets, sponsorships, memberships, sustaining funds, or deficit financing.

767. Enoch Pratt Free Library, Baltimore, MD. $35,000, 1999. For challenge grant for Roland Park Library Initiative expansion, equipment and renovation of Roland Park branch.
768. Planned Parenthood of Maryland, Baltimore, MD. $99,615, 1999. For statewide emergency contraception program, including establishment of statewide toll-free telephone access to information about family planning options.

The Jacob and Hilda Blaustein Foundation, Inc.

Limitations: Giving primarily in MD; no local projects outside Baltimore, MD. No support for unaffiliated schools or synagogues. No grants to individuals, or for fundraising events, or direct mail solicitations; no loans (except for program-related investments).

769. Survivors of the Shoah Visual History Foundation, Los Angeles, CA. $50,000, 1999. For unrestricted support.

The Annie E. Casey Foundation

Limitations: No grants to individuals (except for Casey Children and Family Fellowship program), or for capital projects.

770. Center for Applied Research, Philadelphia, PA. $48,064, 1999. To support site team leaders in building understanding of their roles in their communities, skills required and tools and resources needed.
771. Community Information Exchange, DC. $25,000, 1999. For technical assistance to Rebuilding Communities Initiative (RCI) site.
772. Cross City Campaign for Urban School Reform, Chicago, IL. $100,000, 1999. For systemwide school reform work under way in six cities through cross-site visits, parent and community leadership development and creation of viable national network.
773. Donors Forum of Chicago, Chicago, IL. $50,000, 1999. For conference to examine issues and challenges in strengthening refugee and immigrant families and communities.
774. Enoch Pratt Free Library, Baltimore, MD. $75,000, 1999. For Pratt Center for Technology Training.
775. Enterprise Foundation, Columbia, MD. $85,621, 1999. To support Patty Rouse Resource Center as source of information on best practices in comprehensive community development.
776. Finance Project, DC. $500,000, 1999. For work of Welfare Information Network, clearinghouse and technical assistance broker on welfare reform.
777. Foundation Center, NYC, NY. $150,000, 1999. For organizational membership.
778. HandsNet, San Jose, CA. $250,000, 1999. To strengthen field by linking diverse points of view and providing access to information.
779. Harvard University, Cambridge, MA. $20,000, 1999. For resource guide that will give catalogue of projects, organizations, consultants and Web sites about community institutions.
780. Juvenile Law Center, Philadelphia, PA. $30,000, 1999. To provide resource guide in service delivery system reforms.

781. Metis Associates, NYC, NY. $1,500,000, 1999. To strengthen capacity of Foundation grantees to access and use information.
782. National Governors Association Center for Best Practices, DC. $45,000, 1999. To convene and facilitate Interdisciplinary Learning Network on Effective Youth Policy and Practice.
783. National Housing Institute, Orange, NJ. $82,800, 1999. For technical assistance to Rebuilding Communities Initiative (RCI) site.
784. National Multicultural Institute, DC. $37,000, 1999. To provide review of Foundation's grant making related to race, ethnicity, language, culture and power and develop resource guide.
785. National Youth Information Network, Lawrence, KS. $10,000, 1999. For consultative process with community foundations, United Way agencies and adult-serving agencies.
786. Nonprofit Clinic Consortium, DC. $142,056, 1999. To develop coordinated Management Information System for neighborhood health clinics in District of Columbia as part of health care reform initiatives.
787. Parent Resource Network, Richmond, VA. $40,000, 1999. For further development of Network, grassroots family group affiliated with Mental Health Initiative for Urban Children in East End of Richmond. Grant made through Richmond Community Action Council.
788. Rocky Mountain Media Watch, Denver, CO. $13,000, 1999. To produce communications resource guide.
789. United Neighborhood Houses of New York, NYC, NY. $80,000, 1999. To develop typology of social networks and document strategies used by settlement houses to strengthen social connections among community residents.
790. University of Arizona, Tucson, AZ. $145,000, 1999. To develop model management information tool for community health outreach workers' programs.
791. University of Maine, Portland, ME. $40,000, 1999. To propose set of criteria and provide information for interactive database of programs and practices that improve transition to adulthood of youth leaving foster care system.
792. West Virginia Kids Count Fund, Charleston, WV. $60,000, 1999. For Kids Count state projects.

The Sherman Fairchild Foundation, Inc.

793. Journal Storage Project (JSTOR), NYC, NY. $50,000, 1999. For software development.
794. Millbrook Free Library, Millbrook, NY. $25,000, 1999. For building renovation.

France-Merrick Foundation

Limitations: Giving primarily in the metropolitan Baltimore, MD, area. No grants to individuals.

795. Baltimore Neighborhood Indicators Alliance, Baltimore, MD. $50,000, 2000.
796. Roland Park Library Initiative, Baltimore, MD. $27,000, 2000.
797. Village Learning Place, Baltimore, MD. $50,000, 2000.

Morris Goldseker Foundation of Maryland, Inc.

Limitations: Giving limited to the Baltimore, MD, area. No support for advocacy or political action groups, religious purposes, health, arts or cultural affairs, specific diseases or disabilities, or for projects normally financed with public funds. No grants to individuals, or for building or endowment funds, equipment, land acquisition, renovation projects, deficit financing, annual campaigns, research, or publications.

798. Baltimore Neighborhood Indicators Alliance, Baltimore, MD. $50,000, 1999. For start-up support for organization with mission develop and analyze neighborhood-level data, provide technical assistance to users of the system, award community data partnership grants and coordinate forums to develop city-wide indicators of community well-being.
799. Maryland Regional Practitioners Network for Fathers and Families, Bowie, MD. $45,000, 1999. To establish group as independent nonprofit, with small staff and network of volunteer members, as it expands coordination, training and advocacy efforts.
800. Midtown Community Benefits District, Baltimore, MD. $36,000, 1999. For full-time community organizer to develop network of

block captains and group of neighborhood walkers to work for long-term revitalization of diverse neighborhoods.

801. Village Learning Place, Baltimore, MD. $195,000, 1999. 3-year grant. For positions of full-time program director and part-time community outreach coordinator.

The James M. Johnston Trust for Charitable and Educational Purposes

Limitations: Giving primarily in Washington, DC, and NC. No grants to individuals, or for building or endowment funds or operating budgets.

802. George C. Marshall Research Foundation, Lexington, VA. $25,000, 1999. For continued support for scholarships.

The John W. Kluge Foundation

803. Library of Congress, DC. $2,275,000, 2000. For general support.
804. Ronald Reagan Presidential Foundation, Simi Valley, CA. $125,000, 2000. For general support.

Lockheed Martin Corporation Foundation

Limitations: Giving primarily in areas of company operations. No support for home-based child care/educational services, religious organizations for religious purposes, professional associations, labor or fraternal organizations, social clubs, or athletic groups. No grants to individuals (except for employee-related scholarships), or for advertising in booklets, yearbooks, or journals unrelated to Lockheed Martin's business interests.

805. Council for Basic Education, DC. $10,000, 1999.

Town Creek Foundation, Inc.

Limitations: Giving nationally for major programs; support limited to Talbot County, MD, for social services. No support for primary or secondary schools, hospitals, health care institutions, or religious organizations. No support for colleges or universities except when some aspect of their work is an integral part of a program supported by the foundation. No grants to individuals, or for endowment, capital, or building fund campaigns, purchase of land or buildings, research, scholarship programs, conferences, the publication of books or periodicals, or visual or performing arts projects.

806. Physicians for Social Responsibility, DC. $25,000, 2000. For Disarmament Clearinghouse.
807. Southwest Research and Information Center, Albuquerque, NM. $15,000, 2000. For Nuclear Watch of New Mexico.

The Harry and Jeanette Weinberg Foundation, Inc.

Limitations: No support for colleges, universities, or museums. No grants to individuals.

808. Clay Mountain Housing, Clay, WV. $25,000, 2000.
809. Hawaii State Library Foundation, Honolulu, HI. $10,000, 2000.

MASSACHUSETTS

The George I. Alden Trust

Limitations: Giving limited to the U.S.. No grants to individuals; no loans.

810. American Antiquarian Society, Worcester, MA. $350,000, 2000. For construction.
811. Worcester Free Public Library, Friends of the, Worcester, MA. $250,000, 2000. For construction.

L. G. Balfour Foundation

Limitations: Giving primarily in New England, with emphasis on MA. No grants to individuals.

812. Balfour Gold Dusters, Mansfield, MA. $13,000, 2000. For general support and for emergency medical needs not covered by insurance.
813. Education Resources Institute, Boston, MA. $100,000, 2000. For Higher Education Information Center operating support.

Barr Foundation

Limitations: Giving primarily in the greater Boston, MA, area. No grants to individuals.

814. Folger Shakespeare Library, DC. $100,000, 1999.
815. Library of the Boston Athenaeum, Boston, MA. $20,000, 1999.

Berkshire Taconic Community Foundation

Limitations: Giving limited to northwest Litchfield County, CT, Berkshire County, MA, and northeast Dutchess and Columbia counties, NY.

816. Cornwall Library Associates, Cornwall, CT. $20,000, 1999. For new building.

Boston Foundation, Inc.

Limitations: Giving from discretionary funds limited to the metropolitan Boston, MA, area. No support for religious purposes, private schools, municipalities, or national or international programs. No grants to individuals, or for medical, scientific, or academic research, books or articles, films, radio, or television programs, equipment, travel, scholarships, fellowships, conferences, or capital campaigns; no loans.

817. Associated Day Care Services of Metropolitan Boston, Boston, MA. $36,500, 2000. For Early Education Clearinghouse.
818. Associated Grantmakers of Massachusetts, Boston, MA. $50,000, 2000. For Catalogue for Philanthropy.
819. Associated Grantmakers of Massachusetts, Giving New England, Boston, MA. $25,000, 2000. For efforts to increase base of charitable capital available to communities in central and northern New England.
820. Boston Athenaeum, Boston, MA. $105,000, 2000.
821. Boston Athenaeum, Boston, MA. $50,000, 2000.
822. Boston Public Library Foundation, Boston, MA. $300,000, 2000.
823. Groton Public Library, Groton, MA. $201,486, 2000.
824. Massachusetts Affordable Housing Alliance, Boston, MA. $43,100, 2000. For Building Blocks in Boston campaign.
825. Memphis/Shelby County Public Library, Memphis, TN. $10,000, 2000.
826. Metropolitan Area Planning Council, Boston, MA. $45,000, 2000. For Boston Children and Families Database.
827. Project Parents, Boston, MA. $17,000, 2000. For libraries and literacy workshops at Boston public housing developments.

Community Foundation of Western Massachusetts

Limitations: Giving limited to western MA, including on Hampden County, Hampshire County, and Franklin County. No support for political or religious organizations, private secondary or higher education. No grants to individuals directly, or for operating budgets, endowments, fundraising events, tickets for benefits, courtesy advertising, academic or medical research or multi-year funding.

828. Springfield Library and Museums Association, Springfield, MA. $30,000, 2000. For capital campaign.

Irene E. and George A. Davis Foundation

Limitations: Giving primarily in Hampden County, MA. No grants to individuals or for scholarships (except James E. Davis Memorial Scholarship), for deficit financing, endowment funds, or matching gifts; no loans.

829. Pioneer Institute for Public Policy Research, Boston, MA. $40,000, 1999. For Charter School Resource Center.
830. Springfield Library and Museums Association, Springfield, MA. $25,000, 1999. For The Mystical Arts of Tibet exhibit.

Fidelity Foundation

Limitations: Giving primarily in KY, MA, NH, NY, OH, RI, TX, UT, Toronto, Canada, and in other communities where FMR employees live and work. No support for sectarian organizations, disease-specific associations, or public school systems. No grants to individuals, or for scholarships, civic or start-up organizations, corporate memberships, participation in benefit events, or film or video projects; no multi-year pledges.

831. Huntington Library, Art Collections and Botanical Gardens, San Marino, CA. $50,000, 1999.
832. John F. Kennedy Library Foundation, Boston, MA. $25,000, 1999.
833. Malden Public Library, Malden, MA. $20,000, 1999.
834. Utah Library Association, Orem, UT. $15,000, 1999.

FleetBoston Financial Foundation

Limitations: Giving limited to states where the company subsidiaries do business: CT, MA, ME, NH, NJ, NY, PA, and RI. No support for fraternal or veterans' groups, religious groups, sectarian purposes, national organizations, including state and local chapters, or for organizations that are not open to the general public. No grants to individuals (except for employee-related scholarships), or for scientific or medical research, tours, trips, or conferences, or annual funds for hospitals, colleges, universities, grade schools, or high schools; no loans.

835. Bangor Public Library, Bangor, ME. $20,000, 1999.
836. Buffalo Niagara Enterprise, Buffalo, NY. $12,200, 1999.
837. Hartford Public Library, Hartford, CT. $20,000, 1999.
838. Providence Public Library, Providence, RI. $15,000, 1999.
839. Springfield Library and Museums Association, Springfield, MA. $50,000, 1999.
840. York Public Library Association, York, ME. $10,000, 1999.

George F. and Sybil H. Fuller Foundation

Limitations: Giving primarily in MA, with emphasis on Worcester. No grants to individuals, or for endowments or general operating support; no loans.

841. American Antiquarian Society, Worcester, MA. $150,000, 2000.
842. Worcester Public Library, Worcester, MA. $150,000, 2000.

The Highland Street Connection

Limitations: Giving primarily in MA. No grants to individuals.

843. Morse Institute Library, Natick, MA. $10,000, 1999. For general operating support for annual giving program.

The Hyams Foundation, Inc.

Limitations: Giving primarily in Boston and Chelsea, MA. No support for municipal, state, or federal agencies; institutions of higher learning for standard educational programs; religious organizations for sectarian religious purposes; or national or regional health organizations; support for medical research is being phased out. No grants to individuals, or for endowment funds, hospitals and health centers, capital campaigns, fellowships, publications, conferences, films or videos or curriculum development.

844. Massachusetts Affordable Housing Alliance, Boston, MA. $22,500, 1999. For continued operating support.
845. Project Parents, Boston, MA. $15,000, 1999. For operating support, targeted to creation and maintenance of libraries for youth at Boston Housing Authority sites.

The Henry P. Kendall Foundation

Limitations: Giving primarily in northeastern and northwestern North America (U.S. and Canada) for environmental and natural resource programs. No support for waste clean-ups, toxic or air/water pollution prevention or pollution monitoring initiatives, land trusts, or species-specific preservation efforts. No grants to individuals, or for capital or endowment funds, building construction/operation, basic research, scholarships, fellowships, equipment, debt reduction, or conference participation/travel.

846. Canadian Parks and Wilderness Society, Ottawa, Canada. $10,000, 1999. For work with Miistakis Institute for the Rockies to address legal and financial management challenges associated with becoming independent organization providing electronic communication and biological data services to Y2Y region.

The John Merck Fund

Limitations: Generally, no support for large organizations with well-established funding sources. No grants to individuals, or for endowment or capital fund projects.

847. Citizens Nuclear Information Center, Tokyo, Japan. $30,000, 1999. For continued support to end Japanese plutonium reprocessing.
848. Human Rights Internet, Ottawa, Canada. $40,000, 1999. To continue to assist human rights organizations in developing countries to launch World Wide Web information sites.
849. International Monitor Institute, Los Angeles, CA. $50,000, 1999. To maintain, increase and improve publicly available database of television and radio broadcast and photographic materials on human rights conflicts and issues around the world.
850. National Security Archive Fund, National Security Archive, DC. $25,000, 1999. To reform government secrecy practices and improve human rights accountability in Latin America.
851. Program for Appropriate Technology in Health (PATH), Seattle, WA. $50,000, 1999. To provide information about emergency contraceptives to health care providers with ethnically diverse patient loads and increase awareness among those patients of this means of preventing unintended pregnancy.
852. University of Minnesota, School of Law, Minneapolis, MN. $20,000, 1999. To improve and expand Human Rights Library on the World Wide Web.

Amelia Peabody Charitable Fund

Limitations: Giving primarily in New England with emphasis on MA. No support for tax-supported municipal or government organizations or religious groups. No grants to individuals, or for salaries or operating expenses.

853. Boston Athenaeum, Boston, MA. $500,000, 1999. For climate control.
854. IMAGGHINE, Wellesley, MA. $15,800, 1999. For computer technology.
855. Massachusetts Historical Society, Boston, MA. $85,000, 1999. For library automation.
856. Social Law Library, Boston, MA. $250,000, 1999. For library computer system.

Amelia Peabody Foundation

Limitations: Giving limited to MA. No grants to individuals, or for endowment funds, performances, conferences, research, filmmaking or videos, publications, scholarships, or fellowships; no loans or program-related investments.

857. Benjamin Banneker Charter School, Cambridge, MA. $100,000, 1999. For start-up support to establish Library Media Center.
858. Pioneer Institute for Public Policy Research, Boston, MA. $100,000, 1999. For Charter School Resource Center.

State Street Foundation

Limitations: Giving primarily in the greater Boston, MA, area. No grants to individuals, or for scholarships.

859. Boston Public Library Foundation, Boston, MA. $35,000, 1999.
860. Harry S. Truman Library Institute for National and International Affairs, Independence, MO. $10,000, 1999.

Silva Casa Stiftung Trust

Limitations: Giving on an international basis, with emphasis on Switzerland. No grants to individuals.

861. Staatsarchiv Des Kantons Bern, Bern, Switzerland. $64,400, 1999. For general support.
862. Stadt Und Universitatbibliothek Bern, Bern, Switzerland. $128,880, 1999. For general support.

MICHIGAN

Battle Creek Community Foundation

Limitations: Giving limited to the greater Battle Creek, MI, area. No grants for operating budgets, deficit financing, endowments, or research; no loans (except for program-related investments).

863. Willard Library, Battle Creek, MI. $15,000, 2000. For Community Technology Coordination Project.
864. Willard Library, Nonprofit Alliance, Battle Creek, MI. $10,000, 2000. For community-wide evaluation project.

The Carls Foundation

Limitations: Giving primarily in MI. No grants to individuals, or for publications, film and video, research, travel, conferences, or special event sponsorships.

865. Gerontology Network Resources, Grand Rapids, MI. $22,200, 1999. For Traveling Grannies and Grandpas.

Community Foundation for Southeastern Michigan

Limitations: Giving limited to southeastern MI. No support for sectarian religious programs. No grants to individuals from unrestricted funds, or for capital projects, endowments, annual campaigns, operating budgets (except in initial years of new ventures), conferences, fundraising, annual meetings, building funds, or equipment.

866. Michigan Association of Community Arts Agencies, Detroit, MI. $64,200, 1999. For directory of arts and cultural organizations.

DaimlerChrysler Corporation Fund

Limitations: Giving primarily in areas where company employees live and work, including AL, AZ, DE, IL, IN, MI, MO, NY, OH, and WI. No support for religious, organizations for religious purposes, veterans or labor organizations, fraternal associations, athletic groups, social clubs, political organizations or campaigns, organizations supported by the United Way (except through employee contributions), organizations that limit membership and services based on race, religion, color, creed, sex, age or national origin, or delivery of direct health care, or disease-specific organizations. No grants to individuals (except for employee-related scholarships), or for endowment funds, trips, tours, conferences, seminars, fellowships, fundraising, advertising, deficit financing, vehicle donation, capital campaigns or multi-year pledges; no loans.

867. Charities Aid Foundation, West Malling, England. $550,000, 1999. For operating support.
868. Detroit Public Library, Friends of, Detroit, MI. $100,000, 1999. For operating support.
869. Eisenhower Foundation, Abilene, KS. $25,000, 1999. For operating support.
870. Eisenhower Foundation, Abilene, KS. $25,000, 1999. For operating support.

Dow Chemical Company Foundation

Limitations: No grants to individuals (except for special relief funds).

871. Child Care Concepts, Midland, MI. $28,902, 1999.
872. Clute Public Library Association, Clute, TX. $175,000, 1999.

The Herbert H. and Grace A. Dow Foundation

Limitations: Giving limited to MI, with emphasis on Midland County. No support for political organizations or sectarian religious organizations or programs, other than churches in Midland County. No grants to individuals, or for travel or conferences; no loans.

873. Hoyt Public Library, Saginaw, MI. $40,000, 1999. For parking lot.

Earhart Foundation

Limitations: No grants for capital, building, or endowment funds, operating budgets, continuing support, annual campaigns, seed money, emergency funds, deficit financing, or matching gifts; no loans.

874. Institute of World Politics, DC. $10,000, 1999. To continue to catalogue and computerize holdings of Institute's library.

Ford Motor Company Fund

Limitations: Giving primarily in areas where plants and offices are located and members of the community are employed, with special emphasis on Detroit, MI. No support for religious, sectarian, political or fraternal organizations, animal rights organizations, labor groups, private schools, profitmaking enterprises, or organizations supported by the United Way. No grants to individuals, or for scholarships (except employee-related scholarships), fellowships, endowments, debt reduction, fundraising, or beauty or talent contests; no loans, program-related investments or donations of vehicles.

875. Indian Health Care Resources Center, Tulsa, OK. $150,000, 1999. For capital support.
876. Library Legacy Foundation, Toledo, OH. $25,000, 1999. For program support.
877. National Charities Information Bureau (NCIB), NYC, NY. $10,000, 1999.
878. Non-Profit Enterprise at Work, NEW Center, Ann Arbor, MI. $20,000, 1999.
879. Somos El Futuro, Albany, NY. $10,000, 1999.

The Fremont Area Community Foundation

Limitations: Giving primarily in Newaygo County, MI. No grants to individuals (except for scholarships from specified funds of the foundation), or for contingencies, reserves, or deficit financing.

880. Fremont Area District Library, Fremont, MI. $882,927, 1999. For community contribution for renovation and expansion.
881. Fremont Area District Library, Fremont, MI. $60,000, 1999. For library enhancements.
882. Fremont Area District Library, Fremont, MI. $30,392, 1999. For building security system.
883. Fremont Area District Library, Fremont, MI. $21,600, 1999. For art sculpture for new library building.
884. Fremont Area District Library, Fremont, MI. $20,000, 1999. For book security system.
885. Fremont Area District Library, Fremont, MI. $14,999, 1999. For collection upgrade.
886. Grant Public Library, Grant, MI. $35,000, 1999. For library enhancements.
887. Hesperia Public Library, Hesperia, MI. $25,000, 1999. For consultant fees for new library building.
888. Hesperia Public Library, Hesperia, MI. $25,000, 1999. For library enhancements.
889. Newaygo Carnegie Library, Newaygo, MI. $40,000, 1999. For library enhancements.
890. Newaygo Carnegie Library, Newaygo, MI. $11,800, 1999. For program support and camp registration fees. Grant made through Amazing X Charitable Trust.
891. Newaygo Public Schools, Newaygo, MI. $38,571, 1999. For Joining Forces Child Care Resources and Referral Program.
892. White Cloud Public Library, White Cloud, MI. $35,000, 1999. For library enhancements.
893. Womens Information Service, Fremont, MI. $55,683, 1999. For operating support for Newaygo County domestic violence outreach program.

Frey Foundation

Limitations: Giving primarily in Emmet, Charlevoix, and Kent counties, MI. No support for sectarian charitable activity. No grants to individuals, or for endowment funds, debt retirement, general operating expenses, scholarships, conferences, speakers, travel, or to cover routine, current, or emergency expenses.

894. Child and Family Resource Council, Grand Rapids, MI. $45,770, 1999. For multi-stage process to develop, implement and continually update information infrastructure of resources available to families and children in Kent County.
895. Council of Michigan Foundations, Grand Haven, MI. $50,000, 1999. To establish Dorothy A. Johnson endowment fund supporting speakers for Council's annual conference and to establish research library on philanthropy and voluntarism at Grand Valley State University.
896. Gerald R. Ford Foundation, Grand Rapids, MI. $25,000, 1999. For construction and renovation of new educational exhibits and related programs and materials at Gerald R. Ford Museum.
897. Ryerson Library Foundation, Grand Rapids, MI. $250,000, 1999. For renovation and expansion of Grand Rapids Public Library's main and branch facilities throughout city.

Irving S. Gilmore Foundation

Limitations: Giving primarily in the greater Kalamazoo, MI, area. No grants to individuals.

898. Greater Kalamazoo-Telecity USA, Kalamazoo, MI. $25,000, 1999. For operating support.
899. Portage Public Library, Portage, MI. $35,000, 1999. For facilities.

Grand Rapids Community Foundation

Limitations: Giving limited to Grand Rapids, MI, and surrounding communities. No support for religious organizations, hospitals, K-12 schools, child care centers, nursing homes/retirement facilities, or political or cause-related projects. No grants to individuals (except for scholarships), or for continued operating support, annual campaigns, travel expenses, medical or scholarly research, deficit financing, endowment funds, computers, vehicles, films, videos, or conferences; no student loans; no venture capital for competitive profit-making activities.

900. Ryerson Library Foundation, Grand Rapids, MI. $15,000, 2000. For capital project grant from William and Beatrice Idema Fund.

Herrick Foundation

Limitations: Giving primarily in MI; support also in Washington, DC, IN, MS, NY, OH, TN, and WI. No support for international organizations, or for domestic organizations for international programs. No grants to individuals.

901. Adrian College, Adrian, MI. $100,000, 1999. Toward expansion and renovation of Shipman Library.
902. Croswell, City of, William H. Aitkin Memorial Library, Croswell, MI. $100,000, 1999. Toward building expansion campaign.
903. Spring Arbor College, Spring Arbor, MI. $1,000,000, 1999. Toward construction of new library.

Hudson-Webber Foundation

Limitations: Giving primarily in the city of Detroit, and the tri-county Wayne, Oakland, and Macomb area of southeastern MI. No support for educational institutions or neighborhood organizations, except for projects that fall within current program missions. No grants to individuals (except for J.L. Hudson Co. employees and ex-employees), or for emergency funds, deficit financing, endowment funds, scholarships, fellowships, publications, conferences, fundraising, social events, or exhibits; no loans.

904. Artserve Michigan, Detroit, MI. $84,000, 2000. To conduct survey of arts education programs in Michigan's public and private schools and community arts agencies and to produce publication of best practices in arts education.

W. K. Kellogg Foundation

Limitations: Giving primarily in the U.S., Latin America and the Caribbean, and the south African countries of Botswana, Lesotho, South Africa, Swaziland, Zimbabwe and Mozambique. No support for religious purposes or for capital facilities. No grants to individuals (except through fellowship programs), or for endowment funds, development campaigns, films, equipment, publications, conferences, or radio and television programs unless they are an integral part of a project already being funded; no grants for operating budgets, or capital facilities.

905. Center for Democratic Renewal and Education, Atlanta, GA. $50,000, 2000. Toward youth summit.
906. Donors Forum of Chicago, Chicago, IL. $50,000, 2000. To strengthen health of refugee and immigrant families in 21st century through national conference to build policy, program, and research agenda.
907. Foundation Center, NYC, NY. $175,000, 2000. To provide annual program subsidies.
908. Grand Valley State University, Allendale, MI. $300,000, 2000. To provide resources to sustain comprehensive academic library on subjects of philanthropy and volunteerism.
909. Land Information Access Association, Traverse City, MI. $564,800, 2000. 3-year grant. To develop new intergovernmental cooperative project for planning sustainable communities in rural counties.
910. New York Academy of Medicine, NYC, NY. $150,000, 2000. 2-year grant. To improve public health nationwide through documentation and dissemination of community-based public-private partnerships and models strengthening practices at local level.
911. Robben Island Museum, Cape Town, South Africa. $190,000, 2000. 2-year grant. To promote international understanding and respect for African contributions to global solutions by researching, documenting, and archiving lives of selected former prisoners turned national leaders.
912. Volunteer and Information Services of Battle Creek, Battle Creek, MI. $20,500, 2000. Toward Expert in Residence visit by Points of Light Foundation to educate community on importance of family volunteering.
913. Willard Library, Battle Creek, MI. $108,282, 2000. 2-year grant. To enhance capacity of local nonprofit organizations by supporting collaborative technical assistance program.

Kellogg's Corporate Citizenship Fund

Limitations: Giving primarily in areas of company operations.

914. Volunteer and Information Services of Battle Creek, Battle Creek, MI. $10,000, 1999. For general support.

The Kresge Foundation

Limitations: No support for religious organizations, community colleges, private foundations, or elementary or secondary schools unless they predominantly serve individuals with physical and/or developmental disabilities. No grants to individuals, or for operating or special project budgets, furnishings, conferences, seminars, church building projects, endowment funds, student aid, scholarships, fellowships, research, debt retirement, completed projects, or general purposes; no loans.

915. Berkeley Public Library, Berkeley, CA. $300,000, 2000. For matching grant toward purchase and installation of fixed library shelving.
916. Brockton Public Library, Brockton, MA. $200,000, 2000. For matching grant toward renovation and expansion of Main Library.
917. Carthage College, Kenosha, WI. $800,000, 2000. For matching grant toward construction of Hedberg Library.
918. College of Charleston, Charleston, SC. $700,000, 2000. For matching grant toward construction of library.
919. Eugene Public Library Foundation, Eugene, OR. $325,000, 2000. For matching grant toward construction of replacement Public Library facility.
920. Foundation Center, NYC, NY. $75,000, 2000. For matching grant toward relocation and renovation of Washington, DC, regional Foundation Center.
921. Franklin and Eleanor Roosevelt Institute, Hyde Park, NY. $900,000, 2000. For matching grant toward construction of Orientation Education Conference Center and renovation and landscaping of FDR Library/Museum.
922. New York Public Library, NYC, NY. $2,000,000, 2000. For matching grant toward renovation of Library for the Performing Arts at Lincoln Center.

McGregor Fund

Limitations: Giving primarily in the metropolitan Detroit, MI, area, including Wayne, Oakland, and Macomb counties; grants to private colleges and universities under special program limited to MI and OH. No support for disease-specific organizations (or their local affiliates). No grants to individuals, or for scholarships, fellowships, research, travel, workshops, film or video projects, publications, or conferences; no loans.

923. Council of Michigan Foundations, Grand Haven, MI. $20,000, 2000. For planning and early implementation phase of City Connect Collaborative, initiative to support, strengthen, and connect non-profits in Detroit.
924. Ecumenical Theological Center, Detroit, MI. $50,000, 2000. Toward full implementation of John E. Biersdorf Theological Library, including cataloging of existing materials and acquisition of holdings.
925. HP Devco, Highland Park, MI. $50,000, 2000. For development of renovation plans for McGregor Library in Highland Park.

Charles Stewart Mott Foundation

Limitations: Giving nationally and to emerging countries in Central and Eastern Europe, Russia, and South Africa. No support for religious organizations for religious purposes. No grants to individuals, or generally for building or endowment funds, research, scholarships, or fellowships.

926. Access to Information Programme, Sofia, Bulgaria. $60,000, 2000. 2-year grant. For continued general support.
927. Bank Information Center, DC. $345,000, 2000. 2-year grant. For general support.
928. Bertelsmann Stiftung, Gutersloh, Germany. $150,000, 2000. 4-year grant. Toward establishment of network to address strategic, governance and management issues facing foundations.
929. Bulgarian Charities Aid Foundation, Sofia, Bulgaria. $58,154, 2000. 2-year grant. To research and promote corporate philanthropy in Bulgaria.
930. CEE BankWatch Network, Prague, Czech Republic. $90,000, 2000. For continued general support.

931. Center for Democratic Renewal and Education, Atlanta, GA. $95,000, 2000. 1.25-year grant. To mobilize grassroots activities from the South to participate in United Nations World Conference Against Racism.

932. Center of Nongovernmental Organizations, Riga, Latvia. $25,000, 2000. 2-year grant. For continued general support.

933. Charities Aid Foundation, West Malling, England. $100,000, 2000. 2-year grant. Toward support for Russian office.

934. Charities Aid Foundation, West Malling, England. $100,000, 2000. 2-year grant. To develop community foundations in Russia.

935. Charities Aid Foundation, West Malling, England. $100,000, 2000. To build capacity of Bulgarian third sector.

936. Charities Aid Foundation, West Malling, England. $50,000, 2000. 1.50-year grant. Toward grassroots citizen action and community building in Serbia and Montenegro.

937. Charities Aid Foundation, West Malling, England. $49,280, 2000. To assess state of nonprofit sector in Romania and to identify strengths, weaknesses, needs and opportunities for donor support.

938. Charities Aid Foundation, West Malling, England. $11,640, 2000. For continued support to review training services for Bulgarian nongovernmental organizations.

939. Charities Aid Foundation, West Malling, England. $10,000, 2000. To supplement activities related to thorough review of Romanian nongovernmental organization sector including disseminating review as widely as possible to key stakeholders in both Romanian and English, and carry out follow-up activities.

940. Charities Aid Foundation-Russia, Moscow, Russia. $1,000,000, 2000. 11-year grant. Toward endowment for Russian office.

941. Connecticut Voices for Children, New Haven, CT. $200,000, 2000. 2-year grant. For network that promotes policies to help low-income families achieve economic security.

942. Council of Better Business Bureaus Foundation, Arlington, VA. $75,000, 2000. 1.50-year grant. Toward efforts to update guidelines for the nonprofit sector.

943. Donors Forum, Prague, Czech Republic. $45,000, 2000. 3-year grant. For general support.

944. European Foundation Centre, Brussels, Belgium. $65,000, 2000. 2-year grant. For continued general institutional support and for conference, Building Civil Society Cooperation and Euro-Mediterranean Partnership.

945. European Foundation Centre, Brussels, Belgium. $18,500, 2000. To strengthen capacity of private philanthropies to address problems of at-risk youth through Youth Empowerment: Learning for Active Citizenship Initiative.

946. European Movement of Serbia, Belgrade, Yugoslavia. $70,000, 2000. 2-year grant. To increase citizen participation in decisionmaking process, promote peaceful resolution of political and ethnic issues, foster networks of local communities, and encourage critical thinking and debate at local levels about public policy issues in Yugoslavia and Southeastern Europe.

947. Finance Project, DC. $150,000, 2000. For continued support to maintain and grow capacity of Welfare Information Network which provides one-stop shopping for information pertaining to welfare and poverty issues.

948. Foundation Center, NYC, NY. $300,000, 2000. 2-year grant. Toward additional technological capacity to enable center to provide information and services to wider audiences through Foundation Center Online.

949. Foundation Center, NYC, NY. $50,000, 2000. 1.25-year grant. For relocation and expansion of Washington, D.C. field office and library.

950. Information Centre, Galanta, Slovakia. $40,000, 2000. 1.50-year grant. To build capacity of civil society in Southern Slovakia by supporting informal citizen groups and local nongovernmental organizations.

951. Institute for Democracy in Eastern Europe, Warsaw, Poland. $99,700, 2000. 2-year grant. To provide information and networking opportunities to emerging nongovernmental organizations in Russia and Ukraine.

952. Institute for Social Justice, Little Rock, AR. $150,000, 2000. For ACORN Living Wage Resource Center which provide information, materials, research, technical assistance, training, and strategic advice to organizations, allowing those organizations to save money and time, avoid common pitfalls, and build on the victories of other localities.

953. International Center for Not-for-Profit Law, DC. $100,000, 2000. 2-year grant. Toward Database and Journal Project which aims to exploit power of Internet to make charity law information broadly available by digitizing documents concerning charity laws in 115 countries to create on-line library of information accessible to organizations through the world.

954. Johns Hopkins University, Sar Levitan Center for Social Policy Studies, Baltimore, MD. $23,500, 2000. To strengthen network working to build national youth policy agenda through Levitan Youth Policy Network.

955. Mexican Center for Philanthropy, Mexico City, Mexico. $150,000, 2000. For general support.

956. National Assistance and Information Centre for NGOs in Moldova, Chisinau, Moldova. $25,000, 2000. 2-year grant. For general support.

957. National Center for Black Philanthropy, DC. $100,000, 2000. 1.50-year grant. To examine philanthropic contributions of black people in the U.S. and abroad at National Conference on Black Philanthropy.

958. National Center for Family Philanthropy, DC. $100,000, 2000. 2-year grant. To develop and test strategies that help community foundations attract and develop relationships with donor families.

959. National Charities Information Bureau (NCIB), NYC, NY. $50,000, 2000. Toward merger between NCIB and Council of Better Business Bureaus Foundations, two nationally recognized charity evaluation and accountability organizations.

960. Network of Estonian Nonprofit Organizations, Tallinn, Estonia. $25,000, 2000. 2-year grant. For general support.

961. Nonprofit Information and Training Center Foundation, Budapest, Hungary. $100,000, 2000. 2-year grant. For continued general support.

962. Nonprofit Partnership, Braamfontein, South Africa. $50,000, 2000. To improve financial sustainability of nonprofit sector in South Africa through financial training workshops and seminars.

963. Oxfam America, Boston, MA. $250,000, 2000. Toward development of networks of community organizations in low-income rural areas in effort to meet challenges of globalization.

964. Pro Vobis Volunteer Center, Cluj, Romania. $57,250, 2000. 2-year grant. To encourage voluntarism in Romania through national network of volunteer centers.

965. Sluzhenye Association of Nongovernmental Not-for-Profit Organizations, Nizhny Novgorod, Russia. $100,700, 2000. 2-year grant. For continued support for activities of nongovernmental organization support center in Russia's Volga-Vyatka area.

966. South Central Los Angeles Inter-Religious Sponsoring Committee, Los Angeles, CA. $104,864, 2000. Toward development of network to address problems of Los Angeles metropolitan area.

967. Southern Russia Resource Center, Krasnodar, Russia. $99,995, 2000. 2-year grant. For general support.

968. State Communities Aid Association, Albany, NY. $100,000, 2000. For continued support for collaboration with Child Care, Inc. to develop Universal Prekindergarten Resource Partnership in New York. Effort will support increased communication and resource sharing with development and maintenance of Web site and expand availability of partnership resource materials by traditional means for those unable to access information via the Internet.

969. Synergos Institute, NYC, NY. $40,000, 2000. For continued support for efforts to publish Sourcebook on Building Grantmaking Foundations.

970. Tides Center, San Francisco, CA. $100,000, 2000. Toward Green Media Toolshed project, cooperatively run national clearinghouse offering media-related tools and information for use by participating nonprofit environmental groups.

971. Tides Center, Project Change Anti-RacismNet Web Site, San Francisco, CA. $60,000, 2000. To provide setting through which public and grassroots organizations can be informed and motivated to combat racism and improve race relations.

972. United Way, Minsk, Belarus. $40,000, 2000. For continued general support.

973. Volunteer Consulting Group, NYC, NY. $10,000, 2000. For continued support for travel and accommodation for board placement leaders to meet in New York in order to share information and build skills on board placement programs.

The Skillman Foundation

Limitations: Giving primarily in southeastern MI, with emphasis on metropolitan Detroit, and Macomb, Oakland, and Wayne counties. No support for long-term projects not being aided by other sources, sectarian religious activities, political lobbying or legislative activities, or new organizations which do not have an operational and financial history. The foundation does not make grants to organizations that had public support and revenues of less than $100,000 for the preceding year. No grants to individuals, or for endowment funds, annual campaigns, purchase, construct or renovate facilities, basic research or deficit financing; no loans.

974. Detroit Public Library, Detroit, MI. $5,000,000, 2000. For renovations at downtown branch.
975. Foundation Center, NYC, NY. $10,000, 2000. For general operating support.
976. Oakland Family Services, Pontiac, MI. $370,000, 2000. For Father's Resource Center.

Steelcase Foundation

Limitations: Giving limited to areas of company operations, including Athens, AL, Orange County, CA, Grand Rapids, MI, Asheville, NC, and Markham, Canada. No support for churches, or programs with substantial religious overtones of a sectarian nature. No grants to individuals, or for endowment funds, conferences and seminars.

977. Grand Rapids Center for Independent Living, Grand Rapids, MI. $15,000, 1999. For Advocacy Resource System, collaborative referral service for improved access to services.
978. Wyoming Public Library, Wyoming, MI. $60,000, 1999. For Shape of Things to Come, campaign to renovate and expand library.

Whirlpool Foundation

Limitations: Giving limited to communities where major company units are located: Fort Smith, AR, Evansville and La Porte, IN, Benton Harbor, MI, Oxford, MS, Clyde, Findlay, Greenville, and Marion, OH, and Lavergne and Knoxville, TN. No support for religious or theological schools, religion-related groups, political causes, athletic associations, United Way agencies seeking general support, or for social, labor, veterans', alumni, or fraternal organizations. No grants to individuals (except for employee-related scholarships), or for endowment capital funds; no loans.

979. Council for Basic Education, DC. $10,000, 2000.

Matilda R. Wilson Fund

Limitations: Giving primarily in southeast MI. No grants to individuals; no loans.

980. Detroit Public Library, Friends of, Detroit, MI. $25,000, 1999. For operating support.

MINNESOTA

Andersen Foundation

Limitations: Giving on a national basis. No support for federally funded colleges or universities. No grants to individuals.

981. Bayport Public Library, Bayport, MN. $53,500, 2000.
982. Bayport Public Library Foundation, Bayport, MN. $30,000, 2000.

Hugh J. Andersen Foundation

Limitations: Giving primarily in St. Croix Valley-Washington County, MN, and Pierce, Polk, and St. Croix counties, WI, with a secondary interest in St. Paul and the greater MN area. No support for private foundations or schools, political or religious organizations, athletic teams, child care centers, civic action groups, business or economics education, or immigration and refugee issues and programming. No grants to individuals, or for fundraising dinners and events, travel, curriculum development, independent media productions, scholarships, or fellowships; no loans.

983. Bayport Public Library Foundation, Bayport, MN. $10,000, 2000. For memorial endowment.
984. Community Referral Agency, Milltown, WI. $100,000, 2000. For capital support.
985. Community Referral Agency, Milltown, WI. $15,000, 2000. For continued general operating support.

986. Metropolitan State University Foundation, Saint Paul, MN. $25,000, 2000. For continued support of Community Library and Information Access Center.
987. Project Childcare Resource and Referral, River Falls, WI. $10,000, 2000. For continued general operating support.

Bayport Foundation, Inc.

Limitations: Giving primarily in areas where Andersen Window employees live in the eastern Twin Cities area, MN and the St. Croix Valley area, WI. No grants to individuals.

988. Bayport Public Library Foundation, Bayport, MN. $95,000, 1999.

F. R. Bigelow Foundation

Limitations: Giving limited to the greater metropolitan St. Paul, MN, area; including Ramsey, Washington, and Dakota counties. No support for sectarian religious programs. No grants to individuals, or for annual operating expenses, medical research, and ongoing, open-ended needs.

989. Childrens Home Society of Minnesota, Saint Paul, MN. $100,000, 1999. Toward Information and Technology Systems Project.

The Blandin Foundation

Limitations: Giving limited to rural areas of MN; scholarships limited to graduates of an Itasca County, Hill City, or Remer, MN, high school. No support for religious activities or camping programs. No grants to individuals (except for scholarships), or for operating budgets, annual campaigns, deficit financing, government services, capital funds (outside home community), endowments, publications, travel, medical research, conferences, or seminars (outside of those sponsored by the foundation and related to its grantmaking).

990. First Call for Help of Itasca County, Grand Rapids, MN. $25,000, 2000. For sustaining contribution.
991. First Call for Help of Itasca County, Grand Rapids, MN. $25,000, 2000. For sustaining contribution.

Otto Bremer Foundation

Limitations: Giving limited to cities in MN, ND, and WI where there are Bremer Bank affiliates, and to organizations addressing poverty in the city of St. Paul, MN. No support for national health organizations, sporting activities, or K-12 education. No grants to individuals, or for endowment funds, medical research, professorships, annual fund drives, benefit events, camps, or artistic or media projects.

992. Center for Cross Cultural Health, Minneapolis, MN. $20,000, 2000. For conference on emerging issues in cultural competence.
993. Center for Cross Cultural Health, Minneapolis, MN. $20,000, 2000. For training health providers in meeting health care needs of ethnically, culturally, linguistically, and spiritually diverse patients.
994. Devils Lake, City of, Devils Lake, ND. $25,000, 2000. To renovate site for new public library.
995. Family Pathways, Wyoming, MN. $15,000, 2000. For information and referral service in east central Minnesota.
996. First Call Minnesota, Fergus Falls, MN. $20,000, 2000. To replace furniture and equipment in referral office.
997. Goedel Memorial Library, Warren, MN. $10,000, 2000. To purchase microfilm reader and printer for document maintenance and research.
998. Grantsburg Public Library, Grantsburg, WI. $25,000, 2000. To purchase equipment and increase library collection.
999. Northwest Wisconsin Child Care Resource and Referral, Hayward, WI. $20,000, 2000. For services for child care workers.
1000. Saint Paul Public Library, Friends of the, Saint Paul, MN. $20,000, 2000. To add library's collection of books and other materials for non-English speaking library users.

The Bush Foundation

Limitations: Giving primarily in MN, ND, and SD. No support for private foundations. No grants to individuals (except for fellowships), or for research in biomedical and health sciences. Generally, no grants for continuing operating support; construction of hospitals or medical facilities, church sanctuaries, individual day care centers, municipal buildings, or buildings in public colleges and universities; or for covering operating deficits or to retire mortgages or other debts; no loans.

1001. Battered Womens Legal Advocacy Project, Minneapolis, MN. $73,073, 2000. 2-year grant. To organize and improve legal resource library for attorneys of battered women and for relocation costs.
1002. Bay Mills Community College, Brimley, MI. $60,000, 2000. 2-year grant. To develop faculty resource library and to provide professional development conferences.
1003. Libraries for the Future, NYC, NY. $65,000, 2000. 1.50-year grant. For study of libraries in Minnesota, North Dakota and South Dakota.
1004. Mayo Foundation, Rochester, MN. $210,000, 2000. 3.50-year grant. For Multicultural Healthcare Alliance, helping refugees and immigrants to use health services.
1005. Minnesota Center for Environmental Advocacy, Saint Paul, MN. $132,875, 2000. 3-year grant. To build capacity to produce in-house Geographic Information System maps to communicate environmental issues.
1006. Minnesota Child Care Resource and Referral Network, Rochester, MN. $400,407, 2000. To promote and strengthen integration of Infant Toddler Training Intensive (ITTI) network into underserved populations.
1007. Minnesota Child Care Resource and Referral Network, Rochester, MN. $125,000, 2000. Toward capital campaign for building to house services for children and families.
1008. Minnesota Public Radio, Saint Paul, MN. $335,000, 2000. For equipment for digital audio archive.

Carolyn Foundation

Limitations: Giving primarily in the metropolitan areas of New Haven, CT, and Minneapolis-St. Paul, MN. No support for political or veterans' groups, fraternal societies, or religious organizations for religious purposes. No grants to individuals, or for endowment funds, annual fund drives, conferences, seminars, deficit funding, costs of litigation, or continuing support; no loans.

1009. Aurora Charter School, Minneapolis, MN. $16,500, 2000. For library books, audio tapes, videos, and library furnishings.

General Mills Foundation

Limitations: Giving primarily in areas of major parent company operations. No support for religious purposes, political, social, labor, veterans', alumni or fraternal organizations, recreation, national or local campaigns to eliminate or control specific diseases, or athletic associations. No grants to individuals, or, generally, for endowments, research, publications, films, advertising, athletic events, testimonial dinners, workshops, symposia, travel, fundraising events, or deficit financing; no loans.

1010. American Indian Treaty Council Information Center, Minneapolis, MN. $10,000, 2000. For Farmer to Farmer Program.
1011. Library Foundation of Hennepin County, Minnetonka, MN. $16,000, 2000. For The Story Garden, piece of art provided through Public Art Initiative undertaken by the Foundation which defines the children's area from the rest of the library and invites involvement through small video monitors and windows on both sides and through allusions to nature inside the room.
1012. Minneapolis Neighborhood Employment Network, Minneapolis, MN. $17,000, 2000. For operating support.
1013. Minneapolis Neighborhood Employment Network, Minneapolis, MN. $15,000, 2000. For National Resilience Resources Center's Minnesota Family Investment Program (MFIP) training.
1014. Montana School for the Deaf and Blind Foundation, Great Falls, MT. $20,000, 2000. For library project.
1015. National Practitioners Network for Fathers and Families, DC. $10,000, 2000. For one-time grant for information dissemination project.
1016. Urban Hope Ministries, Minneapolis, MN. $11,800, 2000. For YATA Resource House.

Honeywell Foundation

Limitations: Giving limited to cities where the company has major facilities, with emphasis on Minneapolis, MN; support also in AZ, FL, IL, and NM. No support for religious denominations for support of denominational causes; or political, fraternal, veterans', or professional organizations. No grants to individuals (except for Teacher Mini-Grants), or for general endowment funds, deficit financing, fundraising, land acquisition,

matching or challenge grants, research, demonstration projects, conferences, testimonial events, athletic scholarships, advertising, publications, or production of films or special broadcasts; no loans.

1017. Steve Pascente Charitable Foundation, Phoenix, AZ. $50,000, 1999. To establish centralized information center for families in crisis.

HRK Foundation

Limitations: Giving primarily in MN, with emphasis on the metropolitan Twin Cities and St. Croix Valley areas, and in Ashland and Bayfield counties, WI. No grants to individuals, or for scholarships or fellowships; no loans.

1018. Bayfield Carnegie Library, Bayfield, WI. $30,650, 1999.

The Hubbard Foundation

Limitations: Giving primarily in MN. No grants to individuals.

1019. Saint Paul Public Library, Friends of the, Saint Paul, MN. $53,000, 1999. For operating support.

Jerome Foundation

Limitations: Giving limited to MN and New York, NY. No support for educational programs in the arts and humanities. No grants to individuals (except for Media Arts Program and Minnesota Travel and Study Grant Program), or for undergraduate or graduate student research projects, capital or endowment funds, equipment, scholarships, or matching gifts.

1020. Museum of Modern Art, NYC, NY. $25,000, 2000. To acquire films and videos created by Jerome Foundation-funded artists in Media Arts Program.

Mardag Foundation

Limitations: Giving primarily in the east metropolitan area of Ramsey, Washington, and Dakota counties, MN, and greater MN. No support for programs serving Minneapolis, MN, and the surrounding west metropolitan area. No support for sectarian religious programs, federated campaigns, conservation or environmental programs or programs serving the mentally, developmentally, or physically disabled. No grants to individuals, or for annual operating expenses, medical research, scholarships, fellowships, events or conferences. No grants through fiscal agents.

1021. First Call for Help Southwest, Fergus Falls, MN. $15,000, 2000. For continued start-up support for office in Marshall, MN.

The McKnight Foundation

Limitations: Giving limited to organizations in MN, especially the seven-county Twin Cities, MN, area, except for programs in the environment, international aid, and research. No support for religious organizations for religious purposes. No grants to individuals (except for the Virginia McKnight Binger Awards in Human Service), or for basic research in academic disciplines (except for defined programs in crop research, neuroscience, and eating disorders), endowment funds, scholarships, fellowships, national fundraising campaigns, ticket sales, or conferences.

1022. Helping Industry Resolve Employment Disabilities (HIRED), Minneapolis, MN. $25,000, 2000. To update client- and information-tracking and evaluation system.
1023. Minnesota Center for Community Economic Development, Minneapolis, MN. $75,000, 2000. To develop statewide job and career information system for job seekers, employment organizations, and employers.
1024. Minnesota Council of Nonprofits, Saint Paul, MN. $19,000, 2000. For catalog of evaluation resources.
1025. Prairie Rivers Network, Champaign, IL. $80,000, 2000. For work to protect and preserve rivers in Illinois.

The Medtronic Foundation

Limitations: Giving primarily in areas of company operations, including Phoenix and Tempe, AZ, Goleta, Santa Ana, and Santa Rosa, CA, Louisville and Parker, CO, Warsaw, IN, Danvers, MA, Grand Rapids, MI, Milaca and the Twin Cities-Seven County metro, MN, area, Humacao and Villalba, PR, Memphis, TN, and Redmond, WA, or to national organizations having an effect on these areas; international giving in Medtronic communities. Generally, no support for primarily social organizations, religious, political, or fraternal activities, or general support for educational institutions, reimbursable health treatment, or substance abuse programs or programs that receive support from United Way of the Minneapolis, MN, area. No grants to individuals, or for deficit financing, scientific research, travel, fundraising events, general operating support, advertising, conferences, or multiple-year commitments; grants seldom for capital or endowment funds.

1026. American Pain Foundation, Baltimore, MD. $50,000, 2000. For Patients in Pain.

1027. Center for Cross Cultural Health, Minneapolis, MN. $15,000, 2000. For Cultural Competency Training in Health and Community Services.

1028. Minnesota Senior Federation, Saint Paul, MN. $10,000, 2000. For Health Plan Information Center and Senior Partners Care Outreach Program.

1029. United Hospital Foundation, Saint Paul, MN. $100,000, 2000. For Jesse Edwards Registry.

The Minneapolis Foundation

Limitations: Giving limited to MN, with emphasis on organizations from the City of Minneapolis. No support for national campaigns, political or religious organizations, veterans' or fraternal organizations, or organizations within umbrella organizations. No grants to individuals, or for annual campaigns, deficit financing, building or endowment funds, scholarships, fellowships, conferences courtesy advertising, benefit tickets, telephone solicitations, or memberships.

1030. Greater Minnesota Housing Fund, Saint Paul, MN. $10,000, 2000. For operating support for activities which educate policymakers on housing needs in Greater Minnesota.

1031. Middle School Connection, Minneapolis, MN. $75,000, 2000. To educate Minneapolis families of children grades 4-8 about middle school issues and activities.

1032. Minneapolis American Indian Center, Minneapolis, MN. $132,275, 2000. For Court Monitoring Indian Child Welfare Act Compliance Education Project in Minneapolis and Hennepin County.

Northwest Area Foundation

Limitations: Giving limited to IA, ID, MN, MT, ND, OR, SD, and WA. No support for lobbying activities. No grants to individuals.

1033. Foundation Center, NYC, NY. $15,000, 2000. For annual support.

Oakleaf Foundation

Limitations: Giving primarily in the Minneapolis-St. Paul, MN, area. No grants to individuals.

1034. Library Foundation of Hennepin County, Minnetonka, MN. $15,000, 1999.

The Jay and Rose Phillips Family Foundation

Limitations: Giving primarily in the Twin Cities metropolitan, MN, area. No support for political organizations or religious organizations for sectarian purposes. No grants to individuals, or for endowment campaigns.

1035. Center for Cross Cultural Health, Minneapolis, MN. $11,000, 2000. For revision of Provider's Guide.

1036. Child Care Resource Center/Southside, Minneapolis, MN. $40,000, 2000. For Culturally Responsive Child Care project.

1037. Minnesota Medical Foundation, Minneapolis, MN. $30,000, 2000. For Family Resource Library.

The Saint Paul Foundation, Inc.

Limitations: Giving from restricted and unrestricted funds limited to nonprofit organizations and public entities primarily serving residents of the East Metro area of Ramsey, Washington, and Dakota counties in the metropolitan Saint Paul, MN, area. No support for sectarian religious programs, except from designated funds. No grants to individuals or for annual operating budgets, agency endowment funds, and capital projects located outside the East Metro area.

1038. American-Scandinavian Foundation, NYC, NY. $46,000, 1999. For repatriation of Icelandic books by Arni Magnusson Manuscript Institute.

1039. Augsburg College, Minneapolis, MN. $50,000, 1999. For Lindell Library Fund Endowment for Technology.

1040. Center for Policy Studies, Saint Paul, MN. $60,000, 1999. For information and reporting on developments in financing education.

1041. Childrens Home Society of Minnesota, Saint Paul, MN. $100,000, 1999. For Information and Technology Systems Project.

1042. Frogtown Action Alliance, Saint Paul, MN. $90,000, 1999. Toward operating support for Frogtown-Summit University Business Resource Center.

1043. Model Cities of Saint Paul, Saint Paul, MN. $10,000, 1999. For building renovation for Family Resource Library.

1044. Resources for Child Caring, Saint Paul, MN. $17,000, 1999. Toward position of Hmong Bilingual Referral Counselor.

1045. Saint Paul Public Library, Friends of the, Saint Paul, MN. $25,000, 1999. For Renewal Campaign.

1046. University of Minnesota Foundation, Minneapolis, MN. $35,000, 1999. Toward operating support for Municipal Data Access and Deployment Project of Neighborhood Planning for Community Revitalization Project.

1047. Veterans Affairs Sierra Nevada Health Care System, General Post Fund, Reno, NV. $10,000, 1999. Toward Mental Health Service Line to promote programs for homeless and chronically ill patients.

The St. Paul Companies, Inc. Foundation

Limitations: Giving limited to the Twin Cities, MN, the Baltimore, MD, area, the United Kingdom, and selected locations where the company has a significant presence. No support for sectarian religious organizations, veterans' and fraternal groups, human services, environmental programs, health or disease-specific organizations, hospitals and other health services generally supported by third-party reimbursement mechanisms, or start-up, capital, or operations of public or charter schools. No grants to individuals (including scholarships and emergency assistance), advertising, or revenue-generating events, such as benefits, fundraisers, and telethons.

1048. Center for Management Assistance, Kansas City, MO. $25,000, 1999. For creation of information database on housing, arts and culture, and educational agencies.

1049. European Foundation Centre, Brussels, Belgium. $11,036, 1999. For European foundation and corporate giving programs to promote quality philanthropy in Europe.

1050. NPower, Seattle, WA. $15,000, 1999. For online resource coordinator to help nonprofits in Greater Puget Sound area deliver their services more effectively and efficiently.

1051. Volunteer Resource Center of the Twin Cities, Minneapolis, MN. $75,000, 1999. For transition of Volunteer Center for Saint Paul-only resource to metrowide resource and for ongoing service provision of recruitment and referral services to metro area nonprofit organizations and volunteers.

1052. West End Business Revitalization Corporation, Saint Paul, MN. $20,000, 1999. To provide West Seventh-area businesses with information about resources available for economic development.

Target Foundation

Limitations: Giving primarily in the Minneapolis/St. Paul, MN, metropolitan area. No support for religious organizations for religious purposes; grants rarely made for health organizations, recreation, theraputic programs, living subsidies, or the care of disabled persons. No grants to individuals, or for national ceremonies, memorials, conferences, fundraising dinners, testimonials, or similar events.

1053. Allergy and Asthma Network-Mothers of Asthmatics, Fairfax, VA. $100,000, 2000. For MasterWorks Award.

1054. Frogtown Action Alliance, Saint Paul, MN. $15,000, 2000. For Frogtown Employment Resource Center.

1055. Minneapolis Neighborhood Employment Network, Minneapolis, MN. $12,500, 2000. For general operating support.

1056. Minneapolis Neighborhood Employment Network, Minneapolis, MN. $12,500, 2000. For general operating support.

WEM Foundation

Limitations: Giving primarily in MN. No grants to individuals.

1057. Wayzata Public Library, Wayzata, MN. $600,000, 1999.

MISSOURI

Anheuser-Busch Foundation

Limitations: Giving primarily in areas of major company operations of its breweries and theme parks: St. Louis, MO, Newark, NJ, Los Angeles, Fairfield, and San Diego, CA, San Antonio, TX, Columbus and Cleveland, OH, Jacksonville, Tampa, and Orlando, FL, Merrimack, VA, Baldwinsville, NY, Fort Collins, CO, Cartersville, GA, and Langhorne, PA. No support for organizations whose activities are primarily religious in nature, social or fraternal groups, or political or athletic organizations. No grants to individuals, or for hospital operating budgets.

1058. Health Education Foundation, DC. $55,000, 1999. For general support.
1059. Missouri Development Finance Board, Jefferson City, MO. $90,000, 1999. For Harry S. Truman Library Institute.
1060. William J. Clinton Presidential Foundation, Little Rock, AR. $200,000, 1999. For general support.

The Danforth Foundation

Limitations: Giving limited to the metropolitan St. Louis, MO, area. No grants to individuals.

1061. Charter School Information Center, Saint Louis, MO. $75,000, 2000. To provide information to citizens who are interested in learning about charter schools.
1062. Child Care Resource and Referral Network, Saint Joseph, MO. $11,000, 2000. To develop business plan for Network, which provides information to parents on child care topics.
1063. Citizens for Missouris Children, Saint Louis, MO. $12,500, 2000. To develop system for collecting and disseminating data on effective early childhood care and education programs and activities.
1064. Foundation Center, NYC, NY. $10,000, 2000. For general support.

Emerson Charitable Trust

Limitations: Giving primarily in areas of company operations.

1065. Carnegie-Viersen Public Library, Pella, IA. $10,000, 2000. For building fund.
1066. OASIS Institute, Saint Louis, MO. $30,000, 2000.
1067. Saint Louis County Library Foundation, Saint Louis, MO. $25,000, 2000.

The H & R Block Foundation

Limitations: Giving primarily in the metropolitan bi-state Kansas City, MO, area. No support for religious purposes, businesses, single-disease agencies, or historic preservation projects. No grants to individuals, or for endowment funds, travel, telethons, dinners, advertising, fundraising, research, demonstration projects, publications, or conferences; no loans.

1068. Harry S. Truman Library Institute for National and International Affairs, Independence, MO. $18,750, 1999. For new volunteer coordinator position.
1069. Metropolitan Energy Information Center, Kansas City, MO. $15,000, 1999. To expand services to additional households.

Hall Family Foundation

Limitations: Giving limited to Kansas City, MO. No support for international or religious organizations or for political purposes. No grants to individuals (except for emergency aid to Hallmark Cards employees, and employee-related scholarships), or for endowment funds, travel, operating deficits, conferences, scholarly or medical research, or fundraising campaigns such as telethons.

1070. Kansas City Public Library, Kansas City, MO. $3,000,000, 2000. 2-year grant. For capital campaign.
1071. Mid America Assistance Coalition, Kansas City, MO. $20,000, 2000. For MAACLink, shared social services database.

Hallmark Corporate Foundation

Limitations: Giving limited to the Kansas City, MO, area, and communities where major Hallmark facilities are located, including Enfield, CT, Co-lumbus, GA, Metamora, IL, Lawrence, Leavenworth, and Topeka, KS, Liberty, MO, and Center, TX. No support for religious, fraternal, political, international or veterans' organizations, athletic or labor groups, social clubs, non-tax-exempt organizations, or disease-specific organizations. No grants to individuals, or for scholarships, endowment funds, past operating deficits, travel, conferences, sponsorships, scholarly or health-related research, charitable advertisements, or mass media campaigns such as walk-a-thons or telethons.

1072. Harry S. Truman Library Institute for National and International Affairs, Independence, MO. $40,000, 1999. For volunteer/intern program expansion.

The Greater Kansas City Community Foundation and Affiliated Trusts

Limitations: Giving primarily in the bi-state Kansas City area. No grants to individuals (except through designated scholarship funds), or for deficit financing, endowments, capital or annual campaigns, or operating expenses.

1073. Black Archives of Mid-America, Kansas City, MO. $15,000, 1999.
1074. Harry S. Truman Library Institute for National and International Affairs, Independence, MO. $166,000, 1999.
1075. Kansas City Public Library, Kansas City, MO. $86,810, 1999.
1076. Metropolitan Energy Information Center, Kansas City, MO. $41,000, 1999.
1077. National Youth Information Network, Lawrence, KS. $20,000, 1999.

Ewing Marion Kauffman Foundation

Limitations: Giving limited to the U.S., with emphasis on the metropolitan Kansas City, MO, area for youth development.

1078. Black Archives of Mid-America, Kansas City, MO. $15,000, 2000. Toward educational activities.
1079. Child Care Resource and Referral Network, Saint Joseph, MO. $50,000, 2000. To develop and implement statewide system of child care resource and referral services.
1080. Child Care Resource and Referral Network, Saint Joseph, MO. $10,650, 2000. For consultation services to address hiring of executive director and moving operation to independent office in Jefferson City.
1081. Citizens for Missouris Children, Saint Louis, MO. $25,000, 2000. To update statewide database and Web site for tracking early care and learning services, best practices, model programs and current issues.
1082. Council on Foundations, DC. $50,000, 2000. For communications and education initiative on role and significance of philanthropy and foundations in American life.
1083. Foundation Center, NYC, NY. $60,000, 2000. To foster public understanding of foundations and corporate giving.
1084. Harry S. Truman Library Institute for National and International Affairs, Independence, MO. $250,000, 2000. For educational programs and development and implementation of outreach strategies for students attending Kansas City Missouri School District.
1085. Heart of America Family Services, Kansas City, KS. $333,000, 2000. For expansion of comprehensive child care resource and referral system for metropolitan Kansas City.
1086. Metropolitan Energy Information Center, Kansas City, MO. $49,977, 2000. For Sustainable Community project in Westside neighborhood of Kansas City, MO.
1087. National Assembly of National Health and Human Service Organizations, DC. $10,000, 2000. For National Youth Development Information Center.
1088. National Charities Information Bureau (NCIB), NYC, NY. $10,000, 2000. For Standards of Performance for national nonprofit organizations.
1089. Unified School District No. 500, Kansas City, KS. $40,552, 2000. For school libraries at public elementary schools in Kansas City, KS as part of Just Read Program.

Muriel McBrien Kauffman Foundation

Limitations: Giving primarily in Kansas City, MO, and New York, NY. No loans or program-related investments.

1090. American Cancer Society, Kansas City, MO. $50,000, 1999. For capital campaign to construct Hope Lodge in Kansas City, short-term residential facility offering free short-term housing, counseling, and referral services to patients receiving oncology treatment at local hospitals.

William T. Kemper Foundation

Limitations: Giving primarily in the Midwest with emphasis on MO and surrounding areas. No support for private foundations. No grants to individuals, or for tickets for dinners, benefits, exhibits, conferences, sports and other event activities, advertisements, endowment funds, or fundraising activities.

1091. Harry S. Truman Library Institute for National and International Affairs, Independence, MO. $62,500, 2000.
1092. Springfield-Greene County Library District, Springfield, MO. $20,000, 2000.
1093. University of Missouri, Kansas City, MO. $10,000, 2000. For Western Historical Manuscript Collection.

The May Department Stores Company Foundation, Inc.

Limitations: Giving primarily in areas of company operations.

1094. OASIS Institute, Saint Louis, MO. $932,745, 2000.
1095. OASIS Institute, Saint Louis, MO. $366,000, 2000. For Intergenerational Tutoring Program.

NEBRASKA

The Buffett Foundation

Limitations: No grants to individuals (except for Teacher Awards and through scholarship program).

1096. Homeless Prenatal Program, San Francisco, CA. $10,000, 2000. For project support.
1097. Sexuality Information and Education Council of the U.S. (SIECUS), NYC, NY. $15,000, 2000. For general support.

Durham Foundation

Limitations: Giving primarily in Omaha, NE. No grants to individuals.

1098. Library of Congress, DC. $1,000,000, 2000. For endowment.

Peter Kiewit Foundation

Limitations: Giving limited to Rancho Mirage, CA, western IA, NE, and Sheridan, WY; college scholarships available to high school students in the Omaha, NE-Council Bluffs, IA, area only. No support for elementary or secondary schools, churches, or religious groups. No grants to individuals (except for scholarships), or for endowment funds or annual campaigns.

1099. Bloomfield Library Foundation, Bloomfield, NE. $103,000, 2000. For unrestricted support.
1100. Cambridge, City of, Cambridge, NE. $60,000, 2000. For Butler Memorial Library.
1101. Indiana University Foundation, Indianapolis, IN. $10,000, 2000. For Payton Philanthropic Studies Library.
1102. Ralston, City of, Ralston, NE. $100,000, 2000. For Ralston Public Library.

Omaha Community Foundation

Limitations: Giving primarily in the metropolitan Omaha, NE, area including southwest IA. No support for tax-supported institutions, religious organizations for religious purposes, organizations funded by the United Way, arts groups, social clubs, or veterans', labor, or fraternal organizations. No grants to individuals, or for endowments, capital campaigns, deficit financing, annual drives, fundraising events, dinners, or tickets.

1103. Hope Medical Outreach Coalition, Omaha, NE. $18,100, 2000.
1104. Omaha Public Library, Omaha, NE. $11,400, 2000.
1105. Woodbine Carnegie Public Library, Woodbine, IA. $24,851, 2000.

Union Pacific Foundation

Limitations: Giving primarily in areas of company operations, with emphasis on the midwestern and western U.S.: AR, AZ, CA, CO, IA, ID, IL, KS, LA, MN, MO, MT, NE, NM, NV, OK, OR, TX, UT, WA, WI, and WY. No support for specialized national health and welfare organizations, religious or labor groups, social clubs, or fraternal or veterans' organizations; support for United Way-affiliated organizations restricted to capital projects. No grants to individuals, or for sponsorship of dinners, benefits, seminars, or other special events.

1106. Goshen County Library Foundation, Torrington, WY. $29,000, 1999. Toward computer hardware.
1107. Pennsylvania State University, University Park, PA. $20,000, 1999. For library programs.
1108. Stanfield Library, Stanfield, OR. $10,000, 1999. Toward facility construction.
1109. Wichita Public Library Foundation, Wichita, KS. $10,000, 1999. For Juvenile Literacy Outreach.

NEVADA

The Cord Foundation

Limitations: Giving primarily in northern NV.

1110. Washoe County Law Library, Reno, NV. $75,000, 1999. For renovation of new library facility.
1111. White Pine County Public Library, Ely, NV. $12,000, 1999. For library materials, and project with County Welfare Office.

Lied Foundation Trust

Limitations: Giving primarily in NE and Las Vegas, NV.

1112. University of Nevada at Las Vegas Foundation, Las Vegas, NV. $5,000,000, 1999. For construction of Lied Library.

Donald W. Reynolds Foundation

Limitations: Giving primarily in AR, NV, and OK for Capital Grants and Community Services Center grants. Giving nationally for cardiovascular clinic research and geriatrics training of physicians. No support for elementary or secondary education, or religious institutions or hospitals. No grants to individuals, or for continuing support, program or operating support, or endowment funds.

1113. Philander Smith College, Little Rock, AR. $7,839,294, 2000. For library and technology center.

E. L. Wiegand Foundation

Limitations: Giving primarily in NV and adjoining western states, including AZ, ID, OR, UT and WA; public affairs grants given primarily in CA, Washington, DC, and New York, NY. No support for organizations receiving significant support from the United Way or public tax funds; organizations with beneficiaries of their own choosing; or federal, state, or local government agencies or institutions. No grants to individuals, or for endowment funds, fundraising campaigns, debt reductions, emergency funding, film or media presentations, or operating funds; no loans.

1114. Churchill County Museum and Archives, Fallon, NV. $152,300, 1999. For exhibit on history of Nevada.
1115. Our Lady of Lourdes School, Salt Lake City, UT. $78,000, 1999. To computerize library and classrooms.
1116. Saint Marys High School, Phoenix, AZ. $51,645, 1999. For new technology in library.

NEW JERSEY

Geraldine R. Dodge Foundation, Inc.

Limitations: Giving primarily in NJ, with support for the arts and local humane groups limited to NJ, and support for other local projects limited to the Morristown-Madison area; some giving in the other Middle Atlantic states and New England, and to national organizations. No support for religious, higher education, health, or conduit organizations. No grants for capital projects, equipment purchases, indirect costs, endowment funds, deficit financing, or scholarships.

1117. Educational Information and Resource Center, Sewell, NJ. $100,000, 1999. For programs to improve quality of New Jersey geography and conservation education in K-12 classrooms in collaboration with teachers and students in Costa Rica.

1118. Folger Shakespeare Library, DC. $65,000, 1999. For teacher training workshops on best methods for teaching and performing Shakespeare.

1119. Harvard University, Cambridge, MA. $80,000, 1999. For Project Zero to provide research-based information about teaching and learning to schools, based on Multiple Intelligences theory.

1120. Newark Public Library, Newark, NJ. $45,000, 1999. For Club Success, which provides focused, intensive homework assistance, at branches of Newark Public Library.

1121. Sexuality Information and Education Council of the U.S. (SIECUS), NYC, NY. $60,000, 1999. For publication, A Religious Declaration and Sexual Morality, Justice and Healing.

The Fund for New Jersey

Limitations: Giving primarily in NJ or to regional programs that benefit NJ. No support for recreation, day care centers, drug treatment programs, health care delivery, curricular changes in educational institutions, or arts programs. No grants to individuals, or for capital projects, equipment, endowment funds, scholarships, or fellowships.

1122. Eagleton Institute of Politics, New Brunswick, NJ. $50,000, 2000. For completion of interactive Web site for Star-Ledger/Eagleton-Rutgers Poll in partnership with Scholarly Communication Center of Rutgers University Libraries to provide unrestricted public access to interactive library of opinion polling data on important public issues.

1123. Stony Brook-Millstone Watersheds Association, Pennington, NJ. $65,000, 2000. For renewed support for Geographic Information Systems (GIS) Resource Center and Natural Lands Network.

The Healthcare Foundation of New Jersey

Limitations: Giving primarily in NJ, with emphasis on Newark and Essex, Morris, and Union counties. Limited giving for regional and national programs. No support for political campaigns. No grants to individuals, or for deficit retirement, ongoing general operating expenses, endowments, or fundraising campaigns.

1124. Jewish Family Service of Metrowest, Florham Park, NJ. $15,500, 1999. For Metro-Peers: A Jewish Self-Help Clearinghouse.

1125. New Jersey Poison Information and Education System, Newark, NJ. $30,000, 1999. To create lead poisoning information and referral web site.

Honeywell International Foundation

Limitations: Giving primarily in areas of company operations. No support for church-related programs, special interest groups (such as labor or veterans) unless activity benefits entire community, political organizations, or for international organizations. No grants to individuals, or for endowment funds; no loans.

1126. Linda Hall Library Trust, Kansas City, MO. $10,000, 1999. For continued support to implement electronic on-line catalog system.

The Hyde and Watson Foundation

Limitations: Giving includes the metropolitan New York, NY, region, and primarily Essex, Union and Morris counties in NJ. No giving outside the U.S.. No grants to individuals, or generally for operating budgets, continuing support, annual campaigns, general endowments, deficit financing, scholarships, or fellowships.

1127. Henry H. Kessler Foundation, West Orange, NJ. $19,000, 2000. For equipment for Medical Library and Patient Resource Center.

1128. Literacy Assistance Center, NYC, NY. $10,000, 2000. To expand and modernize Clearinghouse facility.

1129. New York Cares, NYC, NY. $16,000, 2000. To develop interactive Web site and database.

The Robert Wood Johnson Foundation

Limitations: Giving limited to the U.S.. No support for political organizations, international activities, programs or institutions concerned solely with a specific disease or basic biomedical research. No grants to individu-

als, or for ongoing general operating expenses, endowment funds, capital costs, including construction, renovation, or equipment, or research on unapproved drug therapies or devices.

1130. Alcohol Research Information Service, Lansing, MI. $161,000, 2000. For information resources for substance abuse prevention practitioners.

1131. Boston University, School of Public Health, Boston, MA. $6,000,000, 2000. 2-year grant. To provide national resource center for community substance abuse initiatives.

1132. Foundation for Accountability (FACCT), Portland, OR. $394,584, 2000. For examining validity and usefulness of the Internet as tool for collecting and providing health information.

1133. Foundation for Health Care Quality, Seattle, WA. $1,726,212, 2000. For multistate initiative to help build health information infrastructure.

1134. George Washington University, DC. $689,980, 2000. For technical assistance and direction for Making the Grade: State/Local Partnerships for School-Based Health Centers and School-Based Health Care Resource Center.

1135. Georgetown University Medical Center, DC. $749,966, 2000. 2-year grant. For consumer information on access to coverage.

1136. HealthforAll, Buffalo, NY. $700,000, 2000. 3-year grant. For Communities in Charge: Financing and Delivering Health Care to Uninsured — Phase II.

1137. Homeless Prenatal Program, San Francisco, CA. $314,400, 2000. 3-year grant. For jail outreach project for incarcerated women.

1138. Info Line of Middlesex County, New Brunswick, NJ. $100,000, 2000. 2-year grant. For county-wide information and referral service.

1139. Missouri Association of Community Task Forces, Kansas City, MO. $800,000, 2000. 4-year grant. For Reducing Underage Drinking Through Community and State Coalitions.

1140. New Jersey Foundation for Aging, Trenton, NJ. $76,861, 2000. For developing public private partnership for New Jersey's aging services network.

1141. New York Academy of Medicine, NYC, NY. $100,000, 2000. For Expanding David E. Rogers fellowship program.

1142. Task Force for Child Survival and Development, Decatur, GA. $5,000,000, 2000. 3-year grant. For technical resource center to foster development of integrated preventive health information systems for All Kids Count.

1143. University of California, San Francisco, CA. $500,000, 2000. For creating tobacco document archive.

1144. University of Kansas Center for Research, Lawrence, KS. $525,000, 2000. 2-year grant. For Community Tool Box: computer information database and exchange network.

F. M. Kirby Foundation, Inc.

Limitations: Giving primarily in NC, NJ, and PA. No grants to individuals, or for fundraising benefits, dinners, theater, or sporting events; no loans or pledges.

1145. Crohns and Colitis Foundation of America, NYC, NY. $50,000, 2000. Toward development of DNA and Cell Line Bank for inflammatory bowel disease (IBD).

1146. National Kidney Foundation, NYC, NY. $15,000, 2000. Toward Kidney Transplant Recipients Cardiac Registry.

1147. New Jersey Coalition for Battered Women, Trenton, NJ. $15,000, 2000. For matching grant for Legal Services Project.

1148. Wyoming Seminary, Kingston, PA. $27,500, 2000. For Kirby Library.

The Lebensfeld Foundation

Limitations: Giving primarily in NY and PA. No grants to individuals.

1149. Boston College, Chestnut Hill, MA. $12,000, 1999. For Library.
1150. Greenwich Library, Greenwich, CT. $10,000, 1999.
1151. New York Public Library, NYC, NY. $50,000, 1999.
1152. New York Public Library, Lydenberg Society, NYC, NY. $10,000, 1999.
1153. Syracuse University, Syracuse, NY. $10,000, 1999. For Library.

Lucent Technologies Foundation

Limitations: Giving on a national basis. No support for religious or political organizations. No grants to individuals (except for special foundation programs), or for conferences, fundraisers, or endowments.

1154. National Charities Information Bureau (NCIB), NYC, NY. $10,000, 1999.

The Merck Company Foundation

Limitations: Giving primarily in areas of company operations, including CA, GA, NJ, PA, and VA. No support for political, fraternal, veterans', labor or sectarian groups, or elementary/secondary education. No grants to individuals (except for fellowships in clinical pharmacology), or for operating budgets, continuing support, annual campaigns, emergency or endowment funds, deficit financing, land acquisition, travel, conferences, publications, media productions or research; no loans.

1155. Lansdale Public Library, Lansdale, PA. $25,000, 1999.
1156. National Library of Medicine, Friends of the, DC. $20,000, 1999.
1157. Rockingham Public Library, Harrisonburg, VA. $25,000, 1999.
1158. Thomas Beaver Free Library, Danville, PA. $20,000, 1999.

Merrill Lynch & Co. Foundation, Inc.

Limitations: No support for religious purposes or social, fraternal, or athletic organizations, political parties, interests groups, or candidates. No grants to individuals, or for deficit financing, matching funds, or conferences; no loans.

1159. New York Public Library, NYC, NY. $25,000, 1999. For unrestricted support.

Pharmacia Foundation, Inc.

Limitations: Giving primarily in areas where employees and their families live and work. No support for religious organizations. No grants to individuals.

1160. Council of Michigan Foundations, Grand Haven, MI. $10,000, 1999. For Dorothy A. Johnson Educational Fund and Grand Valley State University Research Library.

Howard Phipps Foundation

Limitations: Giving primarily in New York, NY.

1161. Harvard University, Harvard University Library, Cambridge, MA. $10,000, 1999.
1162. Pierpont Morgan Library, NYC, NY. $25,000, 1999.

The Prudential Foundation

Limitations: Giving primarily in areas of company operations, with emphasis on Phoenix, AZ, Los Angeles, CA, Jacksonville, FL, Atlanta, GA, Minneapolis, MN, Newark, NJ, Philadelphia, PA, and Houston, TX. No support for veterans', labor, religious, fraternal, or athletic groups, or general operating funds for single-disease health organizations. No grants to individuals, or for endowment funds, goodwill advertising, or fundraising events.

1163. Newark Public Library, Newark, NJ. $1,000,000, 2000. For one-time grant as part of Prudential's 125th Anniversary.

Fannie E. Rippel Foundation

Limitations: Giving primarily in the Eastern Seaboard states, with emphasis on NJ and the metropolitan New York, NY, area. No grants to individuals, or for general purposes, operating budgets, continuing support, annual campaigns, deficit financing, scholarships, fellowships, or building funds, no loans.

1164. Cathedral Health Services, Saint Michael's Medical Center, Newark, NJ. $32,000, 2001. Toward renovation of Aquinas Medical Library.

The Schumann Fund for New Jersey, Inc.

Limitations: Giving limited to NJ, with emphasis on Essex County. No grants to individuals, or for capital campaigns, annual giving, or endowments.

1165. Child Care Connection, Trenton, NJ. $19,500, 2000. For evaluation of impact of training and technical assistance on quality of child care centers.

Turrell Fund

Limitations: Giving limited to Essex, Union, Hudson and Passaic counties, NJ, and VT. No support for advocacy work, most hospital work, or health delivery services; generally no support for cultural activities. No grants to individuals, or for endowment funds, publications, conferences, or research; no loans.

1166. Citizens for Better Schools, Newark, NJ. $75,000, 1999. For Paterson Project and Charter School Resource Center.
1167. Citizens for Better Schools, Newark, NJ. $50,000, 1999. For Charter School Resource Center.
1168. Elizabeth Public Library, Elizabeth, NJ. $60,000, 1999. For capital support.
1169. Hartland Public Library, Hartland, VT. $37,000, 1999. For capital support of new children's room.
1170. Montclair Public Library, Montclair, NJ. $19,500, 1999. For activities and programs for Black History Month.
1171. Mount Saint Dominic Academy, Caldwell, NJ. $25,000, 1999. For financial aid and library expansion.
1172. Mount Saint Dominic Academy, Caldwell, NJ. $25,000, 1999. For library expansion.
1173. Newark Family Resource Network, Newark, NJ. $60,000, 1999. For program support.
1174. Norman Williams Public Library, Woodstock, VT. $20,000, 1999. For capital support.
1175. Windham Childcare Providers Association, Brattleboro, VT. $30,000, 1999. For program support.

Victoria Foundation, Inc.

Limitations: Giving limited to greater Newark, NJ; environmental grants limited to NJ. No support for organizations dealing with specific diseases or afflictions, geriatric needs, or day care. No grants to individuals, or for publications or conferences.

1176. Bloomfield College, Bloomfield, NJ. $100,000, 1999. For capital campaign to build new library.
1177. Libraries for the Future, NYC, NY. $37,500, 1999. For Youth ACCESS Newark's after-school program using children's computer software to teach communication and leadership skills.
1178. Newark Public Library, Newark, NJ. $100,000, 1999. For renovation and expansion of Vailsburg branch library, improving residents' access to print-based materials and bringing advanced electronic resources and access to neighborhood.

NEW MEXICO

Lannan Foundation

Limitations: No support for political purposes. No grants to individuals (except for Lannan Literary Awards), or for documentary film or video projects, performing arts or theater, or crafts or decorative arts.

1179. Amherst College, Amherst, MA. $21,710, 1999. For reading series at Folger Shakespeare Library in Washington, DC.
1180. Southwest Research and Information Center, Albuquerque, NM. $30,000, 1999. For legal support for court cases involving uranium.

McCune Charitable Foundation

Limitations: Giving limited to NM. No grants to individuals, or for endowments, research or voter registration drives.

1181. Columbus Health Care Organization, Columbus, NM. $15,000, 1999. To establish summer youth and after-school program to keep youth from drugs, alcohol and premature sexual activities, and equipment for Tumbleweed Theater, and matching grant for operating support for public library.
1182. Embudo Valley Library, Dixon, NM. $10,000, 1999. For operating support.
1183. Jemez Pueblo Community Library, Jemez Pueblo, NM. $16,000, 1999. For operating support.
1184. Jemez Pueblo Community Library, Jemez Pueblo, NM. $11,000, 1999. To establish computer educational program for tribal youth.

1185. Las Clinicas del Norte, El Rito, NM. $15,000, 1999. For continued operating support for El Rito Library.

Eugene V. & Clare E. Thaw Charitable Trust

Limitations: Giving on a national basis. No grants to individuals or operating support.

1186. Frick Art Reference Library, NYC, NY. $70,000, 1999. For documentation of auction catalogues.

1187. Medici Archive Project, NYC, NY. $10,000, 1999.

1188. Pierpont Morgan Library, NYC, NY. $3,000,000, 1999. For grant in form of Cezanne sketchbook.

1189. Pierpont Morgan Library, NYC, NY. $1,000,000, 1999. To build Conservation Center.

1190. Pierpont Morgan Library, NYC, NY. $1,000,000, 1999. To build Conservation Center.

1191. Pierpont Morgan Library, NYC, NY. $20,000, 1999. For Director's Roundtable program.

NEW YORK

ABC, Inc. Foundation

Limitations: Giving primarily in areas where company properties are located. No grants to individuals, or for building funds.

1192. Academy of Television Arts and Sciences Foundation, Archive of American Television, North Hollywood, CA. $200,000, 1999.

1193. New York Public Library, NYC, NY. $25,000, 1999.

Louis and Anne Abrons Foundation, Inc.

Limitations: Giving primarily in the metropolitan New York, NY, area. No grants to individuals.

1194. New York Public Library, NYC, NY. $30,000, 2000.

The Achelis Foundation

Limitations: Giving primarily in the New York, NY, area. Generally, no support for colleges and universities, small art, dance, music, or theater groups, national health or mental health organizations, housing, international projects, government agencies, public schools, or nonprofit programs and services significantly funded or wholly reimbursed by the government. No grants to individuals, or for annual appeals, dinner functions, fundraising events, capital campaign, deficit financing, or film or travel; no loans.

1195. Foundation Center, NYC, NY. $10,000, 2000. For new services on website.

1196. Foundation for Individual Rights in Education, Philadelphia, PA. $50,000, 2000. For student information guides.

1197. Institute for Life Coping Skills, NYC, NY. $60,000, 2000. Toward 3rd Edition of the Atkins Life Skills Program for employment and career advancement, including internet enhancements and Spanish version.

1198. Metropolitan Museum of Art, NYC, NY. $100,000, 2000. For enhancements for Thomas J. Watson Jr. Memorial Library.

Altman Foundation

Limitations: Giving limited to NY, with emphasis on the boroughs of New York City. No grants to individuals, or for building funds, or capital equipment.

1199. Archdiocese of New York, NYC, NY. $1,070,000, 1999. 4-year grant. For Patrons Program to launch and support Library Connections in inner-city non-public elementary schools and to evaluate first year of program.

1200. Chess-in-the-Schools, NYC, NY. $30,000, 1999. Toward Cullman After-School Library Program (CASL).

1201. Child Care, Inc., NYC, NY. $40,000, 1999. Toward Child Care implementation of Universal Pre-k in New York City.

1202. Citizens Advice Bureau, Bronx, NY. $40,000, 1999. Toward Project Achieve, after-school program at Girls Club.

1203. New York Public Library, NYC, NY. $1,400,000, 1999. 4-year grant. Toward establishing endowment for future Technology Training Center at Humanities and Social Services Library and for general support of Research Libraries.

1204. Pierpont Morgan Library, NYC, NY. $75,000, 1999. For continued support to develop Library's public programming.

1205. Resources for Children with Special Needs, NYC, NY. $50,000, 1999. For continued support for Publications Program.

American Express Foundation

Limitations: Giving primarily in AZ, CA, FL, GA, MA, MN, NC, NY, TX, and UT; and internationally in Asia/Pacific, Canada, Europe, Latin America, and Japan. No support for religious or fraternal organizations, sporting events or athletic programs, umbrella organizations with active grantmaking programs, or professional, trade, or marketing associations. No grants to individuals (except for employee-related scholarships), or for medical research, endowments, advertising in journals or yearbooks, or publication of books, magazines or articles in professional journals; no grants for endorsements or capital campaigns except on rare occasions.

1206. Charities Aid Foundation, West Malling, England. $120,000, 1999.

1207. Charities Aid Foundation, West Malling, England. $100,000, 1999.

1208. Libraries for the Future, NYC, NY. $10,000, 1999.

AT&T Foundation

Limitations: Giving on a national and international basis, primarily to Los Angeles and San Francisco, CA; Denver, CO; Washington, DC; Miami, FL; Chicago, IL; NJ; NY; Pittsburgh and Philadelphia, PA; and Seattle, WA. No support for religious organizations for sectarian purposes, political campaigns, or disease-related health associations other than AIDS-related programs, child care and elder care centers, sports teams, or sports-related activities, planetariums, zoos, or historic buildings or villages. No grants to individuals, or for capital development, scholarships, endowments, deficit financing, medical research projects, operating expenses or capital campaigns of local health or human service agencies other than hospitals, wiring or other equipment, construction or renovation, competitions, land acquisition, or advertising or sponsorship purchases; no equipment donations.

1209. Americans for the Arts, NYC, NY. $37,500, 2000.

1210. Brooklyn Public Library, Brooklyn, NY. $50,000, 2000.

1211. California State Library Foundation, Sacramento, CA. $25,000, 2000.

1212. Charities Aid Foundation, West Malling, England. $35,000, 2000.

1213. Chicago Public Library Foundation, Chicago, IL. $175,000, 2000.

1214. Coast Community Library, Friends of, Point Arena, CA. $10,000, 2000.

1215. Council for Basic Education, DC. $137,500, 2000.

1216. Eugene Public Library Foundation, Eugene, OR. $18,000, 2000.

1217. Filipino American Heritage Institute, Los Angeles, CA. $25,000, 2000.

1218. Green Business Network, Oakland, CA. $30,000, 2000.

1219. Indianapolis-Marion County Public Library Foundation, Indianapolis, IN. $30,000, 2000.

1220. National Archives, Foundation for the, DC. $250,000, 2000.

1221. San Jose Public Library Foundation, San Jose, CA. $23,000, 2000.

The Atlantic Foundation of New York

Limitations: Giving on a national and international basis. No grants to individuals.

1222. Child Care, Inc., NYC, NY. $18,000, 1999.

1223. Montclair Public Library, Montclair, NJ. $65,250, 1999.

1224. New York Public Library, NYC, NY. $7,900,000, 1999.

AXA Foundation, Inc.

Limitations: Giving on a national basis, with some emphasis on New York, NY. No support for private foundations, member agencies of the United Way, or for religious or international purposes. No grants to individuals, or for capital campaigns, medical research, or media-related projects.

1225. Balch Institute for Ethnic Studies, Philadelphia, PA. $15,000, 1999. For website support.

1226. Brooklyn Childrens Museum, Brooklyn, NY. $50,000, 1999. For Museum Team program.

1227. Children of Aging Parents, Levittown, PA. $25,000, 1999. For Toll Free Help Line.

1228. Children of Aging Parents, Levittown, PA. $25,000, 1999. For Toll Free Help Line and general support.
1229. National Alliance for Caregiving, Bethesda, MD. $35,000, 1999. For Long Term Care Survey.
1230. New York Public Library, NYC, NY. $25,000, 1999. For general support.

The George F. Baker Trust

Limitations: Giving primarily in the eastern U.S., with some emphasis on the New York, NY, area. No grants to individuals, or for scholarships; no loans.

1231. Harvard University, Business School, Cambridge, MA. $250,000, 1999. For continued support for renovation of Baker Library.
1232. Porter Memorial Library, Machias, ME. $10,000, 1999. For renovation and modernization of library building.

The Barker Welfare Foundation

Limitations: Giving primarily in Chicago, IL, Michigan City, IN, and New York, NY. No support for political activities, national health, welfare, or education agencies, institutions or funds. No grants to individuals, or for endowment funds, seed money, emergency funds, deficit financing, scholarships, fellowships, medical or scientific research, films or videos, or conferences; no loans.

1233. Chicago Public Library Foundation, Chicago, IL. $50,000, 2000. For Family Computer Center at Thomas Hughes Children's Library.
1234. Metropolitan Opera Association, NYC, NY. $19,400, 2000. For Radio and Television Archive Restoration Project.
1235. New York Historical Society, NYC, NY. $18,000, 2000. For Historical Artifacts Digitization Project.

The Bodman Foundation

Limitations: Giving primarily in northern NJ and New York, NY. Generally, no support for colleges or universities, international projects, government agencies, public schools, nonprofit programs and services mostly funded or wholly reimbursed by government, small performing arts groups, or national health or mental health organizations. No grants to individuals; generally no grants for travel, publications, endowments, conferences, capital campaigns, housing, annual appeals, dinner functions, fundraising events, deficit financing, or films; no loans.

1236. Child Care, Inc., NYC, NY. $25,000, 2000. To expand Family Day Care Business Resource Center.
1237. Foundation Center, NYC, NY. $10,000, 2000. For new services on website.
1238. George C. Marshall Institute, DC. $50,000, 2000. For independent and alternative Summary for Policymakers to the UN's Third Assessment Report of the Intergovernmental Panel on Climate Change (Global Warming).
1239. Metropolitan Museum of Art, NYC, NY. $100,000, 2000. For enhancements for Thomas J. Watson, Jr. Memorial Library.

Booth Ferris Foundation

Limitations: Giving limited to the New York, NY, metropolitan area for social service agencies and cultural organizations. No support for federated campaigns, community chests, or for work with specific diseases or disabilities. No grants to individuals, or for research; generally no grants to educational institutions for scholarships, fellowships, or unrestricted endowments; no loans.

1240. Pro Bono Net, NYC, NY. $140,000, 2000. For capacity building.

The Bristol-Myers Squibb Foundation, Inc.

Limitations: Giving primarily in Stamford and Wallingford, CT, Evansville, IN, New Brunswick, Princeton, and Skillman, NJ, and Buffalo and Syracuse, NY. No support for political, fraternal, social, or veterans' organizations; religious or sectarian organizations not engaged in a significant project benefiting the entire community; specific public broadcast programs or films; or organizations receiving support through federated campaigns. No grants to individuals (except for employee-related scholarships), or for endowment funds, conferences, or sponsorships or independent medical research; no loans.

1241. Mercantile Library, NYC, NY. $10,000, 1999.

1242. New York Academy of Medicine, NYC, NY. $10,000, 1999. For Being Healthy.

The Samuel Bronfman Foundation, Inc.

Limitations: Giving primarily in New York, NY, and to national U.S. programs. No grants to individuals, or for building or endowment funds.

1243. Child Care, Inc., NYC, NY. $125,000, 2000.
1244. New York Public Library, Schomburg Center for Research in Black Culture, NYC, NY. $250,000, 2000.

The Louis Calder Foundation

Limitations: Giving primarily in the greater New York City metropolitan area. No support for publicly-operated educational and medical institutions, private foundations, or governmental organizations; cultural grants only to well-known and established institutions; grants for endowments are made only occasionally. No grants to individuals.

1245. Brotherhood/Sister Sol, NYC, NY. $20,000, 2000. For capital support for library and computer room.
1246. Citizens Advice Bureau, Bronx, NY. $20,000, 2000. For programming in computer room at Project Achieve after-school program.
1247. Foundation Center, NYC, NY. $10,000, 2000. For program support.
1248. Libraries for the Future, NYC, NY. $30,000, 2000. For Harlem Youth ACCESS, technology-based after-school program.
1249. New York Public Library, NYC, NY. $500,000, 2000. For capital support for Adopt-A-Branch, program to refurbish library branches.
1250. New York Public Library, NYC, NY. $105,000, 2000. For capital support for Sedgwick Branch Library in the Bronx.
1251. Patrons Program, NYC, NY. $100,000, 2000. For capital support for Library Connections program to revitalize libraries of inner-city elementary schools.
1252. Phipps Community Development Corporation, NYC, NY. $20,000, 2000. For capital support for teen and school-age libraries.
1253. Pierpont Morgan Library, NYC, NY. $12,000, 2000. For arts-in-education program for local high schools.
1254. Queens Library Foundation, Jamaica, NY. $30,000, 2000. For Latchkey Enrichment Program.
1255. Salvation Army of Greater New York, NYC, NY. $40,000, 2000. For computer rooms and libraries at Bushwick Community Center.

Carnegie Corporation of New York

Limitations: Giving primarily in the U.S. Some grants in commonwealth Sub-Saharan Africa, South Africa. No support for facilities of educational or human services institutions. No grants for scholarships, fellowships (except for internal fellowhip program), travel, basic operating expenses or endowments; no program-related investments.

1256. Botswana National Library Service, Gaborone, Botswana. $67,000, 2000. To develop strategic plan to revitalize public libraries in Botswana.
1257. Brooklyn Public Library, Brooklyn, NY. $25,000, 2000. Toward expansion of early childhood programs to promote reading.
1258. Center for National Independence in Politics (CNIP), Corvallis, OR. $300,000, 2000. 3-year grant. For final grant for general support.
1259. Council for Basic Education, DC. $450,000, 2000. 3-year grant. For Standards-based Teacher Education Project.
1260. Council on Foreign Relations, NYC, NY. $200,000, 2000. 2-year grant. To develop web-based resource on role of partitions in ethnic conflict and post-conflict reconstruction.
1261. Foundation Center, NYC, NY. $225,000, 2000. 3-year grant. For final grant for general support.
1262. Interhemispheric Resource Center, Silver City, NM. $200,000, 2000. 2.50-year grant. For web-based research and analysis on ethnic self-determination.
1263. International Council of Scientific Unions, Paris, France. $150,000, 2000. To disseminate bibliography and findings of literature review on public libraries in Africa by International Network for the Availability of Scientific Publications.
1264. International Development Research Centre-East African Regional Office, Nairobi, Kenya. $500,000, 2000. 2-year grant. For final grant for African Technology Policy Studies Network

which works to improve science and technology policy making in sub-Saharan Africa.

1265. Kenya National Library Service, Nairobi, Kenya. $75,000, 2000. To develop strategic plan to revitalize public libraries in Kenya.

1266. Library and Information Association of South Africa, South Africa. $249,400, 2000. 3-year grant. For institutional support for staff and operating support.

1267. Library of Congress, DC. $25,000, 2000. Toward planning national commission on adult literacy.

1268. National Endowment for the Humanities, DC. $1,000,000, 2000. 2-year grant. To provide core collection of works by American authors to rural and small public libraries in the U.S. in collaboration with Library of America and American Library Association.

1269. National Security Archive Fund, DC. $500,000, 2000. 2-year grant. For continued support for Russia and Former Soviet Union Initiative.

1270. New School University, NYC, NY. $258,800, 2000. 2-year grant. For Journal Donation Project which assists libraries in the former Soviet Union and in Eastern Europe in obtaining English-language social science and humanities research journals.

1271. New York Public Library, NYC, NY. $25,000, 2000. Toward summer reading programs for children.

1272. Queens Borough Public Library, Jamaica, NY. $25,000, 2000. Toward books and materials for early literacy workshops and summer reading programs.

1273. Rutgers, The State University of New Jersey, New Brunswick, NJ. $16,500, 2000. Toward archival project on Russian political parties.

1274. University of Wisconsin, Consortium for Policy Research in Education, Madison, WI. $450,000, 2000. 3-year grant. To disseminate activities on new forms of teacher compensation.

1275. Wellesley College, National Institute on Out-of-School Time, Wellesley, MA. $297,000, 2000. 2-year grant. To develop cross-city network for after-school leaders.

1276. Woodrow Wilson International Center for Scholars, DC. $2,400,000, 2000. 2-year grant. For creation of Centers for Advanced Study and Education (CASES) in Russia. Centers will serve as umbrellas for advanced interdisciplinary research, professional training, academic mobility and library and publication support. Project administered by Kennan Institute for Advanced Russian Studies and Moscow Public Science Foundation.

China Medical Board of New York, Inc.

Limitations: Giving limited to East and Southeast Asia, including the People's Republic of China, Hong Kong, Indonesia, Korea, Malaysia, the Philippines, Singapore, Taiwan, and Thailand. No support for governments, professional societies, or research institutes not directly under medical school control. No grants to individuals, or for capital funds, operating budgets for medical care, special projects, or the basic equipping of medical schools, nursing schools, or schools of public health that are the responsibility of various governments or universities; no loans.

1277. Institute of Medicine, Myanmar (Burma). $180,000, 2000. For development of medical information center to provide up-to-date medical information for profession.

Citigroup Foundation

Limitations: No support for political causes or religious, veterans' or fraternal organizations, unless they are engaged in a significant project benefiting the entire community. No grants to individuals, or for fundraising events, telethons, marathons, races, benefits, or courtesy advertising.

1278. Brooklyn Public Library, Brooklyn, NY. $50,000, 2000. For Business Library Educational Programming.

1279. Career Development Services, Rochester, NY. $10,000, 2000. For Greater Rochester Unemployed Resources Network.

1280. Charities Aid Foundation, West Malling, England. $100,000, 2000. For Foundation for Support of Women's Work in Turkey.

1281. Charities Aid Foundation, West Malling, England. $60,000, 2000. For Working Women's Forum in India.

1282. Charities Aid Foundation, West Malling, England. $50,000, 2000. For Friends of Women's World Banking in India.

1283. Charities Aid Foundation, West Malling, England. $50,000, 2000. For Society for Promotion of Area Resource Centers in India.

1284. Charities Aid Foundation, West Malling, England. $50,000, 2000. For Shakti Foundation for Disadvantaged Women in Bangladesh.

1285. Charities Aid Foundation, West Malling, England. $50,000, 2000. For Fundacio Tomillo/Teacher Training and Technology Resources in Spain.

1286. Charities Aid Foundation, West Malling, England. $25,000, 2000. For SASHA economic development program in India.

1287. Charities Aid Foundation, West Malling, England. $25,000, 2000. For SHARAN economic development program in India.

1288. Charities Aid Foundation, West Malling, England. $25,000, 2000. For local capital in Spain.

1289. Charities Aid Foundation, West Malling, England. $25,000, 2000. For University of London/TeachNet Pilot Program in the United Kingdom.

1290. Charities Aid Foundation, West Malling, England. $25,000, 2000. For International Program Fund.

1291. Charities Aid Foundation, West Malling, England. $24,000, 2000. For Rural-Urban Encounters: Managing the Environment of Peri-Urban Interface in the United Kingdom.

1292. Charities Aid Foundation, West Malling, England. $20,000, 2000. For Technology Equipment and Software for Sola Kallio School in Finland.

1293. Charities Aid Foundation, West Malling, England. $20,000, 2000. For Bizim Ulke Association/Vocational Computer Education Courses in Turkey.

1294. Charities Aid Foundation, West Malling, England. $20,000, 2000. For KIMEP/Institute of Management Economics and Strategic Research in Kazakhstan.

1295. Charities Aid Foundation, West Malling, England. $16,000, 2000. For South Asia Partnership in Sri Lanka.

1296. Charities Aid Foundation, West Malling, England. $15,000, 2000. For Book Group Pakistan Literacy/Teacher Training and Model School Project.

1297. Charities Aid Foundation, West Malling, England. $15,000, 2000. For SOS Children's Village of Zambia Trust.

1298. Charities Aid Foundation, West Malling, England. $10,000, 2000. For Tsinghua University, School of Economics and Management Scholarship and Faculty Fund in China.

1299. Charities Aid Foundation, West Malling, England. $10,000, 2000. For Peking University, School of Management Scholarship and Faculty Fund in China.

1300. Charities Aid Foundation, West Malling, England. $10,000, 2000. For Fudan University, School of Management Scholarship and Faculty Fund in China.

1301. Charities Aid Foundation, West Malling, England. $10,000, 2000. For Zongshan University Scholarship and Faculty Fund in China.

1302. Child Care, Inc., NYC, NY. $60,000, 2000. For Accreditation and Universal Pre-K Initiatives.

1303. Educational Netcasting Foundation, Cambridge, MA. $146,000, 2000. For Encarta Africana Donation to Schools, Libraries and NGOs in Africa.

1304. Gwinnett Coalition for Health and Human Services, Lawrenceville, GA. $10,000, 2000. For Gwinnett Helpline.

1305. Library Foundation of Los Angeles, Los Angeles, CA. $10,000, 2000. For Children's Reading Club.

1306. Library of Congress, DC. $200,000, 2000. For National Digital Library, African-American Odyssey.

1307. Middle Country Library Foundation, Centereach, NY. $10,000, 2000. For Teen Service Centers.

1308. National Housing Institute, Orange, NJ. $20,000, 2000. For Shelterforce.

1309. Nevada Avenue Elementary School, Los Angeles, CA. $10,000, 2000. For School Library Books.

1310. Nonprofit Connection, Brooklyn, NY. $25,000, 2000. For general operating support.

1311. Nonprofit Connection, Brooklyn, NY. $20,000, 2000. For Nonprofit Days Project.

1312. Parents United for the D.C. Public Schools, DC. $10,000, 2000. For Parent Information Programs.

1313. Queens Library Foundation, Jamaica, NY. $25,000, 2000. For Teen NET Mentor Program.

1314. United Way International, Alexandria, VA. $35,600, 2000. For Pustaka Kelana Foundation/Mobile Library Project in Indonesia.

1315. United Way International, Alexandria, VA. $25,000, 2000. For Abrinq Foundation for Children's Rights/Living Library Project in Hospitals in Brazil.

Liz Claiborne & Art Ortenberg Foundation

Limitations: Giving primarily in Third World countries in the Tropics and in the Northern Rocky Mountain region of the U.S.. No grants for general support, or for underwriting of overhead.

1316. Library of Congress, DC. $227,000, 2000.

Liz Claiborne Foundation

Limitations: Giving only in the four areas where the main operating facilities of Liz Claiborne, Inc. are located: Montgomery, AL, Hudson County, NJ, New York, NY, and Mount Pocono, PA. No support for religious, fraternal, or veterans' organizations. No grants to individuals, or for capital campaigns, equipment, conferences or symposia, endowments, research, technical assistance, media projects, fundraising events, sponsorships, or journal advertisements.

1317. New York Public Library, NYC, NY. $10,120, 1999.

The Clark Foundation

Limitations: Giving primarily in upstate NY and New York City; scholarships restricted to students residing in the Cooperstown, NY, area. No grants to individuals (except as specified in restricted funds), or for deficit financing or matching gifts.

1318. Foundation Center, NYC, NY. $73,000, 2001. For training consultants.

1319. Inner-City Scholarship Fund, NYC, NY. $100,000, 2001. For Library Connections program.

1320. New York Public Library, NYC, NY. $50,000, 2001. For Computer Page Program which hires local, bright high school and college students and trains them to help people use computers, software programs, and the Internet in the Library.

The Edna McConnell Clark Foundation

Limitations: Giving nationally for Children's Program and Student Achievement Program; New York City preference for Program for New York Neighborhoods. No grants to individuals, or for capital funds, construction and equipment, endowments, scholarships, fellowships, annual appeals, deficit financing, or matching gifts; no loans to individuals.

1321. Collaborative Communications Group, DC. $125,000, 2000. To implement comprehensive dissemination plan that engages educators and education organizations in using book and videos to increase middle schools' use of standards.

1322. Foundation Center, NYC, NY. $40,000, 2000. For continuing general support.

1323. National Assembly of National Health and Human Service Organizations, DC. $105,000, 2000. For continuing support to expand capacity of National Youth Development and Information Center, which provides local and national youth-serving organizations with information about youth development field.

Robert Sterling Clark Foundation, Inc.

Limitations: Giving primarily in New York State for the Public Institutions Program and in New York City for the Cultural Program; giving nationally for reproductive freedom projects. No grants to individuals, or for annual campaigns, seed money, emergency funds, deficit financing, capital or endowment funds, matching gifts, scholarships, fellowships, conferences, or films.

1324. Americans for the Arts, DC. $50,000, 2000. For arts advocacy work which includes coordinating national arts leadership and building grassroots support network for arts, as well as for activities of National Arts Policy Board.

1325. DataCenter, Oakland, CA. $25,000, 2000. For CultureWatch, monthly publication and website monitoring people, organizations and issues of far right political and social movements.

1326. National Abortion and Reproductive Rights Action League (NARAL) Foundation, DC. $150,000, 2000. For continued expansion and updating of NARAL's database of reproductive rights-related legislation and court decisions, analysis of data, and compilation of information into report of status of reproductive rights in each of the fifty states.

1327. Poets House, NYC, NY. $25,000, 2000. For fundraising feasibility study to determine Poets House's readiness to undertake possible capital campaign.

1328. Sexuality Information and Education Council of the U.S. (SIECUS), NYC, NY. $60,000, 2000. For public policy initiatives designed to promote comprehensive sexuality education and sexual rights, and educate policymakers and media on these issues.

1329. State Communities Aid Association, Albany, NY. $40,000, 2000. For analysis, advocacy, and public education to inform state policies affecting economic security of poor New Yorkers.

1330. State Communities Aid Association, Albany, NY. $35,000, 2000. To assist policymakers in improving school-based mental health and health services and to educate public and school officials about effective programs.

The Commonwealth Fund

Limitations: No support for religious organizations, or basic biomedical research. No grants to individuals (except through the Commonwealth Fund's fellowship programs), or for building or endowment funds, general support, capital funds, construction or renovation of facilities, purchase of equipment, assistance with operating budgets or deficits of established programs or institutions, scholarships, or major media projects or documentaries; no loans (except program-related investments).

1331. Advocates for Children of New York, Brooklyn, NY. $25,000, 2000. For project, Parent Information Center: Providing a Web-Based Guide to New York City's Public Schools.

1332. American Public Human Services Association, DC. $97,664, 2000. For State Strategies to Enhance Quality of Medicaid Managed Care, Phase Two project to expand development of national information on quality of Medicaid managed care plans to include more states, analyze variations in quality, encourage states to adopt effective strategies for improving quality, and develop funding to sustain activity.

1333. Foundation Center, NYC, NY. $30,000, 2000. For general support.

1334. New York Academy of Medicine, NYC, NY. $25,000, 2000. For project, Recent Contributions of Health Services Research.

1335. New York Academy of Medicine, NYC, NY. $20,000, 2000. For project, The Doctor at the Millennium: Practice in a Changing Environment.

1336. Research Foundation of the City University of New York, NYC, NY. $262,292, 2000. For Providing Medicare Beneficiaries with Report Cards to Compare HMO Quality in New York City Phase Two project to explore how training staff at senior services organizations can assist beneficiaries in using health plan report cards to help elderly Medicare beneficiaries in New York City make informed decisions when choosing a managed care plan.

1337. Rockefeller University, NYC, NY. $357,408, 2000. For transfer, processing, and storage of Commonwealth Fund archival materials at the Rockefeller Archive Center.

Community Foundation for Greater Buffalo

Limitations: Giving limited to western NY; scholarships awarded to students primarily from Erie County. No support for religious purposes, or schools not registered with the State Education Department. No grants to individuals (except from designated scholarship funds) or for annual campaigns, deficit financing, or endowment; no loans.

1338. Computers for Children, Buffalo, NY. $18,275, 1999. For computers and operating systems for libraries in Buffalo Public Schools.

Corning Incorporated Foundation

Limitations: Giving primarily in communities where Corning Incorporated has operations. No support for elementary or secondary schools outside of school systems in plant communities, athletic activities, veterans' organizations, political parties, labor groups, or religious or fraternal organizations. No grants to individuals, or for courtesy advertising, volunteer emergency squads, or fundraising events; no loans.

1339. Corning Area Public Library, Corning, NY. $10,000, 2000. For strategic plan.

Lewis B. & Dorothy Cullman Foundation, Inc.

Limitations: Giving primarily in NY. No grants to individuals.

1340. New York Public Library, NYC, NY. $1,000,000, 2000.
1341. Pierpont Morgan Library, NYC, NY. $20,000, 2000.

The Nathan Cummings Foundation, Inc.

Limitations: Giving primarily in the U.S. and Israel. No grants for endowments, debt reduction, capital campaigns, capital construction, equipment, or museum collections acquisitions.

1342. Americans for the Arts, NYC, NY. $30,000, 1999.
1343. Jewish Womens Archives, Brookline, MA. $25,000, 1999.
1344. New York Academy of Medicine, NYC, NY. $10,000, 1999. For continued support.
1345. Newberry Library, Chicago, IL. $10,000, 1999.

Eleanor Naylor Dana Charitable Trust

Limitations: Giving primarily in areas east of the Mississippi River. No grants to individuals, or for instrumentation other than that required for a specific project, large-scale field studies of a therapeutic or epidemiological nature, or conferences (in biomedical research); or for deficit financing, exhibits, publications, or conclaves (in the arts).

1346. Converse College, Spartanburg, SC. $25,000, 1999. For archives.
1347. Lahey Clinic Hospital, Burlington, MA. $15,000, 1999. For data processing equipment for archival program.

The Ira W. DeCamp Foundation

Limitations: Giving primarily in NY including the metropolitan area and NJ and CT. No support for government-affiliated organizations, or for research on live animals other than rats and mice. No grants to individuals, or for general support, land acquisition, publications, conferences, endowment funds, operating budgets, continuing support, annual campaigns, emergency funds, or deficit financing; no loans.

1348. New York University, School of Law, NYC, NY. $150,000, 2000. To construct computer or library space within new building.
1349. Pius XII Foundation, NYC, NY. $50,000, 2000. To renovate library at Marie Smith Urban Academy.

Beatrice P. Delany Charitable Trust

Limitations: Giving primarily in the metropolitan Chicago, IL, area. No grants to individuals.

1350. Bedford Free Library, Bedford, NY. $50,000, 1999. For general support.

The Gladys Krieble Delmas Foundation

Limitations: Giving on a national basis to organizations, but only in New York, NY, for performing arts grants; giving for individual research projects conducted in Venice or the Veneto, Italy. No grants to individuals (except for advanced research in Venice and the Veneto), or for building campaigns; no loans.

1351. American Academy in Rome, NYC, NY. $40,000, 1999. For Photographic Archive in library.
1352. American Friends of Cambridge University, Scott Polar Research Institute, NYC, NY. $32,000, 1999. For access and preservation to photographic collections in Shackleton Memorial Library.
1353. Art Institute of Chicago, Chicago, IL. $18,000, 1999. For catalogue on web of Mary Reynolds Collection at Ryerson Library.
1354. Centro di Studi Americani, Rome, Italy. $40,000, 1999. For organization, classification, and recording of Archives.
1355. Council on Library and Information Resources, DC. $35,000, 1999. For task force to consider role of artifact in library collections.
1356. Duke University, William R. Perkins Library, Durham, NC. $40,000, 1999. For North Carolina Archives Online Project.
1357. Huntington Library, Art Collections and Botanical Gardens, San Marino, CA. $25,000, 1999. For graduate student seminar in Paleography.
1358. Indiana University, Office of Development and External Affairs, Indianapolis, IN. $10,000, 1999. For Philanthropic Studies Index at University Libraries.

1359. Literary Classics of the United States, NYC, NY. $35,000, 1999. Toward branch libraries in NYC to bring their collections of Library of America volumes up to date.
1360. National Gallery of Canada, Ottawa, Canada. $27,797, 1999. To contribute Canadian holdings to Archival Resources service.
1361. New York Public Library, Astor, Lenox and Tilden Foundations, NYC, NY. $70,000, 1999. For Manuscripts and Archives Access Project.
1362. University of California, Santa Cruz, CA. $14,000, 1999. For preservation, digitizing, and cataloguing of slides from Branson DeCou Collection at the University Library.
1363. University of Maryland Foundation, College Park, MD. $10,000, 1999. For transfer of ACA music archive to University of Maryland Library.
1364. University of Pennsylvania, Office of the Dean Administrative and Financial Services, Philadelphia, PA. $25,000, 1999. For processing and cataloguing of records of American Poetry Review at Annenburg Rare Book and Manuscript Library.

Deutsche Bank Americas Foundation

Limitations: Giving primarily in areas of company operations in the U.S., Canada and Latin America. No support for religious purposes, veterans' and fraternal organizations, United Way agencies unless they provide a fundraising waiver, political parties or their candidates, or legal advocacy. No grants to individuals, or for endowment campaigns.

1365. Charities Aid Foundation America, Alexandria, VA. $380,000, 1999. For Bankers Trust Company Donor Advised Fund.
1366. Charities Aid Foundation America, Investors in Society, Alexandria, VA. $53,000, 1999. For Bankers Trust Company Foundation Donor Advised Fund.
1367. University of Pennsylvania, Wharton Financial Institutions Center, Philadelphia, PA. $10,000, 1999. For Brookings-Wharton Papers on Financial Services.

Irene Diamond Fund

Limitations: Giving primarily in NY. No grants to individuals; no loans.

1368. New York Public Library, NYC, NY. $250,000, 1999. For general support of Research Libraries, for Scholars-in-Residence program at Schomburg Center for Research in Black Culture, and for minority education and professional advancement opportunities at Branch Libraries.
1369. New York Public Library, NYC, NY. $250,000, 1999. For general support of Research Libraries, for Scholars-in-Residence program at Schomburg Center for Research in Black Culture, and for minority education and professional advancement opportunities at Branch Libraries.

Harriet Ford Dickenson Foundation

Limitations: Giving limited to Broome County, NY. No grants to individuals.

1370. Broome Library Foundation, Binghamton, NY. $1,041,000, 2000. For general support.

The Dillon Fund

Limitations: No grants to individuals; no loans.

1371. American Library in Paris, Paris, France. $55,000, 1999. For capital campaign.
1372. Century Association Archives Foundation, NYC, NY. $10,000, 1999. For preservation of archives.
1373. Pierpont Morgan Library, NYC, NY. $21,000, 1999. For annual operating support.
1374. Pierpont Morgan Library, NYC, NY. $15,000, 1999. For anniversary gala benefit.

The William H. Donner Foundation, Inc.

1375. Vetiver Network, Leesburg, VA. $100,000, 2000. For Vetiver 2000: World Wide Project to Support Accelerated Introduction of Vetiver Grass Technology for Natural Resource Conservation and Rehabilitation.

Doris Duke Charitable Foundation

Limitations: Giving on a national basis. No support for water or aquatic issues, air or climate change issues, toxic issues, litigation, the visual arts, museums or galleries, or arts programs for rehabilitative or therapeutic purposes. No grants for to individuals (except through special foundation programs) or for conferences or publications.

1376. Americans for the Arts, DC. $1,000,000, 2000. To develop national public service campaign with Ad Council promoting arts education.
1377. Association for Biodiversity Information, Arlington, VA. $2,200,000, 2000. 3-year grant. For matching grant to develop, test, and market new and improved computer tools that integrate information about biological diversity into land use decision making and to establish endowment for project.
1378. Foundation Center, NYC, NY. $15,000, 2000. For general operating support.
1379. Library of Congress, DC. $1,000,000, 2000. For Library of Congress to acquire Katherine Dunham collection, to preserve materials that document and augment Dunham legacy, and to stabilize operations of Dunham Centers in East Saint Louis, IL.

Dyson Foundation

Limitations: Giving primarily in Dutchess County, NY, and organizations providing services in Dutchess County, NY. National and other grants on a solicited basis. No support for international organizations. No grants to individuals, debt reduction, direct mail campaign or fundraising events.

1380. Franklin and Eleanor Roosevelt Institute, Hyde Park, NY. $1,500,000, 1999. For construction of new Visitor's Center and renovation of library and museum facilities.
1381. Millbrook Free Library, Millbrook, NY. $250,000, 1999. For capital campaign.
1382. New York Academy of Medicine, NYC, NY. $250,000, 1999. For David E. Rogers Fellowship Program.
1383. New York Academy of Medicine, NYC, NY. $62,188, 1999. For Enhancing Community Commitment in Pediatrics.

Eastman Kodak Charitable Trust

Limitations: Giving primarily in high employment locations, including Windsor, CO, Rochester, NY, and Kingsport, TN; giving nationally only for higher education. No grants to individuals, or for matching gifts; low priority given to building or endowment funds; no loans..

1384. Library of Congress, DC. $200,000, 2000.

Fred L. Emerson Foundation, Inc.

Limitations: Giving primarily in Auburn, Cayuga County, and upstate NY. No grants to individuals, or for deficit financing; no loans. Support for operating budgets is discouraged.

1385. Paul Smiths College of Arts and Sciences, Paul Smiths, NY. $250,000, 2000. For Adirondack Information Resource Center Library.
1386. Powers Library, Moravia, NY. $50,000, 2000. For capital campaign.
1387. Roswell Park Cancer Institute, Buffalo, NY. $50,000, 2000. For renovation of Mirand Library.

The Charles Engelhard Foundation

Limitations: Giving on a national basis. No support for international organizations. No grants to individuals.

1388. Amherst College, Amherst, MA. $50,000, 2000. For administration of Folger Shakespeare Library in Washington, DC.
1389. New York Public Library, NYC, NY. $152,000, 2000.
1390. Pierpont Morgan Library, NYC, NY. $45,000, 2000.

The Ford Foundation

Limitations: Giving on an international basis, including the U.S., Eastern Europe, Africa and the Middle East, Asia, Russia, Latin America and the Caribbean. No support for programs for which substantial support from government or other sources is readily available, or for religious sectarian activities as such. No grants for routine operating costs, construction or maintenance of buildings, or undergraduate scholarships; graduate fellow-

ships generally channeled through grants to universities or other organizations; no grants for purely personal or local needs.

1391. Advocacy Institute, DC. $90,000, 2000. Support For Journal And Listserve To Promote Networking And Information Exchange Between Alumni Of International Advocacy Fellows Program And Other Social Justice Advocates Worldwide.
1392. African Small-Scale Farmers Communication Network, Nairobi, Kenya. $95,000, 2000. 3-year grant. Support For Radio Listening Project And Programming On Agriculture And Health Issues For Women In Rural Kenya.
1393. African Women and Child Information Network, Nairobi, Kenya. $148,000, 2000. 3-year grant. Support For African Monitoring And Advocacy Campaign During And After Beijing Plus Five Review.
1394. Afro-American Historical and Genealogical Society, DC. $54,000, 2000. Support For Planning Grant To Explore Ways To Research, Catalog, And Manage Disposition Of Historical Materials On African-Americans.
1395. American Council on Education, DC. $100,000, 2000. 1.25-year grant. Toward Development Of Regional And Statewide Meetings, Network Of Senior Academic Officials, And Web Site To Improve Teacher Education.
1396. American Institute of Indian Studies, Chicago, IL. $300,700, 2000. 2-year grant. Supplemental Support To Undertake Integrated Cataloging Project For Audio-Visual Archiving And To Manage Activities Of National Archival Consortium In India.
1397. American Library Association, DC. $115,000, 2000. Support For Public Education, Advocacy And Constituency Building Around Intellectual Property Policy For Digital Media.
1398. Americans for the Arts, DC. $1,010,500, 2000. 1.25-year grant. Continued Support For National Demonstration Program To Strengthen Arts And Cultural Projects That Stimulate Civic Dialogue On Contemporary Issues.
1399. Arab Network of NGOs for Development, Beirut, Lebanon. $150,000, 2000. Support For Regional NGO Participation In Second World Summit On Social Development.
1400. Archbishopric of Santiago for the Vicariate of Solidarity, Santiago, Chile. $324,000, 2000. 3-year grant. Supplemental Support For Continuity Of Documentation Center And Archives On Human Rights In Chile.
1401. Archive Administration of Saint Petersburg and Leningrad Region, Saint Petersburg, Russia. $100,000, 2000. Support For Creation Of Electronic Catalog And Preservation Of Part Of Photo Collection Of Saint Petersburg Central State Archive Of Video, Photo And Audio Documents.
1402. Arkansas State University, State University, AR. $175,000, 2000. 1.50-year grant. To Develop Electronic Community And Multistate Clearinghouse For Community-Based Organizations In Delta To Support Tourism Development Program For Minority And Distressed Communities.
1403. Asia Monitor Resource Center, Kowloon, Hong Kong. $100,000, 2000. Support For Research, Publications, Networking, Documentation And Training Programs Enabling Asian Workers To Meet Challenges Of Globalization.
1404. Asosiasi Konsultan Pembangunan Permukiman Indonesia, Bandung, Indonesia. $168,300, 2000. 1.50-year grant. Support For Pilot Projects On Establishing Community-Based Information Networks For Development Planning.
1405. Association for Promotion of Cultural Development in Egypt, Oschelbronn, Germany. $173,000, 2000. 1.25-year grant. Support For Workshops And Website To Facilitate Information Exchanges On Organic Farming Techniques, Marketing And Trade Opportunities For Farmers, Merchants, Researchers And Wider Public.
1406. Baikal Environmental Education, Irkutsk, Russia. $50,000, 2000. Support For Preservation Of Archive Of Documentary Films On East Siberia And Creation Of Electronic Catalogue.
1407. Cambridge College, Cambridge, MA. $300,000, 2000. 2-year grant. To Support Development Of Online Virtual Resource Network Designed To Help Community-Based Organizations Operate More Effectively.
1408. Caucus of Development NGO Networks, Manila, Philippines. $56,500, 2000. 2-year grant. Support For Efforts To Sustain Trisectoral Cooperation Among Philippine Civil Society, Government, And Business In Addressing Peace And Development In Mindanao And Other Urgent Social Concerns.

1409. Center for Information Research, Moscow, Russia. $150,000, 2000. Continued Support For Extending Access To Information In Social Sciences Through On-Line Database To Serve Needs Of Russian Academics.

1410. Center for Research and Higher Studies in Social Anthropology, Guadalajara, Mexico. $150,000, 2000. 1.50-year grant. To Consolidate Indigenous Photography Archive Program And Expand Its Links To Cultural Institutions In Southern State Of Chiapas, Mexico.

1411. Centre for Independent Social Research (CISR), Saint Petersburg, Russia. $75,000, 2000. Support For Preservation In Saint Petersburg Of Archive Of Unofficial Press And Documentation On Social Movements In Russia And Neighboring States During Post-1986 Period.

1412. Centre for Independent Social Research (CISR), Saint Petersburg, Russia. $25,000, 2000. Support For Access To Archive Of Unofficial Publications On Developments In U.S.S.R. Post-1986, And Its Integration Into Social Research Center.

1413. Centre National de la Recherche Scientifique (CNRS), Paris, France. $150,000, 2000. Support For Electronic Archiving Of Arabic Manuscripts In Bamako, Mali In Timbuktu Region.

1414. Centre of Contemporary Architecture, Moscow, Russia. $100,000, 2000. Support For Center, Creation Of Archive And Data Base, And For Educational And Television Programs.

1415. Charities Aid Foundation, West Malling, England. $198,200, 2000. Support For Planning And Other Activities To Establish East African Center For Promotion Of Philanthropy And Citizenship.

1416. Charities Aid Foundation, West Malling, England. $90,000, 2000. 1.50-year grant. Support For Research On Indigenous And Religious Philanthropy In India And Diaspora Philanthropy To Indian Nonprofit Sector, And International Research Exchanges.

1417. Charities Aid Foundation, West Malling, England. $50,000, 2000. Support For Journal Alliance, Which Helps Increase Resources To Nonprofit Sector Worldwide By Serving Information Needs Of Philanthropic Organizations And Donor Agencies.

1418. Charities Aid Foundation, West Malling, England. $47,500, 2000. Support For Publication Of Nonprofit Sector Studies On South Asia, Comparative Workshop On Nonprofit Certification, And Community Foundation Explorations In New Delhi.

1419. Charities Aid Foundation-West Africa, Accra, Ghana. $37,000, 2000. Support For Research And Workshop On Development Strategies In Ghana.

1420. China Business Forum, DC. $40,000, 2000. 1.50-year grant. For Establishment Of Small Library Of World Trade Organization And International Trade Law Materials At Department Of Treaties And Laws Of Chinese Ministry Of Foreign Trade And Economic Cooperation.

1421. Chinese Academy of Forestry, Beijing, China. $121,707, 2000. Support For Network And Newsletter On Community-Based Social Forestry In China.

1422. Chinese Womens Health Network, China. $50,000, 2000. 2-year grant. Support For Compilation And Publication Of Oral Histories Of Chinese Women In The 20th Century.

1423. Cinema Museum, Moscow, Russia. $74,000, 2000. Support For Creation Of Russian-English Electronic Catalogue Of Over 400,000 Items In Cinema Museum's Archive.

1424. Communication and Information for Women, Mexico City, Mexico. $150,000, 2000. 2-year grant. Support To Strengthen And Expand Mexico City-Based Network Of NGOs Promoting Women's Health And Sexual And Reproductive Rights.

1425. Community Health Media Trust, Johannesburg, South Africa. $100,000, 2000. For 18 Episodes Of Weekly Television Magazine Program That Provides Reliable Information To People Living With HIV/AIDS And Those In Their Support Systems.

1426. Cooperative Housing Foundation, Silver Spring, MD. $50,000, 2000. To Consolidate U.S.-Mexico Transborder Network To Expand Access To And Enhance Sharing Of Information Among Organizations Providing Housing Options For Low-Income Populations.

1427. Corporation for Enterprise Development (CFED), DC. $100,000, 2000. 2-year grant. Continued Support For Business Incentive Reform Clearinghouse.

1428. Democracy and Sexuality, Mexico City, Mexico. $158,522, 2000. 2-year grant. Support To Strengthen NGO Capacity To Address Challenges Of Decentralization In Public Education With Regard To Sexuality Education.

1429. Democracy and Sexuality, Mexico City, Mexico. $100,000, 2000. 2-year grant. Communications Initiatives In Ten Mexican States Of NGO Network That Promotes Sexuality Education In Framework Of Human Rights, Gender Equity, And Respect For Religious Diversity.

1430. Donors Forum of Chicago, Chicago, IL. $60,000, 2000. 2-year grant. Support For Grantmakers Concerned With Immigrants And Refugees, Affinity Group.

1431. Eduardo Mondlane University, Maputo, Mozambique. $250,000, 2000. 2-year grant. Support To Change Learning Environment In Faculty Of Agronomy And Forestry By Developing And Digitizing Library, Expanding Computer Lab, And Supporting Student Field Work.

1432. Eduardo Mondlane University, Maputo, Mozambique. $200,000, 2000. 2-year grant. Support For Digitalization And Publications At Mozambique Historical Archives.

1433. Euro-Mediterranean Human Rights Network, Copenhagen, Denmark. $45,000, 2000. 2-year grant. Support For Arabic Documentation And Dissemination Of Work Of Human Rights Network.

1434. Foundation Center, NYC, NY. $600,000, 2000. 3-year grant. General Support To Collect, Organize, Analyze, And Disseminate Information On Foundation And Corporate Giving, And Toward Relocation And Construction Of Washington, DC Library.

1435. Foundation Center, NYC, NY. $500,000, 2000. 3-year grant. Supplemental Support For Creating Online Information And Training Services About Foundations.

1436. Futureworks Company, Springfield, MA. $200,000, 2000. Support For Research And Pilot Programs On Engagement Of Corporate-Led Civic Organizations With Small Business Development.

1437. Gaza Library Project, London, England. $50,000, 2000. 1.50-year grant. Support For Expanding Network To Collect Publications Internationally For Palestinian Professional Libraries With Goal Of Building Research Environment In Palestine.

1438. Ghana Book Trust, Accra, Ghana. $140,400, 2000. 2-year grant. Support For Developing Children's Electronic Library In Ghana Through Use Of New Media Technologies.

1439. HandsNet, San Jose, CA. $350,000, 2000. 1.50-year grant. Support For Online Discussion Project For Human Services Professionals Working With Children, Youth, And Family Issues.

1440. Heartland Alliance for Human Needs and Human Rights, Chicago, IL. $150,000, 2000. 2-year grant. Support For U.S.-Mexico Advocates Network, Project That Links Civil Society Organizations To Develop Regional Perspective On Migration And Educate Policy Makers And Public In Both Countries.

1441. Ho Chi Minh National Political Academy, Ho Chi Minh City, Vietnam. $94,000, 2000. 2-year grant. Strengthening Academy's International Cooperation Department Through Staff Development And Library Support.

1442. Homenet International, Leeds, England. $375,000, 2000. 2-year grant. Support For Expanding And Strengthening Homenet International To Organize And Represent Issues Of Homebased Workers, And For Organizational Development Of Streetnet, Network Of Street Vendors.

1443. International Possibilities Unlimited, DC. $75,000, 2000. Support To Plan For U.S. Organizations To Participate In Global Network Of Black Communities Promoting Environmental And Economic Justice.

1444. International Union for Conservation of Nature and Natural Resources, Gland, Switzerland. $100,000, 2000. Support For Initial Development Of Regional Network On Transboundary Natural Resource Management In Southern Africa.

1445. ISIS International, Santiago, Chile. $145,000, 2000. 2-year grant. Follow-On Process To Disseminate And Monitor Implementation Of Platform Of Action From 1995 U.N. Conference On Women.

1446. Kenya Forestry Research Institute, Nairobi, Kenya. $280,000, 2000. 2-year grant. Kenyan Participation In East African Research Network On Community Institutions For Management Of Woodland Resources.

1447. Lontar Foundation, Jakarta, Indonesia. $200,000, 2000. 2-year grant. Support For Oral History Research, Documentation,

Archiving, And Publications On Indonesia During New Order Period.

1448. Memorial Human Rights Center, Moscow, Russia. $40,000, 2000. Support For Information Service On Developments In North Caucasus, With Particular Reference To Refugees In Ingushetiia.

1449. Mexican Center for Philanthropy, Mexico City, Mexico. $240,000, 2000. 5-year grant. To Establish Strategic Plan For Institutional Development And Financial Sustainability Over Five Years, And To Strengthen Its Training, Advocacy And Information Services For Philanthropy Sector.

1450. Mexican Center for Philanthropy, Mexico City, Mexico. $50,000, 2000. For Process Of Dialogue Between Civil Society Organizations And Incoming Government To Define Policy Proposal For Strengthening Sector And Its Role In Social And Political Development.

1451. Ministry of Foreign Affairs, Center for Foreign Affairs and Languages Training, Ho Chi Minh City, Vietnam. $163,000, 2000. Expanded Support For Office In Ho Chi Minh City To Meet Burgeoning Needs For Information Through Electronic Library Development, Language Training And International Seminars.

1452. Moscow State Tchaikovsky Conservatory, Moscow, Russia. $93,500, 2000. Support For Second Phase Of Project By Conservatory To Establish Center For Restoration And Preservation Of Recordings From Archives Of 1930-1990.

1453. Museum for African Art, NYC, NY. $100,000, 2000. Support To Develop African Art Resource Network.

1454. Natarang Pratishthan, India. $175,000, 2000. 5-year grant. Endowment Support To Help Stabilize Organization In Its Core Activities Of Archiving, Documentation, Computerization, And Dissemination.

1455. National Council of Churches of Kenya, Kenya. $100,000, 2000. Establishment Of Telecenters For Information Connectivity To Church Organizations Working On Community Mobilization And Social Justice Advocacy In Kenya.

1456. National Security Archive Fund, DC. $200,000, 2000. Support For Activities To Promote Transparency And Accountability In U.S. Foreign Policy.

1457. National Security Archive Fund, DC. $87,000, 2000. Support To Sustain And Expand Project Of Historical Recovery And International Accountability Concerning Chile.

1458. National Youth Employment Coalition, DC. $200,000, 2000. Toward General Support, And For Expansion Of Promising And Effective Practices Network.

1459. New Visions for Public Schools, NYC, NY. $250,000, 2000. 2.25-year grant. Continued Support For Evaluation Of New York Networks For School Renewal Project.

1460. Nonprofit Partnership, Braamfontein, South Africa. $36,000, 2000. Support For Financial Management Training Courses Targeting Representatives From South African Nongovernmental And Community-Based Organizations.

1461. Ongwediva Teachers Resource Center, Oshakati, Namibia. $47,000, 2000. Support For Project Designed To Promote Preservation And Revitalization Of Traditional Dance And Music.

1462. Palestinian Peace Information Center, Jerusalem, Israel. $100,000, 2000. Support For Series Of Track II Meetings Between Palestinians, Jordanians, And Israelis To Discuss Issues Of Refugees And Water, Within Larger Goal Of Creating Trilateral Security Regime.

1463. Perhimpunan Pengembangan Pesentrean dar Masqarakat, Perhimpunan Lp3es, Jakarta, Indonesia. $220,000, 2000. 1.25-year grant. Toward Coordination of Network Of Nongovernmental Organizations To Monitor State-Initiated Social Safety Net Projects And Facilitate National Dialogue On Poverty Strategies.

1464. Public Agenda Foundation, NYC, NY. $50,000, 2000. Toward Developing Web-Based Clearinghouse On Childcare And Early Childhood Education Issues.

1465. Regional Information and Support Centre for Nongovernmental Organizations, Gdansk, Poland. $120,000, 2000. 2-year grant. Program Support For Development And Enlargement Of Support Center Serving Network Of Six Major Polish Nongovernmental Organizations.

1466. Research and Information Centre Memorial, Saint Petersburg, Russia. $75,000, 2000. Support For Preservation Of Archive In Saint Petersburg Devoted To Political Repression In Soviet Union

And Development Of Educational Programs Based On Its Holdings.

1467. Research and Information Centre Memorial, Saint Petersburg, Russia. $20,000, 2000. Support For Public Use Of Archive In Saint Petersburg Devoted To Political Repression In Soviet Union, And Development Of Educational Programs Based On Its Holdings.

1468. Richard Nixon Library and Birthplace Foundation, Yorba Linda, CA. $235,000, 2000. 2-year grant. Project Designed To Develop Concrete Proposals Addressing Risk Of Nuclear Proliferation In Persian Gulf, Specifically Potential For Development Of Iranian Nuclear Weapons Capability.

1469. Russian Academy of Sciences, Institute Of Economics And Industrial Engineering, Moscow, Russia. $26,500, 2000. To Develop Internet-Based Social Science Information Resources Network To Serve Needs Of Russian Academic Community.

1470. Russian Center for Public Opinion and Market Research, Moscow, Russia. $80,000, 2000. 1.25-year grant. Support For Planning And Creation Of National Public Archive Of Survey Datasets In Russia.

1471. Russian Charitable Foundation, No to Alcoholism and Drug Addiction, Moscow, Russia. $75,000, 2000. 1.50-year grant. Support For Information Clearinghouse To Spread Best Practices Regarding Municipal Funding Innovations That Enable NGO Service Providers To Compete For Municipal Support.

1472. Russian State Archive of Film and Photo Documents, Krasnogorsk, Russia. $100,000, 2000. Support For Preservation Of Unique Documentary Footage From Beginning Of Century In Russian State Archive Of Film And Photo Documents Collection.

1473. Rutgers, The State University of New Jersey, New Brunswick, NJ. $100,000, 2000. Support For Data Gathering And Communications Activities Related To Strengthening Fragile Families Initiative.

1474. Sexuality Information and Education Council of the U.S. (SIECUS), NYC, NY. $200,000, 2000. Continued Core Support For Work On Comprehensive Sexuality Education And Expanded Outreach, Particularly To Underserved Communities.

1475. Sexuality Information and Education Council of the U.S. (SIECUS), NYC, NY. $21,500, 2000. Support For Project On Religion And Sexuality.

1476. Sol Plaatje Educational Trust, Kimberley, South Africa. $54,550, 2000. 3-year grant. Support For Cultural Library Dedicated To Sol Plaatje.

1477. State Pedagogical Institute of Nizhny Tagil, Nizhny Tagil, Russia. $65,000, 2000. 2.25-year grant. Support For Collaboration Between Pedagogical Institute And Department Of Internal Affairs To Catalogue And Rehabilitate Victims Of Gulag, And For Seminar On Victims Of Repression in Russia.

1478. Steve Biko Foundation, Cape Town, South Africa. $60,000, 2000. Support For Extensive Planning Process To Establish Steve Biko Library And Archives.

1479. Thailand Business Coalition on AIDS, Bangkok, Thailand. $255,700, 2000. 3.50-year grant. Building Business Response To AIDS In Thailand, India, And Indonesia Through Training, Strategic Planning, Sharing Of Best Practice, And Facilitating Networks Of Business Implementation Workplace Program.

1480. Tides Center, DC. $500,000, 2000. 2-year grant. Toward Core Operating Support To Build Capacity Of Net Impact, Network Of Emerging Business Leaders Concerned With Linking Business Practice With Social Concerns.

1481. Tomsk Human Rights Research Center, Tomsk, Russia. $30,000, 2000. Support For Database Of Repressed In Tomsk Region During Soviet Period, And For Memorial Museum And Its Public Education Work.

1482. United Nations Educational, Scientific and Cultural Organization (UNESCO), Abuja, Nigeria. $100,000, 2000. Support For Network Of Documentalists, Librarians, And Information Systems Professionals Working In Development Aid Institutions In Nigeria.

1483. University of Cape Town, Institute of Criminology, Rondebosch, South Africa. $225,000, 2000. 3-year grant. Toward Its Policing, Gender, And Criminal Justice Information Projects.

1484. University of North Carolina, Chapel Hill, NC. $75,000, 2000. To Provide Technical Assistance And Networking To Improve Teacher Quality In Southeastern Region Of U.S..

1485. UNNATI Organisation for Development Education, Ahmadabad, India. $56,000, 2000. 2-year grant. Support To Expand And

Strengthen Citizen Participation In Urban Governance In Small And Medium-Sized Towns In Gujarat And Establish State-Level Urban Governance Resource Center.

1486. Volunteer Consulting Group, NYC, NY. $200,000, 2000. 2-year grant. Support For Boardnet, Online Nonprofit Board/Potential Board Member Connector Service And Technical Assistance Project To Enhance Access To And Diversify Composition Of Nonprofit Boards.

1487. Women of Color Resource Center, Berkeley, CA. $50,000, 2000. Support For Participation Of Women Of Color In Beijing Plus 5 Conference And Its Related Activities.

Foundation for Child Development

Limitations: Giving limited to research and policy grants related to foundation focus and restricted to the U.S.; program development grants in New York City only. No grants to individuals, including scholarships, or for capital campaigns, building purchase, construction, renovations, or direct services outside NYC.

1488. Donors Forum of Chicago, Chicago, IL. $10,000, 2000. Toward work of Grantmakers Concerned with Immigrants and Refugees.

1489. Jewish Board of Family and Childrens Services, Institute for Clinical Studies of Infants, Toddlers, and Parents, NYC, NY. $10,000, 2000. Toward creation of special library on infancy and related topics, with particular emphasis on materials related to cultural diversity of New York City's children.

1490. Judge David L. Bazelon Center for Mental Health Law, DC. $10,000, 2000. Toward series of pamphlets about mental health services for children with serious emotional disturbance and low-income families.

1491. New York Academy of Medicine, NYC, NY. $200,000, 2000. For third-year activities of New York Forum for Child Health.

1492. University of Illinois at Chicago, Chicago, IL. $10,000, 2000. Toward expansion of Institute of Government and Public Affairs' web site, Guide To Careers in Child and Family.

The Freeman Foundation

Limitations: Giving primarily in VT for environment and special interest grants; Asian studies grants awarded nationally. No grants to individuals.

1493. American Forum for Global Education, NYC, NY. $300,000, 2000. For China Project.

1494. Brandon Free Public Library, Brandon, VT. $94,000, 2000. For Community Literacy Project of Rutland Northeast Supervisory Union.

1495. Bridge to Asia Foundation, San Francisco, CA. $108,750, 2000. For challenge grant for scholarship, information, and new book internet projects.

1496. Primary Source, New England China Network, Watertown, MA. $828,710, 2000. For China K-12 program and China Studies Partnership.

1497. Vermont Department of Libraries, Montpelier, VT. $5,000,000, 2000. For community libraries in Vermont.

Gebbie Foundation, Inc.

Limitations: Giving primarily in Chautauqua County and, secondarily, in neighboring areas of western NY. No support for sectarian or religious organizations. No grants to individuals.

1498. Anderson-Lee Library, Silver Creek, NY. $25,000, 2000. For renovations.

1499. Chautauqua Connections, Dunkirk, NY. $50,000, 2000. For construction.

1500. Chautauqua Connections, Dunkirk, NY. $23,854, 2000. For Success by Six coordinator.

1501. Chautauqua-Cattaraugus Library System, Jamestown, NY. $26,283, 2000. For book plan and school library journal.

1502. Ripley Free Library, Ripley, NY. $10,000, 2000. For circulation desk.

1503. Sinclairville Free Library, Sinclairville, NY. $75,000, 2000. For new library building.

Gilder Foundation, Inc.

Limitations: Giving primarily in NY. No grants to individuals.

1504. Gilder Lehrman Institute of American History, NYC, NY. $5,141,371, 1999.

1505. New York Public Library, NYC, NY. $10,000, 1999.

1506. Pierpont Morgan Library, NYC, NY. $133,300, 1999.

Horace W. Goldsmith Foundation

Limitations: Giving primarily in AZ, MA, and New York, NY. No grants to individuals.

1507. Archives of American Art of the Smithsonian Institution, DC. $25,000, 1999.

1508. Brooklyn Public Library, Brooklyn, NY. $50,000, 1999.

1509. Center for Jewish History, NYC, NY. $250,000, 1999.

1510. Foundation Center, NYC, NY. $75,000, 1999.

1511. Harry S. Truman Library Institute for National and International Affairs, Independence, MO. $300,000, 1999.

1512. Jewish Womens Archives, Brookline, MA. $75,000, 1999.

1513. Leo Baeck Institute, NYC, NY. $25,000, 1999.

1514. Medici Archive Project, NYC, NY. $30,000, 1999.

1515. Nantucket Atheneum, Nantucket, MA. $100,000, 1999.

1516. National Center for Victims of Crime, Arlington, VA. $25,000, 1999.

1517. New York Academy of Medicine, NYC, NY. $150,000, 1999.

1518. Oxford University, Boldeian Library, Oxford, England. $100,000, 1999.

1519. Pierpont Morgan Library, NYC, NY. $2,000,000, 1999. For Endowment Fund.

The Florence Gould Foundation

Limitations: Giving primarily in the U.S. and France. No grants to individuals.

1520. Folger Shakespeare Library, Folger Library, DC. $12,000, 1999.

1521. Medici Archive Project, NYC, NY. $20,000, 1999.

1522. Mercantile Library Association of the City of New York, NYC, NY. $12,800, 1999.

1523. New York Public Library, NYC, NY. $250,000, 1999.

1524. New York Public Library, NYC, NY. $250,000, 1999.

1525. Pierpont Morgan Library, NYC, NY. $45,000, 1999.

William T. Grant Foundation

Limitations: Giving internationally for research grants and faculty scholars; giving limited to NY, NJ, and CT for youth service grants. No grants to individuals, except for Faculty Scholars Program, or for annual fundraising campaigns, equipment and materials, land acquisition, building or renovation projects, operating budgets, endowments, or scholarships; no loans.

1526. Citizens Advice Bureau, Bronx, NY. $15,000, 2000. To provide after-school enrichment and basic skills development services to youth who attend Community Education School 90 and Junior High School 145.

1527. Columbia University, NYC, NY. $306,365, 2000. To establish information center on child and family policies and programs in industrialized countries and provide support for system of disseminating this information to wide range of groups, and promote comparative social policy research as basis for child and family policy.

1528. Foundation Center, NYC, NY. $25,000, 2000. To create comprehensive online service, Foundation Center Online, for grantseekers, grant-makers, media representatives, policy makers, and others interested in foundations and the philanthropic world.

1529. Harvard University, Cambridge, MA. $499,095, 2000. 4-year grant. To encourage and facilitate multi-disciplinary research on successful adolescent development and on youth as a life stage by strengthening Murray Research Center's existing holdings of longitudinal data on youth; establishing education and training programs that use the data; and sponsoring small grant programs for faculty, graduate, and undergraduate students to use archives.

1530. McGill University, Montreal, Canada. $20,000, 2000. To evaluate strategy to increase readership and impact of interdisciplinary Injury Prevention Journal.

The Green Fund, Inc.
Limitations: Giving primarily in the metropolitan New York, NY, area. No grants to individuals.

1531. New York Public Library, NYC, NY. $12,500, 2000. For continued support.

The Greenwall Foundation
Limitations: Giving primarily in New York, NY, for arts and humanities; giving nationally for bioethics. No grants to individuals, or for building or endowment funds, operating budgets, annual campaigns, deficit financing, publications, or conferences; no loans.

1532. Brooklyn Public Library, Brooklyn, NY. $10,000, 1999. For Lobby Gallery exhibition series.
1533. New York Academy of Medicine, NYC, NY. $10,000, 1999. For project, Bioethics in the Urban Context.
1534. Poets House, NYC, NY. $20,000, 1999. For continued support for Poetry Publication Showcase.

Hagedorn Fund
Limitations: Giving primarily in New York, NY. No grants to individuals, or for continuing support, seed money, emergency funds, deficit financing, endowment funds, matching gifts, scholarships, fellowships, research, special projects, publications, or conferences; no loans.

1535. New York Public Library, NYC, NY. $25,000, 1999. For general support.

Gladys and Roland Harriman Foundation
Limitations: No grants to individuals.

1536. New York Public Library, NYC, NY. $40,000, 1999. For general support.
1537. Patten Free Library, Bath, ME. $10,000, 1999. For general support.

The John A. Hartford Foundation, Inc.
Limitations: Giving primarily on a national basis. No grants to individuals, or for annual or capital campaigns, seed money, emergency or endowment funds, or deficit financing.

1538. New York Academy of Medicine, NYC, NY. $606,054, 2000. 3-year grant. To coordinate implementation of Graduate Geriatric Social Work Practicum.

Charles Hayden Foundation
Limitations: Giving limited to the metropolitan Boston, MA, and the metropolitan New York, NY (including northern NJ), areas. No support for fraternal groups, religious organizations other than community youth-related projects, arts exposure programs, institutions of higher education except to support work on precollegiate programs (other than recruitment programs for a particular college), hospitals, hospices, or projects essentially medical in nature. No grants to individuals, or for endowment funds, operating budgets, fellowships, annual campaigns, emergency funds, deficit financing, publications, or conferences; no loans.

1539. Partnership for After School Education, NYC, NY. $10,000, 2000. Toward completion of Mapping Project and to develop resource directory of youth organizations across New York City.
1540. Saint Philips Academy, Newark, NJ. $150,000, 2000. Toward Library Renovation Project.

The Hearst Foundation, Inc.
Limitations: Giving limited to the U.S. and its territories. No support for public policy. No grants to individuals, or for media projects, conferences, workshops, seminars, building projects, seed funding, multi-year grants, continuing support, equipment of any kind, including computers and transportation, special events, or the purchase of tickets, tables, or advertising for fundraising events; no loans.

1541. Brooklyn Public Library Foundation, Brooklyn, NY. $50,000, 2000. For continued support for William Randolph Hearst Endowed Fund for Family Programs and to help meet challenge grant from National Endowment for Humanities.

1542. Child Care, Inc., NYC, NY. $50,000, 2000. For technical assistance and training services for early childhood programs throughout New York City.
1543. Council of Better Business Bureaus Foundation, Arlington, VA. $40,000, 2000. For public education program of Philanthropic Advisory Service (PAS).
1544. Queens Library Foundation, Jamaica, NY. $50,000, 2000. For William Randolph Hearst Endowed Fund for community-based humanities programs and to help meet National Endowment for the Humanities challenge grant.
1545. University of California, Graduate School of Education and Information Studies, Los Angeles, CA. $100,000, 2000. Toward statewide Governor's Principal Leadership Institute.

William Randolph Hearst Foundation
Limitations: Giving limited to the U.S. and its territories. No support for public policy or public schools. No grants to individuals, or for media projects, conferences, workshops, seminars, multi-year grants, publishing projects, special events, seed funding, equipment and public policy research or the purchase of tickets, tables, or advertising for fundraising events; no loans.

1546. Elizabeth Glaser Pediatric AIDS Foundation, Santa Monica, CA. $100,000, 2000. Toward Glaser Pediatric Research Network, national partnership linking world-class scientific centers to accelerate progress on serious and life-threatening pediatric illnesses.
1547. Fine Arts Museums of San Francisco, San Francisco, CA. $2,000,000, 2000. Toward William Randolph Hearst Public Reading Room in new deYoung Museum in Golden Gate Park.
1548. Foundation Center, NYC, NY. $50,000, 2000. For general support.
1549. Frick Collection, NYC, NY. $250,000, 2000. For continued support for William Randolph Hearst Endowment for Frick Art Reference Library.
1550. Inner-City Scholarship Fund, NYC, NY. $25,000, 2000. For Library Connections initiative at inner-city elementary school libraries in New York Archdiocese.
1551. University of California, Davis, CA. $100,000, 2000. Toward rural medical emergency care network for children.

Drue Heinz Trust
Limitations: Giving primarily in NY and PA.

1552. Charities Aid Foundation America, Alexandria, VA. $16,500, 1999.
1553. Charities Aid Foundation America, Alexandria, VA. $16,500, 1999.
1554. Pierpont Morgan Library, NYC, NY. $20,000, 1999.
1555. Sewickley Public Library, Sewickley, PA. $33,333, 1999.

The F. B. Heron Foundation
Limitations: Giving on a national basis in both urban and rural areas. No grants to individuals.

1556. National Housing Institute, Orange, NJ. $60,000, 2000. For general support.

The Institute for Aegean Prehistory
Limitations: Giving on a national and international basis, with emphasis on Greece. No grants for students obtaining degrees, travel or maintenance of children or spouses, research expenses incurred before the date of a grant, salaries for researchers, purchase of expensive individual items of equipment such as computers, cameras and video recorders, or general activities of other institutions, or entities including "overhead expenses".

1557. British School at Athens, Athens, Greece. $157,835, 2000. For library.
1558. British School at Athens, Athens, Greece. $15,759, 2000. For library.

International Paper Company Foundation
Limitations: Giving primarily in communities where there are company plants and mills, and in Memphis, TN. No support for athletic organizations or religious groups. No grants to individuals, or for endowment funds or capital expenses; no loans.

1559. Foundation for the Memphis Shelby County Public Library, Memphis, TN. $25,000, 1999. For general support.
1560. Southwest Georgia Regional Library, Bainbridge, GA. $10,000, 1999. For general support.

Jesselson Foundation

Limitations: Giving on a national basis, with emphasis on NY.

1561. American Jewish Historical Society, Waltham, MA. $19,375, 1999. For general support.
1562. New York Public Library, NYC, NY. $10,000, 1999. For general support.
1563. YIVO Institute for Jewish Research, NYC, NY. $10,000, 1999. For general support.

The JM Foundation

Limitations: No support for the arts, government agencies, public schools, or international activities. No grants to individuals, or for operating expenses, annual fundraising campaigns, capital campaigns, equipment, or endowment funds; no loans.

1564. Resources for Children with Special Needs, NYC, NY. $15,000, 2000. Toward publications.

Christian A. Johnson Endeavor Foundation

Limitations: Giving limited to the eastern U.S.. No support for government agencies, or for community or neighborhood projects, religious institutions, or for health care. No grants to individuals, or for continuing support, annual campaigns, emergency funds, deficit financing, land acquisitions, building projects, medical research, demonstration projects, publications, or conferences; no loans.

1565. Boricua College, NYC, NY. $100,000, 1999. For computerization of Instructional Module Library.
1566. Foundation Center, NYC, NY. $25,000, 1999. For general operating support and for Foundation Center Online.

Joukowsky Family Foundation

Limitations: Giving primarily in the northeastern U.S..

1567. Providence Public Library, Providence, RI. $10,000, 2000. For special collections.

The J. M. Kaplan Fund, Inc.

Limitations: Giving primarily in NY, with emphasis on New York City. No grants to individuals, including scholarships and fellowships, or for construction or building programs, endowment funds, operating budgets of educational or medical institutions, film or video, or sponsorship of books, dances, plays, or other works of art.

1568. Century Association Archives Foundation, NYC, NY. $10,000, 1999. For photography and conservation of documents and photographs for archives.
1569. City College of the City University of New York, NYC, NY. $750,000, 1999. For endowment to support undergraduates engaged in scientific research, to publish student journal of scientific research, and to purchase new collections for library, including databases, indexes, and journals in sciences, engineering, and architecture - in honor of Maurice Austin.
1570. New York City Public/Private Initiatives, NYC, NY. $150,000, 1999. For Shelter Family Literacy Program that provides libraries and literacy programs for parents and children in emergency shelters.
1571. New York Public Library, NYC, NY. $100,000, 1999. For Preschool Family Literacy Program, and evaluation.
1572. Playwrights Preview Productions, NYC, NY. $15,000, 1999. For continued support for Urban Stages program that presents plays to literacy classes in libraries in underserved communities.
1573. Queens Library Foundation, Jamaica, NY. $50,000, 1999.
1574. Westminster College, Fulton, MO. $15,000, 1999. For general support for Winston Churchill Memorial and Library.

Stephen and Tabitha King Foundation, Inc.

Limitations: Giving primarily in ME.

1575. Belfast Free Library, Belfast, ME. $25,000, 1999.
1576. Bridgton Public Library, Bridgton, ME. $20,000, 1999.
1577. Curtis Memorial Library, Brunswick, ME. $15,000, 1999.
1578. Guilford Memorial Library, Guilford, ME. $12,000, 1999.
1579. Ludden Memorial Library, Dixfield, ME. $10,000, 1999.
1580. Northeast Historic Film, Bucksport, ME. $200,000, 1999.
1581. Porter Memorial Library, Machias, ME. $30,000, 1999.

The Esther A. & Joseph Klingenstein Fund, Inc.

Limitations: No grants to individuals (except for Neuroscience Fellowship Prog.), or for building or endowment funds.

1582. Center for Connecticut Studies, New Haven, CT. $10,000, 2000. To promote separation of church and state.
1583. New York Public Library, NYC, NY. $500,000, 2000. For family programs.
1584. New York Public Library, NYC, NY. $23,350, 2000. For family programs.

Samuel H. Kress Foundation

Limitations: Giving primarily in the U.S. and Europe. No support for art history programs below the pre-doctoral level, or the purchase of works of art. No grants for living artists, or for operating budgets, continuing support, annual campaigns, endowments, deficit financing, capital funds exhibitions, or films; no loans.

1585. Kunsthistorisches Institut, Florence, Italy. $15,000, 2000. For purchase of Cicognara Library Microfiche.
1586. Medici Archive Project, NYC, NY. $25,000, 2000. For fellowship for Kelly Thomas Helmstutler Documentary Sources for Arts and Humanities in Medici Granducal Archive.
1587. Northeast Document Conservation Center, Andover, MA. $18,000, 2000. For Post-Grad Fellow in Paper Conservation.
1588. Northeast Document Conservation Center, Andover, MA. $15,000, 2000. For State Russian Museum in Saint Petersburg exchange program.
1589. Oxford University, Oxford, England. $25,000, 2000. For Bodelian Library Incunabula Project.
1590. University of Illinois at Urbana-Champaign, Urbana, IL. $15,000, 2000. For Cicognara Library Microfiche Kunsthistorisches, Florence.
1591. Yale University, New Haven, CT. $20,000, 2000. For Kress fellowship in art librarianship.

George Link, Jr. Foundation, Inc.

Limitations: Giving primarily in MA, NJ, and NY. No grants to individuals, or for general support, operating budgets, continuing support, annual campaigns, seed money, emergency funds, deficit financing, equipment, land acquisition, renovation projects, or matching gifts; no loans.

1592. New York Public Library, NYC, NY. $25,000, 1999.

Albert A. List Foundation, Inc.

Limitations: No support for political organizations, local community fund drives, medical programs, or ongoing programs that are not essentially innovative. No grants to individuals, or for annual giving, building or capital funds, debt reduction, endowments, museum acquisitions, or scholarships or fellowships (unless initiated by the foundation).

1593. Center for Democratic Renewal and Education, Atlanta, GA. $15,000, 1999. For general operating support.
1594. DataCenter, Oakland, CA. $15,000, 1999. For general operating support and Common Sense Policy Network.
1595. DataCenter, Oakland, CA. $10,000, 1999. For general support and Common Sense Policy Network.
1596. Libraries for the Future, NYC, NY. $35,000, 1999. For Telecommunications Advocacy Project.

The Lucius N. Littauer Foundation, Inc.

Limitations: Giving primarily in NY for medical ethics and environmental projects. No support for synagogues. No grants to individuals, or for capital projects or operating funds.

1597. American Friends of the Medem Library, NYC, NY. $10,000, 2000. For Archives Project.

1598. Emory University, Atlanta, GA. $11,000, 2000. For addition to endowment for Lucius N. Littauer Judaica Book Fund and for library support for additional Hebraica.

1599. Spertus College of Judaica, Chicago, IL. $10,000, 2000. For Asher Library Automation Project.

Richard Lounsbery Foundation, Inc.

Limitations: Giving limited to the U.S., France and Canada. No grants to individuals, or for capital or building funds, conferences or seminars, or endowment funds; no loans.

1600. New York Academy of Medicine, NYC, NY. $215,000, 1999. For Junior Fellows Program.

1601. New York Academy of Medicine, NYC, NY. $20,000, 1999. For Student Exchange Program at American Bureau for Medical Advancement in China.

Leon Lowenstein Foundation, Inc.

Limitations: Giving primarily in the metropolitan New York, NY, area.

1602. Greenwich Library, Greenwich, CT. $260,000, 1999.

The Henry Luce Foundation, Inc.

Limitations: Giving on a national and international basis; international activities limited to East and Southeast Asia. No support for journalism, medical or media projects. No grants to individuals (except for specially designated programs), or for endowments, domestic building campaigns, general operating support, annual fund drives; no loans (except for program-related investments).

1603. American Theological Library Association, Evanston, IL. $330,000, 2000. 3-year grant. Toward setting standards for digital publications in theological studies.

1604. Case Western Reserve University, Cleveland, OH. $270,000, 2000. 3-year grant. For Tibetan Oral History and Archive Project.

1605. Eastern Cluster of Lutheran Seminaries, Columbia, SC. $360,000, 2000. 3-year grant. To develop fully integrated library system for three related Lutheran Seminaries.

1606. Huntington Library, Art Collections and Botanical Gardens, San Marino, CA. $130,000, 2000. 2-year grant. To re-interpret American art collection reinstallation, through American Collections Enhancement (ACE) initiative.

1607. International Center in New York, NYC, NY. $30,000, 2000. For Chairman's Discretionary Grant for expand, modernize and professionalize Center's Library.

1608. Libraries for the Future, NYC, NY. $100,000, 2000. 2-year grant. For Youth Access, after-school program in Harlem designed to enhance educational, literacy, and employment skills opportunities of young people ages 8-18. Participants in Youth ACCESS work together to learn about their community and issues of importance to themselves, distinguish research from opinion, and communicate with the larger world by means of Internet-based media, to enhance their ability to look at the world from a scientific point of view, and to identify and publish stories about positive role models.

1609. Mepkin Abbey, Moncks Corner, SC. $1,500,000, 2000. To complete construction of Clare Boothe Luce Library.

1610. Montclair Art Museum, Montclair, NJ. $250,000, 2000. 2-year grant. For LeBrun Library's relocation and to enhance accessibility of American art resources.

Josiah Macy, Jr. Foundation

Limitations: No grants to individuals, or for travel, capital funds, operating budgets, annual fund appeals, seed money, financing, research, scholarships, or fellowships; no loans.

1611. Columbia University, Eisenhower Center for the Conservation of Human Resources, NYC, NY. $61,000, 2000. 1.50-year grant. For preparation and publication of monograph Supply of U.S. Physicians 2000-2020.

1612. New York Academy of Medicine, NYC, NY. $10,000, 2000. For symposium sponsored by New York Academy of Medicine Center for Urban Bioethics, Bioethics in the Urban Context: A National Symposium.

1613. New York Public Library, NYC, NY. $15,000, 2000. For free access to health information for the public, to expand information collections and train staff for Community Health Onsite Information Centers (CHOICES) program.

M&T Charitable Foundation

Limitations: Giving primarily in NY. No grants to individuals.

1614. Rundel Library Foundation, Rochester, NY. $10,000, 1999.

The John and Mary R. Markle Foundation

Limitations: No support for projects within formal educational institutions. No grants to individuals (except for pensions to specified beneficiaries); generally no grants for general support, operating budgets, continuing support, annual campaigns, seed money, emergency funds, equipment, land acquisition, renovations, capital or endowment funds, matching gifts, scholarships, fellowships, publications, conferences, or film, radio, or video production.

1615. Foundation Center, NYC, NY. $10,000, 1999.

G. Harold & Leila Y. Mathers Charitable Foundation

Limitations: No grants to individuals.

1616. Montecito Library, Friends of, Santa Barbara, CA. $20,000, 1999. For general support.

The Andrew W. Mellon Foundation

Limitations: No support for primarily local organizations. No grants to individuals (including scholarships and fellowships); no loans.

1617. American Antiquarian Society, Worcester, MA. $500,000, 2000. 3-year grant. For Post-Doctoral Fellowships in the Humanities.

1618. American Council of Learned Societies, NYC, NY. $14,000, 2000. 2-year grant. For subscription to Journal Storage Project (JSTOR).

1619. American Music Center, NYC, NY. $2,500,000, 2000. 2-year grant. For matching endowment for core institutional support.

1620. American Political Science Association, DC. $50,000, 2000. 1.25-year grant. To create Online Scholarly Portal in collaboration with Harvard University Library.

1621. Appalachian College Association, Berea, KY. $50,000, 2000. For Archival Digitization Initiative.

1622. Art Institute of Chicago, Chicago, IL. $750,000, 2000. 4-year grant. For Museum Archives.

1623. Associated Colleges of the Midwest, Chicago, IL. $645,000, 2000. 4-year grant. For Libraries Initiative.

1624. Association pour le Rayonnement des Arts Asiatiques, Musee Guimet, Paris, France. $420,000, 2000. 2-year grant. To digitize images for Dunhuang (Chinese) Collection.

1625. Association pour le Rayonnement des Arts Asiatiques, Musee Guimet, Paris, France. $50,000, 2000. 1.50-year grant. For Mellon International Dunhuang (Chinese) Archive.

1626. British Library, London, England. $1,100,000, 2000. 4-year grant. For material for Dunhuang (Chinese) Archive.

1627. Brooklyn Institute of Arts and Sciences, Brooklyn, NY. $750,000, 2000. 4-year grant. For Museum Archives.

1628. Brown University, John Carter Brown Library, Providence, RI. $400,000, 2000. 4-year grant. For Post Doctoral Fellowships in Humanities.

1629. Burlington Magazine Foundation, London, England. $641,000, 2000. 3-year grant. For matching grant to endow program to index archives of magazine and for general support.

1630. Cambridge University, Cambridge, England. $674,000, 2000. 2.25-year grant. To archive Newton Papers.

1631. China Cultural Property Promotion Association, Beijing, China. $43,400, 2000. For Digital Imaging Training Initiative.

1632. Cornell University, Ithaca, NY. $275,000, 2000. 3-year grant. For Library of Natural Sounds, which seeks to promote better understanding of animal behavior and diversity by providing multimedia resources for research, education, and conservation.

1633. Cornell University, Ithaca, NY. $150,000, 2000. To archive Electronic Journals.

1634. Cornell University, Library, Ithaca, NY. $750,000, 2000. 3-year grant. For Project Euclid, collaboration with Duke University Press to advance effective and affordable scholarly communication in theoretical and applied mathematics and statistics.

1635. Eastern Cape Higher Education Association Trust, Port Elizabeth, South Africa. $1,175,000, 2000. 3.50-year grant. For South East Academic Libraries System (SEALS).

1636. Ecological Society of America, DC. $23,000, 2000. For ESA/JSTOR Electronic Journal Archive, which contains every back issue of Ecology, Ecological Monographs, and Ecological Applications prior to 1996 and is available on-line.

1637. Foundation Center, NYC, NY. $900,000, 2000. 3-year grant. Toward design and launch of Online Gateway to Philanthropy.

1638. Foundation Center, NYC, NY. $30,000, 2000. For general support.

1639. Foundation for Library and Information Service Development, Pretoria, South Africa. $400,000, 2000. 1.50-year grant. For National Library of South Africa.

1640. George Mason University, Fairfax, VA. $600,000, 2000. 3.50-year grant. For Population Networks in Developing Countries Initiative.

1641. Grantmakers in the Arts, Seattle, WA. $10,000, 2000. For Research, Publications, and Information Services Program for the Performing Arts.

1642. Great Lakes Colleges Association, Ann Arbor, MI. $650,000, 2000. 4-year grant. For Libraries Initiative.

1643. Harvard University, Cambridge, MA. $145,000, 2000. To archive electronic journals.

1644. Harvard University, Cambridge, MA. $19,000, 2000. For Internet Collections Technology Initiative.

1645. Harvard University, Radcliff Institute for Advanced Study, Schlesinger Library, Cambridge, MA. $295,000, 2000. 2-year grant. For Photographic Access Project.

1646. Huntington Library, Art Collections and Botanical Gardens, San Marino, CA. $390,000, 2000. 4-year grant. For Curatorial Fellowships.

1647. Journal Storage Project (JSTOR), NYC, NY. $2,800,000, 2000. 2-year grant. For Art History Cluster.

1648. Journal Storage Project (JSTOR), NYC, NY. $450,000, 2000. 3-year grant. To archive sociology and demography titles.

1649. Journal Storage Project (JSTOR), NYC, NY. $400,000, 2000. For User Evaluation Study.

1650. Library Information Network Consortium (LINC), Riga, Latvia. $19,000, 2000. For librarian training as part of European Educational Projects (EEP), effort to eliminate violence and xenophobia from European Union.

1651. Library Information Network Consortium (LINC), Riga, Latvia. $16,000, 2000. For training trips as part of European Educational Projects (EEP), effort to eliminate violence and xenophobia from European Union.

1652. Massachusetts Institute of Technology, Cambridge, MA. $215,000, 2000. 1.50-year grant. For Digital Archive.

1653. Massachusetts Institute of Technology, Cambridge, MA. $145,000, 2000. To archive Electronic Journals.

1654. Missouri Botanical Garden, Saint Louis, MO. $200,000, 2000. 2-year grant. To digitize rare book collection.

1655. Museum of Fine Arts, Boston, MA. $750,000, 2000. 4-year grant. For work with Museum archives.

1656. New Jersey Historical Society, Newark, NJ. $18,000, 2000. Toward development of Online Public Access Catalogue.

1657. New York Botanical Garden, Bronx, NY. $195,000, 2000. 2-year grant. To digitize rare books.

1658. New York Public Library, NYC, NY. $2,250,000, 2000. 5-year grant. For matching grant for Preservation Endowment.

1659. New York Public Library, NYC, NY. $150,000, 2000. To archive electronic journals.

1660. New York University, NYC, NY. $2,365,000, 2000. 2-year grant. For maintenance of New York Historical Society Library Collections.

1661. New York University, NYC, NY. $50,000, 2000. For Database of Recorded American Music (DRAM).

1662. Newberry Library, Chicago, IL. $400,000, 2000. 3-year grant. For Post-Doctoral Fellowships in Humanities.

1663. Northeast Document Conservation Center, Andover, MA. $36,000, 2000. For Digital Conversion Projects.

1664. Oxford University, Oxford, England. $775,000, 2000. 4-year grant. For Digital Library Resource Development Fund.

1665. Oxford University, Refugee Studies Centre, Oxford, England. $1,000,000, 2000. 3-year grant. For Digital Library.

1666. Oxford University, Refugee Studies Centre, Oxford, England. $44,000, 2000. For Digital Library.

1667. Philadelphia Museum of Art, Philadelphia, PA. $750,000, 2000. 4-year grant. For work on Museum archives as it relates to art conservation.

1668. Princeton University, Princeton, NJ. $24,000, 2000. To digitally archive manuscripts from Western Europe.

1669. Randolph-Macon Womans College, Lynchburg, VA. $94,500, 2000. 2-year grant. For Journal Storage (JSTOR) Initiative, in conjunction with Hollins University, Mary Baldwin College, Hampden-Sydney College and Lynchburg College.

1670. Recorded Anthology of American Music, NYC, NY. $250,000, 2000. For Database of Recorded American Music (DRAM).

1671. Renaissance Society of America, NYC, NY. $220,000, 2000. 5-year grant. To archive letters of Lorenzo DeMedici.

1672. Rochester Institute of Technology, Rochester, NY. $500,000, 2000. 3-year grant. For Preservation Management Initiative at Image Permanence Institute, university-based, nonprofit research laboratory dedicated to preservation of visual and other forms of recorded information.

1673. Rosenbach Museum and Library, Philadelphia, PA. $50,000, 2000. 5-year grant. For Research Fellowship Endowment.

1674. South African Bibliographic and Information Network (SABINET), Centurion, South Africa. $340,000, 2000. 5-year grant. For Journal Storage (JSTOR) Initiative in South Africa.

1675. Southeastern Pennsylvania Consortium for Higher Education, Glenside, PA. $197,500, 2000. 2-year grant. For Journal Storage (JSTOR) database.

1676. Stanford University, Stanford, CA. $440,000, 2000. To archive Electronic Journals using LOCKSS, (Lots of Copies Keep Stuff Safe), open-source digital preservation appliance, designed to make it practical and affordable for libraries to take custody of web-published journal volumes to which they subscribe.

1677. Stanford University, Stanford, CA. $100,000, 2000. For 3-D Imaging Initiative.

1678. Tsinghua University Education Foundation, Beijing, China. $36,000, 2000. 3-year grant. For Journal Storage Initiative (JSTOR).

1679. Union Theological Seminary, NYC, NY. $1,250,000, 2000. 2.50-year grant. For retrospective conversion of Burke Library Catalogue.

1680. University of California, Berkeley, CA. $670,000, 2000. 2-year grant. For Journal Management Initiative.

1681. University of California, Berkeley, CA. $80,000, 2000. For Journal Management Initiative.

1682. University of Connecticut, Storrs, CT. $665,000, 2000. 3-year grant. For African National Congress (ANC) Archives and Oral History. Grant transferred to University of Connecticut Foundation.

1683. University of Illinois at Urbana-Champaign, Mortenson Center for International Library Programs, Urbana, IL. $250,000, 2000. 3-year grant. For South African Library Leadership Project.

1684. University of Massachusetts, Boston, MA. $15,000, 2000. For New England Resource Center for Higher Education.

1685. University of Michigan, Ann Arbor, MI. $27,000, 2000. For Digital Image Management and Access Systems.

1686. University of Pennsylvania, Philadelphia, PA. $150,000, 2000. To archive Electronic Journals.

1687. University of Pennsylvania, Museum of Archaeology and Anthropology, Philadelphia, PA. $170,000, 2000. To provide access to archival and artifactual collections.

1688. University of Puget Sound, Tacoma, WA. $100,000, 2000. 3-year grant. To archive Records of Early English Drama.

1689. Western Cape Tertiary Institutions Trust, Cape Town, South Africa. $1,000,000, 2000. 3-year grant. For study of bandwith capabilities in South Africa.

1690. Western Cape Tertiary Institutions Trust, Cape Town, South Africa. $50,000, 2000. For staff training in using Cape Library Cooperative (CALICO) software system.

1691. Yale University, New Haven, CT. $150,000, 2000. To archive Electronic Journals.

1692. Yale University, New Haven, CT. $35,000, 2000. 2-year grant. For Journal Storage (JSTOR) Archive for Linguistic Research.

Joyce Mertz-Gilmore Foundation

Limitations: Giving on a national and international basis, with the exception of the New York City Program. No support for private foundations, sectarian religious concerns, or political purposes. No grants to individuals, or for capital or endowment funds, building construction or maintenance, annual campaigns, conferences, travel, publications, film or television production, scholarships, research, or fellowships; no loans (except for program-related investments).

1693. International Monitor Institute, Los Angeles, CA. $40,000, 2000. For general operating support.
1694. Kav LaOved-Workers Hotline for the Protection of Workers Rights, Tel Aviv, Israel. $60,000, 2000. For general operating support.
1695. Nonprofit Connection, Brooklyn, NY. $25,000, 2000. For general operating support.

Metropolitan Life Foundation

Limitations: No support for private foundations, religious, fraternal, athletic, political, social, or veterans' organizations, organizations already receiving support through United Way campaigns, local chapters of national organizations, disease-specific organizations, labor groups, organizations whose activities are mainly international, organizations primarily engaged in patient care or direct treatment, drug treatment centers and community health clinics, or elementary or secondary schools. No grants to individuals (except for medical research awards), or for endowment funds, hospital capital fund campaigns, courtesy advertising, or festival participation.

1696. Americans for the Arts, DC. $250,000, 2000. For Afterschool Youth Arts Initiative.
1697. New York Academy of Medicine, NYC, NY. $25,000, 2000. For school health education curriculum.
1698. New York Public Library, NYC, NY. $22,500, 2000.

Paul and Irma Milstein Foundation

Limitations: Giving primarily in New York, NY. No grants to individuals.

1699. New York Public Library, NYC, NY. $3,000,000, 1999.

The Ambrose Monell Foundation

Limitations: No grants to individuals.

1700. Brooklyn Public Library Foundation, Brooklyn, NY. $40,000, 1999. For Youth Wing programs.
1701. Brooklyn Public Library Foundation, Brooklyn, NY. $10,000, 1999. For general support.
1702. George C. Marshall Research Foundation, Lexington, VA. $10,000, 1999. For general support.
1703. Manpower Demonstration Research Corporation, NYC, NY. $150,000, 1999. For dissemination of information.
1704. New York Public Library, NYC, NY. $100,000, 1999. For general support.
1705. Pierpont Morgan Library, NYC, NY. $100,000, 1999. For general support.
1706. Pierpont Morgan Library, NYC, NY. $100,000, 1999. For Centennial.

The J. P. Morgan Chase Foundation

Limitations: Giving in the tri-state region of NY, NJ, and CT; the states of AZ, CA, DE, FL, IL, LA, MA, and OH; some national programs; and approximately 50 countries where J.P. Morgan Chase has a business presence. No support for religious, fraternal, or veterans' organizations, member organizations of the United Way (when a contribution is made to that particular United Way campaign) or organizations serving people suffering from a single disease (other than HIV/AIDS), health issues, or higher education. No grants to individuals, or for endowment funds or medical research.

1707. Brooklyn Public Library, Brooklyn, NY. $25,000, 1999. For general support.
1708. Brooklyn Public Library, Brooklyn, NY. $20,000, 1999. For general support.
1709. Charities Aid Foundation America, Alexandria, VA. $140,000, 1999. For matching gifts of employees to organizations outside the US, through Donor Advised Fund.

1710. Charities Aid Foundation America, Alexandria, VA. $10,000, 1999. For relief efforts in Taiwan, through Donor Advised Fund.
1711. Child Care, Inc., NYC, NY. $50,000, 1999. For Family Day Care Business Resource Center.
1712. New York Industrial Retention Network, Brooklyn, NY. $25,000, 1999. For general support.
1713. Nonprofit Connection, Brooklyn, NY. $20,000, 1999. For general support.
1714. Project Reach Youth, Brooklyn, NY. $40,000, 1999. For Farragut Reading Room.
1715. Queens Library Foundation, Jamaica, NY. $10,000, 1999. For general support.

The New York Community Trust

Limitations: Giving limited to the metropolitan New York, NY, area. No support for religious purposes. No grants to individuals, or for deficit financing, emergency funds, building campaigns, endowment funds, capital projects or general operating support.

1716. Citizens Advice Bureau, Bronx, NY. $45,000, 2000. To strengthen rent assistance program for families on public assistance in the South Bronx.
1717. Citizens Advice Bureau, Bronx, NY. $25,000, 2000. To expand summer program for children of working poor families.
1718. Education and Research Foundation of the Better Business Bureau of Metropolitan New York, NYC, NY. $20,000, 2000. To expand New York Philanthropic Advisory Service.
1719. Health Care Choices, NYC, NY. $10,000, 2000. To advocate for improved funding and care for persons with cancer.
1720. New York Academy of Medicine, NYC, NY. $115,000, 2000. For fellowship to study dizziness and falls in older people which may result in hip fractures.
1721. New York Industrial Retention Network, Brooklyn, NY. $35,000, 2000. To build broad-based support for land use policy that supports manufacturing.
1722. Primary Care Development Corporation, NYC, NY. $50,000, 2000. To help primary health care providers to develop information systems.
1723. Pro Bono Net, NYC, NY. $40,000, 2000. To coordinate and enhance pro bono and legal service programs that assist indigent New Yorkers.

New York Foundation

Limitations: Giving limited to local programs in the New York, NY, metropolitan area. No support for the arts, medical research, or films. No grants to individuals, or to capital campaigns, renovations, emergency funds, deficit financing, building or endowment funds, equipment, scholarships, fellowships, land acquisition, research, conferences, publications, or demonstration projects.

1724. Infoshare, NYC, NY. $30,000, 1999. To conduct workshop and provide individualized assistance to New York Foundation grantees on use of Infoshare, computer program and database specially developed for New York nonprofits.
1725. Nonprofit Connection, Brooklyn, NY. $30,000, 1999. To provide individual technical assistance to New York Foundation grantees in fundraising, fiscal management, human resource management, strategic planning, board development, staff training and organizational structure.

The New York Times Company Foundation, Inc.

Limitations: Giving primarily in the New York, NY, metropolitan area and in localities served by affiliates of the company. No support for sectarian religious institutions or for health, drug or alcohol therapy purposes; grants for urban affairs seldom made on the neighborhood level. No grants to individuals, or for capital and building funds; no loans.

1726. Brooklyn Public Library, Brooklyn, NY. $10,000, 1999. For preservation of archives.
1727. Columbia University, Rare Book and Manuscript Library, NYC, NY. $15,000, 1999. For collation and preservation of newly acquired papers.
1728. Horticultural Society of New York, NYC, NY. $25,000, 1999. For gardens at community libraries as part of education project.

1729. Library of Congress Millennium Foundation, DC. $15,000, 1999. For conservation of rare 18th century newspapers.

1730. New York Public Library, NYC, NY. $65,000, 1999. For general operating support.

1731. Pierpont Morgan Library, NYC, NY. $20,000, 1999. For 75th anniversary educational programs for children.

1732. Princeton University, Princeton, NJ. $25,000, 1999. For work on papers of Thomas Jefferson.

1733. Resources for Children with Special Needs, NYC, NY. $20,000, 1999. For publications.

1734. University of Illinois at Urbana-Champaign, Urbana, IL. $20,000, 1999. For fellowship to maintain and preserve Scotty Reston Papers.

Samuel I. Newhouse Foundation, Inc.

Limitations: No grants to individuals.

1735. Library of Congress, DC. $12,500, 1999. For continued support.

1736. Library of Congress, Center for the Book, DC. $25,000, 1999. For continued support.

1737. New York Public Library, NYC, NY. $400,000, 1999. For continued support.

1738. Newark Public Library, Newark, NJ. $15,000, 1999. For continued support.

1739. Ryerson Library Foundation, Grand Rapids, MI. $17,000, 1999. For continued support.

Jessie Smith Noyes Foundation, Inc.

Limitations: Giving primarily in the southeast, south central, and southwest regions of the U.S. No grants to individuals, or for scholarships, fellowships, endowment funds, deficit financing, capital construction funds, land acquisition, or general fundraising drives; generally no support for conferences, research, or media; no loans (except for program-related investments).

1740. Arkansas Public Policy Panel, Little Rock, AR. $25,000, 2000. For technical assistance and organizing for community-based groups working on environmental issues, with special focus on people of color and underrepresented areas of southern and eastern Arkansas.

1741. Community Food Security Coalition, Venice, CA. $25,000, 2000. To support advocacy, networking, policy development and training activities.

1742. DataCenter, Oakland, CA. $60,000, 2000. 2-year grant. For ImpactResearch project, providing research and information to community-based organizations working for social, environmental and economic justice.

1743. Environmental Background Information Center, NYC, NY. $25,000, 2000. For general support to provide communities, organizations and journalists with information on environmental histories of corporations and to help them use that information effectively.

1744. Interfaith Center on Corporate Responsibility, NYC, NY. $25,000, 2000. To support shareholder activity on issues of energy, environment and agricultural biotechnology.

1745. Sexuality Information and Education Council of the U.S. (SIECUS), NYC, NY. $30,000, 2000. To track and analyze debates about sexuality education, monitor activities of national opponents of sexuality education, and assist communities in implementing effective programs and resisting attacks from far right groups on sexuality education.

1746. Southwest Research and Information Center, Albuquerque, NM. $60,000, 2000. 2-year grant. For general support for technical assistance to communities in Southwest on health and environmental issues.

1747. Washington Sustainable Food and Farming Network, Bellingham, WA. $45,000, 2000. 2-year grant. To support statewide alliance that mobilizes residents and organizations in order to create sustainable food and farming system.

1748. Watchperson Project, Brooklyn, NY. $20,000, 2000. To provide community residents in Greenpoint and Williamsburg sections of Brooklyn with technical and legal assistance on various organizing campaigns to improve environmental quality.

The Ohrstrom Foundation, Inc.

Limitations: Giving primarily in NY and VA. No grants to individuals, or for deficit financing, scholarships, fellowships, research, special projects, publications, or conferences; no loans.

1749. National Sporting Library, Middleburg, VA. $311,000, 2000. For continued unrestricted support.

F. W. Olin Foundation, Inc.

Limitations: No grants to individuals, or for operating budgets, research, scholarships, fellowships, matching gifts, special projects, general support, or non-academic buildings and facilities funds; no loans.

1750. Rollins College, Winter Park, FL. $318,463, 1999. For addition to library.

John M. Olin Foundation, Inc.

Limitations: No support for programs without significant importance for national affairs. No grants to individuals, or for annual campaigns, operating budgets, or building or endowment funds; no loans.

1751. Gilder Lehrman Institute of American History, NYC, NY. $50,000, 1999. For Historians' Forums series.

Olive Bridge Fund, Inc.

Limitations: Giving primarily in MA and NY. No grants to individuals.

1752. New York Public Library, NYC, NY. $17,000, 1999.

Open Society Institute

Limitations: Giving on a national and international basis.

1753. American Pain Foundation, Baltimore, MD. $100,000, 1999. For general support.

1754. Burma Issues, Bangkok, Thailand. $15,000, 1999. To support documentation center.

1755. Charity Society Bashkechid, Baku, Azerbaijan. $11,979, 1999. To support employment center by providing equipment and necessary materials and supplies, to create extensive database of unemployed individuals, running regular orientation seminars and meetings with potential employers.

1756. Community Resource Services, Poolesville, MD. $95,463, 1999. To support research on economics of inmate labor force participation.

1757. Cornell University, Ithaca, NY. $15,200, 1999. To support library and archives preservation intern from Burma to train at Cornell Library.

1758. Donors Forum of Chicago, Chicago, IL. $150,000, 1999. To support regrant project of Fund for Immigrants and Refugees.

1759. Foundation Center, NYC, NY. $10,000, 1999. For general support.

1760. Goree Institute, Dakar, Senegal. $12,119, 1999. To purchase and ship books and CD-ROMs ordered from Amazon.com for library.

1761. Harvard University, Cambridge, MA. $500,000, 1999. For National Firearm Injury Reporting System, coordinated through Medical School in Boston, which will provide consistent and representative data on firearm-related injuries over time.

1762. International Monitor Institute, Los Angeles, CA. $50,000, 1999. To support Balkan Archive project to process video footage relating to current conflict in Kosovo.

1763. International Monitor Institute, Los Angeles, CA. $20,000, 1999. To support Burma Archives project.

1764. International Monitor Institute, Los Angeles, CA. $14,958, 1999. To increase public awareness of and access to International Monitor Institute archives on the Balkans, Africa, and Southeast Asia through the Internet.

1765. Khazar University, Baku, Azerbaijan. $17,667, 1999. To conduct library automation seminar to help Azerbaijani librarians explore key professional issues and to learn some practical skills and processes.

1766. Libraries for the Future, NYC, NY. $50,000, 1999. To fund Telecommunications Advocacy Project.

1767. Los Angeles Coalition to End Hunger and Homelessness, Los Angeles, CA. $40,000, 1999. To coordinate education, outreach and information efforts targeting immigrant communities impacted by welfare reform.

1768. New York Academy of Medicine, NYC, NY. $62,430, 1999. To develop protocol for Heroin Trial in North America.

1769. Northeast Document Conservation Center, Andover, MA. $40,000, 1999. To fund conservator program for visiting conservators from Mongolia and Estonia at Northeast Document Conservation Center, Williamstown Art Conservation Center, in Williamstown, MA, and Textile Conservation Center.

1770. Northeastern University, Boston, MA. $150,000, 1999. To create interdisciplinary, specialized collaborative practices described in Community Legal Resource Networks proposal.

1771. Ohio State University, School of Journalism and Communication, Columbus, OH. $25,000, 1999. To support work compiling file, film and photo archives of International Brotherhood of Teamsters.

1772. Open Library for Legal Information, Tashkent Legal Institute, Tashkent, Uzbekistan. $13,648, 1999. To fund purchase of equipment, legal materials, and payment of other incidental start-up expenses.

1773. Pro Bono Net, NYC, NY. $250,000, 1999. To improve and expand quality pro bono work though innovative use of technology.

1774. Proyecto Pastoral, Los Angeles, CA. $20,000, 1999. To provide citizenship services, ESL classes, information and referrals to residents of East Los Angeles/Boyle Heights.

1775. Relief International, Iran Quake Relief Association, Los Angeles, CA. $13,572, 1999. To establish libraries for IDP children in Azerbaijan.

1776. Service Employees International Union, Los Angeles Homecare Workers, Los Angeles, CA. $75,000, 1999. To provide bereavement support, information, training and referrals to homecare workers who provide end-of-life assistance to elderly and disabled.

1777. Sexuality Information and Education Council of the U.S. (SIECUS), NYC, NY. $75,000, 1999. To fund monitoring of federally funded state abstinence-only-until-marriage programs, dissemination of information about same, and advocacy work to build national, state and grassroots support for comprehensive sex education.

1778. South Miami Hospital Foundation, Miami, FL. $74,870, 1999. To establish referral network of professionally trained bereavement support programs in faith communities.

1779. University of Maryland Foundation, School of Law, Baltimore, MD. $143,055, 1999. To support creation of community-based demonstration law office and lawyer resource network described in Community Legal Resource Networks proposal.

1780. University of Minnesota Foundation, Minneapolis, MN. $50,000, 1999. To improve capacity and accessibility of University of Minnesota's Human Rights Library on World Wide Web.

The Overbrook Foundation

Limitations: Giving primarily in New York, NY. No grants to individuals.

1781. New York Public Library, NYC, NY. $500,000, 1999. For general support.

Park Foundation, Inc.

Limitations: Giving limited to the East Coast (primarily in central NY) and the southeastern U.S.. No grants to individuals.

1782. Dewitt Historical Society of Tompkins County, Ithaca, NY. $25,000, 1999. For full-time archivist, shelving, computer materials, containers for new location.

1783. Dewitt Historical Society of Tompkins County, Ithaca, NY. $25,000, 1999. For full-time archivist, storage containers, shelving, computing materials.

1784. Summit Free Public Library, Summit, NJ. $10,000, 1999. To provide staff for storytelling time.

1785. W G B H Educational Foundation, Boston, MA. $250,000, 1999. For conditional support for broadcast of Between the Lions.

The PepsiCo Foundation, Inc.

Limitations: Giving primarily in communities where operating divisions are located, including Irvine, CA, Wichita, KS, Louisville, KY, Somers, NY, and Plano, TX. No grants to individuals.

1786. Americans for the Arts, DC. $10,000, 1999.

1787. Charities Aid Foundation America, Alexandria, VA. $32,750, 1999.

1788. Library of Congress, DC. $100,000, 1999.

The Carl and Lily Pforzheimer Foundation, Inc.

Limitations: No grants to individuals, or for building funds; no loans.

1789. New York Public Library, NYC, NY. $88,361, 1999.

The Pincus Family Fund

Limitations: Giving primarily in NY. No loans or grants to individuals, or for capital funds, construction and equipment, scholarships, or fellowships.

1790. New York Public Library, NYC, NY. $100,000, 2000.

The Pinkerton Foundation

Limitations: Giving primarily in New York, NY. No support for medical research, the media, the direct provision of health care, or religious education. Generally no grants to individuals, or for emergency assistance, conferences, publications, media, building renovations, or other capital projects, unless they are integrally related to foundation's program objectives or an outgrowth of grantee's programs; no loans.

1791. Brooklyn Public Library, Brooklyn, NY. $30,000, 2000. For seed support for Youth Career Institute, program for teen and young adult part-timers, which provides mentors and career-related workshops.

1792. New York Public Library, NYC, NY. $52,400, 2000. For computer page program in East and Central Harlem and for upkeep of Web site for computer pages.

1793. Queens Library Foundation, Jamaica, NY. $50,000, 2000. 2-year grant. For Library Page Fellows program, providing additional rung to career ladder for pages interested in considering career in library sciences field.

The Prospect Hill Foundation, Inc.

Limitations: Giving primarily in the northeastern U.S., including NY and RI. No support for religious activities. No grants to individuals, or for research.

1794. Bank Information Center, DC. $15,000, 2000. To improve multilateral lending institutions' policies and projects in the Caribbean and Latin America and to prepare for the Inter-American Development Bank's annual meeting in New Orleans.

1795. New Jersey Historical Society, Newark, NJ. $50,000, 2000. Toward making library's collections electronically accessible.

1796. New York Public Library, NYC, NY. $25,000, 2000. Toward conservation of materials in research libraries.

1797. Providence Public Library, Providence, RI. $15,000, 2000. Toward Family Place, multi-faceted initiative for families with young children.

Reader's Digest Foundation

Limitations: Giving primarily in Westchester County, NY. No support for religious organizations or endeavors, veterans' or fraternal organizations, private foundations, cultural organizations, environmental groups, local chapters of national organizations, medical research or health-related activities. No grants to individuals (except for employee-related scholarships), or for capital, building or endowment funds, operating budgets, annual campaigns, seed money, emergency funds, deficit financing, special projects, charitable dinners or fundraising events, television, film, or video productions, publications, workshops, conferences, or seminars; no loans.

1798. Mid-Hudson Library, Poughkeepsie, NY. $25,000, 2000.

1799. Westchester Library System, Elmsford, NY. $704,500, 2000.

1800. Western Connecticut Library Council, Middlebury, CT. $26,500, 2000.

Rockefeller Brothers Fund, Inc.

Limitations: Giving on a national basis, and in Central and Eastern Europe, East and Southeast Asia, and South Africa. No grants to individuals (including research, graduate study, or the writing of books or dissertations by individuals, with three exceptions: the RBF Fellowships under the education program, which are limited to those students nominated by the colleges that have been selected to participate in this program, the Ramon Magsaysay Awards through the Program for Asian Projects), and the Culpeper Medical Scholarships, or land acquisitions or building funds.

1801. Bank Information Center, DC. $120,000, 2000. For Asia programs, which monitors World Bank policy, lending strategies, and loan portfolios.

1802. Foundation Center, NYC, NY. $60,000, 2000. 2-year grant. For general support.

1803. National Center for Black Philanthropy, DC. $35,000, 2000. Toward National Conference on Black Philanthropy.

1804. National Charities Information Bureau (NCIB), NYC, NY. $20,000, 2000. Toward costs of merger between National Charities Information Bureau and Council of Better Business Bureaus' Foundation.

The Rockefeller Foundation

Limitations: Giving on a national and international basis. No support for the establishment of local hospitals, churches, schools, libraries, welfare agencies, altruistic movements involving private profit, or for the attempts to influence legislation. No grants for capital or endowment funds, general support or scholarships; no loans, except program-related investments.

1805. Africa Centre, London, England. $177,472, 2000. To develop comprehensive digital database of information on Africa and to strengthen its radio program on African affairs that promotes scholarly debates on developmental challenges facing African continent.

1806. Africa University, Mutare, Zimbabwe. $30,000, 2000. To enable University's Faculty of Agriculture to obtain Essential Electronic Agricultural Library to improve access of faculty and students to up-to-date scientific information on all areas of agricultural science for teaching and research.

1807. American Library Association, DC. $100,000, 2000. Toward costs of forum on Digital Technology, Information Policy, and Future of Libraries.

1808. Association of African Universities, Accra, Ghana. $217,677, 2000. Toward costs of project to develop database of African theses and dissertations.

1809. Ateneo de Manila University, Institute of Philippine Culture, Manila, Philippines. $93,900, 2000. For activities related to fostering people-centered public health strategies, and forging networks among several Asian countries to share information about these efforts.

1810. Business for Social Responsibility (BSR) Education Fund, San Francisco, CA. $150,000, 2000. To assist employers in developing career advancement strategies in retail sector through development of issue brief and how-to guide.

1811. Cambridge University, Cambridge, England. $75,000, 2000. Toward cost of developing and extending its Library's rare books and manuscripts reading rooms, used by scholars from all over world.

1812. China National Rice Research Institute, Hangzhou, China. $50,000, 2000. For use by its Research Library for purchase of journals and periodicals.

1813. Circle Foundation, Bethesda, MD. $50,000, 2000. Toward costs of its Vox Populi project, designed to give American public greater voice in public policy process, through interpretation of policy data, a television series, and a website.

1814. Cornell University, Albert R. Mann Library, Ithaca, NY. $85,000, 2000. Toward continued education on and marketing of Essential Electronic Agricultural Library in Africa.

1815. Cornell University, Albert R. Mann Library, Ithaca, NY. $85,000, 2000. Toward additional marketing and training support for Essential Electronic Agricultural Library in Africa.

1816. Food and Agriculture Organization of the United Nations, Rome, Italy. $12,000, 2000. For use by its sub-regional office in southern and eastern Africa to develop information materials to be used in Africa to communicate issues related to development and use of transgenic crop plants.

1817. Foundation Center, NYC, NY. $200,000, 2000. Toward its general operating expenses.

1818. George Coates Performance Works, San Francisco, CA. $20,000, 2000. To support creation and production of Better Bad News, multi-media live and online performance piece.

1819. Grantmakers in Health, DC. $12,000, 2000. For continued support of its efforts to communicate information and generate knowledge about health issues and effective grantmaking strategies to help grantmakers improve nation's health.

1820. International Center for Information on Cover Crops, Tegucigalpa, Honduras. $95,000, 2000. To support development and maintenance of database to store and manage information related to green manure cover crop systems in tropics.

1821. International Center for Not-for-Profit Law, DC. $25,000, 2000. Toward costs of component for sub-Saharan Africa of database project designed to provide useful resources to advance development of better laws affecting civil society organizations in countries around the world.

1822. International Institute for Sustainable Development (IISD), Winnipeg, Canada. $100,000, 2000. Toward costs of reports and on-line coverage of meetings related to intellectual property rights for publication in its Earth Negotiations Bulletin.

1823. International Livestock Research Institute, Nairobi, Kenya. $45,000, 2000. To develop spatially-referenced crop and livestock production database for eastern and southern Africa.

1824. International Maize and Wheat Improvement Center, Mexico City, Mexico. $20,000, 2000. To support development and maintenance of database for storage and management of information related to Green Manure Cover Crops systems in tropics.

1825. International Service for the Acquisition of Agri-biotech Applications, Ithaca, NY. $225,000, 2000. To establish knowledge center on crop biotechnology located in Southeast Asia serving all developing countries and to facilitate dialogue that will enable policymakers and scientists responsible for crop biotechnology in developing countries to better understand positions and concerns of all sides in global debates on this topic.

1826. Library of Congress, DC. $25,000, 2000. To support three symposia on Islamic Societies and Globalization.

1827. Location One, NYC, NY. $187,500, 2000. Toward costs of virtual lab to bring together artists and programmers for exchange of ideas, projects, and practices.

1828. Louisiana State University, Baton Rouge, LA. $23,118, 2000. Toward activities to enhance team residency, Health Maps: A Global Network for Control of Snail-Borne Disease Using Satellite Surveillance and Geographic Information Systems, held at Bellagio Study and Conference Center from April 4 to 14, 2000.

1829. Museum of Modern Art, NYC, NY. $30,000, 2000. Toward costs of website component of Video Rewind project, overview of video's development as art form.

1830. National Committee on American Foreign Policy, NYC, NY. $135,000, 2000. Toward costs of CD-ROM project on humanitarian mine clearance.

1831. Obafemi Awolowo University, Ile-Ife, Nigeria. $45,000, 2000. To provide access to Essential Electronic Agricultural Library to its Faculty of Agriculture to improve access of faculty and students to up-to-date scientific information on all areas of agricultural science for teaching and research.

1832. Photo Archive Group, El Segundo, CA. $48,335, 2000. Toward costs of Danang Phase of American War Project, exhibition and book of Vietnam War-era photographs by Vietnamese photographers.

1833. Project Underground, Berkeley, CA. $20,000, 2000. Toward costs of developing web-based database on conflicts around the world that are based on mining and oil resources and that affect minorities.

1834. Rhizome Communications, NYC, NY. $75,000, 2000. Toward costs of archival and technological development of Rhizome ArtBase, online resource for preservation of Internet art.

1835. Smithsonian Institution, DC. $250,000, 2000. Toward pilot phase of Smithsonian WorldMusicNet.Com, project to promote musical and cultural heritage around the world through use of digital technologies.

1836. Social and Public Art Resource Center, Venice, CA. $133,735, 2000. Toward costs of completing designs for next four sections of Great Wall of Los Angeles mural.

1837. Syracuse University, Syracuse, NY. $200,000, 2000. Toward costs of its Gene Media Forum's project to develop international information system for journalists and public on food and biotechnology.

1838. Tropical Soil Biology and Fertility Programme, Nairobi, Kenya. $10,422, 2000. To support publishing of webpage and preparation of proceedings of Forum for Organic Resource Management and Agricultural Technologies symposium held September 2000 in Nairobi, Kenya.

1839. University of Paris, Paris, France. $75,000, 2000. Toward costs of research and development of DVD-ROM on works of artist Nam June Paik.

1840. University of Pennsylvania, Center for Bioethics, Philadelphia, PA. $19,648, 2000. To explore current state of ownership, patenting and property statutes of genetic and biological material through establishment of international database.

1841. Zimbabwe Ministry of Lands and Agriculture, Zimbabwe. $45,000, 2000. To provide access to Essential Electronic Agricultural Library to Agronomy Research Institute of Department of Research and Specialist Services to improve quality of its scientific research activities.

Frederick P. & Sandra P. Rose Foundation

Limitations: Giving primarily in New York, NY. No grants to individuals.

1842. New York Public Library, NYC, NY. $3,000,000, 1999.
1843. New York Public Library, NYC, NY. $12,040, 1999.
1844. Patrons of the New Haven Public Library, New Haven, CT. $25,000, 1999.
1845. Rye Free Reading Room, Rye, NY. $25,000, 1999.

Daniel and Joanna S. Rose Fund, Inc.

Limitations: Giving primarily in NY. No grants to individuals.

1846. New York Public Library, NYC, NY. $25,000, 1999.
1847. Yale University, New Haven, CT. $10,000, 1999. For library.

Ross Family Charitable Foundation

Limitations: Giving primarily in the greater metropolitan New York, NY, area, including Long Island. No grants to individuals.

1848. Long Now Foundation, San Francisco, CA. $50,000, 1999.
1849. Shoah Foundation, Philadelphia, PA. $50,000, 1999.

Helena Rubinstein Foundation, Inc.

Limitations: Giving primarily in New York, NY. No grants to individuals, or for emergency funds or film or video projects; no loans.

1850. Child Care, Inc., NYC, NY. $20,000, 2001. For continuing general support for child care referral, research, training, and advocacy initiatives.

1851. Libraries for the Future, NYC, NY. $50,000, 2001. For expansion and replication in New York City of program that helps public libraries to provide their local communities with greater access to health information.

1852. National Womens Health Network, DC. $10,000, 2001. For continued support for internship program in health education and advocacy for women.

May and Samuel Rudin Family Foundation, Inc.

Limitations: Giving primarily in New York City.

1853. Gay Mens Health Crisis (GMHC), NYC, NY. $30,000, 2000. For general support for Hotline.

1854. Lower Manhattan Cultural Council, NYC, NY. $40,000, 2000. For downtown web site.

1855. New York Academy of Medicine, NYC, NY. $50,000, 2000. For Lewis Rudin Glaucoma Prize.

1856. New York Public Library, NYC, NY. $25,000, 2000. For computer internships.

1857. Pierpont Morgan Library, NYC, NY. $15,000, 2000. For general support.

The Fan Fox and Leslie R. Samuels Foundation, Inc.

Limitations: Giving limited to New York, NY. No support for social service or education. No grants to individuals, or for scholarships, fellowships, or film or video projects.

1858. George Balanchine Foundation, NYC, NY. $15,000, 2000. For George Balanchine Foundation Interpreters Archive.

1859. Medicare Rights Center, NYC, NY. $58,500, 2000. For Medicare Information Library Outreach.

1860. New York Academy of Medicine, NYC, NY. $51,600, 2000. For project, A Model to Educate Social Work Students for Geriatric Practices in Health and Mental Health Care Settings.

1861. New York Academy of Medicine, NYC, NY. $51,600, 2000. For project, A Model to Educate Social Work Students for Geriatric Practices in Health and Mental Health Care Settings.

1862. New York Academy of Medicine, NYC, NY. $40,000, 2000. For Urban Health Initiative/Homeless Shelter Program.

1863. New York Academy of Medicine, NYC, NY. $28,000, 2000. For Urban Health Initiative/Homeless Shelter Program.

1864. New York Public Library, NYC, NY. $100,000, 2000. To videotape productions in New York City for preservation in Theater on Film and Tape Archive.

The Scherman Foundation, Inc.

Limitations: Giving primarily in New York, NY for arts and social welfare. No support for colleges, universities, or other higher educational institutions. No grants to individuals, or for building or endowment funds, scholarships, fellowships, conferences or symposia, specific media or arts production, or medical, science or engineering research.

1865. City Wide Task Force on Housing Court, NYC, NY. $50,000, 2000. 2-year grant. For general support.

1866. New York Public Library, NYC, NY. $325,000, 2000. 3-year grant. For general support.

1867. Southwest Research and Information Center, Albuquerque, NM. $40,000, 2000. 2-year grant. For general support.

S. H. and Helen R. Scheuer Family Foundation, Inc.

Limitations: Giving primarily in New York, NY.

1868. Center for Jewish History, NYC, NY. $15,000, 1999. For unrestricted support.

1869. YIVO Institute for Jewish Research, NYC, NY. $15,000, 1999. For unrestricted support.

The Peter Jay Sharp Foundation

Limitations: Giving primarily in New York, NY. No grants to individuals.

1870. Juilliard School, NYC, NY. $600,000, 1999. For renovations and renewal of library.

Ralph C. Sheldon Foundation, Inc.

Limitations: Giving limited to southern Chautauqua County, NY. No support for religious organizations. No grants to individuals.

1871. Falconer Public Library, Falconer, NY. $15,000, 1999. For renovation of windows.

1872. James Prendergast Library Association, Jamestown, NY. $65,000, 1999. For books and tapes.

1873. James Prendergast Library Association, Jamestown, NY. $11,580, 1999. For automated infrastructure project.

The Shubert Foundation, Inc.

Limitations: No grants to individuals, or for capital or endowment funds, seed money, research, conduit organizations, renovation projects, audience development, productions for specialized audiences, scholarships, fellowships, or matching gifts; no loans.

1874. Foundation Center, NYC, NY. $10,000, 2000. For general support.

1875. New York Public Library, NYC, NY. $30,000, 2000. For general support for Lincoln Center Library for the Performing Arts.

Skirball Foundation

Limitations: Giving primarily in CA. No grants to individuals.

1876. Center for Jewish History, NYC, NY. $200,000, 1999. For operating support.

Alfred P. Sloan Foundation

Limitations: No support for the creative or performing arts, humanities, religion, or primary or secondary education. No grants to individuals directly, or for endowment or building funds, medical research, or equipment not related directly to foundation-supported projects; no loans.

1877. Anthology Film Archives, NYC, NY. $20,000, 2000. Toward science film series and gallery exhibit.

1878. Council on Competitiveness, DC. $160,000, 2000. For briefings for Congressional staffs on technology-related matters.

1879. Council on Foundations, DC. $45,000, 2000. Toward launching electronic newsletter for foundation-related news, information, and commentary.

1880. Dibner Institute for the History of Science and Technology, Cambridge, MA. $1,335,000, 2000. To build and operate program for history of recent science and technology on the web.

1881. Foundation Center, NYC, NY. $30,000, 2000. To upgrade software license for Grantmaker Web Search search engine.

1882. Franklin W. Olin College of Engineering, Needham, MA. $45,000, 2000. For Asynchronous Learning Networks (ALN) newsletter and speaker's bureau.

1883. Institute of Electrical and Electronics Engineers (IEEE), Piscataway, NJ. $35,000, 2000. To add software careers videotape to careers cornerstone series, as part of Education and Careers in Science and Technology program.

1884. National Research Council, DC. $30,000, 2000. Toward A Guide to Recruiting and Advancing Academic Women in Science and Engineering.

1885. New York Industrial Retention Network, Brooklyn, NY. $30,000, 2000. To create printing industry collaborative.

1886. Rutgers, The State University of New Jersey, Newark, NJ. $30,000, 2000. To institutionalize performance assessment in Montclair, New Jersey and disseminate results of Sloan-sponsored government performance assessment projects.

The Starr Foundation

Limitations: No grants to individuals (except through foundation's scholarship programs), or for matching gifts; no loans.

1887. Abraham Lincoln Presidential Library and Museum Foundation, Springfield, IL. $250,000, 2000. For endowment for new library, museum and educational center.

1888. American Forum for Global Education, NYC, NY. $25,000, 2000. For continued general operating support.

1889. Archdiocese of New York, NYC, NY. $300,000, 2000. 4-year grant. For Library Connections program for disadvantaged children and youth.

1890. Brewster Public Library, Brewster, NY. $15,000, 2000. 3-year grant. For general operating support.

1891. Brooklyn Museum of Art, Brooklyn, NY. $300,000, 2000. 3-year grant. For Libraries Renovation Plan.

1892. Brooklyn Public Library Foundation, Brooklyn, NY. $150,000, 2000. 2-year grant. For educational initiatives, including reading and literacy training for children and adults.

1893. Citizens Advice Bureau, Bronx, NY. $50,000, 2000. For Project Achieve after-school program.

1894. Community Food Resource Center, NYC, NY. $300,000, 2000. 2-year grant. For food programs for disadvantaged, access to benefits project and capacity-building.

1895. Council for Basic Education, DC. $90,000, 2000. 3-year grant. For general support.

1896. Eisenhower Foundation, Presidential Gallery and Learning Center, Abilene, KS. $250,000, 2000. For educational programs.

1897. Foundation Center, NYC, NY. $300,000, 2000. 2-year grant. For Online Project.

1898. Meharry Medical College, Nashville, TN. $1,000,000, 2000. For library endowment.

1899. Multiple Sclerosis Society, National, NYC, NY. $61,000, 2000. To add full-time social worker to MS Care Center at New York Presbyterian Hospital-Weill Medical College of Cornell University.

1900. Queens Library Foundation, Jamaica, NY. $500,000, 2000. 3-year grant. For International Resource Center.

1901. Richard Nixon Library and Birthplace Foundation, Yorba Linda, CA. $1,000,000, 2000. 3-year grant. For general support.

1902. Saint Johns Bread and Life Program, Brooklyn, NY. $300,000, 2000. 2-year grant. For mobile soup kitchen and social service vehicle.

1903. University of Puget Sound, Tacoma, WA. $100,000, 2000. 2-year grant. For renovation of Collins Memorial Library.

The Harold & Mimi Steinberg Charitable Trust

Limitations: Giving primarily in New York, NY. No grants to individuals.

1904. University of California, Library, Berkeley, CA. $10,000, 1999. For continued unrestricted support.

The Judy and Michael Steinhardt Foundation

Limitations: No grants to individuals.

1905. American Jewish Historical Society, NYC, NY. $10,000, 1999. For unrestricted support.

1906. Pierpont Morgan Library, NYC, NY. $10,000, 1999. For unrestricted support.

1907. YIVO Institute for Jewish Research, NYC, NY. $25,000, 1999. For unrestricted support.

The Philip A. and Lynn Straus Foundation, Inc.

Limitations: Giving primarily in NY. No grants to individuals.

1908. Mamaroneck Free Library, Mamaroneck, NY. $1,500,000, 2000.

1909. Mamaroneck Free Library, Mamaroneck, NY. $10,000, 2000.

Surdna Foundation, Inc.

Limitations: No support for international projects. No grants to individuals, or for capital campaigns, building funds, endowments, or land acquisition.

1910. American Communications Foundation, Mill Valley, CA. $100,000, 2000. To develop Internet site that will provide details about nonprofit groups featured in stories produced by American Communications Foundation and aired on major commercial radio and television stations.

1911. American Communications Foundation, Mill Valley, CA. $100,000, 2000. To develop Internet site that will provide details about nonprofit groups featured in stories produced by American Communications Foundation (ACF) and aired on major commercial radio and television stations.

1912. Child Care, Inc., NYC, NY. $100,000, 2000. For Surdna Family Child Care Initiative.

1913. Environmental Defense, NYC, NY. $250,000, 2000. For Internet service that will provide localized and customized environmental information through variety of nonprofit and commercial channels.

1914. Foundation Center, NYC, NY. $20,000, 2000. For general operating support to collect and disseminate information on private foundations and other grantmaking organizations.

1915. New York Academy of Medicine, NYC, NY. $100,000, 2000. For study of state community benefits laws governing nonprofit health-care organizations; research project intended to document how and why states enacted community benefits statutes and how those legal provisions have affected delivery of charitable health-care services.

1916. TechRocks, Philadelphia, PA. $150,000, 2000. For development of ebase, free software package designed to help nonprofits keep track of information on members and donors.

The Teagle Foundation, Inc.

Limitations: Giving limited to the U.S. No grants to community organizations outside New York City. No grants to U.S. organizations for foreign programmatic activities. No grants to individuals; no loans.

1917. Citizens Advice Bureau, Bronx, NY. $25,000, 2000. For Girls Club of New York programs.

1918. Theological Consortium of Greater Columbus, Columbus, OH. $250,000, 2000. To develop joint library as focal point for further collaboration.

The Tinker Foundation Inc.

Limitations: Giving limited to projects related to Latin America, Spain, Portugal, and Antarctica. No support for projects concerned with health or medical issues or the arts and humanities. No grants to individuals, or for building or endowment funds, equipment, annual campaigns, operating budgets, annual appeals of community funds, or production costs for film, television, and radio projects.

1919. Library of Congress, Hispanic and Portuguese Division, DC. $42,500, 1999. Toward conference on 21st Century Public Policy in the Americas, covering topics such as challenges to democracy in Americas, human rights and migration in Americas, sustainable development, and information age in Western Hemisphere.

1920. Synergos Institute, NYC, NY. $100,000, 1999. For project to strengthen philanthropic sector in Latin America, produce profiles of grant-making foundations in Brazil, Mexico and Ecuador, collect information on those elements that strengthen local philanthropy in these countries, conduct tri-country comparative analysis of foundation functions, and refine survey methods for use in other countries.

Tisch Foundation, Inc.

Limitations: Giving primarily in NY. No grants to individuals, or for endowment funds, scholarships, fellowships, or matching gifts; no loans.

1921. Center for Jewish History, NYC, NY. $50,000, 1999.
1922. Library of Congress, DC. $10,000, 1999. For Henry A. Kissinger Chair in Foreign Policy and International Relations.
1923. Rye Free Reading Room, Rye, NY. $25,000, 1999.
1924. Tufts University, Tisch Library, Medford, MA. $1,000,000, 1999.

The Trust for Mutual Understanding

Limitations: Giving for exchanges between the U.S., the former Soviet Union, and the countries of Central and Eastern Europe, primarily the Czech Republic, Hungary, Poland, Russia, Slovakia, and Ukraine. No support for large-scale institutional programs lacking an individual exchange component, youth or undergraduate exchanges, economic development, medicine, public health, agricultural issues, or activities pertaining to nuclear weapons and arms control. No grants to individuals, or for fellowships, capital campaigns, deficit financing, endowments, general program and operating costs, salaries, honoraria, publications, library and equipment purchases, film, media, or one-person exhibitions or performance tours.

1925. Gertrude Stein Repertory Theater, NYC, NY. $18,000, 2000. For representatives from Theater to travel to Russia to develop Russian Performing Arts Database, Internet-based, multilingual theater archive, in collaboration with Bakhrushin Museum in Moscow, Saint Petersburg Academy of Theater Arts, and Museum of Theater and Music in Saint Petersburg.
1926. New York University, School of Law, NYC, NY. $20,000, 2000. For American and Central European participation in meetings on strengthening public access to environmental information, to be held in Central Europe.
1927. Northeast Document Conservation Center, Andover, MA. $32,000, 2000. For exchange with State Russian Museum in Saint Petersburg for Russian conservation specialists to visit United States and work with conservators on preservation techniques that can be used to treat twentieth-century works of art on paper.
1928. Northeast Document Conservation Center, Andover, MA. $25,000, 2000. For conservators from Bulgaria to participate in training program on conservation of photographs at Center.
1929. Northeast Document Conservation Center, Andover, MA. $10,000, 2000. For conservators from Center to visit Academy of Arts and Design in Bratislava, Slovakia, to discuss issues of paper conservation and to develop plan for possible exchange program for faculty members at Academy.
1930. Russian American Exchange Center, San Francisco, CA. $20,000, 2000. For cultural exchange between representatives of Russian Archives Online and American specialists for Russian-American Cultural Documentation Exchange: Archives Online project to increase technological capacity of preservation of and public accessibility to Russian audiovisual archives.

United States-Japan Foundation

Limitations: Giving primarily in the U.S. and Japan. No support for projects in the arts involving performances, exhibitions, or productions, or for sports exchanges or student exchanges. No grants to individuals, or for building or endowment funds, capital campaigns, deficit operations.

1931. National Security Archive Fund, National Security Archive, DC. $132,000, 1999. For continued support for work to analyze US government documents pertaining to US-Japan relations secured by the Freedom of Information Act.

H. van Ameringen Foundation

Limitations: Giving primarily in NY. No grants to individuals.

1932. Body Positive, NYC, NY. $25,000, 2000.

Verizon Foundation

Limitations: Giving primarily in areas of corporate sponsor's operations concentrated in New England, DE, NJ, NY, PA, WV, and the greater metropolitan Washington, DC, area. No support for organizations which duplicate work of federal, state, or local public agencies, or religious organizations. No grants to individuals, or for advertising, or operating expenses of organizations supported by the United Way.

1933. Barbour Community Net, Philippi, WV. $11,000, 1999.
1934. Brooklyn Public Library Foundation, Brooklyn, NY. $25,000, 1999.
1935. Folger Shakespeare Library, DC. $60,000, 1999.
1936. Free Library of Philadelphia, Philadelphia, PA. $10,000, 1999.
1937. James V. Brown Library, Williamsport, PA. $10,000, 1999.
1938. New Hampshire Library Association, Concord, NH. $10,000, 1999.
1939. Nonprofit Connection, Brooklyn, NY. $10,000, 1999.
1940. Olean Public Library, Olean, NY. $11,425, 1999.
1941. Providence Public Library, Providence, RI. $12,000, 1999.
1942. Queens Library Foundation, Jamaica, NY. $15,000, 1999.
1943. Westchester Library System, Elmsford, NY. $10,000, 1999.

Wallace-Readers Digest Funds

Limitations: Giving on a national basis. No support for religious, fraternal, or veterans' organizations; government and public policy organizations, or private foundations. No grants for annual campaigns, endowments, capital purpose, or scholarly research.

1944. Foundation Center, NYC, NY. $25,000, 2000. For general support.
1945. Foundation Center, NYC, NY. $25,000, 2000. For general support.
1946. Project for Public Spaces, NYC, NY. $650,000, 2000. To transform Urban Parks Institute into Web-based national resource center for urban parks, convene urban parks grantees in annual conferences, and support efforts to develop national alliance for urban parks.

The Margaret L. Wendt Foundation

Limitations: Giving primarily in Buffalo and western NY. No grants to individuals, or for scholarships.

1947. King Urban Life Center, Buffalo, NY. $226,700, 2000. For Library Loft Project.
1948. Library Foundation of Buffalo and Erie County, Buffalo, NY. $100,000, 2000. For On-Line Public Access Computer work station.

The Whitehead Foundation

Limitations: Giving primarily in NY.

1949. George C. Marshall Research Foundation, Lexington, VA. $20,000, 2000. For general support.
1950. Library of Congress, DC. $100,000, 2000. For general support.
1951. Library of Congress, DC. $15,000, 2000. For general support.
1952. New York Public Library, NYC, NY. $15,000, 2000. For general support.
1953. Pierpont Morgan Library, NYC, NY. $20,000, 2000. For general support.

1954. Ronald Reagan Presidential Library, Simi Valley, CA. $25,000, 2000. For general support.

The Norman and Rosita Winston Foundation, Inc.

Limitations: Giving primarily in NY. No grants to individuals.

1955. Medici Archive Project, NYC, NY. $20,000, 1999. For Magistrata Suprema Project.
1956. New York Academy of Medicine, NYC, NY. $25,000, 1999. For general support.
1957. New York Public Library, NYC, NY. $30,000, 1999. For general support.
1958. New York Public Library, NYC, NY. $10,000, 1999. For Book Conservation.

NORTH CAROLINA

Mary Reynolds Babcock Foundation, Inc.

Limitations: Giving in the southeastern U.S., with emphasis on eastern AR, GA, LA, MS, NC, SC, TN, north and central FL, and the Appalachian regions of KY and WV. No support for medical or health programs and international activities. No grants for endowment funds, building funds, renovation projects, film or video production, scholarships, fellowships, or research; no student loans.

1959. Nonprofit Resources, Little Rock, AR. $71,000, 1999. For grant made through Organizational Development Program.

Bank of America Foundation, Inc.

Limitations: Giving limited to areas of major company operations, including 21 states and Washington, DC, and other select areas where there is a company presence. No support for organizations lacking 501(c)(3) status, religious organizations for sectarian purposes, athletic events and programs, agencies receiving support from the United Way or arts councils, public or private K-12 schools, or disease advocacy organizations. No grants to individuals, or for book, film, or video development or production.

1960. Childrens Book Press, San Francisco, CA. $10,000, 1999. For literacy project that includes writers, artists, families, libraries, and teachers.
1961. Community Housing Resources of Arizona, Phoenix, AZ. $15,000, 1999. To provide prepurchase and default/delinquency counseling for low-income families.
1962. EdSource, Menlo Park, CA. $10,000, 1999. For Public Information program.
1963. Foundation Center, San Francisco, CA. $15,000, 1999. For capital campaign for expansion.
1964. George Bush Presidential Library Foundation, College Station, TX. $125,000, 1999. For lecture series and volunteerism exhibition.
1965. Harry S. Truman Library Institute for National and International Affairs, Independence, MO. $20,000, 1999.
1966. Home Buyer Assistance and Information Center (HBAIC), Oakland, CA. $50,000, 1999. For housing initiative.
1967. Home Buyer Assistance and Information Center (HBAIC), Oakland, CA. $25,000, 1999. For homebuyer counseling.
1968. Huntington Library, Art Collections and Botanical Gardens, San Marino, CA. $25,000, 1999. For Mount Vernon exhibit.
1969. Huntington Library, Friends of the, San Marino, CA. $15,000, 1999. For annual support.
1970. Jacksonville Public Libraries, Jacksonville, FL. $12,500, 1999.
1971. Jacksonville Public Library Foundation, Jacksonville, FL. $15,000, 1999.
1972. Library Foundation of Los Angeles, Los Angeles, CA. $20,000, 1999. For existing programs projects and services.
1973. Long Beach Public Library Foundation, Long Beach, CA. $25,000, 1999. For family learning center.
1974. Public Library of Charlotte and Mecklenburg County, Charlotte, NC. $30,000, 1999. For Early Intervention Reading Program.
1975. Saint Louis Mercantile Library, Saint Louis, MO. $15,000, 1999. For exhibition, The Taming of the West.
1976. San Francisco AIDS Foundation, San Francisco, CA. $25,000, 1999. For operating support and newsletter, Outreach.
1977. South Carolina Archives and History Foundation, Columbia, SC. $20,000, 1999.

1978. Springfield-Greene County Library District, Springfield, MO. $50,000, 1999. For business resource center at library.
1979. Tampa Bay Partnership Regional Research and Educational Foundation, Tampa, FL. $10,000, 1999. For Business Resource Center in Pinellas County.
1980. Village Learning Place, Baltimore, MD. $10,000, 1999.
1981. Washoe County Public Library System, Reno, NV. $10,000, 1999. For community outreach programs.

Burroughs Wellcome Fund

Limitations: Giving limited to the U.S. and Canada. No grants to individuals, or for building or endowment funds, equipment, operating budgets, continuing support, annual campaigns, deficit financing, publications, conferences, or matching gifts; no loans.

1982. Institute for Science Philanthropy, Fountain Hills, AZ. $50,000, 2000. For general support.

The Cannon Foundation, Inc.

Limitations: Giving primarily in NC, with emphasis on the Cabarrus County area. No grants to individuals, or for operating budgets, seed money, emergency funds, deficit financing, land acquisition, endowment funds, demonstration projects, research, publications, conferences, seminars, scholarships, or fellowships; no loans.

1983. Avery-Mitchell-Yancey Regional Library, Spruce Pine, NC. $25,000, 2000. For renovations.
1984. Belmont Abbey College, Belmont, NC. $50,000, 2000. For library renewal.
1985. Madison County Library, Friends of, Marshall, NC. $25,000, 2000. For construction of new facility.
1986. Scotland Neck, Town of, Scotland Neck, NC. $25,000, 2000. For addition to Library.

The Duke Endowment

Limitations: Giving limited to NC and SC. No grants to individuals (except for internship program), or for deficit financing; no loans.

1987. Cannon Memorial Hospital, Pickens, SC. $175,000, 2000. To develop Partners Healthwise Initiative, community health information program.
1988. Davidson College, Davidson, NC. $253,142, 2000. For library acquisitions, publications, and operating support.
1989. Duke University, Durham, NC. $9,200,000, 2000. For Perkins Library.
1990. Foundation Center, NYC, NY. $20,000, 2000. For annual support.
1991. Furman University, Greenville, SC. $2,000,000, 2000. For capital campaign to renovate and expand James B. Duke Library and for James B. Duke Scholarship Program.
1992. Furman University, Greenville, SC. $575,000, 2000. For library support.
1993. Haywood Regional Medical Center, Clyde, NC. $66,097, 2000. To develop community-based health information system.
1994. Johnson C. Smith University, Charlotte, NC. $194,550, 2000. For administration of library.
1995. University of North Carolina, Chapel Hill, NC. $150,000, 2000. For AHEC Digital Library and Resource System.
1996. WESTCARE Health System, Sylva, NC. $60,152, 2000. To establish community-based computer information and referral system.

Duke Energy Foundation

Limitations: Giving primarily in the company's headquarters and service areas in NC and SC. No support for single sectarian or denominational religious, veterans', or fraternal organizations, organizations where the foundation would be the only donor, hospitals supported by the Duke Endowment, or organizations primarily supported by tax dollars (except for education). No grants to individuals (except for scholarships).

1997. George Bush Presidential Library Foundation, College Station, TX. $20,000, 1999. For operating support.
1998. South Carolina Archives and History Foundation, Columbia, SC. $10,000, 1999. For operating support.

The First Union Foundation

Limitations: Giving limited to CT, Washington, DC, DE, FL, GA, MD, NC, NJ, NY, PA, SC, TN, and VA. No support for political, religious, veterans', or fraternal organizations, retirement homes, precollege level private schools except through employee matching gifts, or organizations supported through the United Way, except for approved capital campaigns, international organizations, or intermediary organizations or agents. No grants to individuals, or for travel or conferences, or capital projects.

1999. Action AIDS, Philadelphia, PA. $10,000, 1999.
2000. Free Library of Philadelphia, Philadelphia, PA. $32,000, 1999.
2001. National Housing Institute, Orange, NJ. $13,000, 1999.

Foundation For The Carolinas

Limitations: Giving primarily to organizations serving the citizens of NC and SC, with emphasis on the greater Charlotte, NC region. No grants to individuals (except for scholarships), or for deficit financing, capital campaigns, operating budgets, publications, conferences, videos, travel, equipment, or endowment funds.

2002. Child Care Resources, Charlotte, NC. $204,391, 1999.
2003. Davidson County Library Foundation, Lexington, NC. $20,000, 1999.
2004. Public Library of Charlotte and Mecklenburg County, Charlotte, NC. $38,300, 1999.
2005. Sandhill Regional Library, Rockingham, NC. $75,000, 1999.

Janirve Foundation

Limitations: Giving primarily in western NC. No support for public and private elementary schools, or churches and religious programs. No grants to individuals, or generally for operating budgets, endowments or for research programs, publication of books or printed material, theatrical productions, videos, radio or television programs; no loans.

2006. Buncombe County Library, Friends of, Asheville, NC. $10,000, 2000. For general support.
2007. Madison County Library, Friends of, Marshall, NC. $450,000, 2000. For general support.

William R. Kenan, Jr. Charitable Trust

Limitations: Giving for secondary schools limited to Eastern Seaboard states. No support for medical, public health, or social welfare; or for designated educational programs, or independent day schools. No grants to individuals, or for building funds, operating budgets, scholarships, fellowships, research, or special programs.

2008. Foundation Center, NYC, NY. $24,000, 2000.
2009. Pierpont Morgan Library, NYC, NY. $100,000, 2000. For educational programming.

Kate B. Reynolds Charitable Trust

Limitations: Giving limited to NC; social welfare grants limited to Winston-Salem and Forsyth County; health care giving, statewide. No support for political organizations. No grants to individuals, or for endowment funds or medical research; grants on a highly selective basis for construction of facilities or purchase of equipment.

2010. Northern Moore Family Resource Center, Robbins, NC. $16,570, 2000. For operating support for second expansion of occupational therapy program for low-income children needing sensory integration therapy.

Z. Smith Reynolds Foundation, Inc.

Limitations: Giving limited to NC. No grants to individuals (except for Nancy Susan Reynolds Awards for community leadership and sabbatical program), or for research; no loans or program-related investments.

2011. Carolina Justice Policy Center, Durham, NC. $15,000, 1999. To develop dialogue with corrections officials about role of nonprofit organizations working in community corrections, and to increase number of organizations that receive and share information about governmental and legislative actions.
2012. Greensboro Housing Coalition, Greensboro, NC. $15,000, 1999. For landlord-renter advocacy, and to acquire and upgrade computers to educate and advocate on behalf of low-wealth renters.

2013. Hope Harbor Home, Supply, NC. $20,000, 1999. For minority outreach program for victims of domestic violence and sexual assault to educate women about available services.
2014. North Carolina Association of County Directors of Social Services, Raleigh, NC. $30,000, 1999. For North Carolina Welfare Resource Exchange, to gather and distribute information about promising practices and resources in welfare reform.
2015. North Carolina Center for International Understanding, Raleigh, NC. $35,000, 1999. For clearinghouse for global educational opportunities for K-12 educators.
2016. REAL Crisis Intervention, Greenville, NC. $25,000, 1999. For El Faro, to provide language and cultural sensitivity training for Pitt County agencies that work with Latino crime victims.
2017. University of North Carolina, Chapel Hill, NC. $30,000, 1999. For Implementing Smart Growth in North Carolina, to provide practical information in communities that will improve their capabilities to accommodate growth in a more sustainable, livable pattern.
2018. Watauga County Hunger Coalition, Boone, NC. $25,000, 1999. For disability advocacy program to assist residents under financial stress in obtaining disability benefits.

C. D. Spangler Foundation, Inc.

Limitations: Giving primarily in NC. No grants to individuals.

2019. Moravian Church in America, Southern Province, Winston-Salem, NC. $25,000, 1999. For building campaign for Archie K. Davis Center, housing Moravian Archives and Moravian Music Foundation.

The Wachovia Foundation, Inc.

Limitations: Giving primarily in FL, GA, NC, SC, and VA. No grants to individuals.

2020. Moravian Music Foundation, Winston-Salem, NC. $50,000, 2000. To construct archival research center.
2021. South Carolina Archives and History Foundation, Columbia, SC. $25,000, 2000. For capital campaign.

OHIO

Britton Fund

Limitations: Giving primarily in OH. No grants to individuals.

2022. Blue Hill Library, Blue Hill, ME. $25,000, 1999. For capital campaign.

Eva L. and Joseph M. Bruening Foundation

Limitations: Giving limited to the greater Cleveland, OH, area. No grants to individuals, or for endowment funds, general operating budgets, research, publications, symposia and seminars, mass mailings, or annual campaigns.

2023. East Cleveland Public Library, East Cleveland, OH. $150,000, 2000. For renovate and expand main library.
2024. Western Reserve Historical Society, Cleveland, OH. $25,000, 2000. For development of science-based educational program and for philanthropic archives.

The Greater Cincinnati Foundation

Limitations: Giving limited to southeastern IN, northern KY, and the greater Cincinnati, OH area. No support for sectarian religious purposes, schools, hospitals, nursing homes, or retirement centers. No grants to individuals, or for operating budgets, annual campaigns, deficit financing, scholarships, endowments, travel grants, fellowships, internships, exchange programs, or scholarly or medical research.

2025. Chatfield College, Saint Martin, OH. $10,000, 1999. To furnish library at Chatfield College's Cincinnati Branch.

The Cleveland Foundation

Limitations: Giving limited to the greater Cleveland, OH, area, with primary emphasis on Cleveland, Cuyahoga, Lake, and Geauga counties, unless specified by donor. No support for sectarian or religious activities, community services such as fire and police protection, and library and welfare services. No grants to individuals, or for endowment funds, operating costs, debt reduction, fundraising campaigns, publications, films and audiovisual materials (unless they are an integral part of a program already being supported), memberships, travel for bands, sports teams, classes and similar groups; no capital support for planning, construction, renovation, or purchase of buildings, equipment and materials, land acquisition, or renovation of public space unless there is strong evidence that the program is of priority to the foundation.

2026. Cleveland Museum of Natural History, Cleveland, OH. $30,000, 2000. For Access to Harold Terry Clark Library.

2027. Donors Forum of Ohio, Columbus, OH. $381,191, 2000. 1.50-year grant. For operating and transition support.

2028. East Cleveland Public Library, East Cleveland, OH. $1,000,000, 2000. 2-year grant. For Capital Campaign.

2029. Foundation Center, NYC, NY. $300,000, 2000. For building new facility.

2030. Foundation Center, NYC, NY. $124,605, 2000. For operating support.

The Columbus Foundation and Affiliated Organizations

Limitations: Giving limited to Franklin County, OH, from unrestricted and other discretionary funds. No support for religious purposes, or for projects normally the responsibility of a public agency. No grants to individuals, or generally for budget deficits, conferences, scholarly research, or endowment funds.

2031. Childrens Hospital, Columbus, OH. $35,000, 2000. For production of training materials and informational brochures, website development, and half-time coordinator to create Center for Injury and Research Policy.

2032. Columbus Academy, Gahanna, OH. $25,000, 2000. For Library/Technology Center Campaign and annual support.

2033. Columbus Academy, Gahanna, OH. $20,000, 2000. For Library/Technology Center.

2034. Columbus Regional Information Service, Columbus, OH. $60,000, 2000. For Columbus Workforce Development initiative.

2035. Columbus Regional Information Service, Columbus, OH. $50,000, 2000. For high school internship program as part of graduation requirements for Columbus Public Schools.

2036. Fairfield County Library Foundation, Lancaster, OH. $20,000, 2000. For capital campaign to build new branch library in Village of Bremen.

2037. Logan Elm Board of Education, Circleville, OH. $20,000, 2000. For Salt Creek Township Elementary School's Project 2000 Focus on Children, enhancement of Library/Media Center, enhancement of book collection, etc.

2038. Methodist Theological School in Ohio, Delaware, OH. $25,000, 2000. For renovation of Dickhaut Library building.

2039. National First Ladies Library, Canton, OH. $15,000, 2000. For event.

2040. New Albany-Plain Local Schools Board of Education, New Albany, OH. $10,000, 2000. For elementary school's lower school library, or other support.

2041. Parenting Project, Boca Raton, FL. $15,000, 2000. For operating support and completion of advocacy manual.

The Community Foundation of Greater Lorain County

Limitations: Giving limited to Lorain County, OH, and immediate vicinity. No support for religious purposes, street repair, government services, public or non-public school services required by law, or self-help clubs that meet the needs of a small population. No grants to individuals (except for scholarships), or for annual campaigns, medical research, deficit financing, membership fees, equipment, group travel, or capital campaigns.

2042. Child Care Resource Center of Lorain County, Elyria, OH. $34,000, 1999. To raise quality of childcare services with training and continuing technical assistance.

Charles H. Dater Foundation, Inc.

Limitations: Giving primarily in the greater Cincinnati, OH, area.

2043. Cincinnati Center for Developmental Disorders, Jack H. Rubinstein Libraries, Cincinnati, OH. $25,000, 1999.

2044. Public Library of Cincinnati and Hamilton County, Cincinnati, OH. $20,000, 1999. For Westwood Branch Children's Library fund.

Firstar Foundation, Inc.

Limitations: Giving primarily in the areas where Firstar Bank does business. No support for institutions supported mainly by taxes (except specific programs at publicly funded educational institutions), or for agencies that receive large donations from United Way or Fine Arts Fund, or for political or religious (exclusively serving their own membership) organizations, or for controversial social causes on which there are strong divergences of opinion. No grants to individuals.

2045. Athenaeum of Ohio, Cincinnati, OH. $10,000, 2000. For Our Faith, Our Future, Preserving Affordable Housing.

2046. Combined Generations of the Holocaust of Greater Cincinnati, Cincinnati, OH. $25,000, 2000.

2047. Council Bluffs Library Foundation, Council Bluffs, IA. $20,000, 2000.

2048. Milwaukee Public Library Foundation, Milwaukee, WI. $20,000, 2000.

FirstEnergy Foundation

Limitations: Giving limited to areas served in OH and western PA. Generally, no grants to individuals, or for deficit financing, research, scholarships, or fellowships; no gifts to other foundations; no loans.

2049. Toledo-Lucas County Public Library, Toledo, OH. $35,000, 1999. For capital campaign.

The Agnes Gund Foundation

Limitations: Giving primarily in New York, NY. No grants to individuals.

2050. City College of the City University of New York, NYC, NY. $10,000, 2000. For Library.

2051. New York Public Library, NYC, NY. $15,000, 2000.

2052. Pierpont Morgan Library, NYC, NY. $50,000, 2000.

The George Gund Foundation

Limitations: Giving primarily in northeastern OH and the greater Cleveland, OH, area. No support for political groups, services for the physically, mentally or developmentally disabled, or the elderly. Generally, no grants to individuals, or for building or endowment funds, political campaigns, debt reduction, equipment, renovation projects, or to fund benefit events.

2053. Child Care Resource Center of Cuyahoga County, Cleveland, OH. $150,000, 2000. For operating, scholarship and workplace development support.

2054. East Cleveland Public Library, East Cleveland, OH. $200,000, 2000. For expansion and renovation.

2055. Foundation Center, Cleveland, OH. $20,000, 2000. For continued support.

2056. River Network, Portland, OR. $45,000, 2000. Toward development of Resource Center, technical information resource for local river protection groups.

2057. Westside-Eastside Congregations Acting Now (WE-CAN), Cleveland, OH. $29,000, 2000. To map demographic trends in Northeast Ohio.

The Hoover Foundation

Limitations: Giving primarily in Stark County, OH. No grants to individuals.

2058. Minerva Public Library, Minerva, OH. $25,000, 2000. For educational program.

2059. National First Ladies Library, Canton, OH. $215,000, 2000. For educational program.

2060. North Canton Public Library Association, North Canton, OH. $575,000, 2000. For educational program.

John P. Murphy Foundation

Limitations: Giving primarily in the greater Cleveland, OH, area. No grants to individuals, or for endowment funds; no loans (except for program-related investments).

2061. Artists Archives of the Western Reserve, Beachwood, OH. $20,000, 1999.
2062. Irish American Archives Society, Cleveland, OH. $10,000, 1999.

Nationwide Foundation

Limitations: Giving primarily in OH, with emphasis on Columbus, and other communities where the company maintains offices. No support for public elementary and secondary schools, or fraternal or veterans' organizations. No grants to individuals, or for building funds or research; no loans.

2063. Asociacion de Intercambio Cultural, Guaynabo, PR. $12,713, 1999. For program materials and capital improvements to the library, English lab, and entrance.

NCC Charitable Foundation II

Limitations: Giving primarily in the northeastern U.S., with emphasis on OH. No grants to individuals.

2064. Carnegie Library of Pittsburgh, Pittsburgh, PA. $13,000, 1999. For general support.
2065. Columbus Metropolitan Library, Columbus, OH. $10,000, 1999. For general support.
2066. Library Legacy Foundation, Toledo, OH. $25,000, 1999. For general support.
2067. Louisville Free Public Library Foundation, Louisville, KY. $12,500, 1999. For general support.
2068. Rock Island Public Library, Rock Island, IL. $10,000, 1999. For general support.

The Nord Family Foundation

Limitations: Giving primarily in the Lorain and Cuyahoga County, OH, areas; also gives secondarily in Denver, CO, Boston, MA, and Columbia, SC. No grants to individuals, or for deficit financing, research, capital campaigns, general operations, scholarships, fellowships, tickets, advertising for fundraising activities, or conferences.

2069. Child Care Resource Center of Lorain County, Elyria, OH. $28,571, 2000. For fundraising challenge.
2070. Donors Forum of Ohio, Columbus, OH. $75,000, 2000. For Promotion of Philanthropy Initiative.
2071. Oberlin Public Library, Oberlin, OH. $67,500, 2000. For The Bridge computer-based technology center designed to address digital divide in Oberlin and serve as model for Lorain County.

The Nordson Corporation Foundation

Limitations: Giving limited to the Monterey Peninsula and San Diego County, CA, Atlanta, GA, and northern OH areas.

2072. Child Care Resource Center of Lorain County, Elyria, OH. $10,000, 1999.

The Procter & Gamble Fund

Limitations: Giving primarily in areas in the U.S. where the company and its subsidiaries have large concentrations of employees; national giving for higher education and economic and public affairs. No grants to individuals (except for employee-related scholarships).

2073. National First Ladies Library, Canton, OH. $50,000, 2000.

Jacob G. Schmidlapp Trust No. 1 and No. 2

Limitations: Giving primarily in the greater Cincinnati, OH, area. No support for religious or political purposes. No grants to individuals, or for annual campaigns, deficit financing, general support, fellowships, operating budgets, or continuing support; no loans.

2074. Athenaeum of Ohio, Cincinnati, OH. $50,000, 1999.

Scripps Howard Foundation

Limitations: Giving primarily in areas of company operations for scholarships, internships and literary grants, and nationally for special grants and awards. No support for private foundations, political causes or candidates, veterans', fraternal or labor groups. No grants for courtesy advertising.

2075. Interreligious Information Center, NYC, NY. $10,000, 1999.

2076. Tulsa Library Trust, Tulsa, OK. $10,000, 1999. For literacy programs.

The Kelvin and Eleanor Smith Foundation

Limitations: Giving primarily in the greater Cleveland, OH, area. No grants to individuals, or for endowment funds, scholarships, or fellowships, no loans.

2077. Case Western Reserve University, Cleveland, OH. $2,195,000, 1999. For capital support for Kelvin Smith Library.

Stark Community Foundation, Inc.

Limitations: Giving limited to Stark County, OH. No support for religious organizations for religious purposes. No grants for endowment funds, operating budgets, continuing support, annual campaigns, publications, conferences or deficit financing; no grants or loans to individuals (except to college students who are permanent residents of Stark County, OH).

2078. Carroll County District Library, Carrollton, OH. $100,000, 1999. For Malvern Branch.
2079. Info Line, Akron, OH. $30,000, 1999. For plan to implement 211 services in Ohio.
2080. National First Ladies Library, Canton, OH. $261,434, 1999. For challenge grant.
2081. National First Ladies Library, Canton, OH. $32,500, 1999. For website curriculum development.
2082. Rotary Club of Canton, Canton, OH. $25,000, 1999. For Carroll County branch library.

Timken Foundation of Canton

Limitations: Giving primarily in local areas of Timken Co. domestic operations in Ashland, Bucyrus, Canton, Columbus, Eaton, New Philadelphia, Wauseon, and Wooster, OH; Ashboro, Columbus, and Lincolnton, NC; Concord, Keene, and Lebanon, NH; Latrobe, PA; Gaffney, SC; and Altavista, VA. Giving also in local areas in Australia, Brazil, Canada, France, Great Britain, Italy, Poland, Romania, and South Africa where Timken Co. has manufacturing facilities. No grants to individuals, or for operating budgets.

2083. Ashland City Schools Academic Foundation, Ashland, OH. $25,000, 2000. Toward LinkNet project.
2084. Ligonier Valley Library, Ligonier, PA. $20,000, 2000. For capital campaign to replace existing facility.
2085. Saluda Community Help, Saluda, NC. $30,000, 2000. To renovate donated building.

TRW Foundation

Limitations: Giving primarily in TRW plant communities, particularly AL, AZ, CA, CO, Washington, DC, IL, IN, MA, MD, MI, MN, MT, NM, NY, NV, OH, PA, TN, TX, UT, and VA. No support for religious purposes, fraternal or labor organizations, or private elementary or secondary schools. No grants to individuals (except for employee-related scholarships), or for endowment funds.

2086. National Archives, DC. $25,000, 1999.

The Raymond John Wean Foundation

Limitations: Giving primarily in Allegheny County, PA, and northeast OH, with emphasis on Cuyahoga, Mahoning, and Trumbull counties. No support for sectarian religious activities, veterans' or fraternal organizations, or local or national offices of organizations combating a particular disease or family of diseases. No grants to individuals; or for endowment funds, debt reduction, foreign operations, national fundraising campaigns or film or video production.

2087. Donors Forum of Ohio, Columbus, OH. $10,000, 2000. For general operating support.
2088. East Cleveland Public Library, East Cleveland, OH. $50,000, 2000. For capital expansion.
2089. Miss Porters School, Farmington, CT. $200,000, 2000. For library unrestricted endowment fund.

Wolfe Associates, Inc.

Limitations: Giving primarily in central OH. No grants to individuals, or for research, demonstration projects, publications, or conferences.

2090. Ohio Dominican College, Columbus, OH. $60,000, 2000. For Chair of Learning and Information Services.

2091. Ohio State University Foundation, Cartoon Research Library, Columbus, OH. $10,000, 2000. For Celebration.

2092. Ohioana Library Association, Columbus, OH. $20,000, 2000. For Enrichment Campaign.

OKLAHOMA

The Mervin Bovaird Foundation

Limitations: Giving limited to the Tulsa, OK, area. No grants to individuals; no loans.

2093. Indian Health Care Resources Center, Tulsa, OK. $20,000, 1999.

2094. Tulsa Area Book Bank, Tulsa, OK. $15,000, 1999.

2095. University of Tulsa, Tulsa, OK. $312,500, 1999. For Legal Center and Legal Clinic.

H. A. and Mary K. Chapman Charitable Trust

Limitations: Giving primarily in Tulsa, OK.

2096. Indian Health Care Resources Center, Tulsa, OK. $50,000, 1999.

2097. Kellyville Public Library, Friends of the, Kellyville, OK. $15,000, 1999.

The Helmerich Foundation

Limitations: Giving limited to the Tulsa, OK, area. No grants to individuals, or for general support, continuing support, annual campaigns, seed money, emergency funds, deficit financing, matching gifts, scholarships, fellowships, program support, operating budgets, research, demonstration projects, publications, or conferences; generally, no support for endowment funds; no loans.

2098. Monte Cassino School, Tulsa, OK. $100,000, 2000. For library.

2099. Talbot Library and Museum Association, Colcord, OK. $10,000, 2000. For Endowment Fund.

2100. Tulsa Area Book Bank, Tulsa, OK. $10,000, 2000. For van.

McCasland Foundation

Limitations: Giving primarily in OK.

2101. University of Oklahoma, Norman, OK. $10,000, 1999. 5-year grant. For continued support for Bizzell Library.

The Samuel Roberts Noble Foundation, Inc.

Limitations: Giving primarily in the Southwest, with emphasis on OK. No grants to individuals (except through the scholarship program for children of employees of Noble organizations); no loans.

2102. Arbuckle Drug and Alcohol Information Center, Ardmore, OK. $30,000, 1999. For operating support.

Sarkeys Foundation

Limitations: Giving limited to OK. No support for direct-to-government agencies or individual public or private elementary or secondary schools, unless they are serving the needs of a special population which are not met elsewhere; generally, no support for hospitals or local programs appropriately financed within the community. No grants to individuals, or for operating support, permanent financing, profitmaking programs, grants which trigger expenditure responsibility, direct mail solicitations, start-up funding for new organizations, feasibility studies, or vehicles.

2103. Kellyville Public Library, Friends of the, Kellyville, OK. $75,000, 2000. For construction of building.

2104. University of Tulsa, College of Law, Tulsa, OK. $200,000, 2000. To build library addition.

Charles and Lynn Schusterman Family Foundation

Limitations: Giving primarily to nonsectarian organizations in OK; giving on a local, national, and international basis for Jewish organizations. No grants to individuals, or for endowment funds, or deficit funds.

2105. Indian Health Care Resources Center, Tulsa, OK. $10,000, 1999. For children's playroom at health care center serving Native Americans in Northeastern Oklahoma.

2106. Jewish Womens Archives, Brookline, MA. $15,000, 1999. To establish intern position to maintain Internet archive.

2107. Tulsa Library Trust, Tulsa, OK. $10,000, 1999. For general support to Schusterman-Benson Library.

OREGON

The Collins Foundation

Limitations: Giving limited to OR, with emphasis on Portland. No support for elementary, secondary or public higher educational institutions. No grants to individuals, or for deficit financing, endowment funds, general purposes, scholarships, fellowships, operating budgets, annual campaigns, or annual fundraising activities.

2108. Jackson County Library Foundation, Medford, OR. $35,000, 2000. For land for new and expanded library facilities in Jackson County communities.

The Ford Family Foundation

Limitations: Giving primarily in rural OR, with special interest in Douglas and Coos counties and in Siskiyou County, CA. No support for churches. No grants to individuals (except for scholarships), or for endowment funds.

2109. Douglas County Headquarters Library, Roseburg, OR. $37,500, 2000. For library computer upgrade.

2110. Etna Public Library, Friends of the, Etna, CA. $50,000, 2000. For building project.

2111. Jackson County Library Foundation, Medford, OR. $125,000, 2000. For site acquisition capital campaign.

2112. Stanfield Library, Stanfield, OR. $30,000, 2000. For building fund.

Intel Foundation

Limitations: Giving primarily in major operating areas in Phoenix, AZ, Santa Clara and Folsom, CA, Colorado Springs, CO, Albuquerque, NM, Hudson, MA, Portland, OR, Fort Worth, TX, Provo, UT, and Tacoma, WA. No support for religious, sectarian, fraternal, or political organizations, or publicly funded academic institutions. No grants to individuals (except through special programs), or for endowments, capital improvement campaigns, general operating expenses, general fund drives, annual appeals, fundraising events, or equipment.

2113. Community Technology Institute, Seattle, WA. $69,230, 2000. For operating support.

The Jeld-Wen Foundation

Limitations: Giving primarily in areas of company operations in AZ, FL, IA, KY, NC, OH, OR, SD, and WA for projects serving communities in which company plants exist; projects in adjacent communities may be accepted if sufficient numbers of employees reside in the area and would benefit. No support for activities that are specifically religious or that duplicate services provided by other government or private agencies. No grants to individuals; no loans.

2114. Dalles-Wasco County Public Library, The Dalles, OR. $25,000, 1999.

2115. John R. Kaufman Jr. Public Library, Sunbury, PA. $50,000, 1999.

2116. Ogema Public Library, Ogema, WI. $27,000, 1999.

Meyer Memorial Trust

Limitations: Giving primarily in OR and Clark County, WA. No support for sectarian or religious organizations for religious purposes. No grants to individuals or for endowment funds, annual campaigns, deficit financing, scholarships, fellowships, or indirect or overhead costs, except as specifically and essentially related to the grant project; occasional program-related loans only.

2117. Cathedral School, Portland, OR. $500,000, 2001. 2-year grant. For matching grant toward construction of new library.

2118. Coos County Cooperative Library Service District, Coos Bay, OR. $100,000, 2001. For matching grant for purchase of equipment and software to upgrade and improve efficiency of library network in Coos County. Grant made through southwestern Oregon Community College.

2119. Eastern Oregon State College, Pierce Library, La Grande, OR. $750,000, 2001. 2-year grant. For matching grant for equipment, software, training, and other services to merge three library networks involving libraries in eastern Oregon counties so residents have improved access to library and information resources.

2120. Foundation Center, NYC, NY. $45,000, 2001. 3-year grant. For general support.

2121. Langlois Public Library Foundation, Langlois, OR. $60,000, 2001. To build new library.

2122. Molalla, City of, Molalla Public Library, Molalla, OR. $100,000, 2001. To remodel and equip former Molalla High School library for use as community library and technology learning center.

2123. Oregon Child Care Resource and Referral Network, Salem, OR. $12,000, 2001. To increase supply of quality day care in Oregon by helping child care providers increase their business skills.

2124. Oregon Library Association, Salem, OR. $35,000, 2001. To promote statewide reading program for children.

2125. Portland State University, Portland, OR. $83,668, 2001. For equipment to add library to ORBIS union catalog, which links library collections of colleges and universities in Oregon.

2126. Western Seminary, Portland, OR. $170,000, 2001. 2-year grant. To upgrade technology and information resources for library, classrooms, and auditorium.

2127. Yoncalla, City of, Yoncalla, OR. $35,000, 2001. Toward construction of new library for rural community in Douglas County.

The Oregon Community Foundation

Limitations: Giving limited to OR. No support for religious organizations for religious purposes, projects in individual schools, or political activities. No grants to individuals (except for scholarships), or for emergency funding, endowments, annual campaigns, deficit financing, research, publications, films, or conferences, unless so designated by a donor; no loans.

2128. Douglas County Library Foundation, Roseburg, OR. $12,750, 2000.

2129. Eugene Public Library Foundation, Eugene, OR. $119,300, 2000.

2130. Institute for the Northwest, Portland, OR. $11,000, 2000.

2131. Jackson County Library Foundation, Medford, OR. $10,000, 2000.

2132. Jefferson County Library Association, Madras, OR. $12,465, 2000.

2133. Josephine County Library Foundation, Grants Pass, OR. $20,000, 2000.

2134. Multnomah County Library, Portland, OR. $722,319, 2000.

2135. Newport Public Library Foundation, Newport, OR. $23,800, 2000.

2136. Oregon Trail Library District, Boardman, OR. $19,608, 2000.

2137. Wallowa County Library, Enterprise, OR. $10,000, 2000.

2138. Yoncalla Library Foundation, Yoncalla, OR. $90,000, 2000.

PENNSYLVANIA

Alcoa Foundation

Limitations: Giving primarily in areas of company operations, national and international; emphasis on local communities: Davenport, IA, Evansville, IN, Massena, NY, Cleveland, OH, Pittsburgh, PA, Knoxville, TN, and Rockdale, TX. No support for sectarian or religious organizations, or political purposes. No grants to individuals (except for employee-related scholarships), or for endowment funds, deficit reduction, documentaries and videos, tickets, souvenir programs, advertising, golf outings, trips, tours, or student exchange programs.

2139. Carnegie Library of Homestead, Munhall, PA. $13,000, 2000. For space planning feasibility study.

2140. Charities Aid Foundation, West Malling, England. $25,000, 2000. For support of charitable grantmaking efforts in Russia.

2141. Giddings, City of, Giddings, TX. $30,000, 2000. 3-year grant. For relocation of Rufus Young King Library.

2142. IESP Chaminade Marianistas, Callao, Peru. $26,733, 2000. For renovation of library into information center.

2143. Joint Center for Political and Economic Studies, DC. $30,000, 2000. For continued support for Databank project on national population.

2144. Ministry of Education of Jamaica, Kingston, Jamaica. $10,000, 2000. For renovation at Mitchel Town All Age for school library.

2145. Tippecanoe County Public Library Foundation, Lafayette, IN. $15,000, 2000. 3-year grant. For purchase of books for additional library in Lafayette area.

The Annenberg Foundation

Limitations: No grants to individuals, or for basic research, capital construction, or general operating expenses.

2146. American Friends of the British Museum, NYC, NY. $1,919,000, 2000. For Walter and Leonore Annenberg Information Center in Round Reading Room.

2147. American Library in Paris USA Foundation, Paris, France. $25,000, 2000.

2148. Colonial Williamsburg Foundation, Williamsburg, VA. $3,000,000, 2000. Toward construction and to endow programs at Bruton Heights School Education Center.

2149. Eisenhower Foundation, Abilene, KS. $50,000, 2000. For continued support for K-12 education programs.

2150. Harry S. Truman Library Institute for National and International Affairs, Independence, MO. $20,000, 2000.

2151. Library Foundation of Los Angeles, Los Angeles, CA. $40,000, 2000. For K-12 education programs.

2152. Library of Congress, DC. $500,000, 2000.

2153. Library of Congress, DC. $200,000, 2000. For continued support for trust fund board.

2154. Library of Congress, DC. $150,000, 2000.

2155. Los Angeles County Public Library Foundation, Downey, CA. $50,000, 2000. For K-12 education programs.

2156. Rancho Mirage Public Library, Rancho Mirage, CA. $20,000, 2000.

2157. Ronald Reagan Presidential Foundation, Simi Valley, CA. $200,000, 2000.

2158. Survivors of the Shoah Visual History Foundation, Los Angeles, CA. $200,000, 2000.

Barra Foundation, Inc.

Limitations: Giving primarily in the Philadelphia, PA, area. No grants to individuals, or for annual or capital campaigns, building or endowment funds, operating budgets, deficit drives, scholarships, fellowships, ongoing programs, publications, catalogues or exhibitions; no loans.

2159. Athenaeum of Philadelphia, Philadelphia, PA. $50,000, 2000. For retroconversion project.

2160. Balch Institute for Ethnic Studies, Philadelphia, PA. $22,500, 2000. For Chautauqua Conferences.

2161. Free Library of Philadelphia Foundation, Philadelphia, PA. $10,000, 2000. For general support.

2162. Library Company of Philadelphia, Philadelphia, PA. $500,000, 2000. For Zinman Collection.

2163. Library Company of Philadelphia, Philadelphia, PA. $50,000, 2000. For retrospective conversion.

Claude Worthington Benedum Foundation

Limitations: Giving limited to southwestern PA and WV. No support for national health and welfare campaigns, medical research, religious activities, national organizations, or individual elementary or secondary schools. No grants to individuals, or for student aid, fellowships, travel, ongoing operating expenses, annual appeals, membership drives, conferences, films, books, or audio-visual productions, unless an integral part of a foundation supported program.

2164. Burnsville Public Library, Burnsville, WV. $25,000, 1999. For library facility expansion.

2165. Clay Mountain Housing, Clay, WV. $25,000, 1999. For continued program support.

2166. Family Service of Marion and Harrison Counties, Fairmont, WV. $45,000, 1999. For seed money for comprehensive, parenting information service.

2167. Pocahontas County Free Libraries, Hillsboro, WV. $25,000, 1999. For matching grant for construction of library in Marlinton.

2168. Richwood Public Library, Richwood, WV. $13,900, 1999. For renovation for library facility in Nicholas County.

2169. Shadyside Hospital Foundation, Pittsburgh, PA. $1,000,000, 1999. For Oncology Informatics Center at Hillman Cancer Center.

The Buhl Foundation

Limitations: Giving primarily in southwestern PA, with emphasis on the Pittsburgh area. No support for religious or political activities, or nationally funded organizations. No grants to individuals, or for building or endowment funds, operating budgets, scholarships, fellowships, equipment, land acquisition, annual campaigns, emergency funds, deficit financing, fundraising campaigns, renovation projects, publications, conferences or seminars (unless grant-related).

2170. Allegheny Intermediate Unit, Pittsburgh, PA. $15,500, 2000. For dinner program in connection with development of Southwestern Pennsylvania Educator Clearinghouse.

2171. Allegheny Intermediate Unit, Pittsburgh, PA. $12,500, 2000. For scanners in connection with development of Southwestern Pennsylvania Educator Clearinghouse.

2172. Carnegie Library of Pittsburgh, Pittsburgh, PA. $250,000, 2000. For customer research component of Agenda for Change: Planning for the Future.

2173. La Roche College, Pittsburgh, PA. $131,050, 2000. For integrated online library system for college library.

2174. Pittsburgh Regional Alliance, Pittsburgh, PA. $26,675, 2000. For ERISS Project.

2175. 3 Rivers Connect, Pittsburgh, PA. $35,000, 2000. For Information Commons 2000, Smart Building Project.

E. Rhodes & Leona B. Carpenter Foundation

Limitations: Giving primarily in areas east of the Mississippi River. No support for local church congregations or parishes, private secondary education, or large public charities. No grants to individuals.

2176. Duke University, Perkins Library, Durham, NC. $1,000,000, 1999. To construct seminar rooms.

2177. Harvard University, Divinity School, Cambridge, MA. $250,000, 1999. To renovate Andover-Harvard Theological Library.

2178. Pierpont Morgan Library, NYC, NY. $100,000, 1999. Toward digitizing books and artwork.

2179. Queens Library Foundation, Jamaica, NY. $25,000, 1999. Toward exhibition, Visible Traces: Rare Books and Special Collections from China.

2180. Seattle University, Seattle, WA. $25,000, 1999. To augment Lemieux Library resources in theological studies.

2181. Temple Public Library, Foundation of, Temple, TX. $55,305, 1999. To improve circulation desk.

2182. Temple Public Library, Foundation of, Temple, TX. $44,006, 1999. To expand genealogy section.

2183. Yale University, Divinity School, New Haven, CT. $100,000, 1999. Toward library renovation.

Connelly Foundation

Limitations: Giving primarily in the Philadelphia, PA, and Delaware Valley areas. No grants to individuals, or for research.

2184. Academy of Natural Sciences of Philadelphia, Philadelphia, PA. $150,000, 1999. For renovation of Dinosaur Hall and integrated electronic library system for Ewell Sale Stewart Library.

2185. Balch Institute for Ethnic Studies, Philadelphia, PA. $40,000, 1999. To build support and audience for Institute through multi-faceted marketing program - including salaries, printing costs, advertising, computers, postage and supplies.

2186. Crime Prevention Association, Philadelphia, PA. $75,000, 1999. For Samuel S. Fels Community Center to be built to house senior citizen program, day care program, recreational or athletic program and library for community residents and offices for staff.

2187. Euphrasia House, Philadelphia, PA. $12,000, 1999. For general operating support and hotline that connects homeless and abused women with support services as they transition to independence.

2188. Holy Ghost Preparatory School, Bensalem, PA. $504,235, 1999. For capital campaign for construction of buildings for library, info and technology center; conversion of existing library to art studio, renovation of main entrance way, and installation of elevator.

2189. Iona College, New Rochelle, NY. $50,000, 1999. For expansion and renovation of Ryan Library in form of multimedia classroom in which instructional services programs will be provided.

2190. Little Flower Catholic High School for Girls, Philadelphia, PA. $45,000, 1999. To enhance student and faculty research and learning capacity in all disciplines via installation of state-of-the-art library/information center.

2191. Malvern Preparatory School, Malvern, PA. $750,000, 1999. For capital campaign Building From Within: The Campaign for Malvern, for renovations to dining hall and math and science center; also construction of new athletic facility and library or technology center.

2192. Rosenbach Museum and Library, Philadelphia, PA. $25,000, 1999. For restoration of historic buildings that house museum on Delancey Place.

The Eberly Foundation

Limitations: Giving primarily in OK, PA, and WV.

2193. George C. Marshall Research Foundation, Lexington, VA. $47,000, 1999. For Phase II of construction of Marshall Memorial Plaza.

2194. Waynesburg College, Waynesburg, PA. $50,000, 1999. For continued capital support for library.

Eden Hall Foundation

Limitations: Giving limited to western PA. No support for private foundations. No grants to individuals, or for operating budgets, deficit financing, or general fundraising campaigns.

2195. Butler County Federated Library System, Butler, PA. $100,000, 1999. To upgrade automation systems of member libraries.

2196. Ligonier Valley Library, Ligonier, PA. $75,000, 1999. For outreach programming and children's center.

Grable Foundation

Limitations: Giving primarily in southwestern PA. No grants to individuals, or for scholarships, endowment funds, or capital campaigns.

2197. Pauline Auberle Foundation, McKeesport, PA. $100,000, 1999. For library and computer center.

2198. 3 Rivers Connect, Pittsburgh, PA. $100,000, 1999. For Internet Education Consortium.

Howard Heinz Endowment

Limitations: Giving limited to activities which directly benefit the citizens of PA, with emphasis on Pittsburgh and western PA. No grants to individuals.

2199. Duquesne University, Institute for Economic Transformation, Pittsburgh, PA. $350,000, 1999. For manufacturing workforce clearinghouse focused on low-income residents and inner-city manufacturing firms, and on building network of partnerships with faith based communities.

2200. Pittsburgh Regional Alliance, Pittsburgh, PA. $250,000, 1999. For creation of regional labor information clearinghouse(PROWL); significant expansion of regional internship development capacity; and joint projects between old/new economy community leaders.

2201. 3 Rivers Connect, Pittsburgh, PA. $500,000, 1999. Toward creation of Pittsburgh I-Net telecommunications network.

2202. 3 Rivers Connect, Pittsburgh, PA. $125,000, 1999. For regional robotics and science initiative for high schools.

Vira I. Heinz Endowment

Limitations: Giving primarily directed to Pittsburgh and western PA, although in certain cases support may be considered on a national or international basis. No grants to individuals.

2203. Allegheny Intermediate Unit, Pittsburgh, PA. $110,000, 1999. For regional clearinghouse for teacher recruitment.

2204. Carnegie Library of Pittsburgh, Pittsburgh, PA. $10,000, 1999. For program services, newsletter, and professional development activities for Foundation Center Library.

2205. Carnegie-Mellon University, Pittsburgh, PA. $20,000, 1999. For initial business-planning and conference-organizing efforts by

MBA and computer science department students to create and hold National High-Tech Conference in Pittsburgh.

2206. Corporation for Enterprise Development (CFED), DC. $20,000, 1999. For website that will collect and share 21st century, new economy economic development strategies and benchmarking case studies, to benefit economic development groups and professionals in Pennsylvania and other states.

2207. 3 Rivers Connect, Pittsburgh, PA. $200,000, 1999. For regional technology for learning initiatives.

2208. 3 Rivers Connect, Pittsburgh, PA. $100,000, 1999. For regional teacher and technology initiatives among schools.

2209. 3 Rivers Connect, Pittsburgh, PA. $20,000, 1999. For Pittsburgh Greenmap Project, Internet-based regional information system highlighting Pittsburgh's green assets.

Heinz Family Foundation

Limitations: No grants to individuals (except for Heinz Awards).

2210. Brashear Association, Pittsburgh, PA. $10,000, 1999. For general operating support for OASIS (Older Adult Service and Information System).

2211. Folger Shakespeare Library, DC. $20,250, 1999. For general operating support.

2212. Library of Congress, DC. $50,000, 1999. For congressional education project.

The Hillman Foundation, Inc.

Limitations: Giving primarily in Pittsburgh and southwestern PA. No grants to individuals, or for operating budgets, annual campaigns, deficit financing, travel, or conferences; no loans.

2213. Oakmont Carnegie Library, Oakmont, PA. $50,000, 2000. Toward renovation and expansion of facility.

2214. University of Pittsburgh, Pittsburgh, PA. $2,500,000, 2000. 5-year grant. Toward establishment of endowed chair for University Librarian/University Library Services Director.

Independence Foundation

Limitations: Giving primarily in Philadelphia, PA, and Bucks, Chester, Delaware, and Montgomery counties. No grants to individuals, or for building and development funds, travel, research, publications, or matching gifts.

2215. Balch Institute for Ethnic Studies, Philadelphia, PA. $10,000, 1999. For general support.

2216. Free Library of Philadelphia, Philadelphia, PA. $100,000, 1999. 2-year grant. For project support.

2217. Library Company of Philadelphia, Philadelphia, PA. $30,000, 1999. 3-year grant. For project support.

2218. Rosenbach Museum and Library, Philadelphia, PA. $10,000, 1999. For general support.

The Mary Hillman Jennings Foundation

Limitations: Giving primarily in the Pittsburgh, PA, area. No grants to individuals.

2219. Ligonier Valley Library, Ligonier, PA. $25,000, 1999.

2220. Sewickley Public Library, Sewickley, PA. $20,000, 1999.

The Sidney Kimmel Foundation

Limitations: Giving primarily in NY and PA. No grants to individuals.

2221. Center for Jewish History, NYC, NY. $25,000, 1999.

2222. Survivors of the Shoah Visual History Foundation, Los Angeles, CA. $250,000, 1999.

Laurel Foundation

Limitations: Giving primarily in southwestern PA. No grants to individuals, or for multi-year support.

2223. Carnegie Library of Pittsburgh, Pittsburgh, PA. $20,000, 1999. For Beginning with Books program to encourage children to read and enjoy books.

2224. Ligonier Valley Library Association, Ligonier, PA. $50,000, 1999. For capital campaign.

John R. McCune Charitable Trust

Limitations: Giving primarily in southwestern PA.

2225. Carnegie Library of Pittsburgh, Pittsburgh, PA. $30,000, 1999. For general support.

McCune Foundation

Limitations: Giving primarily in southwestern PA, with emphasis on the Pittsburgh area. No grants to individuals, or for general operating purposes.

2226. B. F. Jones Memorial Library, Aliquippa, PA. $75,000, 2000. To complete building renovations.

2227. Carnegie Library of Pittsburgh, Pittsburgh, PA. $250,000, 2000. To install air conditioning and upgrade related systems in Homewood Branch Library.

2228. Ligonier Valley Library Association, Ligonier, PA. $50,000, 2000. For capital improvements.

Richard King Mellon Foundation

Limitations: Giving primarily in Pittsburgh and southwestern PA, except for nationwide conservation programs. No grants outside the U.S.. No grants to individuals, or for fellowships or scholarships, or conduit organizations.

2229. Carnegie Library of Pittsburgh, Pittsburgh, PA. $750,000, 2000. For capital campaign to modernize Pittsburgh's Carnegie Library.

2230. Chatham College, Pittsburgh, PA. $2,000,000, 2000. For capital campaign to renovate Jennie King Mellon Library.

2231. Earth Action Network, Norwalk, CT. $25,000, 2000. Toward publication of E-The Environmental Magazine's issue on Urban Sprawl.

2232. 3 Rivers Connect, Pittsburgh, PA. $200,000, 2000. For Airport Concierge Project that provides information through use of technology.

2233. 3 Rivers Connect, Pittsburgh, PA. $50,000, 2000. For greenpittsburgh.net, searchable map of region's natural amenities, recreation areas, and environmental resources.

The William Penn Foundation

Limitations: Giving limited to Camden, NJ and Philadelphia, Bucks, Chester, Delaware, and Montgomery counties, PA; environmental giving in northern DE, small portion of northeastern MD, southern NJ, and larger area of southeastern PA; no national or international giving (except at foundation's initiative). No support for sectarian religious activities, recreational programs, political lobbying or legislative activities, nonpublic schools, pass-through organizations, mental health or retardation treatment programs, or programs focusing on a particular disease, disability, or treatment for addiction, or profit-making enterprises. No grants to individuals, or for debt reduction, hospital capital projects, medical research, programs that replace lost government support, housing construction or rehabilitation, scholarships, or fellowships; no loans or program-related investments.

2234. American Youth Work Center, DC. $16,500, 2000. Toward providing Philadelphia area coverage, in Youth Today newspaper, of best practices of youth-serving agencies, and toward increase in Youth Today circulation over 3 years to program staff and youth policy makers.

2235. Balch Institute for Ethnic Studies, Philadelphia, PA. $396,000, 2000. 3-year grant. Toward Educating for Philadelphia's Changing Diversity: New Immigrants Project, which will give voice to experiences and increase public understanding of new immigrants.

2236. Central Philadelphia Development Corporation, Philadelphia, PA. $82,500, 2000. Toward development of three-dimensional, virtual reality model and web site of Center City Philadelphia.

2237. Free Library of Philadelphia, Philadelphia, PA. $272,250, 2000. 3-year grant. Toward project LEAP, program providing homework and technology assistance and ethnic and cultural enrichment programs to children in branch libraries.

2238. Library Company of Philadelphia, Philadelphia, PA. $880,000, 2000. 4-year grant. Toward renovation of historic Cassatt House as research center and acquisition of Michael Zinman Collection of Early American Imprints.

2239. Manomet Center for Conservation Sciences, Manomet, MA. $49,500, 2000. 1.50-year grant. Toward development of information on wading bird management techniques and dissemination of this information to local organizations participating in Special Area Management Plan for Pea Patch Island Heronry Region.

2240. Maternal Child Health Consortium of Chester County, West Chester, PA. $302,500, 2000. 2-year grant. Toward Latina Health Initiative, providing low-income pregnant and parenting Latina women and their children with linkages to health insurance and prenatal and pediatric care.

2241. National Center for Family Philanthropy, DC. $38,500, 2000. Toward development and production of planning workbook for families and foundations interested in philanthropy.

2242. Parents Union for Public Schools in Philadelphia, Philadelphia, PA. $290,000, 2000. 2-year grant. For support and expansion of Parent Resource Center, which would provide information to parents in MLK and West Philadelphia Clusters of Philadelphia School District.

2243. Philadelphia Health Management Corporation, Philadelphia, PA. $383,180, 2000. 2-year grant. Toward development of Health Data Resource Center and dissemination of information to health and social service providers in southeastern Pennsylvania.

2244. Philadelphia Museum of Art, Philadelphia, PA. $156,062, 2000. Toward collaboration with other institutions of Philadelphia Area Consortium of Special Collections Libraries in presenting Leaves of Gold: Treasures of Manuscript Ilumination from Philadelphia Collections.

2245. Temple University, College of Education, Philadelphia, PA. $78,822, 2000. To complete evaluation of impact of Foundation grant to Free Library of Philadelphia on children's library use and educational outcomes.

The Pew Charitable Trusts

Limitations: Giving on a national basis, with a special commitment to the Philadelphia, PA, region. No support for political organizations. No grants to individuals, or for endowment funds, capital campaigns, construction, equipment, deficit financing, scholarships, or fellowships (except those identified or initiated by the trusts).

2246. Action AIDS, Philadelphia, PA. $160,000, 2000. 2-year grant. To provide mental health services in conjunction with housing counseling and employment services, to HIV-positive individuals in Philadelphia.

2247. Alliance for Better Campaigns, DC. $175,000, 2000. For efforts to encourage television broadcasters to provide five minutes per night of candidate-centered discourse in 30 days before primary and general elections.

2248. American Academy of Religion, Atlanta, GA. $1,200,000, 2000. 3-year grant. To establish referral service that would link members of news media with academic experts on religion and public life issues.

2249. American Red Cross, Lower Bucks County Chapter, Levittown, PA. $11,000, 2000. 2-year grant. For technology and staff training to improve data management.

2250. Association of American Universities, DC. $1,200,000, 2000. 3-year grant. For matching grant for work to create Association of American Universities Clearinghouse to translate state standards and performance assessments for high school graduation into criteria for university admissions.

2251. Bucks County Housing Group, Langhorne, PA. $88,000, 2000. 2-year grant. To establish comprehensive organizational database to enhance ability to monitor and assess shelter programs.

2252. Calcutta House, Philadelphia, PA. $34,000, 2000. 2-year grant. To develop database to track resident outcomes and assess program results.

2253. Center for Public Integrity, DC. $176,000, 2000. For matching grant toward project designed to shine light on role of issue advocacy in campaigns by providing information on sponsors of issue ads to journalists, citizens and academics.

2254. Center for Responsive Politics, DC. $550,000, 2000. 2-year grant. To expand nation's understanding of role and implications of money in politics.

2255. Childrens Hospital Foundation, Philadelphia, PA. $2,000,000, 2000. 4-year grant. For Asthma Network Initiative, which focuses on improving delivery of pediatric asthma care, coordinating educational outreach for families and promoting clinical research.

2256. Consultative Group on Biological Diversity, San Francisco, CA. $60,000, 2000. 2-year grant. For continued support to create information partnerships among foundations and other nonprofits to strategically address loss of biodiversity.

2257. Delaware County Intermediate Unit Education Foundation, Media, PA. $30,000, 2000. 2-year grant. For management information system for data collection, client tracking and outcomes measurement for Delaware County Family Centers.

2258. Eleutherian Mills-Hagley Foundation, Wilmington, DE. $105,000, 2000. 3-year grant. For general operating support for library and Center for Advanced Study.

2259. Energy Coordinating Agency of Philadelphia, Philadelphia, PA. $45,000, 2000. 2-year grant. To enhance new database to integrate information across several programs and train staff in its use.

2260. Foundation Center, NYC, NY. $255,000, 2000. 3-year grant. For general operating support.

2261. Frankford Group Ministry, Philadelphia, PA. $20,000, 2000. 2-year grant. To develop computerized database to better track client outcomes.

2262. Free Library of Philadelphia, Philadelphia, PA. $160,000, 2000. 2-year grant. For continued support of Learning, Enjoyment and Play (LEAP) program providing year-round educational support and enrichment to disadvantaged children and youth.

2263. George Junior Republic, Grove City, PA. $300,000, 2000. 2-year grant. To renovate Memorial Home into Multimedia Technology Center and Library and for construction of two new homes and Special Needs Unit.

2264. Library Company of Philadelphia, Philadelphia, PA. $250,000, 2000. For capital project to renovate historic townhouse into residential research center for study of early American history and culture.

2265. Library Company of Philadelphia, Philadelphia, PA. $150,000, 2000. 3-year grant. For matching grant toward general operations, as part of Philadelphia Cultural Leadership Program.

2266. Lutheran Social Mission Society of Philadelphia, Lutheran Settlement House, Philadelphia, PA. $50,000, 2000. 2-year grant. For support of agencywide database and improved technology for job counseling program.

2267. Montgomery County MH/MR Emergency Service, Norristown, PA. $95,000, 2000. 2-year grant. For clinical systems database for emergency behavioral health care facility in Montgomery County.

2268. Peoples Emergency Center, Philadelphia, PA. $40,000, 2000. 2-year grant. To develop customized database for job training program for homeless clients.

2269. Philadelphia Fight, Philadelphia, PA. $92,000, 2000. 2-year grant. To expand Project TEACH, providing information about treatment options and need for compliance with their medication regimens to low-income Philadelphians living with HIV/AIDS.

2270. Physicians for Social Responsibility, DC. $296,000, 2000. To build network of health care providers interested in environmental health issues.

2271. Princeton University, Princeton, NJ. $1,924,000, 2000. 3-year grant. For fully searchable, digital archive containing policy-relevant information on arts and culture, to be housed at and managed by University Library's Social Science Reference Center.

2272. Quebec-Labrador Foundation/Atlantic Center for the Environment, Ipswich, MA. $360,000, 2000. 3-year grant. For ministry serving people and clergy of Quebec Lower North Shore, and of establishing archival collection that will document ministry's accomplishments in that region.

2273. Rosenbach Museum and Library, Philadelphia, PA. $180,000, 2000. 3-year grant. For general operations, as part of Philadelphia Cultural Leadership Program.

2274. Southern Home Services, Philadelphia, PA. $75,000, 2000. 2-year grant. To complete efforts to upgrade management information system in relation to abuse prevention services.

2275. Stanford University, Department of Communications, Stanford, CA. $585,000, 2000. 2-year grant. For matching grant toward work to support technological initiative designed to provide public with more information about candidates, thereby increasing voter participation.

2276. Supportive Child/Adult Network (SCAN), Philadelphia, PA. $81,000, 2000. 2-year grant. For technical support for efforts to improve communication and technological infrastructure.

2277. Tabor Childrens Services, Doylestown, PA. $89,000, 2000. 2-year grant. For technical assistance toward development of management information system to measure outcomes of in-home services.

2278. Temple University, Center for Public Policy, Philadelphia, PA. $400,000, 2000. 2-year grant. For project to develop and assess ways to network local efforts to engage young adults in civic life of their communities.

2279. Thomas Jefferson University Hospitals, Chinese Community Partnership for Health, Philadelphia, PA. $122,000, 2000. 2-year grant. To provide support services and information about community resources for children to Chinese-speaking families.

2280. Unemployment Information Center, Philadelphia, PA. $65,000, 2000. 2-year grant. For continued operating support to provide benefits counseling and job club services to poor and unemployed adults.

2281. University of Virginia Law School Foundation, Charlottesville, VA. $500,000, 2000. 2-year grant. To develop and disseminate practice guide to current campaign finance regulation for use by citizens, public interest groups and policy makers.

The Philadelphia Foundation

Limitations: Giving limited to Bucks, Chester, Delaware, Montgomery, and Philadelphia counties in southeastern PA, except for designated funds. No support for religious teachings; generally, low priority given to national organizations, government agencies, large budget agencies, private schools, or umbrella funding organizations. No grants to individuals, or for annual or capital campaigns, building funds, land acquisition, endowment funds, research, publications, tours or trips, conferences, or deficit financing; no loans.

2282. Balch Institute for Ethnic Studies, Philadelphia, PA. $25,000, 2000. For general operating support.

2283. Bayard Taylor Memorial Library, Kennett Square, PA. $10,000, 2000. For Adult Literacy Program.

2284. Institute for the Study of Civic Values, Philadelphia, PA. $10,000, 2000. For Neighborhood Builders Online website.

2285. Northwest Interfaith Movement, Philadelphia, PA. $14,000, 2000. For Long Term Care Connection Project.

2286. Rosenbach Museum and Library, Philadelphia, PA. $40,000, 2000. For continued support for education department.

The Pittsburgh Foundation

Limitations: Giving from unrestricted funds limited to Pittsburgh and Allegheny County, PA. No support for churches, private and parochial schools, or hospitals (from unrestricted funds). No grants to individuals (from discretionary funds except for the Isabel P. Kennedy Award) or for annual campaigns, endowment funds, travel, operating budgets, scholarships, fellowships, internships, awards, special events or research of a highly technical or specialized nature; no loans to individuals.

2287. Butler Area Public Library, Butler, PA. $20,000, 2000. For furnishings.

2288. Carnegie Library of Pittsburgh, Pittsburgh, PA. $250,000, 2000. To revitalize facility system and customer focus to insure its place as important 21st Century Pittsburgh institution.

2289. Focus on Renewal-Sto-Rox Neighborhood Corporation, McKees Rocks, PA. $75,000, 2000. To expand Focus on Renewal Sto-Rox Library's services to include children's programming.

2290. Friends of the Music Library, Carnegie Library of Pittsburgh, Pittsburgh, PA. $15,587, 2000. For general support.

2291. Supreme Council Charities, Pittsburgh, PA. $24,152, 2000. For Masonic Museum and Library, Scholarship Fund and Schizophrenia Research Programs.

2292. University of Pittsburgh, Pittsburgh, PA. $15,034, 2000. For Theodore M. Finney Musical Library.

2293. Western Pennsylvania Hospital Foundation, Pittsburgh, PA. $15,000, 2000. To equip medical library with upgraded technology and internet capacity.

2294. 3 Rivers Connect, Pittsburgh, PA. $130,000, 2000. For Smart Building Project in Regional Enterprise Tower.

The PNC Foundation

Limitations: Giving primarily in headquarters and company locations: DE, IN, KY, NJ, OH, and PA. No support for churches or for religious purposes. No grants to individuals, or for endowment funds; no loans.

2295. Free Library of Philadelphia, Philadelphia, PA. $30,000, 1999.

2296. West Shore Public Library, Camp Hill, PA. $20,000, 1999.

PPG Industries Foundation

Limitations: Giving primarily in areas of company operations, with emphasis on the Pittsburgh, PA, region. No support for religious groups for religious purposes, or political activities. No grants to individuals, or for endowment funds, advertising, benefits, or operating support of United Way member agencies; no loans or grants of less than $100 (except for matching gifts).

2297. Carnegie Library of Pittsburgh, Pittsburgh, PA. $30,000, 1999.

2298. Community Center and Library Association, Pittsburgh, PA. $10,000, 1999.

2299. Mount Zion Public Library, Mount Zion, IL. $10,000, 1999.

Sarah Scaife Foundation, Inc.

Limitations: No support for nationally organized fundraising groups. No grants to individuals, or for deficit financing or scholarships; no loans.

2300. George C. Marshall Research Foundation, Lexington, VA. $100,000, 1999. For capital campaign.

R. P. Simmons Family Foundation

Limitations: Giving primarily in PA, with emphasis on Pittsburgh. No grants to individuals.

2301. Sewickley Public Library, Sewickley, PA. $150,000, 1999. For capital campaign.

John Templeton Foundation

Limitations: Giving on a national and international basis. No grants to individuals, (except for awards chosen by trustees) or for scholarships, endowment funds, building funds, capital campaigns, or artistic productions; no loans.

2302. Alister Hardy Trust, Religious Experience Research Centre, Oxford, England. $23,320, 1999. For computerization of archives.

2303. Churches Uniting in Global Mission, Apple Valley, CA. $125,000, 1999. For Journal of Church Growth.

2304. Good News Communication, Atlanta, GA. $120,835, 1999. For Movieguide Awards program.

Harry C. Trexler Trust

Limitations: Giving limited to Lehigh County, PA. No grants to individuals, or for endowment funds, research, scholarships, or fellowships; no loans.

2305. Allentown Public Library, Allentown, PA. $206,000, 2000. For debt reduction.

2306. Whitehall Public Library, Whitehall, PA. $15,000, 2000. For additions to recorded book section.

USX Foundation, Inc.

Limitations: Giving primarily in areas of company operations in the U.S., including AK, AL, CO, IL, IN, LA, MI, MN, OH, OK, western PA, and TX. No support for religious organizations for religious purposes, economic development projects, or preschool to grade 12 education, hospitals or nursing homes. No grants to individuals (except for employee-related scholarships), or for conferences, seminars, symposia, travel, exhibits, special or fundraising events, fellowships, publication of papers, books or magazines, production of films, videotapes, or other audio-visual materials, or operating support of United Way agencies; no loans.

2307. Braddock Carnegie Library and Community Center, Braddock, PA. $20,000, 1999. For capital support.

The Helen F. Whitaker Fund

Limitations: Giving on a national basis, additional regional programs for the Naples, FL, area and the Harrisburg and Philadelphia, PA, areas. No grants to individuals.

2308. American Music Center, NYC, NY. $25,000, 1999. For Copying Assistance Program.

2309. Philharmonic Center for the Arts, Naples, FL. $71,871, 1999. To expand music library.

RHODE ISLAND

The Champlin Foundations

Limitations: Giving primarily in RI. No support for religious schools, books, films, videos, or plays. No grants to individuals, or for general support, program or operating budgets, matching gifts, special projects, research, publications, conferences, or continuing support; no loans.

2310. Barrington Public Library, Barrington, RI. $80,075, 2000. For carpet, PCs and cable, sound system, and collection development.

2311. Brown University, Providence, RI. $500,000, 2000. For equipment for School of Medicine, medical education scholarships, undergraduate scholarships, Champlin Memorial stamp collection, and librarian's discretionary fund.

2312. Brown University, John Carter Brown Library, Providence, RI. $55,200, 2000. Toward Bolivar Room construction woodworking, marble floor, antique furniture repair, furnishings, microfilm storage cabinet, stack chairs, work stations, and plate glass shelves.

2313. Central Falls Free Public Library, Central Falls, RI. $142,082, 2000. For various repairs and improvements.

2314. Clark Memorial Library, Carolina, RI. $57,300, 2000. For renovations to roof, tower, windows and wall and for PCs, end panels, shelving units, Images of Rhode Island, revolving bookcase, audio books, and books.

2315. Cooperating Libraries Automated Network (CLAN), Providence, RI. $34,580, 2000. For conversion of non-MARC records in CLAN database, security cabinet, PCs and furniture.

2316. Coventry Public Library, Coventry, RI. $38,695, 2000. For PCs, laser printers, cabling, laptop computer, switch and cascade attachment, picture book bins, children's tables, and reference and general collection materials.

2317. Cranston Public Library, Cranston, RI. $46,475, 2000. To retrofit computer lab, install sound system at Hall Library, and for collection development, electronic readers for E-books, and book and newspaper display.

2318. Cross Mills Public Library, Charlestown, RI. $22,017, 2000. For PCs, printers, window blinds, oak table, displays, storage room, and book storage in cabin.

2319. Cumberland Public Library, Cumberland, RI. $22,700, 2000. For PCs, Tapecheck for videos, computer DVD drive, and collection development.

2320. Davisville Free Library Association, North Kingstown, RI. $164,500, 2000. For book acquisition, computer software, furniture and equipment, book and artifact restoration, library expansion, tree removal, and CLAN data entry.

2321. East Providence Public Library, East Providence, RI. $58,500, 2000. For exterior painting at Fuller, gutter and window repair at Weaver, upgrading PCs, printers, and Reliance, and Walker picture display.

2322. George Hail Free Library, Warren, RI. $36,560, 2000. To replace furnaces and condensers, clean and protect chimneys and tower, and for renovations, furniture, and collection development.

2323. Greene Public Library, Greene, RI. $90,000, 2000. For library addition, for design and installation of sand filter system, and for well drilling and installation.

2324. Greenville Public Library, Greenville, RI. $42,000, 2000. For health books, computers, Novell 5.0 upgrade to make wireless connections to the Internet and network hub, new telephone system, and tables and chairs.

2325. Harmony Library, Harmony, RI. $13,638, 2000. For computers, printers, reference shelves, collection development, supplies, and floor seating.

2326. Hope Library Association, Hope, RI. $162,850, 2000. For renovating basement, adding circulation workroom on main level, and furnishings for new children's room and new young adult space, and shed.

2327. Island Free Library, Block Island, RI. $55,245, 2000. For CLAN related equipment, including PCs and Images of Rhode Island.

2328. Jamestown Philomenian Library, Jamestown, RI. $24,800, 2000. For meeting hall, sound system, book drop, file and supplies for state mandated preservation plan, shelving, equipment for computer study room, and chairs.

2329. Jesse M. Smith Memorial Library, Harrisville, RI. $13,000, 2000. For PCs, printer, and collection development.

2330. Lincoln Public Library, Lincoln, RI. $16,410, 2000. For display Kiosk, collection development, Ellison letter machine, hanging bag display, projector, DVD player, and printer.

2331. Louttit Library, West Greenwich, RI. $35,845, 2000. For outdoor lighting and electrical work, landscaping, sidewalks and curbing, entrance sign, dehumidifiers, and computer tables.

2332. Marian J. Mohr Memorial Library, Johnston, RI. $37,800, 2000. For circulation desk, carpeting, reference materials, laptop, digital projector, CD-ROM recorder, computers, and network server.

2333. Memorial and Library Association of Westerly, Westerly, RI. $197,315, 2000. For roof repairs, painting, PCs, scanners, and laptop.

2334. Middletown Public Library, Middletown, RI. $12,333, 2000. For PCs, adapter cables, CD and audio displays, and media display shelves.

2335. Narragansett Public Library, Narragansett, RI. $30,173, 2000. For desks, chairs, file cabinets, book cases, computer upgrades including PC, laser scanner, software, licenses, CD-ROM, digital printers and camera, and digital reader printer.

2336. Newport Public Library, Newport, RI. $300,000, 2000. Toward library addition.

2337. North Providence Union Free Library, North Providence, RI. $51,975, 2000. For switch, computers, printers, cable runs, sled for LAN, digital camera, surge protectors, and computer monitoring system.

2338. North Scituate Public Library, North Scituate, RI. $16,900, 2000. For PCs, collection development, book trucks, shelves and display units, digital camera, and refrigerator.

2339. North Smithfield Public Library, Slatersville, RI. $173,692, 2000. For mobile compact shelving in stack area.

2340. Pascoag Public Library, Pascoag, RI. $11,755, 2000. For PC, collection development, lavatory fixtures, and children's room shelving.

2341. Pawtucket Public Library, Pawtucket, RI. $30,000, 2000. To construct group study rooms, buy and move shelving, move public access computers, and add security cameras.

2342. Portsmouth Free Public Library, Portsmouth, RI. $125,000, 2000. For addition to existing library building.

2343. Providence College, Providence, RI. $184,318, 2000. For computers, book scanners, and microfiche reader/printers for Phillips Memorial Library.

2344. Providence Public Library, Providence, RI. $1,796,000, 2000. For capital campaign, books, and personal computers.

2345. Providence Public Library, Providence, RI. $400,000, 2000. To replace current system with new third generation client/server library automation system.

2346. Redwood Library and Athenaeum, Newport, RI. $33,840, 2000. For library and technology equipment and purchase of reference sources.

2347. Rhode Island Natural History Survey, Kingston, RI. $33,590, 2000. For equipment for Biodiversity Center Biota of Rhode Island project, reference materials, upgraded computer system, and display materials.

2348. Rhode Island School of Design, Providence, RI. $202,000, 2000. For air-conditioning for Reading Room and other spaces of library.

2349. South Kingstown Public Library, Peace Dale, RI. $176,800, 2000. For microfilm reader and printer, collection of audiobooks, and renovations to Kingston Free Library.

2350. Tiverton Library Services, Tiverton, RI. $53,935, 2000. For young adult area, PCs, printers, rebinding, wiring and lights at union, and collection development.

2351. University of Rhode Island, Kingston, RI. $542,587, 2000. For Library, Pharmacy, Chemistry, Chemical Engineering programs and for Rhode Island Fish and Wildlife to study problems causing loss of native Ruffed Grouse.

2352. Warwick Public Library, Warwick, RI. $81,000, 2000. For compact stacks, reception desk, and chairs.

2353. West Warwick Public Library System, West Warwick, RI. $51,793, 2000. For PCs, laptop, printers, scanner, shelving, displays, and books.

2354. Woonsocket Harris Public Library, Woonsocket, RI. $415,840, 2000. For library addition and uploading of slides for Images of Rhode Island project.

Dorot Foundation

Limitations: Giving primarily in the U.S.; some giving also in Israel.

2355. Brown University, John Carter Brown Library, Providence, RI. $50,000, 2000.
2356. Jewish Womens Archives, Brookline, MA. $100,000, 2000.
2357. New York Public Library, NYC, NY. $800,000, 2000.

The Rhode Island Foundation

Limitations: Giving limited to RI. No support for religious organizations for sectarian purposes (except as specified by donors). No grants to individuals (except from donor-advised and designated funds), or for endowment funds, research, hospital equipment, capital needs of health organizations, annual campaigns, deficit financing, or educational institutions for general operating expenses; no loans.

2358. Greene Public Library, Greene, RI. $15,500, 2000. For addition to library.
2359. Memorial and Library Association of Westerly, Westerly, RI. $27,418, 2000. For operating support.
2360. Providence Plan, Providence, RI. $25,000, 2000. For community opportunity zone information network.
2361. Providence Public Library, Providence, RI. $50,000, 2000. For Family Reading Program.
2362. Providence Public Library, Providence, RI. $31,124, 2000. For operating support.
2363. Warwick Public Library, Warwick, RI. $61,304, 2000. For operating support.

The Thomas J. Watson Foundation

Limitations: No grants to individuals (except for seniors attending the 50 member colleges of The Watson Fellowship Program)..

2364. New York Society Library, NYC, NY. $20,000, 1999. For general operating support.
2365. Norwich Public Library Association, Norwich, VT. $10,000, 1999. For general operating support.

SOUTH CAROLINA

The Self Family Foundation

Limitations: Giving limited to SC, with primary emphasis on Greenwood. No grants to individuals, or for endowment funds, land acquisition, operating budgets, continuing support, annual campaigns, deficit financing, publications, conferences, scholarships, fellowships, or research-related programs; no loans.

2366. Greenwood School District No. 51, Ware Shoals, SC. $10,000, 1999. To purchase laptop computers for Ware Shoals Community Library.

TENNESSEE

The Assisi Foundation of Memphis, Inc.

Limitations: Giving primarily in Memphis and Shelby County, TN. No grants for endowments or building funds.

2367. Foundation for the Library, Memphis, TN. $200,000, 1999. For Consumer Health Center.
2368. Foundation for the Library, Memphis, TN. $50,000, 1999. For Consumer Health Center.
2369. Grant Center, Memphis, TN. $60,000, 1999. For programming support and technical assistance fund.

Benwood Foundation, Inc.

Limitations: Giving primarily in the Chattanooga, TN, area. No support for political organizations or causes. No grants to individuals, or for general operating expenses, financial deficits, fundraising, endowments, or multi-year grants; no loans (except for program related investments).

2370. Chattanooga-Hamilton County Library, Chattanooga, TN. $100,000, 2000.

Bridgestone/Firestone Trust Fund

Limitations: Giving primarily in areas of major company operations: AR, CO, CT, FL, IA, IL, IN, KY, LA, MI, NC, OH, OK, PA, SC, TN, TX, and UT. No support for religious or partisan political organizations or organizations who will use funds outside the U.S.. No grants to individuals, or for deficit financing, equipment, land acquisition, fellowships, publications, or conferences; no loans.

2371. Nashville Public Library Foundation, Nashville, TN. $250,000, 1999.

Community Foundation of Greater Memphis

Limitations: Giving limited to Crittenden County, AR, DeSoto County, MS, and metropolitan Memphis, including Fayette, Shelby, and Tipton counties, TN. No grants to individuals, (except for scholarships) or for budget deficits, endowments, capital or building funds, or annual campaigns.

2372. Charter School Resource Center of Tennessee, Memphis, TN. $15,000, 2000.
2373. Foundation for the Memphis Shelby County Public Library, Memphis, TN. $25,000, 2000.
2374. Foundation for the Memphis Shelby County Public Library, Memphis, TN. $20,000, 2000.
2375. Foundation for the Memphis Shelby County Public Library, Memphis, TN. $10,000, 2000.
2376. Grant Center, Memphis, TN. $10,000, 2000.

Joe C. Davis Foundation

Limitations: Giving primarily in the Nashville, TN, area.

2377. Nashville Public Library Foundation, Nashville, TN. $525,000, 2000. For capital campaign.

The Frist Foundation

Limitations: Giving primarily in Nashville, TN. No support for political activities, start-up expenses, disease-specific organizations seeking support for national projects, private foundations, religious organizations for religious purposes, hospitals, nursing homes, or retirement homes. No grants to individuals, or for endowment funds, biomedical or clinical research, social events or similar fundraising events, promotional materials including goodwill advertising, telethons, sponsorships, publications, trips, or tours.

2378. Country Music Foundation, Nashville, TN. $333,000, 2000. For library within new Country Music Hall of Fame.
2379. Family and Childrens Service, Nashville, TN. $67,000, 2000. To develop Internet-based management information system and joint human resource management program to serve seven-agency collaborative. Grant made through Fund for Collaboration.
2380. Friends of the Public Library of Nashville and Davidson County, Nashville, TN. $75,000, 2000. To revamp library card system, to raise awareness of library, and offer opportunities for people to contribute. Grant made through Ansley Fund.

Lyndhurst Foundation

Limitations: Giving limited to the southeastern U.S., with emphasis on Chattanooga, TN. Education grants are limited to two clusters of public schools, one in AL and one in Chattanooga, TN.

2381. Foundation Center, NYC, NY. $15,000, 1999. For general support.

Plough Foundation

Limitations: Giving primarily in Shelby County, TN, with an emphasis on Memphis. No grants to individuals, and generally no grants for annual operating funds; no loans.

2382. Grant Center, Memphis, TN. $200,000, 1999. For general operating support.
2383. Grant Center, Memphis, TN. $30,000, 1999. For general operating support.

TEXAS

Abell-Hanger Foundation

Limitations: Giving limited to TX, with emphasis within the Permian Basin. No grants to individuals, or for individual scholarships or fellowships; no loans.

2384. Austin College, Sherman, TX. $50,000, 2000. For challenge grant for renovation of existing space in Abell Library for Archives and Special Collections.

2385. Dickens County-Spur Public Library, Friends of the, Spur, TX. $25,000, 2000. To renovate newly purchased building.

2386. Ector County Library, Friends of the, Odessa, TX. $10,000, 2000. For challenge grant to renovate and automate Children's Department.

2387. Floyd County Library, Friends of the, Floydada, TX. $50,000, 2000. For challenge grant to construct new library and learning resource center.

2388. Midland Energy Library, Midland, TX. $25,000, 2000. Toward moving library to Midland Tower Building.

2389. Midland Public Library, Friends of the, Midland, TX. $30,000, 2000. To update automation system and expand public internet service.

2390. Nita Stewart Haley Memorial Library, Midland, TX. $25,000, 2000. For general operating support.

2391. Nita Stewart Haley Memorial Library, Midland, TX. $10,000, 2000. For Endowment Fund.

2392. Permian Basin Petroleum Museum, Library and Hall of Fame, Midland, TX. $160,960, 2000. For matching grant for permanent endowment fund.

2393. Permian Basin Petroleum Museum, Library and Hall of Fame, Midland, TX. $125,000, 2000. For general operating support.

2394. Recording Library for the Blind and Physically Handicapped, Midland, TX. $10,000, 2000. For general operating support.

2395. Wink Branch Library, Wink, TX. $25,000, 2000. To purchase servers, computers, hardware, software, printer, network wiring and internet service.

Albert and Margaret Alkek Foundation

Limitations: Giving limited to TX. No grants to individuals.

2396. Southwest Texas State University, San Marcos, TX. $200,000, 1999. For library electronic classroom and faculty technology development.

Amarillo Area Foundation, Inc.

Limitations: Giving limited to the 26 northernmost counties of the TX Panhandle. No support for private or parochial schools. No grants to individuals (except for scholarship program), or for operating budgets, annual campaigns, deficit financing, endowment funds, publications, or conferences; no loans.

2397. Collingsworth County Public Library, Wellington, TX. $40,357, 1999.

M. D. Anderson Foundation

Limitations: Giving limited to TX, primarily the Houston area. No grants to individuals, or for endowment funds or operating budgets.

2398. Houston Academy of Medicine, Texas Medical Center Library, Houston, TX. $50,000, 1999. For programs.

The Brown Foundation, Inc.

Limitations: Giving primarily in TX, with emphasis on Houston. No support for political organizations, religious organizations for religious purposes, or private foundations. No grants to individuals, or for operating deficits, debt retirement, advertising, testimonial dinners, deficit financing, or fundraising events; no loans.

2399. Anson Public Library, Anson, TX. $50,000, 2000. For new state-of-the-art rural library.

2400. Archives of American Art of the Smithsonian Institution, DC. $184,479, 2000. For matching grant to supplement endowment funds on hand to guarantee Journal and expand readership.

2401. Bonham Public Library, Bonham, TX. $25,000, 2000. For contingency grant for dry pipe fire protection system and meeting room construction.

2402. Danbury Community Library, Danbury, TX. $25,000, 2000. For renovation of donated building.

2403. Dilley Public Library, Dilley, TX. $10,000, 2000. To renovate and furnish building for use as library.

2404. Dimmit County Public Library, Carrizo Springs, TX. $10,000, 2000. For construction of multi-use museum addition.

2405. Giddings, City of, Giddings, TX. $100,000, 2000. For expansion of library facility.

2406. Goliad County Library, Goliad, TX. $10,000, 2000. For renovations and expansions.

2407. Jeff Davis County Library, Fort Davis, TX. $50,000, 2000. For matching grant for information center, rest area with picnic and restroom facilities, and performing arts amphitheater area.

2408. Kountze Public Library, Kountze, TX. $25,000, 2000. For building project.

2409. Mental Health Association of Houston and Harris County, Houston, TX. $30,000, 2000. For continued support for Self-Help Resource Center for Greater Houston Clearinghouse.

2410. Santa Fe Chamber Music Festival, Santa Fe, NM. $75,000, 2000. For audience campaign, cash reserve fund, and archive at University of New Mexico.

2411. Smithsonian Institution, DC. $4,000,000, 2000. To acquire Victor Building and specifically for Archives of American Art.

2412. Wimberley Village Library, Wimberley, TX. $10,000, 2000. For implementation of technological internet access program.

Amon G. Carter Foundation

Limitations: Giving largely restricted to Fort Worth and Tarrant County, TX. No grants to individuals, or for ongoing operating budgets, deficit financing, publications, or conferences; no loans.

2413. Crime Prevention Resource Center, Fort Worth, TX. $27,500, 1999. For special programs.

2414. Gill Childrens Services, Fort Worth, TX. $50,000, 1999. For children's medical services.

The CH Foundation

Limitations: Giving primarily in Lubbock, TX and surrounding counties.

2415. Texas Tech University, Texas Tech University Libraries, Lubbock, TX. $48,257, 2000. For Southwest Collection maintenance.

The Challenge Foundation

Limitations: No grants to individuals.

2416. East Waco Innovative School Development, Waco, TX. $35,000, 1999. For library development at East Waco School.

2417. Encino Save Our School Corporation, Encino, TX. $20,000, 1999. For library and reference books at Encino School.

2418. Liberty City Charter School Project, Miami, FL. $22,500, 1999. For matching grant to establish Library Media Center.

2419. North Hills School, Irving, TX. $37,500, 1999. For matching funds for library.

2420. NYOS Charter School, Austin, TX. $42,000, 1999. For library resources.

2421. Project Yes, Houston, TX. $15,100, 1999. For library resources.

2422. Star Academy, Tucson, AZ. $15,000, 1999. For library books.

2423. Tempe Preparatory Academy, Tempe, AZ. $18,000, 1999. For matching funds for Reference Libraries for distinct subject areas.

2424. USF Charter School, Tampa, FL. $16,882, 1999. For ongoing staff development, professional library and resource materials for teachers.

Communities Foundation of Texas, Inc.

Limitations: Giving primarily in the Dallas, TX, area (for grants from unrestricted funds). No support for religious purposes from general fund or organizations which redistribute funds to other organizations. No grants to individuals, or for continuing support, media projects or publications, deficit financing, endowment funds, scholarships, fellowships, or salaries.

2425. Allan Shivers Library and Museum, Woodville, TX. $14,961, 2000.
2426. Anson Public Library, Anson, TX. $37,000, 2000.
2427. Consortium for the National Equal Justice Library, DC. $15,000, 2000.
2428. Library of Congress, DC. $25,000, 2000.
2429. San Miguel County Public Library District, Telluride, CO. $26,000, 2000.

The Dallas Foundation

Limitations: Giving limited to the City and County of Dallas, TX. No support for religious purposes. No grants for discretionary funds to individuals, or for endowment or emergency funds, operating budgets, annual campaigns, seed money, land acquisition, conferences and seminars, continuing support, publications, deficit financing, debt retirement, consulting services, technical assistance, research, scholarships or fellowships; no loans.

2430. Dallas Public Library, Dallas, TX. $10,000, 1999. To support youth poetry competition program.
2431. Dallas Public Library, Friends of the, Dallas, TX. $50,000, 1999. For renovations.
2432. Dallas Symphony Association, Dallas, TX. $15,940, 1999. For annual support and to purchase music for library.
2433. Wilkinson Center, Dallas, TX. $10,000, 1999. For general operating support.

Dodge Jones Foundation

Limitations: Giving primarily in Abilene, TX. No grants to individuals.

2434. Anson Public Library, Anson, TX. $93,000, 1999. For new library automation software.
2435. Blanco Library, Blanco, TX. $10,000, 1999. For new facility.
2436. Floyd County Library, Friends of the, Floydada, TX. $25,000, 1999. For new building.

ExxonMobil Foundation

Limitations: No grants to individuals, or for institutional scholarship or fellowship programs, capital or building funds, land acquisition, equipment, renovation projects, or endowment purposes; no loans.

2437. California State Library Foundation, Sacramento, CA. $10,000, 2000. For Governor's Book Fund.
2438. Charter School Resource Center of Texas, San Antonio, TX. $25,000, 2000. For operating support.
2439. Florham Park Public Library, Florham Park, NJ. $10,000, 2000. For library expansion.
2440. Foundation Center, NYC, NY. $20,000, 2000. For general support.
2441. Southeast Texas Family Resource Center, Beaumont, TX. $15,000, 2000. For general operating support.

Leland Fikes Foundation, Inc.

Limitations: Giving primarily in the Dallas, TX, area. No grants to individuals; no loans.

2442. Dallas Public Library, Friends of the, Dallas, TX. $50,000, 1999. For renovations.

The Fondren Foundation

Limitations: Giving primarily in TX, with emphasis on Houston. No grants to individuals, or for annual or operating fund drives.

2443. Rice University, Houston, TX. $1,000,000, 2000. For enhancement of Fondren Library.
2444. Texas Medical Center, Jesse H. Jones Library, Houston, TX. $300,000, 2000. For enhancement of common facility and surrounding areas.
2445. University of Houston-University Park, Houston, TX. $250,000, 2000. For renovation of M. D. Anderson Library and Honors College.

The Ewing Halsell Foundation

Limitations: Giving limited to TX, with emphasis on southwestern TX, particularly San Antonio. No grants to individuals, or for deficit financing, emergency funds, general endowments, matching gifts, scholarships, fel-

lowships, demonstration projects, general purposes, or conferences; no loans.

2446. Dimmit County Public Library, Carrizo Springs, TX. $60,000, 2000. Toward new library and new museum construction.
2447. San Antonio Public Library Foundation, San Antonio, TX. $50,000, 2000. Toward purchase of books.

Hillcrest Foundation

Limitations: Giving limited to TX, with emphasis on Dallas County. No grants to individuals, or for endowment funds, scholarships, or fellowships; no loans.

2448. Bonham Public Library, Bonham, TX. $50,000, 2000. To install fire protection system and construct meeting room.
2449. Coldspring Area Public Library, Coldspring, TX. $25,000, 2000. For construction of new library building.
2450. Dallas Public Library, Friends of the, Dallas, TX. $100,000, 2000. To renovate J Erik Jonsson Central Library's Genealogy Reference Collections, History and Social Sciences Divisions.
2451. Jourdanton Library and Community Center Foundation, Jourdanton, TX. $20,000, 2000. To construct library and community center.
2452. Kountze Public Library, Kountze, TX. $25,000, 2000. For construction of new library.
2453. Universities Center of Dallas, Dallas, TX. $100,000, 2000. To equip and furnish Virtual Library.

Hobby Family Foundation

Limitations: Giving primarily in TX. No grants to individuals.

2454. University of Texas, Harry Ransom Humanities Research Center, Austin, TX. $100,000, 1999. For endowment fund for Senior Librarian Position.

Hoblitzelle Foundation

Limitations: Giving limited to TX, primarily Dallas. No support for religious organizations for sectarian purposes. No grants to individuals; only occasional board-initiated support for operating budgets, debt reduction, research, scholarships, or endowments; no loans.

2455. University of Texas, Harry Ransom Humanities Research Center, Austin, TX. $500,000, 2000. Toward facility improvements and modernization.

Houston Endowment Inc.

Limitations: Giving primarily in Houston, TX; no grants outside the continental U.S.. No support for religious organizations for religious purposes, or organizations that are the responsibility of the government. No grants to individuals; or for fundraising activities including galas, testimonial dinners, or advertising; or the purchase of uniforms, equipment or trips for school related organizations; no loans.

2456. Alliance for the Mentally Ill of the Gulf Coast, Alvin, TX. $30,000, 2000. Toward education, resource information, coordination of volunteer activities and support for families with members who suffer from mental illnesses.
2457. Association of Fundraising Professionals, Houston, TX. $15,000, 2000. Toward scholarships to send representatives from small and/or emerging nonprofit organizations to seminar about seeking grants from corporations and foundations.
2458. Body Positive, Houston, TX. $25,000, 2000. Toward nutrition, counseling, and exercise programs that address AIDS wasting syndrome and other autoimmune diseases and chronic neuromuscular disorders.
2459. Crisis Intervention of Houston, Houston, TX. $50,000, 2000. Toward crisis counseling, referral services, and advocacy for Hispanic women who are victims of domestic abuse.
2460. Houston Education Resource Network (HERN), Houston, TX. $75,000, 2000. Toward technological assistance for schools and community-based organizations, and toward Internet-linked inventory of broad range of programs and resources.
2461. San Antonio Public Library Foundation, San Antonio, TX. $740,000, 2000. Toward three-year pilot program to reduce illiteracy in San Antonio through Little Read Wagons, vans that are driven by library staff who distribute books and other materials in

Spanish and English and train child care workers to read to young children.

2462. University of Houston-University Park, Houston, TX. $5,000,000, 2000. Toward renovating and expanding M.D. Anderson Library.

Albert & Bessie Mae Kronkosky Charitable Foundation

Limitations: Giving limited to Bandera, Bexar, Comal, and Kendall counties, TX.

2463. Arts San Antonio, San Antonio, TX. $60,000, 1999. For Arts San Antonio Web Page Development and to expand outreach to senior centers, community centers, schools, and other venues.

2464. Bandera County Library, Friends of, Bandera, TX. $49,500, 1999. For Rural Library Initiative Grant.

2465. Boerne Public Library, Friends of, Boerne, TX. $50,000, 1999. For matching grant to improve services through facility enhancements resources for persons with disabilities, furniture and equipment, and improved communication and access to materials, as part of Rural Library Initiative.

2466. Bulverde Public Library, Bulverde, TX. $30,000, 1999. For matching grant for improvements, facility enhancements, children's services, and literacy programs as part of Rural Library Initiative.

2467. Comfort Public Library, Comfort, TX. $130,000, 1999. For capital campaign for renovation and expansion.

2468. Comfort Public Library, Comfort, TX. $30,000, 1999. For matching grant to improve collection, enhance access, and train staff and board, as part of Rural Library Initiative Grant.

2469. Converse Area Public Library, Converse, TX. $50,000, 1999. For matching grant for facility enhancements and up-to-date resources, as part of Rural Library Initiative.

2470. Jewish Family Service of San Antonio, San Antonio, TX. $100,000, 1999. For comprehensive senior services program, including assessment, counseling, referral, and visitation.

2471. Lakehills Library and Community Association, Lakehills, TX. $25,000, 1999. For matching grant to acquire plans for permanent building, fencing, and septic system, as part of Rural Library Initiative.

2472. Leon Valley Public Library, Friends of the, San Antonio, TX. $49,960, 1999. For matching grant to improve collection, improve facilities, and upgrade technology to assist special populations, as part of Rural Library Initiative.

2473. New Braunfels Public Library Foundation, New Braunfels, TX. $75,000, 1999. For matching grant to expand access to information in print and electronic formats, as part of Rural Library Initiative.

2474. San Antonio Public Library Foundation, San Antonio, TX. $1,000,000, 1999. To acquire children's books and books about parenting.

2475. San Antonio Public Library Foundation, San Antonio, TX. $29,976, 1999. For electronic database for rural counties.

2476. Seton Home, San Antonio, TX. $50,000, 1999. For social service outreach to homeless adolescent mothers and their babies, linking them to community support services.

2477. Sunshine Cottage School for Deaf Children, San Antonio, TX. $80,000, 1999. For Regional Diagnostic, Information, Referral and Intervention Center for newborns with potential hearing loss.

2478. Tye Preston Memorial Library of Canyon Lake, Canyon Lake, TX. $40,230, 1999. For matching grant for computers, furniture, and other equipment, as part of Rural Library Initiative.

2479. Universal City Public Library, Universal City, TX. $49,950, 1999. For matching grant to improve appearance and utilization of facility, as part of Rural Library Initiative.

The Eugene McDermott Foundation

Limitations: Giving primarily in Dallas, TX. No grants to individuals.

2480. Dallas Public Library, Friends of the, Dallas, TX. $600,000, 2000. For renovation of J. Erik Jonsson Library.

2481. Dallas Public Library, Friends of the, Dallas, TX. $25,000, 2000. For Xavier Corbero Art Piece.

2482. University of Texas at Dallas, Richardson, TX. $1,000,000, 2000. To complete renovation of Eugene McDermott Library.

John P. McGovern Foundation

Limitations: Giving primarily in TX, with emphasis on Houston; giving also in the Southwest. No grants to individuals.

2483. Council on Library and Information Resources, DC. $15,000, 2000. For A.R. Zipf Fellowship Fund.

2484. Duke University, School of Medicine, Durham, NC. $10,000, 2000. For Friends of the Trent Collection which maintains Josiah Charles Trent collection in Duke University Medical Library.

2485. Duke University Medical Center, Durham, NC. $10,000, 2000. For Library Endowment Fund.

2486. Giddings, City of, Giddings, TX. $10,000, 2000. For Rufus King Library.

2487. Houston Academy of Medicine, Texas Medical Center Library, Houston, TX. $20,000, 2000. For John P. McGovern History of Medicine Collection.

2488. Houston Academy of Medicine, Texas Medical Center Library, Houston, TX. $10,000, 2000. For position of curator and director of John P. McGovern Historical and Research Center.

2489. Houston Public Library, Friends of the, Houston, TX. $10,000, 2000.

2490. McGill University, Friends of, Montreal, Canada. $10,000, 2000. For Friends of the Osler Library.

2491. Medical Library Association, Chicago, IL. $25,000, 2000. For John P. McGovern Lectureship Endowment Fund.

2492. National Library of Medicine, Friends of the, DC. $10,000, 2000.

2493. Rosenberg Library, Friends of, Galveston, TX. $10,000, 2000.

2494. University of Houston-University Park, Houston, TX. $500,000, 2000. For M.D. Anderson Library/Honors College Capital Campaign.

McGovern Fund

Limitations: Giving primarily in TX, with emphasis on Houston; giving also in the Southwest. No grants to individuals.

2495. Houston Academy of Medicine, Texas Medical Center Library, Houston, TX. $170,000, 2000. For John P. McGovern Historical Collections and Research Center Endowment Fund.

2496. Houston Academy of Medicine, Texas Medical Center Library, Houston, TX. $50,000, 2000. For McGovern Endowment Fund challenge grant for John P. McGovern Historical Collection and Research Center Endowment Fund.

2497. Ronald Reagan Presidential Foundation, Simi Valley, CA. $25,000, 2000. For Ronald Reagan Freedom Award Dinner.

2498. Ronald Reagan Presidential Foundation, Simi Valley, CA. $25,000, 2000.

2499. University of Houston-University Park, Houston, TX. $500,000, 2000. For M.D. Anderson Library and Honors College Capital Campaign.

The Robert and Janice McNair Foundation

Limitations: Giving primarily in Houston, TX. No grants to individuals.

2500. Charter School Resource Center of Texas, San Antonio, TX. $25,000, 1999.

2501. Houston Education Resource Network (HERN), Houston, TX. $224,179, 1999.

2502. Houston Public Library, Houston, TX. $10,000, 1999.

The Meadows Foundation, Inc.

Limitations: Giving limited to TX. No grants to individuals; generally, no grants for annual campaigns, fundraising events, professional conferences and symposia, travel expenses for groups to perform or compete outside of TX, or construction of churches and seminaries.

2503. American Farmland Trust, San Marcos, TX. $90,500, 2000. Toward developing interactive mapping system to provide statewide information on land fragmentation for policy-makers and conservationists.

2504. Canyon, City of, Canyon Area Library, Canyon, TX. $100,000, 2000. Toward constructing new public library.

2505. Danbury, City of, Danbury Community Library, Danbury, TX. $12,775, 2000. Toward renovating building for use as community library.

2506. Dimmit County Public Library, Carrizo Springs, TX. $56,000, 2000. Toward constructing multi-use museum addition to library building.

2507. Goliad, County of, Goliad, TX. $38,200, 2000. Toward expanding Goliad County Library.

2508. Greater Dallas Planning Council, Dallas, TX. $40,400, 2000. Toward creating online environmental information clearinghouse.

2509. Howe Community Library, Friends of the, Howe, TX. $65,000, 2000. Toward renovating location for combined community and school library.

2510. Muenster Public Library, Friends of the, Muenster, TX. $69,000, 2000. Toward constructing new public library.

2511. Nixon, City of, Nixon Public Library, Nixon, TX. $20,400, 2000. Toward renovating new library facility.

2512. Texas Childrens Hospital, Houston, TX. $117,800, 2000. Toward start-up expenses associated with establishing Texas-based Pediatric HIV Resource Center to provide consultation and information to Texas healthcare professionals caring for HIV-affected children.

2513. Texas Heart Institute, Houston, TX. $500,000, 2000. Toward constructing telemedicine center in new facility to house current and expanded programs and services.

Hal & Charlie Peterson Foundation

Limitations: Giving primarily in Kerr County, TX, and adjacent counties, and to state or national organizations with a local chapter in this area. No support for religious purposes. No grants to individuals, or for operating budgets, debt retirement, media productions, publications, or endowments; no loans.

2514. Comfort Public Library, Comfort, TX. $65,576, 1999. Towards renovations for Library building.

2515. Edwards, County of, Rocksprings, TX. $89,750, 1999. Toward purchase of furniture and fixtures in new County Library Building.

Bernard and Audre Rapoport Foundation

Limitations: Giving on a national basis, with major emphasis on Waco, TX, including McKennan and surrounding counties; some support also in Israel. No grants to individuals.

2516. Austin Public Library, Friends of the, Austin, TX. $10,000, 1999. For general support.

2517. Carelinc Network, Waco, TX. $27,000, 1999. For general support.

2518. Waco-McClennan County Library, Waco, TX. $27,714, 1999. For children's books.

Reliant Energy Foundation

Limitations: No grants to individuals.

2519. Houston Public Library, Friends of the, Houston, TX. $11,265, 1999. For printing of Power Card applications.

Sid W. Richardson Foundation

Limitations: Giving limited to TX, with emphasis on Fort Worth for the arts and human services, and statewide for health and education. No support for religious organizations. No grants to individuals, or for scholarships or fellowships; no loans.

2520. Arlington Public Library Foundation, Arlington, TX. $66,400, 1999. Toward establishing Learning Center for Children in new Southeast Branch Library.

2521. Fort Worth Public Library Foundation, Fort Worth, TX. $50,000, 1999. For continued support to provide office space in new facility.

Rockwell Fund, Inc.

Limitations: Giving primarily in TX, with emphasis on Houston. No grants to individuals or for medical or scientific research projects, underwriting benefits, dinners, galas, and fundraising special events, or mass appeal solicitations; grants primarily awarded on a year-to-year basis only.

2522. Blanco Library, Blanco, TX. $10,000, 1999. For building addition and renovations.

2523. Childrens Museum of Houston, Houston, TX. $25,000, 1999. For Library for Early Childhood.

2524. South Texas College of Law, Houston, TX. $25,000, 1999. For capital support for addition to library.

2525. University of Houston-Downtown, Houston, TX. $20,000, 1999. For entry fee for the JSTOR consortium.

SBC Foundation

Limitations: Giving primarily in AR, CA, CT, IL, IN, KS, MI, MO, NV, OH, OK, TX, and WI. No support for for-profit organizations; religious organizations for sectarian purposes; fraternal, veterans', or labor groups (when serving only their membership); individual K-12 schools or districts; political activities or organizations; disease-specific organizations; religious schools; or groups that discriminate by race, color, creed, gender, sexual orientation, age, or nationality. No grants to individuals, or for hospital operating or capital funds, capital campaigns, endowment funds, operating expenses for United Way-supported organizations, advertising, ticket/dinner purchases, sports programs/events, cause-related marketing, or donation of products or services.

2526. Abraham Lincoln Presidential Library and Museum Foundation, Springfield, IL. $1,300,000, 2000. For Holavision Theater Sponsorship.

2527. Association for Retarded Citizens of Indiana, Indianapolis, IN. $25,000, 2000. For ARC/Ameritech HelpNet.

2528. Childrens Museum of Houston, Houston, TX. $20,000, 2000. To underwrite traveling library kiosks, special arm of Parent Resource Library.

2529. Coalition of Wisconsin Aging Groups, Madison, WI. $25,000, 2000. For Ameritech Training Center and Ameritech Consumer Information Series.

2530. Corpus Christi Public Library Foundation, Corpus Christi, TX. $20,000, 2000. For Library Information Network.

2531. Council for Aid to Education (CFAE), NYC, NY. $25,000, 2000. For Voluntary Support of Education (VSE) survey, national source of information on private giving to higher education and private K-12 schools.

2532. Detroit Institute for Children, Detroit, MI. $73,000, 2000. For Ameritech Compuplay Lending Library for low-income, undeserved children with disabilities.

2533. Fort Worth Public Library, Friends of the, Fort Worth, TX. $25,000, 2000. For Library Card Campaign.

2534. Leland Stanford Mansion Foundation, Sacramento, CA. $50,000, 2000. For Family Library, Media and Technology Room at Governor's Mansion.

2535. Milwaukee Public Library Foundation, Milwaukee, WI. $92,000, 2000. For Make Friends at the Milwaukee Public Library project.

2536. Museum Library and Arts Foundation, Las Vegas, NV. $10,000, 2000. For Nevada Traveling History Trunk Program.

2537. New Haven Free Public Library, Friends of the, New Haven, CT. $50,000, 2000. For Fair Haven Technology Access Center.

2538. Nonprofit Resource Center of Texas, San Antonio, TX. $25,000, 2000. For nonprofit training effort for participants entitled, Drucker Self-Assessment Tool Training and for Annual Campaign.

2539. Northeastern Illinois Area Agency on Aging, West Chicago, IL. $25,000, 2000. For Aging Connections, computerized information system.

2540. OASIS Institute, Saint Louis, MO. $15,000, 2000. For Intergenerational Tutoring Program in Saint Louis.

2541. Older Adult Service and Information System (OASIS), Indianapolis, IN. $20,000, 2000. For Intergenerational Internet Mentoring Program.

2542. Our Lady of the Lake University of San Antonio, San Antonio, TX. $150,000, 2000. For capital campaign for new library and educational technology center.

2543. San Antonio Public Library Foundation, San Antonio, TX. $100,000, 2000. For The Centennial Achievement Plan, in celebration of Library's 100th birthday.

2544. San Gabriel Valley Foundation for Economic Growth, Irwindale, CA. $25,000, 2000. For ValleyNet Regional Marketing Connection Project.

2545. Texas A & M University Development Foundation, College Station, TX. $100,000, 2000. For Bush Presidential Library Campaign to prepare students for leadership roles.

2546. Texas Library Association, Austin, TX. $10,000, 2000. Toward Annual TLA Conference.

2547. Texas Nonprofit Management Assistance Network, San Antonio, TX. $50,000, 2000. To develop statewide Network to provide technical assistance, marketing and technology resources to Texas nonprofit resource centers.

2548. Tulsa Library Trust, Tulsa, OK. $10,000, 2000. To make teleconferencing available to businesses that cannot afford their own equipment.

2549. University of California, Berkeley, CA. $50,000, 2000. For new Information Arcade within James K. Moffett Library.

2550. University of Texas M.D. Anderson Cancer Center, Houston, TX. $200,000, 2000. For Telehealth Center.

2551. Wilkinson Center, Dallas, TX. $10,000, 2000. For Safe Haven Youth Program.

Shell Oil Company Foundation

Limitations: Giving primarily in areas of company operations in the U.S.. No support for special requests of colleges, universities, and college fundraising associations, or hospital operating expenses. No grants to individuals, or for endowment funds, capital campaigns of national organizations, no in-kind contributions or product contributions, or development funds; no loans.

2552. Charter School Resource Center of Texas, San Antonio, TX. $10,000, 1999.

2553. George Bush Presidential Library Center, College Station, TX. $50,000, 1999.

2554. Houston Education Resource Network (HERN), Houston, TX. $10,000, 1999.

2555. Houston Public Library, Houston, TX. $10,000, 1999.

2556. Library of Congress, DC. $100,000, 1999.

2557. People with AIDS Coalition (PWAC) Houston, Houston, TX. $10,000, 1999.

Roy and Christine Sturgis Charitable and Educational Trust

Limitations: Giving primarily in AR and the Dallas, TX, area. No grants to individuals or for seminars; no loans.

2558. Barton Library, El Dorado, AR. $25,000, 1999. For computer software.

2559. Grant County Library Foundation, John Day, OR. $25,000, 1999. To construct children's wing addition.

T. L. L. Temple Foundation

Limitations: Giving primarily in counties in TX constituting the East Texas Pine Timber Belt. No support for private foundations. No grants to individuals, or for deficit financing.

2560. Burkeville Independent School District, Burkeville, TX. $50,786, 2000. To automate library, and purchase computers for computer lab.

2561. Christian Information and Service Center, Lufkin, TX. $80,000, 2000. For general support.

2562. Christian Information and Service Center, Lufkin, TX. $40,000, 2000. For budget deficit.

2563. Kurth Memorial Library, Lufkin, TX. $73,227, 2000. To construct new library facility.

2564. Medical University of South Carolina (MUSC), Charleston, SC. $200,000, 2000. To operate registry for research on hypertrophic cardiomyopathy.

2565. Newton, County of, Newton, TX. $12,000, 2000. For computer workstations and book shelving for Newton County Public Library.

2566. San Augustine Public Library, San Augustine, TX. $184,250, 2000. For renovations and additions.

2567. T.L.L. Temple Memorial Library, Diboll, TX. $159,993, 2000. For Archive.

2568. T.L.L. Temple Memorial Library, Diboll, TX. $75,000, 2000. For general support.

2569. T.L.L. Temple Memorial Library, Diboll, TX. $20,000, 2000. For budget deficit.

Temple-Inland Foundation

Limitations: Giving primarily in areas of company operations. No grants to individuals (except for employee-related scholarships).

2570. T.L.L. Temple Memorial Library, Diboll, TX. $29,620, 2000.

USAA Foundation, A Charitable Trust

Limitations: Giving primarily in AZ, CA, CO, Washington, DC, FL, TX, and VA. No grants to individuals.

2571. George C. Marshall Research Foundation, Lexington, VA. $10,000, 2000.

2572. San Antonio Public Library Foundation, San Antonio, TX. $125,000, 2000.

UTAH

The George S. and Dolores Dore Eccles Foundation

Limitations: Giving primarily in the intermountain area, particularly UT. No grants to individuals, or for endowment funds.

2573. Andrew S. Rowan Reading Room for the Blind, Salt Lake City, UT. $10,000, 1999. For continued general support.

2574. Brigham Young Academy Foundation, Provo, UT. $750,000, 1999. For restoration of Brigham Young Academy building.

2575. Child Abuse Prevention Center, Ogden, UT. $10,000, 1999. For information support and referral service on Shaken Baby Syndrome.

2576. Community Services Council, Salt Lake City, UT. $10,000, 1999. To expand Utah's Health Line through Information and Referral Center.

2577. Sanpete Trade Association, Ephraim, UT. $10,000, 1999. To donate copies of The Blackhawk War: Cultures in Conflict to public elementary schools, public libraries and private schools in Utah.

2578. Utah State Library Division, Salt Lake City, UT. $50,000, 1999. For study to assess building needs of state's public libraries.

The Jon and Karen Huntsman Foundation

Limitations: Giving on a national basis. No grants to individuals.

2579. Brigham Young University, Hunter Law School, Provo, UT. $1,000,000, 1999. For construction of Law Library.

2580. Southern Utah University Foundation, Cedar City, UT. $100,000, 1999. To construct campus library.

Stewart Education Foundation

Limitations: Giving primarily in Ogden, UT.

2581. Weber County Library Development Fund, Ogden, UT. $25,000, 1999.

VIRGINIA

The Robert G. Cabell III and Maude Morgan Cabell Foundation

Limitations: Giving limited to VA. No support for special interest groups. No grants to individuals, or for endowment funds, operating programs, or research projects.

2582. Mathews Memorial Library, Friends of the, Mathews, VA. $50,000, 2000. For renovation and expansion.

2583. Thomas Jefferson Memorial Foundation, Charlottesville, VA. $500,000, 2000. For Jefferson Research Library.

The Community Foundation Serving Richmond & Central Virginia

Limitations: Giving limited to residents of metropolitan Richmond, the tri-cities area, including Hopewell, Colonial Heights, and Petersburg, and Chesterfield, Hanover, and Henrico counties, VA. No grants for annual campaigns, deficit financing, land acquisition, or building funds.

2584. Bar Association of the City of Richmond, Richmond, VA. $15,000, 2000. For operating support for Pro Bono Clearinghouse, which will match attorneys with nonprofits in need of legal assistance.

2585. Mathews Memorial Library, Mathews, VA. $10,000, 2000.

2586. Salvation Army of Richmond, Richmond, VA. $30,000, 2000. For capital support for Library Renovation Project, creating environment promoting positive behavior, academic achievement, and character-building.

2587. Waverly Library, Friends of the, Waverly, VA. $150,000, 2000. To move to new facility.

Freddie Mac Foundation

Limitations: Giving primarily in the metropolitan Washington, DC, area, as well as statewide initiatives in MD and VA. Funding also for groups providing services on a national scope and to organizations located in areas of the corporation's regional offices. No support for sectarian purposes. No grants to individuals, or for incurring debt liability or endowment campaigns.

2588. Foreign Born Information and Referral Network, Columbia, MD. $20,000, 1999. To assist at-risk children of low-income, foreign-born families with homework and reading by setting-up or expanding homework clubs in elementary schools.

2589. Illinois Department of Children and Family Services, Springfield, IL. $896,250, 1999. For Wednesday's Child - Chicago, televised adoption program which features children in foster care in need of adoptive placement.

2590. La Clinica del Pueblo, DC. $20,000, 1999. For Family Mental Health Program, providing culturally-appropriate mental health counseling and referral services to low-income Latino families.

2591. Metropolitan Washington Council of Governments, DC. $511,250, 1999. For Wednesday's Child - Washington DC, televised adoption program which features children in foster care in need of adoptive placement.

2592. National Adoption Center, Philadelphia, PA. $99,508, 1999. To establish new customized component of national Faces of Adoption web-site, Wednesday's Child USA, consisting of web pages for each Wednesday's Child program with links to local child-placing agencies.

2593. National Childrens Alliance, DC. $25,000, 1999. To expand capacity to respond to inquiries for information resulting from increased public awareness and interest in child abuse.

2594. National Fatherhood Initiative, Gaithersburg, MD. $25,000, 1999. To expand capacity and programming of Clearinghouse and Resource Center, which provides educational materials, technical assistance, training and advocacy services nationwide to promote fatherhood involvement.

2595. New Yorkers for Children, NYC, NY. $1,297,800, 1999. For Wednesday's Child-New York, televised adoption program which features children in foster care in need of adoptive placement.

2596. Prince Georges Child Resource Center, Largo, MD. $25,000, 1999. For staff support and transportation for center and to develop evaluation instrument to determine long-term effects of Challenger program.

2597. Project WORD, Arlington, VA. $25,000, 1999. To build capacity to help mentally challenged parents provide appropriate care for their children.

2598. Washington Child Development Council, DC. $20,000, 1999. To expand quality child care in the District of Columbia by addressing identified child care communtiy needs.

Freedom Forum, Inc.

Limitations: Giving on a national and international basis.

2599. Brian Bex Report, Hagerstown, IN. $25,000, 1999. For The Remnant Trust project, archive which collects and lends documents on freedom and democracy for public display.

2600. Foundation Center, NYC, NY. $15,000, 1999.

2601. Freedom Channel, DC. $100,000, 1999. For planning of FreedomChannel.com internet and broadband service providing voters with video, audio and text material on candidates and issues in 2000 campaign.

2602. John F. Kennedy Library Foundation, Boston, MA. $12,500, 1999. For general support.

2603. New York Public Library, NYC, NY. $100,000, 1999. For partnership between The Freedom Forum and the Library.

Gannett Foundation, Inc.

Limitations: Giving limited to organizations in Gannett-served communities, including the U.S., Canada, and the U.S. territory of Guam. No support for religious purposes, elementary or secondary schools (except special initiatives not provided by regular school budgets), medical or other research, fraternal, political, or veterans' organizations, athletic teams, bands, volunteer firefighters, or similiar groups, or national or regional programs. No grants to individuals, or for endowments or multiple-year pledge campaigns.

2604. Saint John Dialysis Center Corporation, Detroit, MI. $11,000, 2000. For books and library equipment to expand Open Arms Program for children's grief counseling, in collaboration with Saint John Community Health Investment Corporation.

2605. Westchester Community College Foundation, Library Resource Center, Valhalla, NY. $25,000, 2000. For capital campaign to upgrade equipment and technological resources for programs.

W. Alton Jones Foundation, Inc.

Limitations: No support for conduit organizations. No grants to individuals, or for building construction or renovation, endowment funds, general support, basic research, scholarships, conferences, international exchanges, or fellowships.

2606. Arms Control Association (ACA), DC. $150,000, 1999. For continued support to provide information and analysis on arms control and disarmament issues for media, officials, experts and journalists in U.S. and abroad.

2607. British Columbia Environmental Network (BCEN) Educational Foundation, Vancouver, Canada. $40,000, 1999. For continued support to assist and coordinate efforts of grassroots forest groups in British Columbia to educate public and to serve as central hub for information to network of forest activists throughout province.

2608. Citizens Nuclear Information Center, Tokyo, Japan. $100,000, 1999. For analysis and public criticism of Japan's energy policy, especially reliance on nuclear power, and to disseminate findings to the public and policymakers.

2609. Environmental Protection Information Center (EPIC), Garberville, CA. $40,000, 1999. To protect Northern California's coastal forest ecosystems and watersheds.

2610. Nautilus of America, Berkeley, CA. $240,000, 1999. To promote projects through television, radio, newspapers and NAPSNet, daily electronic bulletin that collects news reports pertaining to Northeast Asian security, energy and environmental issues for distribution to NGOs.

2611. Programme for Promoting Nuclear Non-Proliferation, NYC, NY. $180,000, 1999. To facilitate information exchange and consensus building among diplomats and media of countries key to preserving and strengthening Nuclear Non-Proliferation Treaty regime, through meetings and publications.

2612. Silva Forest Foundation, Slocan Park, Canada. $40,000, 1999. For continued support to provide communities, forest activists and policymakers with accurate, up-to-date mapped data and analysis to promote ecosystem-based planning and sustainable forestry operations.

The Norfolk Foundation

Limitations: Giving limited to Norfolk, VA, and a 50-mile area from its boundaries. No support for national or international organizations, or religious organizations for religious purposes, hospitals and similar health care facilities, or projects normally the responsibility of the government. No grants to individuals (except for donor-designated scholarships), or for operating budgets, annual campaigns, research, endowment funds, or deficit financing; no loans.

2613. Norfolk Public Library, Friends of the, Norfolk, VA. $66,744, 2000. To help install computer labs at branch locations.

The Mary Morton Parsons Foundation

Limitations: Giving primarily in Richmond, VA. No grants to individuals; or for debt reduction, endowments, research, or general operating expenses.

2614. Eastern Virginia Medical School, Norfolk, VA. $50,000, 2000. For Medical Sciences Library.

2615. Ferrum College, Ferrum, VA. $100,000, 2000. To expand Stanley Library.

2616. Steward School, Richmond, VA. $100,000, 2000. To construct library.

Robins Foundation

Limitations: Giving primarily in Richmond, VA. No grants to individuals, or for annual funds or special events.

2617. Childrens Health Involving Parents, Richmond, VA. $25,000, 1999. For Child Health Linkages, collaboration of CHIP of Richmond, Communities in Schools, and VCU School of Nursing.

The Whitaker Foundation

Limitations: Giving limited to the U.S. and Canada for Biomedical Engineering Research and Special Opportunity Awards Programs; Regional Program limited to Collier County, FL; other programs are limited to the U.S.. No support for sectarian religious purposes. No grants to individuals, or for deficit financing, annual campaigns, emergency funds, or endowment funds.

2618. Dauphin County Library System, Harrisburg, PA. $10,000, 2000. For annual support.
2619. Foundation Center, NYC, NY. $10,000, 2000. For annual support.
2620. West Shore Public Library, Camp Hill, PA. $10,000, 2000. For annual grant.

WASHINGTON

E. K. and Lillian F. Bishop Foundation

Limitations: Giving limited to WA, with emphasis on Grays Harbor County; scholarship applicants must be Grays Harbor County residents entering their 3rd year of college or beyond. No support for preschool or similar daycare facilities, private secondary education, university-level youth activities, or public educational programs. No grants for fellowships; no loans.

2621. Seattle Public Library, Seattle, WA. $50,000, 2000.

The Bullitt Foundation

Limitations: Giving exclusively in the Pacific Northwest. No support for political organizations. No grants to individuals, or for capital campaigns or multi-year grants.

2622. Montana Environmental Information Center, Helena, MT. $30,000, 1999. For continued support for efforts to educate and persuade citizens, leaders, public officials and power providers regarding energy issues and environmental consequences, emphasizing conservation and renewables.
2623. YMCA of Greater Seattle, Seattle, WA. $30,000, 1999. To implement and maintain Salmonweb Internet site to communicate background knowledge and monitoring techniques, and to collect and store data on conditions of region's streams and rivers to aid their preservation and restoration.

Ben B. Cheney Foundation

Limitations: Giving limited to the seven northernmost counties in CA, southwestern OR, with emphasis on Medford, Tacoma and Pierce County, and southwestern WA. No support for religious organizations for sectarian purposes. No grants to individuals, or for operating budgets, basic research, endowment funds, conferences or seminars, book, film, video production or school-related tours; no loans.

2624. Josephine County Library Foundation, Grants Pass, OR. $35,000, 2000. To build new Wolf Creek Branch Library.
2625. Langlois Public Library, Langlois, OR. $30,000, 2000. To build new public library.
2626. Linfield College, McMinnville, OR. $50,000, 2000. Toward capital campaign for new library.
2627. Living Alternatives for Retired Citizens (LARC), Medford, OR. $25,000, 2000. To stabilize agency operations.
2628. Saint Martins College, Lacey, WA. $50,000, 2000. To complete campaign for new library.
2629. Washington Poison Center, Seattle, WA. $25,000, 2000. To upgrade technology that supports database of poisons and treatments.

Bill & Melinda Gates Foundation

Limitations: Giving on a national and international basis to support initiatives in health and learning; the foundation also supports community giving in the Pacific Northwest. No support for religious purposes. No grants to individuals.

2630. Alberta Library, Edmonton, Canada. $901,296, 2000. To provide Alberta's public libraries serving low-income communities with gift of public access computers, internet access, and training of library staff.
2631. Alliance for Education, Seattle, WA. $191,950, 2000. 2-year grant. To contribute to academic achievement of all Seattle School District students by making them effective users of ideas and information through their school librarians.
2632. Arizona, State of, Phoenix, AZ. $2,133,376, 2000. For U.S. Library Program, providing computers with Internet access and training to libraries serving low-income communities.
2633. Biblioteca Nacional de Chile, Direccion de Bibliotecas, Archivos y Museos (DIBAM), Santiago, Chile. $7,387,000, 2000. To provide public access to computers and Internet access to libraries in Chile.
2634. Boston Public Library, Boston, MA. $339,250, 2000. For U.S. Library Program, providing computers with Internet access and training to libraries serving low-income communities.
2635. Bremerton, City of, Bremerton, WA. $100,000, 2000. For matching support for library improvements.
2636. California, State of, Sacramento, CA. $4,344,907, 2000. For U.S. Library Program, providing computers with Internet access and training to libraries serving low-income communities.
2637. Center for Collaborative Education-Metro Boston, Boston, MA. $4,914,021, 2000. 5-year grant. For existing small schools to work with districts to launch new small schools, serve as clearinghouse of research on small schools, and develop cadre of new small school leaders.
2638. Colorado, State of, Denver, CO. $308,000, 2000. For U.S. Library Program, providing computers with Internet access and training to libraries serving low-income communities.
2639. Community Studies, NYC, NY. $100,000, 2000. 4-year grant. For Teacher Center.
2640. Crownpoint Institute of Technology, Crownpoint, NM. $103,357, 2000. For library internship program, as part of Native American Access to Technology initiative.
2641. Education Resources Institute, Boston, MA. $75,000, 2000. To increase college preparation, access, and success for students from groups currently underrepresented in higher education.
2642. EdVisions, Henderson, MN. $4,430,000, 2000. 5-year grant. To develop new schools, create network of these schools, and disseminate successful practices of New Country School and network nationwide.
2643. Foundation Center, NYC, NY. $175,000, 2000. For general support.
2644. Fund for Americas Libraries, Chicago, IL. $20,000, 2000. For U.S. Library Program in Washington, DC, providing computers with Internet access and training to libraries serving low-income communities.
2645. Georgia, State of, Atlanta, GA. $4,286,376, 2000. For U.S. Library Program, providing computers with Internet access and training to libraries serving low-income communities.
2646. Helsinki City Library, Helsinki, Finland. $1,000,000, 2000. To confer Access to Learning Award in recognition of efforts to provide public access to computers and the Internet in useful and innovative ways.
2647. Idaho, State of, Boise, ID. $1,084,898, 2000. For U.S. Library Program, providing computers with Internet access and training to libraries serving low-income communities.
2648. Illinois, State of, Springfield, IL. $777,400, 2000. For U.S. Library Program, providing computers with Internet access and training to libraries serving low-income communities.
2649. Indiana, State of, Indianapolis, IN. $173,400, 2000. For U.S. Library Program, providing computers with Internet access and training to libraries serving low-income communities.
2650. Institute of American Indian Arts Foundation, Santa Fe, NM. $23,379, 2000. For library internship program, as part of Native American Access to Technology initiative.
2651. Las Vegas-Clark County Library District, Las Vegas, NV. $148,350, 2000. For U.S. Library Program, providing computers with Internet access and training to libraries serving low-income communities.

2652. Louisiana State University and A & M College, Baton Rouge, LA. $14,178, 2000. For U.S. Library Program, providing computers with Internet access and training to libraries serving low-income communities.

2653. Maryland, State of, Annapolis, MD. $363,050, 2000. For U.S. Library Program, providing computers with Internet access and training to libraries serving low-income communities.

2654. Medical Library Association, Chicago, IL. $30,000, 2000. To enable international librarians to attend International Federation of Library Associations and Institutions (IFLA) Conference in Boston, MA.

2655. Michigan, State of, Detroit, MI. $5,508,626, 2000. For U.S. Library Program, providing computers with Internet access and training to libraries serving low-income communities.

2656. Milwaukee Public Library, Milwaukee, WI. $86,300, 2000. For U.S. Library Program, providing computers with Internet access and training to libraries serving low-income communities.

2657. Ministere de la Culture et des Communications du Quebec, Quebec, Canada. $5,471,562, 2000. To provide Quebec's public libraries serving low-income communities with gift of public access computers, Internet access, and training of library staff.

2658. Minneapolis Public Library, Minneapolis, KS. $121,150, 2000. For U.S. Library Program, providing computers with Internet access and training to libraries serving low-income communities.

2659. Missouri, State of, Jefferson City, MO. $166,100, 2000. For U.S. Library Program, providing computers with Internet access and training to libraries serving low-income communities.

2660. Montana, State of, Helena, MT. $792,190, 2000. For U.S. Library Program, providing computers with Internet access and training to libraries serving low-income communities.

2661. Multnomah County Library, Portland, OR. $35,650, 2000. For U.S. Library Program, providing computers with Internet access and training to libraries serving low-income communities.

2662. New Mexico State Library, Santa Fe, NM. $28,410, 2000. For Tribal Library Online Public Access Catalog (OPAC) program, as part of Native American Access to Technology initiative.

2663. New York, State of, Albany, NY. $7,603,773, 2000. For U.S. Library Program, providing computers with Internet access and training to libraries serving low-income communities.

2664. North Carolina, State of, Raleigh, NC. $5,801,080, 2000. For U.S. Library Program, providing computers with Internet access and training to libraries serving low-income communities.

2665. Northwest Territories Public Library Services, Hay River, Canada. $219,219, 2000. To provide Northwest Territories' public libraries serving low-income communities with gift of public access computers, Internet access, and training of library staff.

2666. Ohio, State of, Columbus, OH. $492,300, 2000. For U.S. Library Program, providing computers with Internet access and training to libraries serving low-income communities.

2667. Omaha Public Library, Omaha, NE. $90,300, 2000. For U.S. Library Program, providing computers with Internet access and training to libraries serving low-income communities.

2668. Pennsylvania, Commonwealth of, Harrisburg, PA. $2,460,950, 2000. For U.S. Library Program, providing computers with Internet access and training to libraries serving low-income communities.

2669. Salt Lake County Library System, Salt Lake City, UT. $67,900, 2000. For U.S. Library Program, providing computers with Internet access and training to libraries serving low-income communities.

2670. Santa Fe Indian School, Santa Fe, NM. $24,579, 2000. For library internship program, as part of Native American Access to Technology initiative.

2671. Saskatchewan Library Association, Regina, Canada. $636,956, 2000. To provide Saskatchewan's public libraries serving low-income communities with gift of public access computers, Internet access, and training of library staff.

2672. Southwestern Indian Polytechnic Institute, Albuquerque, NM. $58,478, 2000. For library internship program, as part of Native American Access to Technology initiative.

2673. Tennessee, State of, Nashville, TN. $214,950, 2000. For U.S. Library Program, providing computers with Internet access and training to libraries serving low-income communities.

2674. Texas, State of, Austin, TX. $7,108,836, 2000. For U.S. Library Program, providing computers with Internet access and training to libraries serving low-income communities.

2675. Tides Center, DC. $100,000, 2000. For Brave Kids program to develop directory of health care resources for seriously ill children in Washington State.

2676. Tilden Library Foundation, Tilden, NE. $41,250, 2000. To establish technology center.

2677. University of Washington, Seattle, WA. $393,435, 2000. For Tribal Connections Online Health Information for Native Americans project in Four Corners area.

2678. Virginia, Commonwealth of, Richmond, VA. $3,791,558, 2000. For U.S. Library Program, providing computers with Internet access and training to libraries serving low-income communities.

2679. Washington Womens Foundation, Seattle, WA. $100,000, 2000. To develop best practices hand book on philanthropy using foundation as model.

2680. Washington, State of, Olympia, WA. $550,548, 2000. For U.S. Library Program, providing computers with Internet access and training to libraries serving low-income communities.

2681. Wichita Public Library Foundation, Wichita, KS. $99,550, 2000. For U.S. Library Program, providing computers with Internet access and training to libraries serving low-income communities.

2682. Yukon Department of Education, Whitehorse, Canada. $150,364, 2000. To provide Yukon's public libraries serving low-income communities with gift of public access computers, Internet access, and training of library staff.

2683. Yukon Department of Education, Whitehorse, Canada. $52,055, 2000. To assist Yukon's public libraries serving low-income communities by establishing workstation computer-training lab.

M. J. Murdock Charitable Trust

Limitations: Giving primarily in the Pacific Northwest (AK, ID, MT, OR, and WA). No support for government programs; projects common to many organizations without distinguishing merit; sectarian or religious organizations whose principal activities are for the benefit of their own members. No grants to individuals, or for annual campaigns, general support, continuing support, deficit financing, endowment funds, operating budgets, emergency funds, scholarships, fellowships, political activities, or matching gifts; no loans.

2684. Lewis and Clark College, Northwestern School of Law, Portland, OR. $1,000,000, 2000. For library expansion and renovation and for infrastructure technology.

2685. National Strategy Information Center, DC. $350,000, 2000. For research project analyzing nontraditional security challenges.

2686. University of Puget Sound, Tacoma, WA. $1,000,000, 2000. For Collins Library renovation.

The Seattle Foundation

Limitations: Giving limited to the greater Puget Sound region, WA. No support for political or religious organizations. No grants to individuals, or for scholarships, fellowships, endowment funds, research, operating budgets, general purposes, matching gifts, conferences or seminars, exhibits, film or video production, or publications; no loans.

2687. Charities Aid Foundation America, Alexandria, VA. $90,000, 1999. For general support.

2688. Charities Aid Foundation America, Alexandria, VA. $60,000, 1999. For Allen Memorial School in India, including Science Laboratory, Uniforms Fund, Library Books Fund, Computer Science Room and Equipment and school construction.

2689. Charities Aid Foundation America, Alexandria, VA. $30,000, 1999. For Allen Memorial School in India's land acquisition and fax machine.

2690. Huntington Library, Art Collections and Botanical Gardens, San Marino, CA. $10,000, 1999. For Melvin S. and Virginia Morse Book Fund.

2691. Lake Forest Country Day School, Lake Forest, IL. $10,000, 1999. For Kathleen Moore McAllister Library Fund to enhance endowment.

2692. Seattle Public Library Foundation, Seattle, WA. $100,000, 1999. For capital campaign through NEH Challenge Grant Program.

2693. Seattle Public Library Foundation, Seattle, WA. $50,000, 1999. For capital campaign.

WASHINGTON—Seattle

2694. Seattle Public Library Foundation, Seattle, WA. $25,000, 1999. For Books, Bytes, and Believers program.
2695. Seattle Public Library Foundation, Seattle, WA. $10,451, 1999. For general support.
2696. Seattle School District No. 1, Seattle, WA. $60,000, 1999. For elementary library book collection development.
2697. University of Washington Foundation, Seattle, WA. $19,000, 1999. For Allen Library.
2698. Washington Literacy, Seattle, WA. $43,568, 1999. For Day Care Link Program.

The Stewardship Foundation

Limitations: Giving internationally, nationally and in western WA, especially in Tacoma and Pierce County and the Puget Sound Region. No support for churches; religious support only to Christian parachurch organizations. No grants to individuals, or for seed money, endowment funds, deficit financing, research, videos, media time or program production.

2699. Interdev, Seattle, WA. $100,000, 1999. For continued general operating support.
2700. Interdev, Seattle, WA. $25,000, 1999. For Interlink's Adopt a People Partnership for UK Churches.
2701. Night Ministry International, Tacoma, WA. $10,000, 1999. For general operating support.
2702. Pacific Association for Theological Studies, Seattle, WA. $30,000, 1999. For library resources.

Washington Mutual Foundation

Limitations: Giving primarily in areas of company operations in CA, FL, ID, IL, MA, NY, NV, OR, TX, UT, and WA. No support for religious organizations for religious purposes, veterans' or labor organizations. No grants to individuals.

2703. Orange County Affordable Housing Clearinghouse, Lake Forest, CA. $10,000, 2000.
2704. Seattle Public Library Foundation, Seattle, WA. $250,000, 2000.

Weyerhaeuser Company Foundation

Limitations: Giving limited to areas of company operations, especially AL, AR, MS, NC, southeastern OK, western OR, and western WA (including Tacoma, Seattle, and Federal Way); giving to national organizations in fields related to the forest products industry. No support for religious organizations for religious purposes, operating funds for United Way-supported organizations, political campaigns, or for the influence of legislation. No grants to individuals, or for deficit financing, indirect costs, conferences outside the forest products industry, endowments, or memorials.

2705. Amory Municipal Library, Amory, MS. $38,000, 1999. For improvements to Library.

WISCONSIN

Helen Bader Foundation, Inc.

Limitations: Giving primarily in the greater Milwaukee, WI, area for education and economic development; giving locally and nationally for Alzheimer's disease and dementia; giving in Israel for early childhood development. No grants to individuals.

2706. Donors Forum of Wisconsin, Milwaukee, WI. $75,000, 2000. 3-year grant. For Technical Assistance Program for Philanthropists.
2707. Planning Council for Health and Human Services, Milwaukee, WI. $25,000, 2000. To establish 211, phone number for 24 hour Community Information and Referral assistance on non-emergency health and human services.
2708. Southeastern Wisconsin Area Agency on Aging, Brookfield, WI. $40,000, 2000. 2-year grant. For Wisconsin Statewide Dementia Directory.

Pat and Jay Baker Foundation, Inc.

Limitations: Giving primarily in Milwaukee, WI. No grants to individuals.

2709. Milwaukee Public Library, Milwaukee, WI. $50,000, 1999.

The Lynde and Harry Bradley Foundation, Inc.

Limitations: Giving primarily in Milwaukee, WI; giving also on a national and international basis. No support for strictly denominational projects. No grants to individuals, or for endowment funds.

2710. D.C. Parents for School Choice, DC. $50,000, 2000. For continued general operating support.
2711. Donors Forum of Wisconsin, Milwaukee, WI. $30,000, 2000. For Wisconsin Entrepreneurs in Philanthropy Initiative, part of New Ventures in Philanthropy project.
2712. Educational Reviewer, NYC, NY. $65,000, 2000. For book project on recovering traditional precepts of American public philosophy.
2713. European Foundation Centre, Brussels, Belgium. $10,000, 2000. For Annual Assembly and Conference.
2714. Foundation Center, NYC, NY. $12,000, 2000. For continued general operating support.
2715. Gilder Lehrman Institute of American History, NYC, NY. $102,506, 2000. For start-up support for history high school in Milwaukee and development of History On-Line.
2716. Libro Libre, Escazu, Costa Rica. $40,000, 2000. For continued general operating support.
2717. National Strategy Information Center, DC. $250,000, 2000. For continued general operating support.
2718. New Hope Project, Milwaukee, WI. $20,000, 2000. For Milwaukee Workers' Website.
2719. Richard Nixon Library and Birthplace Foundation, Yorba Linda, CA. $90,000, 2000. For strategic assessment.
2720. Ukrainian Catholic Education Foundation, Chicago, IL. $20,000, 2000. For general operating support and for Religious Information Service of Institute for Religion and Society at Lviv Theological Academy in Ukraine.
2721. Wisconsin, State of, Department of Administration, Madison, WI. $118,000, 2000. For preservation of Governor Tommy G. Thompson's official papers by electronic archive.

Fleck Foundation

Limitations: Giving primarily in Milwaukee, WI. No grants to individuals.

2722. Donors Forum of Wisconsin, Milwaukee, WI. $10,000, 1999. To increase services to organizations in Wisconsin.

Johnson Controls Foundation

Limitations: No support for religious purposes, public or private preschools, elementary or secondary schools, industrial groups or trade associations supported by industrial groups, foreign-based institutions, or fraternal, veterans', or labor groups. No grants to individuals (except for employee-related scholarships), or for fundraising events, courtesy advertising, deficit financing, equipment, land acquisition, special projects, research, publications, conferences, or seminars; no loans.

2723. Milwaukee Public Library Foundation, Milwaukee, WI. $20,000, 1999.

Faye McBeath Foundation

Limitations: Giving limited to WI, with emphasis on the greater Milwaukee area. No grants to individuals, or for annual campaigns, capital projects, scholarships, fellowships, or specific medical or scientific research projects; grants rarely for emergency funds; no loans.

2724. Special Needs Adoption Network, Milwaukee, WI. $15,000, 1999. For operating support for resource center, providing post-adoption services to families of children with special needs.
2725. United Way of Greater Milwaukee, Milwaukee, WI. $25,000, 1999. For capital support to establish 211, 24-hour health and human services hotline in Milwaukee County.

Greater Milwaukee Foundation

Limitations: Giving primarily in the greater Milwaukee, WI, area. No support for the general use of churches or for sectarian religious purposes, or for specific medical or scientific projects, except from components of the foundation established for such purposes. No grants to individuals (except for established awards), or for operating budgets, continuing support, annual campaigns, endowment funds, or deficit financing.

2726. Milwaukee Public Library, Milwaukee, WI. $10,000, 2000. For Home Work Help, program to expand homework assistance, art workshops, and field trips for students at Prince of Peace middle school in Clarke Square neighborhood.

2727. Oconomowoc Public Library, Oconomowoc, WI. $12,000, 2000. Toward repair and replacement of zinc alloy griffin statues that formerly stood at entrance.

2728. University of Wisconsin Foundation, Center for Urban Initiatives and Research, Milwaukee, WI. $300,000, 2000. For scholarship/financial aid clearinghouse.

Northwestern Mutual Foundation

Limitations: Giving primarily in the greater Milwaukee, WI, area. No grants to individuals.

2729. Milwaukee Public Library Foundation, Milwaukee, WI. $30,000, 2000.

Jane Bradley Pettit Foundation

Limitations: Giving primarily in the greater Milwaukee, WI, area. No grants to individuals.

2730. Donors Forum of Wisconsin, Milwaukee, WI. $20,000, 1999.

Reiman Charitable Foundation, Inc.

2731. Denver Public Library, Denver, CO. $20,000, 1999. For After School Is Cool program.

2732. Denver Public Library, Denver, CO. $13,000, 1999. For teen summer reading program.

2733. Denver Public Library Friends Foundation, Denver, CO. $10,000, 1999. For Booklover's Ball.

Rockwell International Corporation Trust

Limitations: Giving nationally in areas of corporate operations, except for selected national organizations and universities which are sources of recruits or whose research is of interest; giving internationally where the company has formal programs. No support for religious organizations for religious purposes. No grants to individuals, or for hospital building campaigns or general endowments; no loans.

2734. National Czech and Slovak Museum and Library, Cedar Rapids, IA. $10,000, 2000.

Siebert Lutheran Foundation, Inc.

Limitations: Giving primarily in WI. No grants to individuals, or for endowment funds, scholarships, or fellowships; no loans.

2735. Bethany Lutheran College, Mankato, MN. $25,000, 1999. For new library enhancement and construction.

Wisconsin Energy Corporation Foundation, Inc.

Limitations: Giving primarily in service territories in the Upper Peninsula, MI, area and the southeastern and Fox Valley, WI, areas.

2736. Wisconsin Womens Health Foundation, Madison, WI. $25,000, 1999.

Recipient Index

Child Abuse Prevention Center, UT, 2575
Child and Family Resource Council, MI, 894
Child Care Concepts, MI, 871
Child Care Connection, NJ, 1165
Child Care Resource and Referral, FL, 572, 675
Child Care Resource and Referral Network, MO, 1062, 1079, 1080
Child Care Resource Center of Cuyahoga County, OH, 2053
Child Care Resource Center of Lorain County, OH, 2042, 2069, 2072
Child Care Resource Center/Southside, MN, 1036
Child Care Resources, NC, 2002
Child Care, Inc., NY, 1201, 1222, 1236, 1243, 1302, 1542, 1711, 1850, 1912
Children of Aging Parents, PA, 1227, 1228
Childrens Book Press, CA, 1960
Childrens Council of San Francisco, CA, 173
Childrens Health Involving Parents, VA, 2617
Childrens Home Society of Minnesota, MN, 989, 1041
Childrens Hospital, OH, 2031
Childrens Hospital Foundation, PA, 2255
Childrens Hospital Medical Center of Northern California, CA, 155
Childrens Museum of Houston, TX, 2523, 2528
China Business Forum, DC, 1420
China Cultural Property Promotion Association, China, 1631
China National Rice Research Institute, China, 1812
Chinese Academy of Forestry, China, 1421
Chinese Womens Health Network, China, 1422
Christar, PA, 531
Christian Heritage College, CA, 386
Christian Information and Service Center, TX, 2561, 2562
Churches Uniting in Global Mission, CA, 2303
Churchill County Museum and Archives, NV, 1114
Cincinnati Center for Developmental Disorders, OH, 2043
Cinema Museum, Russia, 1423
Circle Foundation, MD, 1813
Citizens Advice Bureau, NY, 1202, 1246, 1526, 1716, 1717, 1893, 1917
Citizens for Better Schools, NJ, 1166, 1167
Citizens for Missouris Children, MO, 1063, 1081
Citizens Information Service of Illinois, IL, 695
Citizens Nuclear Information Center, Japan, 847, 2608
City College of the City University of New York, NY, 1569, 2050
City Wide Task Force on Housing Court, NY, 1865
Claremont University Center and Graduate School, CA, 758
Clark Atlanta University, GA, 589
Clark County Legal Services Program, NV, 472
Clark Memorial Library, RI, 2314
Clay Mountain Housing, WV, 808, 2165
Clean Air Task Force, MA, 115
Cleveland Housing Network, OH, 473
Cleveland Museum of Natural History, OH, 2026
Cleveland Public Library, OH, 743
Clifton Heights Senior Center, MO, 702
Clute Public Library Association, TX, 872
Coalition of Wisconsin Aging Groups, WI, 2529
Coast Community Library, Friends of, CA, 1214
Coldspring Area Public Library, TX, 2449
Coletivo Feminista Sexualidade e Saude, Brazil, 667

Collaborative Communications Group, DC, 1321
College Misericordia, PA, 500
College of Charleston, SC, 918
Collingsworth County Public Library, TX, 2397
Colonial Williamsburg Foundation, VA, 2148
Colorado Office of Resource and Referral Agencies, CO, 377
Colorado State University Foundation, CO, 402
Colorado, State of, CO, 2638
Columbia Basin College Foundation, WA, 117
Columbia University, NY, 1527, 1611, 1727
Columbine High School, CO, 373
Columbus Academy, OH, 2032, 2033
Columbus Health Care Organization, NM, 1181
Columbus Metropolitan Library, OH, 2065
Columbus Regional Information Service, OH, 2034, 2035
Combined Generations of the Holocaust of Greater Cincinnati, OH, 2046
Comfort Public Library, TX, 2467, 2468, 2514
Commission on Presidential Debates, DC, 551
Communication and Information for Women, Mexico, 1424
Communication Works, CA, 590
Community AIDS Treatment Information Exchange (CATIE), Canada, 329
Community Center and Library Association, PA, 2298
Community Food Resource Center, NY, 1894
Community Food Security Coalition, CA, 1741
Community Health Councils, CA, 70
Community Health Library of Los Gatos, CA, 338, 345
Community Health Media Trust, South Africa, 1425
Community Health Partnership of Santa Clara County, CA, 245, 346
Community Home Ownership Center, WA, 474
Community Housing Development Corporation of North Richmond, CA, 371
Community Housing Resources of Arizona, AZ, 1961
Community Information and Referral Services, AZ, 676
Community Information Exchange, DC, 771
Community Referral Agency, WI, 984, 985
Community Resource Services, MD, 1756
Community Service Education and Research Fund of the Sacramento-El Dorado Medical Society, CA, 71
Community Services Council, UT, 2576
Community Studies, NY, 2639
Community Technology Alliance, CA, 552
Community Technology Institute, WA, 2113
Computers for Children, NY, 1338
Concord Pike Library, Friends of the, DE, 447
Congregation Beth Israel, CA, 358
Connecticut Historical Society, CT, 431
Connecticut Humanities Council, CT, 432
Connecticut Policy and Economic Council, CT, 427
Connecticut State Library, CT, 428
Connecticut Voices for Children, CT, 941
Connection Resource Services, IL, 628, 677
Conservation Fund, VA, 246
Consortium for the National Equal Justice Library, DC, 2427
Consortium of Universities of the Washington Metropolitan Area, DC, 498
Consultative Group on Biological Diversity, CA, 2256
Converse Area Public Library, TX, 2469
Converse College, SC, 1346

Cooperating Libraries Automated Network (CLAN), RI, 2315
Cooperative Housing Foundation, MD, 1426
Coordinated Advice and Referral Program for Legal Services, IL, 629, 696
Coos County Cooperative Library Service District, OR, 2118
Cornell University, NY, 1632-1634, 1757, 1814, 1815
Corning Area Public Library, NY, 1339
Cornwall Library Associates, CT, 497, 816
Corporation for Enterprise Development (CFED), DC, 1427, 2206
Corpus Christi Public Library Foundation, TX, 2530
Cortez Public Library, CO, 374, 395
Council Bluffs Library Foundation, IA, 2047
Council for Advancement and Support of Education, DC, 475
Council for Aid to Education (CFAE), NY, 2531
Council for Basic Education, DC, 422, 457, 553, 711, 715, 805, 979, 1215, 1259, 1895
Council of Better Business Bureaus Foundation, VA, 942, 1543
Council of Michigan Foundations, MI, 895, 923, 1160
Council on Competitiveness, DC, 1878
Council on Foreign Relations, NY, 1260
Council on Foundations, DC, 1082, 1879
Council on Library and Information Resources, DC, 599, 1355, 2483
Country Music Foundation, TN, 2378
Coventry Public Library, RI, 2316
Cranston Public Library, RI, 2317
Crime Prevention Association, PA, 2186
Crime Prevention Resource Center, TX, 2413
Crisis Intervention of Houston, TX, 2459
Crohns and Colitis Foundation of America, NY, 1145
Cross City Campaign for Urban School Reform, IL, 772
Cross Mills Public Library, RI, 2318
Croswell, City of, MI, 902
Crownpoint Institute of Technology, NM, 2640
Cumberland Public Library, RI, 2319
Curtis Memorial Library, ME, 1577

D.C. Parents for School Choice, DC, 2710
Dallas Public Library, TX, 2430
Dallas Public Library, Friends of the, TX, 2431, 2442, 2450, 2480, 2481
Dallas Symphony Association, TX, 2432
Dalles-Wasco County Public Library, OR, 2114
Damien High School, CA, 31
Danbury Community Library, TX, 2402
Danbury, City of, TX, 2505
DataCenter, CA, 517, 1325, 1594, 1595, 1742
Dauphin County Library System, PA, 2618
Davidson College, NC, 1988
Davidson County Library Foundation, NC, 2003
Davisville Free Library Association, RI, 2320
Decatur Public Library, TX, 612
Delaware County Intermediate Unit Education Foundation, PA, 2257
Delray Beach Library, FL, 568
Democracy and Sexuality, Mexico, 1428, 1429
Denver Public Library, CO, 378, 406, 2731, 2732
Denver Public Library Friends Foundation, CO, 379, 388, 678-680, 2733
Desert Foothills Library, AZ, 14
Detroit Institute for Children, MI, 2532
Detroit Public Library, MI, 974
Detroit Public Library, Friends of, MI, 868, 980

Metropolitan Museum of Art, NY, 139, 1198, 1239
Metropolitan Opera Association, NY, 1234
Metropolitan State University Foundation, MN, 986
Metropolitan Washington Council of Governments, DC, 460, 2591
Mexican Center for Philanthropy, Mexico, 670, 955, 1449, 1450
Miami Workers Center, FL, 521
Miami-Dade Public Library, Friends of, FL, 538
Michigan Association of Community Arts Agencies, MI, 866
Michigan, State of, MI, 2655
Mid America Assistance Coalition, MO, 1071
Mid-Hudson Library, NY, 1798
Middle Country Library Foundation, NY, 1307
Middle School Connection, MN, 1031
Middletown Public Library, RI, 2334
Midland Energy Library, TX, 2388
Midland Public Library, Friends of the, TX, 2389
Midtown Community Benefits District, MD, 800
Millbrook Free Library, NY, 794, 1381
Milwaukee Public Library, WI, 2656, 2709, 2726
Milwaukee Public Library Foundation, WI, 2048, 2535, 2723, 2729
Minerva Public Library, OH, 2058
Ministere de la Culture et des Communications du Quebec, Canada, 2657
Ministry of Education of Jamaica, Jamaica, 2144
Ministry of Foreign Affairs, Vietnam, 1451
Minneapolis American Indian Center, MN, 1032
Minneapolis Neighborhood Employment Network, MN, 364, 1012, 1013, 1055, 1056
Minneapolis Public Library, KS, 2658
Minnesota Center for Community Economic Development, MN, 1023
Minnesota Center for Environmental Advocacy, MN, 1005
Minnesota Child Care Resource and Referral Network, MN, 1006, 1007
Minnesota Council of Nonprofits, MN, 1024
Minnesota Medical Foundation, MN, 1037
Minnesota Public Radio, MN, 1008
Minnesota Senior Federation, MN, 1028
Miss Porters School, CT, 2089
Missionary Franciscan Sisters of the Immaculate Conception, Papua New Guinea, 451
Missouri Association of Community Task Forces, MO, 1139
Missouri Botanical Garden, MO, 1654
Missouri Development Finance Board, MO, 1059
Missouri, State of, MO, 2659
Mobile Public Library, AL, 5, 11
Model Cities of Saint Paul, MN, 1043
Moffat Consolidated School District No. 2, CO, 381
Molalla, City of, OR, 2122
Monroe County Public Library, AL, 6
Montana Environmental Information Center, MT, 592, 2622
Montana School for the Deaf and Blind Foundation, MT, 1014
Montana, State of, MT, 2660
Montclair Art Museum, NJ, 1610
Montclair Public Library, NJ, 1170, 1223
Monte Cassino School, OK, 2098
Montecito Library, Friends of, CA, 1616

Monterey County Free Libraries, Foundation for, CA, 182, 183, 263
Montgomery County MH/MR Emergency Service, PA, 2267
Moravian Church in America, Southern Province, NC, 2019
Moravian Music Foundation, NC, 2020
Moriarty Community Library, NM, 411, 412
Morse Institute Library, MA, 843
Moscow State Tchaikovsky Conservatory, Russia, 1452
Mount Saint Dominic Academy, NJ, 1171, 1172
Mount Saint Marys College, CA, 212
Mount Zion Public Library, IL, 2299
Mountain Brook Library Foundation, AL, 7
Mountain Resource Center, CO, 376, 391, 397, 407
Muenster Public Library, Friends of the, TX, 2510
Multiple Sclerosis Society, National, NY, 1899
Multnomah County Library, OR, 2134, 2661
Muncie Public Library, IN, 719, 721
Murray Public Library, IA, 726
Museum Associates, CA, 42, 140
Museum for African Art, NY, 1453
Museum Library and Arts Foundation, NV, 2536
Museum of Chinese-American History, CA, 185
Museum of Fine Arts, MA, 1655
Museum of Modern Art, NY, 141, 1020, 1829

Nantucket Atheneum, MA, 1515
Narika, CA, 78
Narragansett Public Library, RI, 2335
Nashville Public Library Foundation, TN, 2371, 2377
Natarang Pratishthan, India, 1454
National Abortion and Reproductive Rights Action League (NARAL) Foundation, DC, 162, 1326
National Adoption Center, PA, 2592
National Alliance for Caregiving, MD, 1229
National Archives, DC, 2086
National Archives, Foundation for the, DC, 1220
National Assembly of National Health and Human Service Organizations, DC, 1087, 1323
National Assistance and Information Centre for NGOs in Moldova, Moldova, 956
National Association for Visually Handicapped, CA, 350
National Center for Black Philanthropy, DC, 957, 1803
National Center for Family Philanthropy, DC, 179, 204, 264, 736, 958, 2241
National Center for Victims of Crime, VA, 1516
National Charities Information Bureau (NCIB), NY, 601, 877, 959, 1088, 1154, 1804
National Childrens Alliance, DC, 2593
National Committee on American Foreign Policy, NY, 1830
National Conference of State Legislatures, CO, 657
National Consumer Law Center, MA, 116
National Council of Churches of Kenya, Kenya, 1455
National Czech and Slovak Museum and Library, IA, 739, 2734
National Endowment for the Humanities, DC, 1268
National Fatherhood Initiative, MD, 2594
National First Ladies Library, OH, 27, 484, 621, 744, 2039, 2059, 2073, 2080, 2081

National Funding Collaborative on Violence Prevention, DC, 429
National Gallery of Canada, Canada, 1360
National Governors Association Center for Best Practices, DC, 782
National Health Foundation, CA, 89
National Health Law Program, CA, 213
National Housing Institute, NJ, 193, 783, 1308, 1556, 2001
National Kidney Foundation, NY, 1146
National Library of Medicine, Friends of the, DC, 609, 1156, 2492
National Library of New Zealand, New Zealand, 142
National Low Income Housing Coalition and Low Income Housing Information Service, DC, 485
National Multicultural Institute, DC, 784
National Practitioners Network for Fathers and Families, DC, 1015
National Religious Vocation Conference, IL, 566
National Research Council, DC, 1884
National Security Archive Fund, DC, 106, 671, 850, 1269, 1456, 1457, 1931
National Sporting Library, VA, 1749
National Strategy Information Center, DC, 2685, 2717
National Womens Health Network, DC, 163, 400, 510, 1852
National Womens Law Center, DC, 511
National Yiddish Book Center, MA, 299, 642
National Youth Employment Coalition, DC, 1458
National Youth Information Network, KS, 785, 1077
Natural History Museum of Los Angeles County Foundation, CA, 143
Nautilus of America, CA, 2610
Network of Estonian Nonprofit Organizations, Estonia, 960
Nevada Avenue Elementary School, CA, 1309
New Albany-Plain Local Schools Board of Education, OH, 2040
New Beginnings, CA, 334
New Braunfels Public Library Foundation, TX, 2473
New Haven Free Public Library, Friends of the, CT, 2537
New Hope Project, WI, 2718
New Israel Fund, DC, 529
New Jersey Coalition for Battered Women, NJ, 1147
New Jersey Foundation for Aging, NJ, 1140
New Jersey Historical Society, NJ, 1656, 1795
New Jersey Poison Information and Education System, NJ, 1125
New Mexico State Library, NM, 2662
New School University, NY, 1270
New Vision Partners, CA, 205
New Visions for Public Schools, NY, 1459
New York Academy of Medicine, NY, 486, 658, 910, 1141, 1242, 1334, 1335, 1344, 1382, 1383, 1491, 1517, 1533, 1538, 1600, 1601, 1612, 1697, 1720, 1768, 1855, 1860-1863, 1915, 1956
New York Botanical Garden, NY, 1657
New York Cares, NY, 1129
New York City Public/Private Initiatives, NY, 1570
New York Farms, NY, 527
New York Historical Society, NY, 1235
New York Industrial Retention Network, NY, 1712, 1721, 1885

New Hampshire Library Association, NH, 1938

South Austin Job Referral Service, IL, 636, 688

South Carolina Archives and History Foundation, SC, 1977, 1998, 2021

South Central Los Angeles Inter-Religious Sponsoring Committee, CA, 966

South Kingstown Public Library, RI, 2349

South Miami Hospital Foundation, FL, 1778

South Pasadena Educational Foundation, CA, 281

South San Francisco Library, CA, 294

South Texas College of Law, TX, 2524

South Wings, TN, 513

Southeast Texas Family Resource Center, TX, 2441

Southeastern Pennsylvania Consortium for Higher Education, PA, 1675

Southeastern Wisconsin Area Agency on Aging, WI, 2708

Southern Connecticut Library Council, CT, 430

Southern Home Services, PA, 2274

Southern Russia Resource Center, Russia, 967

Southern Utah University Foundation, UT, 2580

Southwest Center for Biological Diversity, AZ, 119

Southwest Georgia Regional Library, GA, 1560

Southwest Research and Information Center, NM, 523, 595, 807, 1180, 1746, 1867

Southwest Texas State University, TX, 2396

Southwestern Indian Polytechnic Institute, NM, 2672

Special Needs Adoption Network, WI, 2724

Spertus College of Judaica, IL, 1599

Sprawl Watch Clearinghouse, DC, 421

Spring Arbor College, MI, 903

Springfield Library and Museums Association, MA, 828, 830, 839

Springfield-Greene County Library District, MO, 1092, 1978

Staatsarchiv Des Kantons Bern, Switzerland, 861

Stadt Und Universitatbibliothek Bern, Switzerland, 862

Stanfield Library, OR, 1108, 2112

Stanford University, CA, 1676, 1677, 2275

Star Academy, AZ, 2422

State Communities Aid Association, NY, 968, 1329, 1330

State Pedagogical Institute of Nizhny Tagil, Russia, 1477

Sterling Public Library, IL, 647

Steve Biko Foundation, South Africa, 1478

Steve Pascente Charitable Foundation, AZ, 1017

Steward School, VA, 2616

Stony Brook-Millstone Watersheds Association, NJ, 1123

Stowe-Day Foundation, CT, 436

Summit Free Public Library, NJ, 1784

Sunshine Cottage School for Deaf Children, TX, 2477

Supportive Child/Adult Network (SCAN), PA, 2276

Supreme Council Charities, PA, 2291

Survivors of the Shoah Visual History Foundation, CA, 92, 126, 357, 611, 644, 664, 769, 2158, 2222

Synergos Institute, NY, 969, 1920

Syracuse University, NY, 563, 1153, 1837

Syracuse-Turkey Creek Township Public Library, IN, 729

T.L.L. Temple Memorial Library, TX, 2567-2570

Tabor Childrens Services, PA, 2277

Talbot Library and Museum Association, OK, 2099

Tallahassee-Leon County Cultural Resources Commission, FL, 564

Tampa Bay Partnership Regional Research and Educational Foundation, FL, 1979

Task Force for Child Survival and Development, GA, 1142

TechRocks, PA, 1916

Tempe Preparatory Academy, AZ, 2423

Temple Public Library, Foundation of, TX, 2181, 2182

Temple University, PA, 2245, 2278

Tennessee, State of, TN, 2673

Texas A & M University Development Foundation, TX, 2545

Texas Childrens Hospital, TX, 2512

Texas Heart Institute, TX, 2513

Texas Library Association, TX, 2546

Texas Medical Center, TX, 2444

Texas Nonprofit Management Assistance Network, TX, 2547

Texas Tech University, TX, 2415

Texas, State of, TX, 2674

Thailand Business Coalition on AIDS, Thailand, 1479

Theological Consortium of Greater Columbus, OH, 1918

Thomas Beaver Free Library, PA, 1158

Thomas Jefferson Memorial Foundation, VA, 2583

Thomas Jefferson University Hospitals, PA, 2279

Tides Center, CA, 84, 970, 971

Tides Center, DC, 1480, 2675

Tilden Library Foundation, NE, 2676

Tippecanoe County Public Library Foundation, IN, 2145

Tiverton Library Services, RI, 2350

Toledo-Lucas County Public Library, OH, 2049

Tomsk Human Rights Research Center, Russia, 1481

Tropical Soil Biology and Fertility Programme, Kenya, 1838

Tsinghua University Education Foundation, China, 1678

Tufts University, MA, 1924

Tulsa Area Book Bank, OK, 2094, 2100

Tulsa Library Trust, OK, 2076, 2107, 2548

Tye Preston Memorial Library of Canyon Lake, TX, 2478

Ukrainian Catholic Education Foundation, IL, 2720

Unemployment Information Center, PA, 524, 2280

Unified School District No. 500, KS, 1089

Union of Pan Asian Communities of San Diego County, CA, 494

Union Springs Library, AL, 2

Union Theological Seminary, NY, 738, 1679

United Hospital Foundation, MN, 1029

United Nations Educational, Scientific and Cultural Organization (UNESCO), Nigeria, 1482

United Negro College Fund, VA, 228

United Neighborhood Houses of New York, NY, 789

United States Catholic Conference, DC, 567

United Way, Belarus, 972

United Way International, VA, 1314, 1315

United Way of Fresno County, CA, 206

United Way of Greater Milwaukee, WI, 2725

United Way of the Chattahoochee Valley, GA, 565

United Way of Tulare County, CA, 85

UniTEQ/PipeVine, CA, 101, 102

Universal City Public Library, TX, 2479

Universities Center of Dallas, TX, 2453

University of Arizona, AZ, 790

University of California, CA, 86, 314, 315, 335, 363, 1143, 1362, 1545, 1551, 1680, 1681, 1904, 2549

University of California at Los Angeles Foundation, CA, 46-48, 114

University of Cape Town, South Africa, 1483

University of Colorado, CO, 405

University of Connecticut, CT, 1682

University of Delaware, DE, 450

University of Houston-Downtown, TX, 2525

University of Houston-University Park, TX, 2445, 2462, 2494, 2499

University of Illinois at Chicago, IL, 1492

University of Illinois at Urbana-Champaign, IL, 1590, 1683, 1734

University of Kansas Center for Research, KS, 1144

University of Maine, ME, 791

University of Maryland Foundation, MD, 1363, 1779

University of Massachusetts, MA, 1684

University of Michigan, MI, 1685

University of Minnesota, MN, 852

University of Minnesota Foundation, MN, 1046, 1780

University of Missouri, MO, 1093

University of Nevada at Las Vegas Foundation, NV, 1112

University of New Mexico, NM, 366

University of North Carolina, NC, 1484, 1995, 2017

University of Oklahoma, OK, 2101

University of Paris, France, 1839

University of Pennsylvania, PA, 1364, 1367, 1686, 1687, 1840

University of Pittsburgh, PA, 2214, 2292

University of Puget Sound, WA, 1688, 1903, 2686

University of Rhode Island, RI, 2351

University of Richmond, VA, 49

University of Southern California, CA, 149

University of Texas, TX, 2454, 2455

University of Texas at Dallas, TX, 2482

University of Texas M.D. Anderson Cancer Center, TX, 2550

University of Tulsa, OK, 2095, 2104

University of Virginia Law School Foundation, VA, 2281

University of Washington, WA, 2677

University of Washington Foundation, WA, 2697

University of Wisconsin, WI, 714, 1274

University of Wisconsin Foundation, WI, 2728

UNNATI Organisation for Development Education, India, 1485

Upper Montgomery Volunteer Network, MD, 468

Urban Hope Ministries, MN, 1016

Urban League of San Diego, CA, 87

USF Charter School, FL, 2424

Utah Library Association, UT, 834

Utah State Library Division, UT, 2578

Valparaiso University, IN, 718

Venice Family Clinic, CA, 282

Vermont Department of Libraries, VT, 1497

Geographic Index

ALABAMA

Greenville Butler County Public Library 12
Grove Hill Public Library 3
Ina Pullen Smallwood Memorial Library 4
Mobile Public Library 5, 11
Monroe County Public Library 6
Mountain Brook Library Foundation 7
Nonprofit Resource Center of Alabama 8
Parnell Memorial Library Foundation 9, 13
Union Springs Library 2

ARIZONA

Arizona, State of 2632
Community Housing Resources of Arizona 1961
Community Information and Referral Services 676
Desert Foothills Library 14
Institute for Science Philanthropy 1982
Library Friends of Payson 15
Phoenix Public Library 20
Phoenix Public Library Foundation 686
Phoenix Public Library, Friends of the 687
Phoenix Seminary 535
Saint Marys High School 1116
Scottsdale, City of 16
Sedona Public Library 692
Southwest Center for Biological Diversity 119
Star Academy 2422
Steve Pascente Charitable Foundation 1017
Tempe Preparatory Academy 2423
University of Arizona 790
Yuma County Library District 17
Yuma Library Foundation 18, 19

ARKANSAS

Arkansas Public Policy Panel 1740
Arkansas River Valley Library 24
Arkansas River Valley Regional Library System 25, 26
Arkansas State University 1402
Barton Library 2558
Institute for Social Justice 952
Nonprofit Resources 1959
Philander Smith College 1113
William J. Clinton Presidential Foundation 127, 1060

AUSTRIA

Osterreichische Akademie der Wissenschaften 147

AZERBAIJAN

Charity Society Bashkechid 1755
Khazar University 1765

BELARUS

United Way 972

BELGIUM

European Foundation Centre 944, 945, 1049, 2713

BOTSWANA

Botswana National Library Service 1256

BRAZIL

Coletivo Feminista Sexualidade e Saude 667

BULGARIA

Access to Information Programme 926
Bulgarian Charities Aid Foundation 929

CALIFORNIA

Academy of Television Arts and Sciences Foundation 1192
AIDS Resources Information and Services of Santa Clara County 99, 284
Alameda County Library Foundation 151
Alameda County Network of Mental Health Clients 369, 370
Alameda, County of 240
Alliance for Technology Access 229
Allied Fellowship Service 187
Altadena Library, Friends of the 283
American Communications Foundation 1910, 1911
Antelope Valley Indian Museum Interpretive Association, Friends of the 129
Art Resources and Technical Services (Arts Inc.) 197
Athenaeum Music and Arts Library 302
Aviva Family and Childrens Services 277
Bancroft Library, Friends of the 285
Berkeley Public Library 108, 239, 915
Berkeley Public Library Foundation 51, 214, 305
Biola University 30, 208, 385
Bolinas-Stinson Beach Library Improvement Society 109
Boys and Girls Club of Los Angeles, Watts/Willowbrook 60
Boys and Girls Club, Variety 278
Bridge to Asia Foundation 1495
Business for Social Responsibility (BSR) Education Fund 1810
California Advocates for Nursing Home Reform 172
California Association of Food Banks 61
California Health Foundation and Trust 62, 63
California Heritage Museum 279
California History Center Foundation 244

California Pacific Medical Center Foundation 152
California Primary Care Association 64, 65
California State Foster Parents Association 66
California State Library Foundation 1211, 2437
California State University at Long Beach Foundation 550
California, State of 2636
Catholic Charities of Santa Clara County 153, 198, 199
Center for Governmental Studies 67
Center for Health Care Rights (CHCR) 68
Center for the Study of Political Graphics 131
Central California Blood Bank 69
Childrens Book Press 1960
Childrens Council of San Francisco 173
Childrens Hospital Medical Center of Northern California 155
Christian Heritage College 386
Churches Uniting in Global Mission 2303
Claremont University Center and Graduate School 758
Coast Community Library, Friends of 1214
Communication Works 590
Community Food Security Coalition 1741
Community Health Councils 70
Community Health Library of Los Gatos 338, 345
Community Health Partnership of Santa Clara County 245, 346
Community Housing Development Corporation of North Richmond 371
Community Service Education and Research Fund of the Sacramento-El Dorado Medical Society 71
Community Technology Alliance 552
Congregation Beth Israel 358
Consultative Group on Biological Diversity 2256
Damien High School 31
DataCenter 517, 1325, 1594, 1595, 1742
Disability Rights Advocates 72
Dominican Santa Cruz Hospital 73
Eden Information and Referral Service 348
EdSource 189, 200, 306, 1962
Elizabeth Glaser Pediatric AIDS Foundation 1546
Environmental Protection Information Center (EPIC) 103, 105, 118, 2609
Etna Public Library, Friends of the 2110
Familia Unida Living with Multiple Sclerosis 74
Family Helpline 58
Filipino American Heritage Institute 1217
Fine Arts Museums of San Francisco 1547
Foundation Center 104, 157, 307, 319, 332, 372, 1963
Franklin-McKinley School District 286
Friends and Foundation of the San Francisco Public Library 158, 175, 196, 308, 322, 353
Future Families 252
George Coates Performance Works 1818
Greater Bay Area Family Resource Network 169

Grover Regional Library Association 396
Hotchkiss Public Library 375
Inter-Faith Task Force for Community Services 383
Jefferson County Public Schools 389
League of Women Voters of Denver Education Fund 390
Moffat Consolidated School District No. 2 381
Mountain Resource Center 376, 391, 397, 407
National Conference of State Legislatures 657
Parent Education and Assistance for Kids 392
Penrose-Saint Francis Health Care System 393
Pikes Peak Library District 394
Providers Resource Clearinghouse 384, 408
Rocky Mountain Media Watch 788
San Miguel County Public Library District 2429
University of Colorado 405

CONNECTICUT

American Public Information on the Environment 525
Center for Connecticut Studies 1582
Connecticut Historical Society 431
Connecticut Humanities Council 432
Connecticut Policy and Economic Council 427
Connecticut State Library 428
Connecticut Voices for Children 941
Cornwall Library Associates 497, 816
Earth Action Network 2231
Greenwich Library 1150, 1602
Hartford Public Library 415, 433-435, 837
Miss Porters School 2089
New Haven Free Public Library, Friends of the 2537
Patrons of the New Haven Public Library 1844
Southern Connecticut Library Council 430
Stowe-Day Foundation 436
University of Connecticut 1682
Western Connecticut Library Council 1800
Yale University 542, 1591, 1691, 1692, 1847, 2183

COSTA RICA

Libro Libre 2716

CZECH REPUBLIC

CEE BankWatch Network 930
Donors Forum 943

DELAWARE

Arden Archives and Museum 446
Catalyst Project 452
Concord Pike Library, Friends of the 447
Eleutherian Mills-Hagley Foundation 2258
Family and Workplace Connection 444, 449, 453
Hagley Museum and Library 454
University of Delaware 450
Wilmington Institute Free Library 455
Wilmington Library Foundation 445

DENMARK

Euro-Mediterranean Human Rights Network 1433

DISTRICT OF COLUMBIA

Advocacy Institute 1391

Afro-American Historical and Genealogical Society 1394
Alliance for Better Campaigns 2247
American Council on Education 1395
American Library Association 665, 1397, 1807
American Political Science Association 1620
American Public Human Services Association 1332
American Youth Work Center 2234
Americans for the Arts 241-243, 1324, 1376, 1398, 1696, 1786
Archives of American Art of the Smithsonian Institution 1507, 2400
Arms Control Association (ACA) 2606
Association of American Universities 2250
Bank Information Center 398, 504-506, 515, 588, 927, 1794, 1801
Calvary Bilingual Multicultural Learning Center 507
Center for Public Integrity 2253
Center for Responsive Politics 2254
China Business Forum 1420
Collaborative Communications Group 1321
Commission on Presidential Debates 551
Community Information Exchange 771
Consortium for the National Equal Justice Library 2427
Consortium of Universities of the Washington Metropolitan Area 498
Corporation for Enterprise Development (CFED) 1427, 2206
Council for Advancement and Support of Education 475
Council for Basic Education 422, 457, 553, 711, 715, 805, 979, 1215, 1259, 1895
Council on Competitiveness 1878
Council on Foundations 1082, 1879
Council on Library and Information Resources 599, 1355, 2483
D.C. Parents for School Choice 2710
EarthRights International 156
Ecological Society of America 1636
Edmund S. Muskie Foundation 653
Essential Information 247
Finance Project 250, 776, 947
Folger Shakespeare Library 458, 499, 814, 1118, 1520, 1935, 2211
Freedom Channel 2601
Genetic Resources Communications Systems 526
George C. Marshall Institute 1238
George Washington University 1134
Georgetown University Medical Center 1135
Grantmakers in Health 1819
Greater D.C. Cares 502
Health Education Foundation 1058
Institute of World Politics 874
International Center for Not-for-Profit Law 953, 1821
International Possibilities Unlimited 1443
Joint Center for Political and Economic Studies 2143
Judge David L. Bazelon Center for Mental Health Law 1490
La Clinica del Pueblo 2590
Library of Congress 190, 191, 464, 756, 803, 1098, 1267, 1306, 1316, 1379, 1384, 1735, 1736, 1788, 1826, 1919, 1922, 1950, 1951, 2152-2154, 2212, 2428, 2556
Library of Congress Millennium Foundation 1729
Marie Stopes International 509
Metropolitan Washington Council of Governments 460, 2591

National Abortion and Reproductive Rights Action League (NARAL) Foundation 162, 1326
National Archives 2086
National Archives, Foundation for the 1220
National Assembly of National Health and Human Service Organizations 1087, 1323
National Center for Black Philanthropy 957, 1803
National Center for Family Philanthropy 179, 204, 264, 736, 958, 2241
National Childrens Alliance 2593
National Endowment for the Humanities 1268
National Funding Collaborative on Violence Prevention 429
National Governors Association Center for Best Practices 782
National Library of Medicine, Friends of the 609, 1156, 2492
National Low Income Housing Coalition and Low Income Housing Information Service 485
National Multicultural Institute 784
National Practitioners Network for Fathers and Families 1015
National Research Council 1884
National Security Archive Fund 106, 671, 850, 1269, 1456, 1457, 1931
National Strategy Information Center 2685, 2717
National Womens Health Network 163, 400, 510, 1852
National Womens Law Center 511
National Youth Employment Coalition 1458
New Israel Fund 529
Nonprofit Clinic Consortium 786
Parents United for the D.C. Public Schools 1312
Partners for Livable Communities 461
Physicians for Social Responsibility 806, 2270
Pinchot Institute for Conservation 593
Population Services International 265
Scenic America 270
Smithsonian Institution 418, 1835, 2411
Sprawl Watch Clearinghouse 421
Tides Center 1480, 2675
United States Catholic Conference 567
Washington Child Development Council 462, 469, 2598
Washington Council of Agencies 503
Women in Government (WIG) 659
Woodrow Wilson International Center for Scholars 1276
Woodstock Theological Center 709

EGYPT

Integrated Care Society 581

ENGLAND

Africa Centre 1805
Alister Hardy Trust 2302
British Library 1626
Burlington Magazine Foundation 1629
Cambridge University 1630, 1811
Charities Aid Foundation 327, 328, 619, 620, 867, 933-939, 1206, 1207, 1212, 1280-1301, 1415-1418, 2140
Gaza Library Project 1437
Homenet International 1442
Oxford University 1518, 1589, 1664-1666
World Conservation Monitoring Centre 276

ESTONIA

Network of Estonian Nonprofit Organizations 960

FINLAND

Finnish Committee for the Restoration of the Viipuri Library 133
Helsinki City Library 2646

FLORIDA

Bass Museum, Friends of 548
Black Archives, History and Research Foundation of South Florida 549
Body Positive Resource Center 324
Broward Alliance 689
Broward Public Library Foundation 571, 673
Child Care Resource and Referral 572, 675
Delray Beach Library 568
Donors Forum of Miami 554
First Call for Help of Broward 682
Flagler College 540
Florida College 532
Jacksonville Public Libraries 1970
Jacksonville Public Library Foundation 1971
Liberty City Charter School Project 2418
Lutheran Social Services of Northeast Florida 536
Miami Workers Center 521
Miami-Dade Public Library, Friends of 538
Parenting Project 2041
Philharmonic Center for the Arts 2309
Restore Orlando 491
Rollins College 1750
Selby Public Library, Friends of the 573
South Miami Hospital Foundation 1778
Tallahassee-Leon County Cultural Resources Commission 564
Tampa Bay Partnership Regional Research and Educational Foundation 1979
USF Charter School 2424
Yulee Elementary School 537

FRANCE

American Library in Paris 1371
American Library in Paris USA Foundation 2147
Association pour le Rayonnement des Arts Asiatiques 1624, 1625
Centre National de la Recherche Scientifique (CNRS) 1413
Fondation Le Corbusier 134
International Council of Scientific Unions 1263
University of Paris 1839

GEORGIA

Agnes Scott College 598
American Academy of Religion 2248
Atlanta University Center 579
CDC Foundation 749
Center for Democratic Renewal and Education 1, 325, 516, 905, 931, 1593
Cherokee Garden Club Library 584, 587
Clark Atlanta University 589
Emory University 1598
Environmental Justice Resource Center 518
Georgia School-Age Care Association 574
Georgia, State of 2645
Good News Communication 2304

Gwinnett Coalition for Health and Human Services 1304
Metro Fair Housing Services 585
Nonprofit Resource Center 576
Quality Care for Children 586
Southwest Georgia Regional Library 1560
Task Force for Child Survival and Development 1142
United Way of the Chattahoochee Valley 565

GERMANY

Association for Promotion of Cultural Development in Egypt 1405
Bertelsmann Stiftung 928

GHANA

Association of African Universities 1808
Charities Aid Foundation-West Africa 1419
Ghana Book Trust 1438

GREECE

British School at Athens 1557, 1558

HAWAII

Hawaii State Library Foundation 809
Saint John Vianney School 603
Saint Joseph School 604

HONDURAS

International Center for Information on Cover Crops 1820

HONG KONG

Asia Monitor Resource Center 1403

HUNGARY

Nonprofit Information and Training Center Foundation 961

IDAHO

Boise State University 605
Idaho State Library 606
Idaho, State of 2647
Information and Referral - Volunteer Connection 607

ILLINOIS

Abraham Lincoln Presidential Library and Museum Foundation 1887, 2526
Alzheimers Disease and Related Disorders Association 706
American Institute of Indian Studies 1396
American Library Association 442, 545
American Theological Library Association 731, 1603
Art Institute of Chicago 1353, 1622
Associated Colleges of the Midwest 1623
Chicago Public Library Foundation 614, 626, 660, 674, 699, 700, 707, 1213, 1233
Chicago Reporter 627
Citizens Information Service of Illinois 695
Connection Resource Services 628, 677
Coordinated Advice and Referral Program for Legal Services 629, 696

Cross City Campaign for Urban School Reform 772
Donors Forum of Chicago 476, 477, 610, 630, 631, 639, 652, 661, 662, 681, 697, 703, 704, 712, 716, 773, 906, 1430, 1488, 1758
Everett McKinley Dirksen Endowment Fund 625
Fund for Americas Libraries 2644
Genesis Center for Health and Empowerment 622
Gerber-Hart Gay and Lesbian Archives and Library 717
Heartland Alliance for Human Needs and Human Rights 1440
Illinois Department of Children and Family Services 2589
Illinois Network of Child Care Resource and Referral Agencies 683
Illinois, State of 2648
Lake Forest Country Day School 2691
Lake Forest Library 623
Legal Assistance Foundation of Chicago 648
Little Company of Mary Hospital Foundation 693
Medical Library Association 2491, 2654
Metropolitan Chicago Information Center 633, 669, 685
Mount Zion Public Library 2299
National Religious Vocation Conference 566
Newberry Library 440, 615, 624, 634, 641, 643, 650, 651, 663, 690, 698, 708, 1345, 1662
North Suburban Library System Foundation 640
Northeastern Illinois Area Agency on Aging 2539
Northwestern University 635, 649, 701
Peoria Heights Public Library 616
Prairie Rivers Network 1025
Rock Island Public Library 646, 2068
South Austin Job Referral Service 636, 688
Spertus College of Judaica 1599
Sterling Public Library 647
Ukrainian Catholic Education Foundation 2720
University of Illinois at Chicago 1492
University of Illinois at Urbana-Champaign 1590, 1683, 1734
W B E Z 637
W T T W Chicago Public Television 638

INDIA

Natarang Pratishthan 1454
UNNATI Organisation for Development Education 1485

INDIANA

Allen County Public Library Foundation 730
Association for Retarded Citizens of Indiana 2527
Bethany Theological Seminary 539
Brian Bex Report 2599
Indiana Cooperative Library Services Authority 733
Indiana Institute of Technology 557
Indiana University 1358
Indiana University Foundation 1101
Indiana, State of 2649
Indianapolis-Marion County Public Library Foundation 722, 1219
International Center of Indianapolis 734, 735
Kendallville Public Library 723
Ligonier Public Library 725
Muncie Public Library 719, 721
Noble County Public Library 727, 728

Older Adult Service and Information System
(OASIS) 2541
Remnant Trust 720
Syracuse-Turkey Creek Township Public
Library 729
Tippecanoe County Public Library Foundation
2145
Valparaiso University 718

INDONESIA

Asosiasi Konsultan Pembangunan Permukiman
Indonesia 1404
Kelola 257
Lontar Foundation 1447
Perhimpunan Pengembangan Pesentrean dar
Masqarakat 1463

IOWA

Barlow Memorial Library 745
Carnegie-Viersen Public Library 1065
Council Bluffs Library Foundation 2047
Dunlap Public Library 741
Iowa Coalition for Housing and the Homeless
480
Lamoni Public Library 724
Matthias M. Hoffman Public Library 746
Murray Public Library 726
National Czech and Slovak Museum and
Library 739, 2734
Northeast Iowa Regional Library System 747
W. H. Johnston Foundation 367
Wartburg College 740, 748
Woodbine Carnegie Public Library 742, 1105

ISRAEL

Kav LaOved-Workers Hotline for the
Protection of Workers Rights 1694
Palestinian Peace Information Center 1462
Workers Hotline 514

ITALY

Centro di Studi Americani 1354
Ente Raccolta Vinciana 132
Food and Agriculture Organization of the
United Nations 1816
Istituto di Studi Rinascimentali 138
Kunsthistorisches Institut 1585

JAMAICA

Ministry of Education of Jamaica 2144

JAPAN

Citizens Nuclear Information Center 847, 2608

KANSAS

Eisenhower Foundation 869, 870, 1896, 2149
Heart of America Family Services 1085
Kansas Action for Children 750
Kansas Advocates for Better Care 751
Kansas Health Institute 752
Kansas University Endowment Association 21,
753
Minneapolis Public Library 2658
National Youth Information Network 785, 1077
Ottawa County Health Planning Commission
754
Unified School District No. 500 1089

University of Kansas Center for Research 1144
Wichita Public Library Foundation 569, 1109,
2681
Wichita State University Endowment
Association 755

KENTUCKY

Appalachian College Association 1621
Louisville Free Public Library Foundation 596,
759, 2067
Recovery Network of Northern Kentucky 522

KENYA

African Small-Scale Farmers Communication
Network 1392
African Women and Child Information
Network 1393
International Development Research
Centre-East African Regional Office 1264
International Livestock Research Institute 1823
Kenya Forestry Research Institute 1446
Kenya National Library Service 1265
National Council of Churches of Kenya 1455
Tropical Soil Biology and Fertility Programme
1838

LATVIA

Center of Nongovernmental Organizations 932
Library Information Network Consortium
(LINC) 1650, 1651

LEBANON

Arab Network of NGOs for Development 1399

LOUISIANA

Cancer Association of Greater New Orleans 337
Louisiana State University 1828
Louisiana State University and A & M College
2652
Volunteer and Information Agency 757

MAINE

American Newspaper Repository 546
Bangor Public Library 835
Belfast Free Library 760, 1575
Blue Hill Library 761, 2022
Bridgton Public Library 1576
Curtis Memorial Library 1577
Guilford Memorial Library 762, 1578
Ludden Memorial Library 1579
Northeast Historic Film 1580
Norway Memorial Library 763
Patten Free Library 1537
Porter Memorial Library 1232, 1581
Rangeley Library Association 764
Rockland Public Library Endowment
Association 765
University of Maine 791
William A. Farnsworth Library and Art
Museum 443
York Public Library Association 766, 840

MARYLAND

American Pain Foundation 1026, 1753
Baltimore Neighborhood Indicators Alliance
795, 798
Circle Foundation 1813

Community Resource Services 1756
Cooperative Housing Foundation 1426
Enoch Pratt Free Library 767, 774
Enterprise Foundation 775
Foreign Born Information and Referral
Network 2588
Foundation for International Arts and
Education 713
Intensive Family Preservation Services
National Network 254
Johns Hopkins University 255, 954
Maryland Regional Practitioners Network for
Fathers and Families 799
Maryland, State of 2653
Midtown Community Benefits District 800
National Alliance for Caregiving 1229
National Fatherhood Initiative 2594
Peoples Homesteading Group 489
Planned Parenthood of Maryland 768
Prince Georges Child Resource Center 466,
2596
Prince Georges County Hotline and Suicide
Prevention Center 467
Roland Park Library Initiative 796
University of Maryland Foundation 1363, 1779
Upper Montgomery Volunteer Network 468
Village Learning Place 797, 801, 1980

MASSACHUSETTS

American Antiquarian Society 29, 810, 841,
1617
American Jewish Historical Society 495, 617,
1561
Amherst College 1179, 1388
Associated Day Care Services of Metropolitan
Boston 817
Associated Grantmakers of Massachusetts 818,
819
Balfour Gold Dusters 812
Benjamin Banneker Charter School 857
Boston Athenaeum 820, 821, 853
Boston College 1149
Boston Public Library 2634
Boston Public Library Foundation 463, 822, 859
Boston University 1131
Brockton Public Library 916
Cambridge College 1407
Center for Collaborative Education-Metro
Boston 2637
Clean Air Task Force 115
Dibner Institute for the History of Science and
Technology 416, 1880
Education Resources Institute 813, 2641
Educational Netcasting Foundation 1303
Franklin W. Olin College of Engineering 1882
Futureworks Company 1436
Groton Public Library 823
Harvard University 33, 34, 779, 1119, 1161,
1231, 1529, 1643-1645, 1761, 2177
Higher Education Resource Center 575
IMAGGHINE 854
Impact Project 219
Jewish Womens Archives 298, 310, 1343,
1512, 2106, 2356
John F. Kennedy Library Foundation 354, 355,
582, 832, 2602
Lahey Clinic Hospital 1347
Library of the Boston Athenaeum 815
Malden Public Library 833
Manomet Center for Conservation Sciences
2239
Massachusetts Affordable Housing Alliance
483, 824, 844
Massachusetts Historical Society 855

Massachusetts Institute of Technology 1652, 1653
Metropolitan Area Planning Council 826
Morse Institute Library 843
Museum of Fine Arts 1655
Nantucket Atheneum 1515
National Consumer Law Center 116
National Yiddish Book Center 299, 642
Northeast Document Conservation Center 144, 1587, 1588, 1663, 1769, 1927-1929
Northeastern University 1770
Oxfam America 963
Pioneer Institute for Public Policy Research 829, 858
Primary Source 1496
Project Parents 827, 845
Quebec-Labrador Foundation/Atlantic Center for the Environment 2272
Social Law Library 856
Springfield Library and Museums Association 828, 830, 839
Tufts University 1924
University of Massachusetts 1684
W G B H Educational Foundation 1785
Wellesley College 1275
Worcester Free Public Library, Friends of the 811
Worcester Public Library 842
YouthBuild USA 577

MEXICO

Amigos Contra el SIDA 666
Center for Research and Higher Studies in Social Anthropology 1410
Communication and Information for Women 1424
Democracy and Sexuality 1428, 1429
International Maize and Wheat Improvement Center 1824
Mexican Center for Philanthropy 670, 955, 1449, 1450
North American Center of Environmental Information and Communication 424

MICHIGAN

Adrian College 901
Alcohol Research Information Service 1130
Arts and Scraps 547
Artserve Michigan 904
Bay Mills Community College 1002
Child and Family Resource Council 894
Child Care Concepts 871
Council of Michigan Foundations 895, 923, 1160
Croswell, City of 902
Detroit Institute for Children 2532
Detroit Public Library 974
Detroit Public Library, Friends of 868, 980
Ecumenical Theological Center 924
Fremont Area District Library 880-885
Gerald R. Ford Foundation 896
Gerontology Network Resources 865
Grand Rapids Center for Independent Living 977
Grand Valley State University 908
Grant Public Library 886
Great Lakes Colleges Association 1642
Greater Kalamazoo-Telecity USA 898
Harbor Springs Library 691
Hesperia Public Library 887, 888
Hoyt Public Library 873
HP Devco 925
Land Information Access Association 656, 909

Michigan Association of Community Arts Agencies 866
Michigan, State of 2655
Newaygo Carnegie Library 889, 890
Newaygo Public Schools 891
Non-Profit Enterprise at Work 878
Oakland Family Services 976
Portage Public Library 899
Ryerson Library Foundation 897, 900, 1739
Saint John Dialysis Center Corporation 2604
Spring Arbor College 903
University of Michigan 1685
Volunteer and Information Services of Battle Creek 912, 914
White Cloud Public Library 892
Willard Library 863, 864, 913
Womens Information Service 893
Wyoming Public Library 978

MINNESOTA

American Indian Treaty Council Information Center 1010
Augsburg College 1039
Aurora Charter School 1009
Battered Womens Legal Advocacy Project 1001
Bayport Public Library 981
Bayport Public Library Foundation 982, 983, 988
Bethany Lutheran College 2735
Center for Cross Cultural Health 992, 993, 1027, 1035
Center for Policy Studies 1040
Child Care Resource Center/Southside 1036
Childrens Home Society of Minnesota 989, 1041
EdVisions 2642
Family Pathways 995
First Call for Help of Itasca County 990, 991
First Call for Help Southwest 1021
First Call Minnesota 996
Friends of the Campbell Library 556
Frogtown Action Alliance 1042, 1054
Goedel Memorial Library 997
Greater Minnesota Housing Fund 1030
Helping Industry Resolve Employment Disabilities (HIRED) 1022
Library Foundation of Hennepin County 1011, 1034
Mayo Foundation 1004
Metropolitan State University Foundation 986
Middle School Connection 1031
Minneapolis American Indian Center 1032
Minneapolis Neighborhood Employment Network 364, 1012, 1013, 1055, 1056
Minnesota Center for Community Economic Development 1023
Minnesota Center for Environmental Advocacy 1005
Minnesota Child Care Resource and Referral Network 1006, 1007
Minnesota Council of Nonprofits 1024
Minnesota Medical Foundation 1037
Minnesota Public Radio 1008
Minnesota Senior Federation 1028
Model Cities of Saint Paul 1043
Resources for Child Caring 1044
Saint Paul Public Library, Friends of the 365, 1000, 1019, 1045
United Hospital Foundation 1029
University of Minnesota 852
University of Minnesota Foundation 1046, 1780
Urban Hope Ministries 1016
Volunteer Resource Center of the Twin Cities 1051

Wayzata Public Library 1057
West End Business Revitalization Corporation 1052

MISSISSIPPI

Amory Municipal Library 2705
Project Connect 22

MISSOURI

American Cancer Society 1090
Black Archives of Mid-America 1073, 1078
Center for Management Assistance 1048
Charter School Information Center 1061
Child Care Resource and Referral Network 1062, 1079, 1080
Citizens for Missouris Children 1063, 1081
Clifton Heights Senior Center 702
Educational and Research Trust of the Missouri Hospital Association 339, 340
Harry S. Truman Library Institute for National and International Affairs 645, 860, 1068, 1072, 1074, 1084, 1091, 1511, 1965, 2150
Kansas City Public Library 1070, 1075
Linda Hall Library Trust 1126
Metropolitan Energy Information Center 1069, 1076, 1086
Mid America Assistance Coalition 1071
Missouri Association of Community Task Forces 1139
Missouri Botanical Garden 1654
Missouri Development Finance Board 1059
Missouri, State of 2659
OASIS Institute 1066, 1094, 1095, 2540
Saint Louis County Library Foundation 1067
Saint Louis Mercantile Library 1975
Saint Louis Public Library 492
Springfield-Greene County Library District 1092, 1978
University of Missouri 1093
Westminster College 1574

MOLDOVA

National Assistance and Information Centre for NGOs in Moldova 956

MONTANA

Montana Environmental Information Center 592, 2622
Montana School for the Deaf and Blind Foundation 1014
Montana, State of 2660

MOZAMBIQUE

Eduardo Mondlane University 1431, 1432

MYANMAR (BURMA)

Institute of Medicine 1277

NAMIBIA

Ongwediva Teachers Resource Center 1461

NEBRASKA

Bloomfield Library Foundation 1099
Cambridge, City of 1100
Hope Medical Outreach Coalition 1103

Omaha Botanical Center 43
Omaha Public Library 1104, 2667
Ralston, City of 1102
Schuyler Public Library 413, 414
Tilden Library Foundation 2676

NEVADA

Churchill County Museum and Archives 1114
Clark County Legal Services Program 472
Help of Southern Nevada 217
Las Vegas-Clark County Library District 2651
Museum Library and Arts Foundation 2536
University of Nevada at Las Vegas Foundation 1112
Veterans Affairs Sierra Nevada Health Care System 1047
Washoe County Law Library 1110
Washoe County Public Library System 1981
White Pine County Public Library 1111

NEW HAMPSHIRE

New Hampshire Library Association 1938

NEW JERSEY

Bloomfield College 1176
Cathedral Health Services 1164
Child Care Connection 1165
Citizens for Better Schools 1166, 1167
Eagleton Institute of Politics 1122
Educational Information and Resource Center 1117
Elizabeth Public Library 1168
Florham Park Public Library 2439
Henry H. Kessler Foundation 1127
Info Line of Middlesex County 1138
Institute of Electrical and Electronics Engineers (IEEE) 1883
Jewish Family Service of Metrowest 1124
Montclair Art Museum 1610
Montclair Public Library 1170, 1223
Mount Saint Dominic Academy 1171, 1172
National Housing Institute 193, 783, 1308, 1556, 2001
New Jersey Coalition for Battered Women 1147
New Jersey Foundation for Aging 1140
New Jersey Historical Society 1656, 1795
New Jersey Poison Information and Education System 1125
Newark Family Resource Network 1173
Newark Public Library 1120, 1163, 1178, 1738
Princeton University 1668, 1732, 2271
Rutgers, The State University of New Jersey 1273, 1473, 1886
Saint Philips Academy 1540
Stony Brook-Millstone Watersheds Association 1123
Summit Free Public Library 1784

NEW MEXICO

Columbus Health Care Organization 1181
Crownpoint Institute of Technology 2640
Embudo Valley Library 1182
Family Voices 248, 249
Institute of American Indian Arts Foundation 2650
Interhemispheric Resource Center 1262
Jemez Pueblo Community Library 1183, 1184
Las Clinicas del Norte 1185
Moriarty Community Library 411, 412
New Mexico State Library 2662

Santa Fe Chamber Music Festival 2410
Santa Fe Indian School 2670
Southwest Research and Information Center 523, 595, 807, 1180, 1746, 1867
Southwestern Indian Polytechnic Institute 2672
University of New Mexico 366

NEW YORK

Advocates for Children of New York 1331
American Academy in Rome 1351
American Council of Learned Societies 1618
American Forum for Global Education 1493, 1888
American Friends of Cambridge University 1352
American Friends of the British Museum 2146
American Friends of the Medem Library 1597
American Jewish Historical Society 50, 1905
American Music Center 188, 1619, 2308
American-Scandinavian Foundation 1038
Americans for the Arts 1209, 1342
Anderson-Lee Library 1498
Anthology Film Archives 1877
Archdiocese of New York 1199, 1889
Bedford Free Library 1350
Body Positive 1932
Boricua College 1565
Brewster Public Library 1890
Brooklyn Childrens Museum 1226
Brooklyn Institute of Arts and Sciences 1627
Brooklyn Museum of Art 1891
Brooklyn Public Library 1210, 1257, 1278, 1508, 1532, 1707, 1708, 1726, 1791
Brooklyn Public Library Foundation 1541, 1700, 1701, 1892, 1934
Broome Library Foundation 1370
Brotherhood/Sister Sol 1245
Buffalo Niagara Enterprise 836
Career Development Services 1279
Center for Constitutional Rights 399
Center for Jewish History 154, 439, 496, 1509, 1868, 1876, 1921, 2221
Century Association Archives Foundation 1372, 1568
Chautauqua Connections 1499, 1500
Chautauqua-Cattaraugus Library System 1501
Chess-in-the-Schools 1200
Child Care, Inc. 1201, 1222, 1236, 1243, 1302, 1542, 1711, 1850, 1912
Citizens Advice Bureau 1202, 1246, 1526, 1716, 1717, 1893, 1917
City College of the City University of New York 1569, 2050
City Wide Task Force on Housing Court 1865
Columbia University 1527, 1611, 1727
Community Food Resource Center 1894
Community Studies 2639
Computers for Children 1338
Cornell University 1632-1634, 1757, 1814, 1815
Corning Area Public Library 1339
Council for Aid to Education (CFAE) 2531
Council on Foreign Relations 1260
Crohns and Colitis Foundation of America 1145
Dewitt Historical Society of Tompkins County 1782, 1783
Education and Research Foundation of the Better Business Bureau of Metropolitan New York 1718
Educational Reviewer 2712
Environmental Background Information Center 1743
Environmental Defense 1913
Falconer Public Library 1871

Foundation Center 32, 174, 195, 201, 218, 251, 301, 331, 359, 423, 459, 501, 519, 520, 555, 591, 600, 632, 705, 732, 777, 907, 920, 948, 949, 975, 1033, 1064, 1083, 1195, 1237, 1247, 1261, 1318, 1322, 1333, 1378, 1434, 1435, 1510, 1528, 1548, 1566, 1615, 1637, 1638, 1759, 1802, 1817, 1874, 1881, 1897, 1914, 1944, 1945, 1990, 2008, 2029, 2030, 2120, 2260, 2381, 2440, 2600, 2619, 2643, 2714
Franklin and Eleanor Roosevelt Institute 921, 1380
Frick Art Reference Library 1186
Frick Collection 1549
Gay Mens Health Crisis (GMHC) 1853
George Balanchine Foundation 1858
Gertrude Stein Repertory Theater 1925
Gilder Lehrman Institute of American History 1504, 1751, 2715
Health Care Choices 1719
HealthforAll 1136
Horticultural Society of New York 1728
Infoshare 1724
Inner-City Scholarship Fund 1319, 1550
Institute for Life Coping Skills 1197
Interfaith Center on Corporate Responsibility 1744
International Center in New York 1607
International Service for the Acquisition of Agri-biotech Applications 1825
Interreligious Information Center 2075
Iona College 2189
James Prendergast Library Association 1872, 1873
Javne Fund 297
Jewish Board of Family and Childrens Services 1489
Jewish Theological Seminary of America 508
Journal Storage Project (JSTOR) 668, 793, 1647-1649
Juilliard School 1870
King Urban Life Center 1947
Leo Baeck Institute 1513
Libraries for the Future 1003, 1177, 1208, 1248, 1596, 1608, 1766, 1851
Library Foundation of Buffalo and Erie County 1948
Literacy Assistance Center 1128
Literary Classics of the United States 1359
Location One 1827
Lower Manhattan Cultural Council 1854
Mamaroneck Free Library 1908, 1909
Manpower Demonstration Research Corporation 1703
Medicare Rights Center 1859
Medici Archive Project 1187, 1514, 1521, 1586, 1955
Mercantile Library 1241
Mercantile Library Association of the City of New York 1522
Metis Associates 781
Metropolitan Museum of Art 139, 1198, 1239
Metropolitan Opera Association 1234
Mid-Hudson Library 1798
Middle Country Library Foundation 1307
Millbrook Free Library 794, 1381
Multiple Sclerosis Society, National 1899
Museum for African Art 1453
Museum of Modern Art 141, 1020, 1829
National Charities Information Bureau (NCIB) 601, 877, 959, 1088, 1154, 1804
National Committee on American Foreign Policy 1830
National Kidney Foundation 1146
New School University 1270

New Visions for Public Schools 1459
New York Academy of Medicine 486, 658, 910, 1141, 1242, 1334, 1335, 1344, 1382, 1383, 1491, 1517, 1533, 1538, 1600, 1601, 1612, 1697, 1720, 1768, 1855, 1860-1863, 1915, 1956
New York Botanical Garden 1657
New York Cares 1129
New York City Public/Private Initiatives 1570
New York Farms 527
New York Historical Society 1235
New York Industrial Retention Network 1712, 1721, 1885
New York Mortgage Coalition 487
New York Public Library 570, 922, 1151, 1152, 1159, 1193, 1194, 1203, 1224, 1230, 1244, 1249, 1250, 1271, 1317, 1320, 1340, 1368, 1369, 1389, 1505, 1523, 1524, 1531, 1535, 1536, 1562, 1571, 1583, 1584, 1592, 1613, 1658, 1659, 1698, 1699, 1704, 1730, 1737, 1752, 1781, 1789, 1790, 1792, 1796, 1842, 1843, 1846, 1856, 1864, 1866, 1875, 1952, 1957, 1958, 2051, 2357, 2603
New York Public Library, Astor, Lenox and Tilden Foundations 1361
New York Society Library 2364
New York University 1348, 1660, 1661, 1926
New York, State of 2663
New Yorkers for Children 2595
Nonprofit Connection 1310, 1311, 1695, 1713, 1725, 1939
Nyack College 534
Olean Public Library 1940
Partnership for After School Education 1539
Patrons Program 1251
Paul Smiths College of Arts and Sciences 1385
Phipps Community Development Corporation 1252
Pierpont Morgan Library 1162, 1188-1191, 1204, 1253, 1341, 1373, 1374, 1390, 1506, 1519, 1525, 1554, 1705, 1706, 1731, 1857, 1906, 1953, 2009, 2052, 2178
Pius XII Foundation 1349
Playwrights Preview Productions 1572
Poets House 1327, 1534
Powers Library 1386
Primary Care Development Corporation 1722
Pro Bono Net 1240, 1723, 1773
Programme for Promoting Nuclear Non-Proliferation 2611
Project for Public Spaces 1946
Project Reach Youth 1714
Public Agenda Foundation 1464
Putnam Valley Library 417
Queens Borough Public Library 1272
Queens Library Foundation 1254, 1313, 1544, 1573, 1715, 1793, 1900, 1942, 2179
Quogue Free Library 425, 426
Recorded Anthology of American Music 1670
Renaissance Society of America 1671
Research Foundation of the City University of New York 1336
Resource Center for Community Development 597
Resources for Children with Special Needs 1205, 1564, 1733
Rhizome Communications 1834
Ripley Free Library 1502
Rochester Institute of Technology 1672
Rockefeller University 1337
Roswell Park Cancer Institute 1387
Rundel Library Foundation 1614
Rye Free Reading Room 1845, 1923
Saint Johns Bread and Life Program 1902
Salvation Army of Greater New York 1255

Sexuality Information and Education Council of the U.S. (SIECUS) 107, 194, 271, 272, 401, 420, 512, 594, 1097, 1121, 1328, 1474, 1475, 1745, 1777
Sinclairville Free Library 1503
Somos El Futuro 879
State Communities Aid Association 968, 1329, 1330
Synergos Institute 969, 1920
Syracuse University 563, 1153, 1837
Union Theological Seminary 738, 1679
United Neighborhood Houses of New York 789
Volunteer Consulting Group 275, 973, 1486
Watchperson Project 1748
Westchester Community College Foundation 2605
Westchester Library System 1799, 1943
YIVO Institute for Jewish Research 419, 1563, 1869, 1907

NEW ZEALAND

National Library of New Zealand 142

NIGERIA

Obafemi Awolowo University 1831
United Nations Educational, Scientific and Cultural Organization (UNESCO) 1482

NORTH CAROLINA

Avery-Mitchell-Yancey Regional Library 1983
Belmont Abbey College 1984
Buncombe County Library, Friends of 2006
Carolina Justice Policy Center 2011
Child Care Resources 2002
Davidson College 1988
Davidson County Library Foundation 2003
Duke University 1356, 1989, 2176, 2484
Duke University Medical Center 2485
Greensboro Housing Coalition 2012
Haywood Regional Medical Center 1993
Hope Harbor Home 2013
Johnson C. Smith University 1994
Madison County Library, Friends of 1985, 2007
Moravian Church in America, Southern Province 2019
Moravian Music Foundation 2020
North Carolina Association of County Directors of Social Services 2014
North Carolina Center for International Understanding 2015
North Carolina Community Development Initiative 488
North Carolina, State of 2664
Northern Moore Family Resource Center 2010
Public Library of Charlotte and Mecklenburg County 560, 1974, 2004
REAL Crisis Intervention 2016
Saluda Community Help 2085
Sandhill Regional Library 2005
Scotland Neck, Town of 1986
University of North Carolina 1484, 1995, 2017
Watauga County Hunger Coalition 2018
WESTCARE Health System 1996

NORTH DAKOTA

Altru Health Foundation 544
Devils Lake, City of 994

OHIO

Artists Archives of the Western Reserve 2061
Ashland City Schools Academic Foundation 2083
Athenaeum of Ohio 2045, 2074
Carroll County District Library 2078
Case Western Reserve University 1604, 2077
Chatfield College 2025
Child Care Resource Center of Cuyahoga County 2053
Child Care Resource Center of Lorain County 2042, 2069, 2072
Childrens Hospital 2031
Cincinnati Center for Developmental Disorders 2043
Cleveland Housing Network 473
Cleveland Museum of Natural History 2026
Cleveland Public Library 743
Columbus Academy 2032, 2033
Columbus Metropolitan Library 2065
Columbus Regional Information Service 2034, 2035
Combined Generations of the Holocaust of Greater Cincinnati 2046
Donors Forum of Ohio 2027, 2070, 2087
East Cleveland Public Library 2023, 2028, 2054, 2088
Fairfield County Library Foundation 2036
Federation for Community Planning 655
Foundation Center 2055
Info Line 2079
Irish American Archives Society 2062
Library Legacy Foundation 876, 2066
Logan Elm Board of Education 2037
Methodist Theological School in Ohio 2038
Minerva Public Library 2058
National First Ladies Library 27, 484, 621, 744, 2039, 2059, 2073, 2080, 2081
New Albany-Plain Local Schools Board of Education 2040
North Canton Public Library Association 2060
Oberlin Public Library 2071
Ohio Dominican College 2090
Ohio State University 1771
Ohio State University Foundation 2091
Ohio, State of 2666
Ohioana Library Association 2092
Public Library of Cincinnati and Hamilton County 2044
Rotary Club of Canton 2082
Theological Consortium of Greater Columbus 1918
Toledo-Lucas County Public Library 2049
Western Reserve Historical Society 2024
Westside-Eastside Congregations Acting Now (WE-CAN) 2057

OKLAHOMA

Arbuckle Drug and Alcohol Information Center 2102
Indian Health Care Resources Center 875, 2093, 2096, 2105
Kellyville Public Library, Friends of the 2097, 2103
Little Dixie Community Action Agency 482
Monte Cassino School 2098
Talbot Library and Museum Association 2099
Tulsa Area Book Bank 2094, 2100
Tulsa Library Trust 2076, 2107, 2548
University of Oklahoma 2101
University of Tulsa 2095, 2104

OREGON

Cathedral School 2117
Center for National Independence in Politics (CNIP) 1258
Coos County Cooperative Library Service District 2118
Dalles-Wasco County Public Library 2114
Douglas County Headquarters Library 2109
Douglas County Library Foundation 2128
Eastern Oregon State College 2119
Ecotrust 231, 232
Eugene Public Library Foundation 919, 1216, 2129
Foundation for Accountability (FACCT) 1132
Grant County Library Foundation 2559
Institute for the Northwest 2130
Jackson County Library Foundation 2108, 2111, 2131
Jefferson County Library Association 2132
Josephine County Library Foundation 2133, 2624
Langlois Public Library 2625
Langlois Public Library Foundation 2121
Lewis and Clark College 2684
Linfield College 2626
Living Alternatives for Retired Citizens (LARC) 2627
Molalla, City of 2122
Multnomah County Library 2134, 2661
Newport Public Library Foundation 2135
Oregon Child Care Resource and Referral Network 2123
Oregon Library Association 2124
Oregon Trail Library District 2136
Portland State University 2125
River Network 2056
Stanfield Library 1108, 2112
Wallowa County Library 2137
Western Seminary 2126
Yoncalla Library Foundation 2138
Yoncalla, City of 2127

PAPUA NEW GUINEA

Missionary Franciscan Sisters of the Immaculate Conception 451

PENNSYLVANIA

Academy of Natural Sciences of Philadelphia 2184
Action AIDS 1999, 2246
Allegheny Intermediate Unit 2170, 2171, 2203
Allentown Public Library 2305
American Red Cross 2249
Art Museum Image Consortium 130
Athenaeum of Philadelphia 2159
B. F. Jones Memorial Library 2226
Balch Institute for Ethnic Studies 1225, 2160, 2185, 2215, 2235, 2282
Bayard Taylor Memorial Library 2283
Bethlehem Area Public Library 694
Braddock Carnegie Library and Community Center 2307
Brashear Association 2210
Bucks County Housing Group 2251
Butler Area Public Library 2287
Butler County Federated Library System 2195
Calcutta House 2252
Carnegie Library of Homestead 2139
Carnegie Library of Pittsburgh 2064, 2172, 2204, 2223, 2225, 2227, 2229, 2288, 2297
Carnegie-Mellon University 2205
Center for Applied Research 770

Central Philadelphia Development Corporation 2236
Chatham College 2230
Children of Aging Parents 1227, 1228
Childrens Hospital Foundation 2255
Christar 531
College Misericordia 500
Community Center and Library Association 2298
Crime Prevention Association 2186
Dauphin County Library System 2618
Delaware County Intermediate Unit Education Foundation 2257
Downingtown Good Neighbor Center 448
Duquesne University 2199
Energy Coordinating Agency of Philadelphia 2259
Euphrasia House 2187
Focus on Renewal-Sto-Rox Neighborhood Corporation 2289
Foundation for Individual Rights in Education 1196
Frankford Group Ministry 2261
Free Library of Philadelphia 543, 580, 1936, 2000, 2216, 2237, 2262, 2295
Free Library of Philadelphia Foundation 2161
Friends of the Music Library, Carnegie Library of Pittsburgh 2290
George Junior Republic 2263
Health Promotion Council of Southeastern Pennsylvania 341
Holy Ghost Preparatory School 2188
Institute for the Study of Civic Values 2284
James V. Brown Library 1937
John R. Kaufman Jr. Public Library 2115
Juvenile Law Center 780
La Roche College 2173
Lancaster Theological Seminary 533
Lansdale Public Library 1155
Library Company of Philadelphia 2162, 2163, 2217, 2238, 2264, 2265
Ligonier Valley Library 2084, 2196, 2219
Ligonier Valley Library Association 2224, 2228
Little Flower Catholic High School for Girls 2190
Lutheran Social Mission Society of Philadelphia 2266
Malvern Preparatory School 2191
Maternal Child Health Consortium of Chester County 2240
Montgomery County MH/MR Emergency Service 2267
National Adoption Center 2592
North Country Community Development Center 28
Northwest Interfaith Movement 2285
Oakmont Carnegie Library 2213
Parents Union for Public Schools in Philadelphia 2242
Pauline Auberle Foundation 2197
Pennsylvania State University 737, 1107
Pennsylvania, Commonwealth of 2668
Peoples Emergency Center 2268
Philadelphia Fight 2269
Philadelphia Health Management Corporation 2243
Philadelphia Museum of Art 1667, 2244
Pittsburgh Regional Alliance 2174, 2200
Resources for Human Development 267
Rosenbach Museum and Library 562, 1673, 2192, 2218, 2273, 2286
Sewickley Public Library 1555, 2220, 2301
Shadyside Hospital Foundation 2169
Shoah Foundation 1849

Southeastern Pennsylvania Consortium for Higher Education 1675
Southern Home Services 2274
Supportive Child/Adult Network (SCAN) 2276
Supreme Council Charities 2291
Tabor Childrens Services 2277
TechRocks 1916
Temple University 2245, 2278
Thomas Beaver Free Library 1158
Thomas Jefferson University Hospitals 2279
Unemployment Information Center 524, 2280
University of Pennsylvania 1364, 1367, 1686, 1687, 1840
University of Pittsburgh 2214, 2292
Waynesburg College 2194
West Shore Public Library 2296, 2620
Western Pennsylvania Hospital Foundation 2293
Whitehall Public Library 2306
Wyoming Seminary 1148
3 Rivers Connect 2175, 2198, 2201, 2202, 2207-2209, 2232, 2233, 2294

PERU

IESP Chaminade Marianistas 2142

PHILIPPINES

Ateneo de Manila University 1809
Caucus of Development NGO Networks 1408
Linangan Ng Kababaihan 259
Remedios AIDS Foundation 266

POLAND

Institute for Democracy in Eastern Europe 951
Regional Information and Support Centre for Nongovernmental Organizations 1465

PUERTO RICO

Asociacion de Intercambio Cultural 2063

RHODE ISLAND

Barrington Public Library 2310
Brown University 1628, 2311, 2312, 2355
Central Falls Free Public Library 2313
Clark Memorial Library 2314
Cooperating Libraries Automated Network (CLAN) 2315
Coventry Public Library 2316
Cranston Public Library 2317
Cross Mills Public Library 2318
Cumberland Public Library 2319
Davisville Free Library Association 2320
East Providence Public Library 2321
George Hail Free Library 2322
Greene Public Library 2323, 2358
Greenville Public Library 2324
Harmony Library 2325
Hope Library Association 2326
Island Free Library 2327
Jamestown Philomenian Library 2328
Jesse M. Smith Memorial Library 2329
Lincoln Public Library 2330
Louttit Library 2331
Marian J. Mohr Memorial Library 2332
Memorial and Library Association of Westerly 2333, 2359
Middletown Public Library 2334
Narragansett Public Library 2335
Newport Public Library 2336

North Providence Union Free Library 2337
North Scituate Public Library 2338
North Smithfield Public Library 2339
Pascoag Public Library 2340
Pawtucket Public Library 2341
Portsmouth Free Public Library 2342
Providence College 2343
Providence Plan 2360
Providence Public Library 838, 1567, 1797, 1941, 2344, 2345, 2361, 2362
Redwood Library and Athenaeum 530, 2346
Rhode Island Natural History Survey 2347
Rhode Island School of Design 2348
South Kingstown Public Library 2349
Tiverton Library Services 2350
University of Rhode Island 2351
Warwick Public Library 2352, 2363
West Warwick Public Library System 2353
Woonsocket Harris Public Library 2354

ROMANIA

Pro Vobis Volunteer Center 964

RUSSIA

Archive Administration of Saint Petersburg and Leningrad Region 1401
Baikal Environmental Education 1406
Center for Information Research 1409
Centre for Independent Social Research (CISR) 1411, 1412
Centre of Contemporary Architecture 1414
Charities Aid Foundation-Russia 940
Cinema Museum 1423
Memorial Human Rights Center 1448
Moscow State Tchaikovsky Conservatory 1452
Research and Information Centre Memorial 1466, 1467
Russian Academy of Sciences 1469
Russian Center for Public Opinion and Market Research 1470
Russian Charitable Foundation 1471
Russian State Archive of Film and Photo Documents 1472
Saratov Legal Reform Project 672
Sluzhenye Association of Nongovernmental Not-for-Profit Organizations 965
Southern Russia Resource Center 967
State Pedagogical Institute of Nizhny Tagil 1477
Tomsk Human Rights Research Center 1481

SENEGAL

Goree Institute 1760

SLOVAKIA

Information Centre 950

SOUTH AFRICA

Community Health Media Trust 1425
Eastern Cape Higher Education Association Trust 1635
Foundation for Library and Information Service Development 1639
Library and Information Association of South Africa 1266
Nonprofit Partnership 962, 1460
Robben Island Museum 911
Sol Plaatje Educational Trust 1476
South African Bibliographic and Information Network (SABINET) 1674

Steve Biko Foundation 1478
University of Cape Town 1483
Western Cape Tertiary Institutions Trust 1689, 1690

SOUTH CAROLINA

Cannon Memorial Hospital 1987
College of Charleston 918
Converse College 1346
Eastern Cluster of Lutheran Seminaries 1605
Furman University 1991, 1992
Greenwood School District No. 51 2366
Medical University of South Carolina (MUSC) 2564
Mepkin Abbey 1609
South Carolina Archives and History Foundation 1977, 1998, 2021

SOUTH DAKOTA

Northern State University 559

SWITZERLAND

International Union for Conservation of Nature and Natural Resources 1444
Staatsarchiv Des Kantons Bern 861
Stadt Und Universitatbibliothek Bern 862

TENNESSEE

Charter School Resource Center of Tennessee 2372
Chattanooga-Hamilton County Library 2370
Country Music Foundation 2378
Family and Childrens Service 2379
Foundation for the Library 2367, 2368
Foundation for the Memphis Shelby County Public Library 1559, 2373-2375
Friends of the Public Library of Nashville and Davidson County 2380
Grant Center 2369, 2376, 2382, 2383
Meharry Medical College 1898
Memphis/Shelby County Public Library 825
Nashville Public Library Foundation 2371, 2377
South Wings 513
Tennessee, State of 2673

TEXAS

Allan Shivers Library and Museum 2425
Alliance for the Mentally Ill of the Gulf Coast 2456
American Farmland Trust 2503
Anson Public Library 2399, 2426, 2434
Arlington Public Library Foundation 2520
Arts San Antonio 2463
Association of Fundraising Professionals 2457
Austin College 2384
Austin Public Library, Friends of the 2516
Bandera County Library, Friends of 2464
Blanco Library 2435, 2522
Body Positive 608, 2458
Boerne Public Library, Friends of 2465
Bonham Public Library 2401, 2448
Bulverde Public Library 2466
Burkeville Independent School District 2560
Canyon, City of 2504
Carelinc Network 2517
Center for Entrepreneurship and Economic Development 326
Center for Nonprofit Management 471

Charter School Resource Center of Texas 2438, 2500, 2552
Childrens Museum of Houston 2523, 2528
Christian Information and Service Center 2561, 2562
Clute Public Library Association 872
Coldspring Area Public Library 2449
Collingsworth County Public Library 2397
Comfort Public Library 2467, 2468, 2514
Converse Area Public Library 2469
Corpus Christi Public Library Foundation 2530
Crime Prevention Resource Center 2413
Crisis Intervention of Houston 2459
Dallas Public Library 2430
Dallas Public Library, Friends of the 2431, 2442, 2450, 2480, 2481
Dallas Symphony Association 2432
Danbury Community Library 2402
Danbury, City of 2505
Decatur Public Library 612
Dickens County-Spur Public Library, Friends of the 2385
Dilley Public Library 2403
Dimmit County Public Library 2404, 2446, 2506
East Waco Innovative School Development 2416
Ector County Library, Friends of the 2386
Edwards, County of 2515
El Paso Community College 330
Encino Save Our School Corporation 2417
Floyd County Library, Friends of the 2387, 2436
Fort Worth Public Library Foundation 2521
Fort Worth Public Library, Friends of the 2533
George Bush Presidential Library Center 2553
George Bush Presidential Library Foundation 613, 1964, 1997
Giddings, City of 2141, 2405, 2486
Gill Childrens Services 2414
Goliad County Library 2406
Goliad, County of 2507
Greater Dallas Planning Council 2508
Houston Academy of Medicine 2398, 2487, 2488, 2495, 2496
Houston Education Resource Network (HERN) 2460, 2501, 2554
Houston Public Library 2502, 2555
Houston Public Library, Friends of the 100, 2489, 2519
Howe Community Library, Friends of the 2509
Jeff Davis County Library 2407
Jewish Family Service of San Antonio 2470
Jourdanton Library and Community Center Foundation 2451
Kountze Public Library 2408, 2452
Kurth Memorial Library 2563
Lakehills Library and Community Association 2471
Leon Valley Public Library, Friends of the 2472
Lyndon Baines Johnson Foundation 356
Mental Health Association of Houston and Harris County 2409
Midland Energy Library 2388
Midland Public Library, Friends of the 2389
Muenster Public Library, Friends of the 2510
New Braunfels Public Library Foundation 2473
Newton, County of 2565
Nita Stewart Haley Memorial Library 2390, 2391
Nixon, City of 2511
Nonprofit Resource Center of Texas 2538
North Hills School 2419
NYOS Charter School 2420

Subject Index

Archives, collections management/preservation 114, 129, 131, 139-141, 143, 145-150, 185, 546, 668, 758, 911, 1038, 1093, 1234, 1235, 1337, 1351, 1354, 1356, 1363, 1372, 1379, 1394, 1401, 1414, 1423, 1452, 1454, 1457, 1467, 1470, 1472, 1529, 1622, 1624-1627, 1630, 1631, 1633, 1643, 1647, 1648, 1652-1655, 1657-1660, 1663, 1667, 1668, 1671, 1672, 1675-1677, 1679-1682, 1686-1688, 1691, 1726, 1727, 1729, 1732, 1734, 1757, 1771, 1858, 2271, 2302

Archives, computer systems/equipment 709, 793, 826, 1235, 1347, 1685, 1782, 1783

Archives, curriculum development 1634

Archives, electronic media/online services 129, 131, 140, 143, 145, 146, 148-150, 279, 709, 1122, 1235, 1356, 1401, 1406, 1413, 1414, 1423, 1432, 1454, 1481, 1618, 1621, 1624, 1631, 1633, 1634, 1636, 1643, 1644, 1652-1654, 1657, 1659, 1663-1666, 1668, 1669, 1672, 1675-1677, 1679-1681, 1685, 1686, 1691, 1692, 1764, 1925, 1930, 2106, 2271

Archives, endowments 1629, 1658, 2400

Archives, equipment 1008, 1782, 1783

Archives, exhibitions 1114, 1687

Archives, faculty/staff development 1782, 1783

Archives, fellowships 1586, 1734

Archives, film/video/radio 318, 611, 1406, 1414, 1762, 1864

Archives, gays/lesbians 717

Archives, immigrants/refugees 1665, 1666

Archives, income development 2400, 2410

Archives, internships 1757, 2106

Archives, minorities 561

Archives, Native Americans 129

Archives, offenders/ex-offenders 911

Archives, program evaluation 1649

Archives, publication 1143, 1367, 1394, 1432, 1447, 1454, 1629, 1634, 2400

Archives, research 671, 713, 737, 911, 1143, 1273, 1394, 1457, 1470, 1478, 1529, 1634, 1649, 1672, 1692

Archives, student aid 2525

Archives, technical aid 2567

Archives, women 148, 298, 310, 1343, 1512, 1669, 2106, 2356

Archives, youth 1529

Armenia, community improvement/development 1755

Armenia, employment 1755

Arms control 806, 807, 847, 1468, 2606

Arms control, conferences/seminars 2611

Arms control, publication 2611

Art conservation 1927

Art conservation, Asians/Pacific Islanders 185

Art conservation, building/renovation 1189, 1190

Art conservation, collections management/preservation 185, 1189, 1190, 1622, 1624-1627, 1631, 1655, 1667, 1929

Art conservation, electronic media/online services 1624, 1631

Art conservation, faculty/staff development 1769, 1928

Art conservation, fellowships 1587

Art conservation, management development 1929

Art history, building/renovation 1610

Art history, collections acquisition 33, 34, 42

Art history, collections management/preservation 1647

Art history, endowments 1549, 1629

Art history, fellowships 184

Art history, publication 1629

Arts councils 274

Arts education 1376, 1896

Arts education, blacks 549

Arts education, boys & young men 2188

Arts education, building/renovation 549, 2188

Arts education, children & youth 443, 904, 1011, 1461, 1696, 1731, 2726

Arts education, collections management/preservation 1461

Arts education, curriculum development 1253, 1731

Arts education, economically disadvantaged 2726

Arts education, equipment 49

Arts education, minorities 2726

Arts education, publication 904

Arts education, research 904

Arts education, youth 1253

Arts/cultural programs 302, 1827

Arts/cultural programs, collections management/preservation 1372

Arts/cultural programs, fellowships 1591

Arts/culture/humanities, Africa 1453, 1805

Arts/culture/humanities, Belarus 668

Arts/culture/humanities, Bulgaria 1928

Arts/culture/humanities, China 1422, 1604, 1624-1626, 1631

Arts/culture/humanities, China & Mongolia 830, 2610

Arts/culture/humanities, Eastern Europe 297, 1270

Arts/culture/humanities, England 1352, 1626, 1629, 1805, 2146

Arts/culture/humanities, Estonia 1769

Arts/culture/humanities, Finland 133

Arts/culture/humanities, France 134, 1624, 1625, 1839

Arts/culture/humanities, global programs 92, 126, 357, 611, 644, 664, 769, 849, 911, 1451, 1482, 1826, 1827, 1835, 1837, 1849, 2158, 2222, 2606

Arts/culture/humanities, Greece 1557, 1558

Arts/culture/humanities, Iceland 1038

Arts/culture/humanities, India 1396, 1454

Arts/culture/humanities, Indonesia 1447

Arts/culture/humanities, Italy 132, 138, 1187, 1351, 1514, 1521, 1585, 1586, 1955

Arts/culture/humanities, Japan 2610

Arts/culture/humanities, Kenya 1392

Arts/culture/humanities, Korea 2610

Arts/culture/humanities, Mexico 1410

Arts/culture/humanities, Mongolia 1769

Arts/culture/humanities, Mozambique 1432

Arts/culture/humanities, Myanmar (Burma) 1754

Arts/culture/humanities, Namibia 1461

Arts/culture/humanities, Nigeria 1482

Arts/culture/humanities, Russia 668, 1401, 1406, 1411, 1414, 1423, 1452, 1466, 1472, 1481, 1925, 1927

Arts/culture/humanities, Slovakia 1929

Arts/culture/humanities, South Africa 911, 1425, 1476

Arts/culture/humanities, Southern Africa 1682

Arts/culture/humanities, Soviet Union (Former) 508, 1270, 1411, 1466, 1481

Arts/culture/humanities, Thailand 1754

Arts/culture/humanities, Ukraine 2720

Arts/culture/humanities, United Kingdom 2700

Arts/culture/humanities, Vietnam 1451, 1832

Arts, administration/regulation 904

Arts, aging 2463

Arts, alliance 242, 243, 1209, 1342, 1786

Arts, artist's services 150, 2308

Arts, Asians/Pacific Islanders 1217

Arts, awards/prizes/competitions 2304

Arts, blacks 1453, 2237

Arts, building/renovation 547

Arts, capital campaigns 154

Arts, children & youth 904, 1226, 1461, 2237, 2463

Arts, collections management/preservation 144, 150, 1414, 1461, 1631, 2271

Arts, commissioning new works 1818

Arts, computer systems/equipment 2650

Arts, cultural/ethnic awareness 154, 299, 419, 439, 496, 508, 642, 735, 830, 1217, 1461, 1509, 1513, 1563, 1835, 1836, 1868, 1869, 1876, 1907, 1921, 2221, 2237, 2650

Arts, economically disadvantaged 2237

Arts, electronic media/online services 150, 188, 197, 268, 548, 1414, 1631, 1661, 1670, 1818, 1829, 1834, 1835, 1839, 1854, 2271, 2463

Arts, endowments 1549, 1619

Arts, ethics 2304

Arts, exhibitions 830

Arts, film/video/radio 1414

Arts, Hispanics 735

Arts, immigrants/refugees 735

Arts, information services 188, 197, 241-243, 268, 274, 547, 548, 563, 564, 866, 904, 1048, 1209, 1342, 1414, 1453, 1549, 1619, 1641, 1661, 1670, 1786, 1818, 1827, 1829, 1834, 1835, 1839, 1854, 2304, 2463

Arts, internships 2650

Arts, management development 197

Arts, management/technical aid 144, 545, 1324, 1453, 1631, 1641

Arts, minorities 1836

Arts, multipurpose centers/programs 150, 197, 545, 1226, 1324, 1396, 1398, 2463

Arts, Native Americans 2650

Arts, performance/productions 1818

Arts, public education 1376

Arts, public policy 241, 274, 1324, 2271

Arts, publication 904, 1641

Arts, research 274, 904, 1398, 1641, 1835

Arts, seed money 564

Asia, education 1495

Asia, health—general 1809

Asia, international affairs/development 969, 1295, 1495

Asia, philanthropy/voluntarism 969

Asia, public affairs/government 1495, 1801

Asians/Pacific Islanders, arts/culture/humanities 185, 1217

Asians/Pacific Islanders, community improvement/development 1416

Asians/Pacific Islanders, education 185, 1217

Asians/Pacific Islanders, health—general 78, 2279

Asians/Pacific Islanders, housing/shelter 494

Asians/Pacific Islanders, human services—multipurpose 78, 494, 1044, 2279

Asians/Pacific Islanders, international affairs/development 1416

Asians/Pacific Islanders, philanthropy/voluntarism 1416

Asthma research, children & youth 2255

Asthma, awards/prizes/competitions 1053

Asthma, children & youth 1053, 2255

Athletics/sports, boys & young men 2191

Athletics/sports, building/renovation 2191

Athletics/sports, capital campaigns 2191

Athletics/sports, school programs 2191

Austria, education 147

Azerbaijan, community improvement/development 1755

Azerbaijan, education 1765, 1775

Economic development, faculty/staff development 1431

Economic development, Hispanics 2530

Economic development, minorities 771, 783, 1402

Economic development, research 952, 1416, 1419

Economic development, technical aid 771, 783

Economic development, visitor/convention bureau 1402

Economically disadvantaged, arts/culture/humanities 788, 1392, 1482, 1572, 1887, 2237, 2726

Economically disadvantaged, civil rights 327, 328, 477, 780, 784, 931, 1142, 1281, 1393, 1408, 1429, 1442, 1443, 1445, 1487, 1694, 1742, 2427

Economically disadvantaged, community improvement/development 67, 82, 223, 224, 450, 488, 517, 577, 771, 773, 775, 779, 783, 787, 788, 790, 800, 952, 963, 966, 1042, 1052, 1236, 1281, 1392, 1402, 1408, 1416, 1427, 1436, 1443, 1463, 1740, 1742, 1743, 2199, 2206, 2584

Economically disadvantaged, crime/courts/legal services 213, 472, 511, 648, 780, 1240, 1723, 1742, 1748, 1773, 2274, 2584, 2593

Economically disadvantaged, education 382, 461, 472, 507, 575, 577, 772, 774, 787, 827, 845, 968, 1006, 1043, 1185, 1199-1201, 1245, 1246, 1249-1251, 1255, 1303, 1312, 1319, 1330, 1331, 1349, 1482, 1500, 1550, 1572, 1608, 1774, 1887, 1889, 2237, 2242, 2262, 2427, 2532, 2586, 2588, 2617, 2630, 2632-2634, 2636-2638, 2644-2649, 2651-2653, 2655-2661, 2663-2669, 2671, 2673, 2674, 2678, 2680-2683, 2726

Economically disadvantaged, employment 521, 524, 577, 790, 952, 1013, 1022, 1054, 1281, 1442, 1694, 1703, 2199, 2246, 2266, 2280, 2718

Economically disadvantaged, environment 116, 517, 1443, 1740, 1742, 1743, 1748

Economically disadvantaged, food/nutrition/agriculture 61, 296, 1392, 1741, 1816, 1825, 1894, 1902

Economically disadvantaged, health—general 60, 62, 64, 65, 69-71, 75, 76, 80, 82, 84, 86, 213, 282, 341, 479, 507, 622, 786, 790, 1028, 1043, 1047, 1103, 1136, 1142, 1304, 1330, 1332, 1392, 1393, 1429, 1445, 1474, 1487, 1491, 1551, 1722, 1915, 2010, 2240, 2269, 2279, 2285, 2532, 2590, 2617

Economically disadvantaged, health—specific diseases 327, 328, 2269

Economically disadvantaged, housing/shelter 193, 220, 223, 224, 371, 450, 460, 468, 472-474, 478, 480-483, 485, 487-489, 491, 492, 494, 552, 710, 775, 783, 808, 824, 844, 1030, 1308, 1426, 1556, 1716, 1961, 1966, 1967, 2001, 2012, 2045, 2165, 2246, 2703

Economically disadvantaged, human services—multipurpose 75, 76, 84, 213, 252, 253, 258, 289, 347, 382-384, 408, 468, 474, 477, 478, 481, 482, 487, 488, 491, 492, 494, 507, 511, 521, 552, 710, 770, 773, 778-780, 782, 785, 787-789, 791, 792, 941, 947, 968, 995, 1006, 1013, 1015-1017, 1028, 1043, 1142, 1222, 1236, 1243, 1255, 1304, 1439, 1463, 1473, 1499, 1500, 1542, 1711, 1717, 1767, 1774, 1850, 1894, 1902, 1912, 1961, 2018, 2053, 2259, 2261, 2262,

2269, 2274, 2279, 2285, 2433, 2551, 2701, 2718

Economically disadvantaged, international affairs/development 327, 328, 931, 963, 969, 1281, 1284, 1286, 1287, 1393, 1416, 1426, 1440, 1443, 1445, 1482, 1487, 1816, 1825, 1920

Economically disadvantaged, mental health/substance abuse 710, 787, 1047, 1330, 2246, 2590

Economically disadvantaged, philanthropy/voluntarism 784, 945, 969, 1416, 1920

Economically disadvantaged, public affairs/government 62, 65, 67, 82, 84, 220, 250, 253, 473, 477, 552, 774, 776, 778, 779, 947, 968, 1030, 1303, 1329-1331, 1402, 1408, 1440, 1608, 1703, 1722, 1767, 1773, 1774, 2014, 2143, 2206, 2630, 2632-2634, 2636-2638, 2644-2649, 2651-2653, 2655-2661, 2663-2669, 2671, 2673, 2674, 2678, 2680-2683, 2718

Economically disadvantaged, recreation/sports/athletics 60, 382, 2532

Economically disadvantaged, religion 966, 1429, 2199, 2701

Economically disadvantaged, science 1816, 1825

Economically disadvantaged, social sciences 82, 941, 947, 1303, 1463, 1920, 2143

Economically disadvantaged, youth development 60, 289, 327, 328, 577, 945, 1200, 1323, 1608, 2586

Economics, faculty/staff development 1298

Economics, offenders/ex-offenders 1756

Economics, research 1294, 1756

Economics, scholarships 1298

Ecuador, international affairs/development 1920

Ecuador, philanthropy/voluntarism 1920

Ecuador, social sciences 1920

Education, administration/regulation 711, 1603

Education, Africa 1263, 1303, 1764, 1808, 1814

Education, aging 1095, 1538, 2540, 2541

Education, alliance 1918

Education, Asia 1495

Education, association 442, 834, 1266, 1800, 1938, 2195, 2491, 2546

Education, Austria 147

Education, Azerbaijan 1765, 1775

Education, Belarus 668

Education, bilingual programs 507

Education, blacks 228, 1245, 2237, 2242

Education, Botswana 1256

Education, boys & young men 278, 2197, 2263

Education, Brazil 1315

Education, building/renovation 51, 278, 396, 445, 447, 764, 765, 811, 816, 897, 900, 925, 1128, 1245, 1255, 1873, 1985, 2036, 2103, 2110, 2197, 2228, 2263, 2385-2387, 2431, 2442, 2465, 2471, 2472, 2480, 2510, 2559, 2574, 2582, 2586, 2613, 2624

Education, Canada 1360, 2272, 2490, 2630, 2657, 2665, 2671, 2682, 2683

Education, capital campaigns 181, 2032, 2224, 2377, 2542, 2692, 2693

Education, children & youth 198, 199, 205-207, 229, 263, 291, 380, 388, 389, 427, 507, 537, 558, 583, 607, 707, 714, 772, 774, 827, 968, 1063, 1084, 1095, 1177, 1181, 1184, 1233, 1246, 1248, 1254, 1275, 1331, 1493, 1526, 1539, 1573, 1608, 1696, 1700, 1797, 1888, 1893, 1973, 2198, 2237, 2242, 2245, 2262, 2386, 2474, 2520, 2540, 2541, 2559, 2588, 2617, 2726, 2731

Education, Chile 1400, 1457, 2633

Education, China 1298-1301, 1420, 1493, 1496, 1601, 1604, 1624-1626, 1631, 1678, 1812, 2179

Education, collections acquisition 316, 317, 1000, 1872, 2145, 2447, 2472, 2474

Education, collections management/preservation 142, 285, 1355, 1529, 1675

Education, community/cooperative 389, 427

Education, computer systems/equipment 210, 278, 352, 722, 1106, 1233, 1245, 1255, 1565, 1690, 1948, 2033, 2071, 2171, 2195, 2197, 2315, 2380, 2386, 2396, 2613, 2683

Education, conferences/seminars 550, 711, 1118, 1395, 1765, 1807, 2491, 2546

Education, Costa Rica 2716

Education, Cuba 671

Education, curriculum development 1289, 1538, 2198

Education, disabled 229, 1331, 2465, 2472

Education, Eastern Europe 297, 1270, 1764

Education, economically disadvantaged 382, 461, 507, 575, 772, 774, 827, 968, 1245, 1246, 1255, 1312, 1331, 1608, 1774, 2237, 2242, 2262, 2586, 2588, 2617, 2637, 2683, 2726

Education, Egypt 581

Education, electronic media/online services 182, 183, 210, 229, 607, 968, 1289, 1331, 1395, 1495, 1603, 1669, 1675, 1948, 2315, 2396, 2460

Education, endowments 983, 2491

Education, England 1285, 1289, 1292-1294, 1296, 1298-1301, 1352, 1437, 1518, 1589, 1626, 1629, 1630, 1664-1666, 1811, 2146, 2302

Education, equal rights 2641

Education, equipment 26, 316, 317, 352, 556, 1181, 1255, 1873, 2181, 2315, 2424, 2465, 2472

Education, ESL programs 1774

Education, Europe 1650, 1651, 1666, 1668

Education, faculty/staff development 1118, 1266, 1276, 1296, 1690, 1765, 2396, 2424, 2683

Education, fellowships 1793, 2483

Education, Finland 133, 1292, 2646

Education, France 134, 1263, 1371, 1413, 1597, 1624, 1625, 2147

Education, fund raising 59, 96, 97, 109, 110, 128, 168, 182, 183, 210, 235, 368, 571, 673, 730, 1034, 1067, 1106, 1370, 1614, 1948, 1972, 2036, 2107, 2108, 2111, 2128, 2131, 2133, 2145, 2559, 2581, 2624

Education, Ghana 1438, 1808

Education, girls & young women 278, 1202

Education, global programs 92, 126, 357, 456, 611, 644, 664, 671, 769, 849, 852, 874, 911, 1420, 1441, 1451, 1478, 1482, 1607, 1665, 1693, 1780, 1849, 1888, 1900, 2015, 2158, 2222

Education, government agencies 17, 25, 26, 394, 1092, 1981, 2136

Education, Greece 1557, 1558

Education, Hispanics 1000, 1245, 1565, 1774, 2530

Education, Iceland 1038

Education, immigrants/refugees 1774, 2588

Education, income development 2380, 2497, 2733

Education, India 1396, 1454, 2688, 2689

Education, Indonesia 1314, 1447

Education, information services 189, 198-200, 205-207, 228, 287, 291, 306, 335, 389, 422, 427, 457, 461, 498, 537, 550, 575, 607,

International affairs/development, Eastern Europe 930, 946, 1764, 1926

International affairs/development, Ecuador 1920

International affairs/development, Egypt 1405

International affairs/development, England 327, 328, 933, 1281-1284, 1286-1288, 1295, 1416, 1665, 1666, 1710, 1805

International affairs/development, Estonia 1769

International affairs/development, Europe 944, 1295, 1650, 1651, 1666

International affairs/development, France 1263

International affairs/development, Germany 328, 1405

International affairs/development, global programs 106, 156, 267, 456, 504, 671, 734, 806, 807, 847, 849, 852, 911, 931, 953, 963, 971, 1238, 1260, 1262, 1282, 1391, 1393, 1399, 1403, 1420, 1430, 1441, 1443, 1445, 1451, 1456, 1478, 1482, 1487, 1594, 1595, 1665, 1693, 1758, 1780, 1822, 1826, 1830, 1833, 1837, 1888, 1922, 2606, 2611, 2685, 2717

International affairs/development, Guatemala 509

International affairs/development, Honduras 1820

International affairs/development, Hong Kong 1403

International affairs/development, Iceland 1038

International affairs/development, India 1281-1283, 1286, 1287, 1416

International affairs/development, Indonesia 1314

International affairs/development, Iran 1468, 1775

International affairs/development, Israel 529, 1462

International affairs/development, Italy 1816

International affairs/development, Japan 847, 1931, 2610

International affairs/development, Jordan 1462

International affairs/development, Kenya 1393, 1823, 1838

International affairs/development, Korea 2610

International affairs/development, Latin America 398, 850, 969, 1400, 1794, 1919

International affairs/development, Latvia 1650, 1651

International affairs/development, Lebanon 1399

International affairs/development, Mexico 506, 671, 1426, 1440, 1824, 1920

International affairs/development, Middle East 1399, 1433, 1462

International affairs/development, Mongolia 1769

International affairs/development, Myanmar (Burma) 1754, 1757, 1763

International affairs/development, Nigeria 267, 1482, 1831

International affairs/development, Russia 668, 672, 933, 1269, 1411, 1412, 1448, 1466, 1467, 1477, 1481, 1927, 1930

International affairs/development, Scotland 327

International affairs/development, Slovakia 1929

International affairs/development, South Africa 911, 1478

International affairs/development, Southeast Asia 1764, 1825

International affairs/development, Southern Africa 1823

International affairs/development, Soviet Union (Former) 1269, 1411, 1412, 1448, 1466, 1467, 1477, 1481

International affairs/development, Spain 1288

International affairs/development, Sri Lanka 1295

International affairs/development, Sub-Saharan Africa 1815, 1821

International affairs/development, Taiwan 1710

International affairs/development, Thailand 1754

International affairs/development, Ukraine 2720

International affairs/development, United Kingdom 1295

International affairs/development, Vietnam 1441, 1451

International affairs/development, West Bank/Gaza 1462

International affairs/development, Yugoslavia 946, 1762, 1764

International affairs/development, Zimbabwe 1806, 1841

International affairs, blacks 1443

International affairs, children & youth 1393, 1493, 1888

International affairs, collections management/preservation 668, 911

International affairs, conferences/seminars 931, 944, 1399, 1451, 1487, 1826, 1919, 2611, 2654

International affairs, economically disadvantaged 931, 963, 1393, 1440, 1443, 1487

International affairs, electronic media/online services 848, 953, 1260, 1262, 1451, 1821, 1830, 1833, 2610

International affairs, ethics 1456

International affairs, faculty/staff development 1451, 1650, 1651

International affairs, film/video/radio 1805

International affairs, goodwill promotion 668, 911, 944, 1295, 1441, 1451, 1493, 1650, 1651, 1888, 2654

International affairs, immigrants/refugees 1440, 1448

International affairs, information services 399, 806, 848, 953, 1260, 1262, 1399, 1433, 1440, 1443, 1448, 1594, 1595, 1640, 1754, 1805, 1821, 1830, 1833, 2606, 2610, 2611

International affairs, management/technical aid 848

International affairs, minorities 931, 1262, 1487, 1650, 1651, 1833

International affairs, national security 106, 671, 1269, 1456, 2685, 2717

International affairs, offenders/ex-offenders 911

International affairs, public education 849

International affairs, public policy 504, 963, 1238, 1260, 1269, 1919, 2606, 2611

International affairs, publication 953, 1433, 2611

International affairs, reform 506

International affairs, research 671, 911, 1262, 1433, 2685

International affairs, U.N. 931, 1393, 1487

International affairs, women 931, 1393, 1487

International agricultural development 1820, 1823, 1824, 1837

International agricultural development, collections acquisition 1812

International agricultural development, conferences/seminars 1405

International agricultural development, economically disadvantaged 1816, 1825

International agricultural development, electronic media/online services 1405, 1806, 1814, 1815, 1831, 1838, 1841

International agricultural development, publication 1838

International agricultural development, research 1405, 1831, 1841

International conflict resolution 946

International conflict resolution, conferences/seminars 1462

International conflict resolution, electronic media/online services 1260, 1262

International conflict resolution, faculty/staff development 1650, 1651

International conflict resolution, immigrants/refugees 1462

International conflict resolution, minorities 1262, 1650, 1651

International conflict resolution, research 1262

International development 398, 588, 933, 1314, 2720

International development, blacks 1443

International development, building/renovation 529

International development, children & youth 1315, 1393

International development, collections acquisition 529

International development, conferences/seminars 267, 1487

International development, economically disadvantaged 327, 328, 969, 1393, 1426, 1443, 1445, 1482, 1487, 1920

International development, electronic media/online services 1495

International development, film/video/radio 1805

International development, minorities 1487

International development, People with AIDS (PWA) 327, 328

International development, publication 969, 1263, 1495

International development, research 1263, 1920

International development, scholarships 1495

International development, women 1393, 1426, 1445, 1487

International development, youth 327, 328

International economic development 504-506, 930, 1283, 1288

International economic development, Asians/Pacific Islanders 1416

International economic development, conferences/seminars 1281, 1399, 1919

International economic development, economically disadvantaged 963, 1281, 1284, 1286, 1287, 1416

International economic development, faculty/staff development 1403

International economic development, publication 1403

International economic development, research 1403, 1416

International economic development, women 1281, 1282, 1284

International economics/trade policy 504, 1420

International economics/trade policy, conferences/seminars 1794

International exchange, arts 734, 1038, 1769, 1927-1930

International exchange, building/renovation 2063

International exchange, collections management/preservation 1038, 1757, 1929

International exchange, conferences/seminars 1926

International exchange, electronic media/online services 1930

International exchange, equipment 2063

Libraries/library science, minorities 845, 1650, 1651
Libraries/library science, professorships 2090
Libraries/library science, publication 1276
Libraries/library science, research 1276, 1368, 1369, 1437
Libraries/library science, seed money 1775
Libraries/library science, youth 1714, 1793
Literature 227, 1361
Literature, awards/prizes/competitions 2430
Literature, capital campaigns 1327, 2092
Literature, children & youth 2430, 2577
Literature, collections acquisition 1268
Literature, collections management/preservation 1038, 1359, 1364
Literature, conferences/seminars 640, 1118
Literature, faculty/staff development 1118
Literature, income development 1327
Literature, performance/productions 1179
Literature, publication 1534
Literature, research 1327
Literature, technical aid 436
Literature, youth 458
Lung research, children & youth 155

Mali, education 1413
Mali, science 1413
Marine science 276
Mathematics, boys & young men 2191
Mathematics, building/renovation 2191
Mathematics, capital campaigns 2191
Mathematics, curriculum development 1634
Mathematics, electronic media/online services 1634
Mathematics, publication 1634
Mathematics, research 1634
Media/communications 271, 590, 849, 970, 1082, 1376, 1396, 1827, 1837, 2146, 2534, 2606, 2699, 2700
Media/communications, blind 2306
Media/communications, building/renovation 44, 2148, 2189
Media/communications, children & youth 202, 788, 2418
Media/communications, collections acquisition 2037, 2306
Media/communications, collections management/preservation 1234, 1401
Media/communications, computer systems/equipment 283, 2037
Media/communications, economically disadvantaged 788, 1482
Media/communications, electronic media/online services 429, 1401, 2236, 2610
Media/communications, endowments 2148
Media/communications, mentally disabled 2306
Media/communications, program evaluation 202
Media/communications, publication 429, 788, 2275
Media/communications, research 1632
Media/communications, seed money 857, 2418
Medical care, Asians/Pacific Islanders 2279
Medical care, children & youth 60, 76, 479, 1491, 2031, 2279, 2414, 2532
Medical care, computer systems/equipment 2532
Medical care, disabled 72, 2532
Medical care, drug/alcohol abusers 1853
Medical care, economically disadvantaged 60, 62, 76, 479, 1103, 1491, 1722, 2279, 2532
Medical care, electronic media/online services 2031
Medical care, equipment 1127
Medical care, faculty/staff development 2031

Medical care, gays/lesbians 1853
Medical care, homeless 1103, 1862, 1863
Medical care, immigrants/refugees 60, 340, 1004
Medical care, minorities 60, 62, 340, 479, 1004, 1722, 2532
Medical care, outpatient care 60, 62, 63, 72, 76, 334, 340, 479, 1004, 1103, 1491, 1722, 1853, 1862, 1863, 2279, 2414, 2550
Medical care, People with AIDS (PWA) 1853, 2458
Medical care, physically disabled 1127, 2458
Medical care, publication 72, 2031
Medical care, rehabilitation 1127, 2031, 2458, 2532
Medical care, research 340
Medical care, women 60
Medical research 1768
Medical research, global programs 1840
Medical research, information services 1840
Medical school/education 1601
Medical school/education, collections acquisition 2311
Medical school/education, equipment 2311
Medical school/education, fellowships 1141
Medical school/education, scholarships 2311
Medicine/medical care, administration/regulation 1777
Medicine/medical care, aging 68, 83, 172, 213, 702, 751, 854, 1028, 1336, 1776, 1859
Medicine/medical care, alliance 400, 910, 1777
Medicine/medical care, Asians/Pacific Islanders 78, 2279
Medicine/medical care, awards/prizes/competitions 1053
Medicine/medical care, building/renovation 875, 1090, 2513
Medicine/medical care, children & youth 60, 65, 70, 76, 80, 84, 86, 155, 249, 428, 479, 490, 1053, 1134, 1142, 1491, 1546, 1551, 1777, 2031, 2240, 2255, 2279, 2477, 2512, 2617, 2675
Medicine/medical care, collections acquisition 1613
Medicine/medical care, community health systems 393, 910, 1996
Medicine/medical care, computer systems/equipment 80, 282, 400, 854, 1326, 1993, 1996
Medicine/medical care, conferences/seminars 213, 906, 992, 1132
Medicine/medical care, crime/abuse victims 78
Medicine/medical care, deaf 2477
Medicine/medical care, disabled 72, 213, 249, 1776
Medicine/medical care, drug/alcohol abusers 87, 1130, 1137, 1853
Medicine/medical care, economically disadvantaged 60, 62, 64, 65, 69-71, 76, 80, 84, 86, 213, 282, 341, 479, 786, 1028, 1103, 1136, 1142, 1304, 1332, 1474, 1491, 1551, 1722, 1915, 2240, 2269, 2279, 2617
Medicine/medical care, electronic media/online services 83, 84, 89, 107, 428, 666, 667, 751, 1125, 1132, 1142, 1144, 1326, 1993, 1996, 2031, 2677
Medicine/medical care, equal rights 72, 213, 1136, 1137
Medicine/medical care, equipment 80, 1127
Medicine/medical care, ethics 1840
Medicine/medical care, faculty/staff development 80, 249, 272, 993, 1027, 1613, 1899, 2031
Medicine/medical care, fellowships 1382, 1600

Medicine/medical care, film/video/radio 83, 753, 1425
Medicine/medical care, gays/lesbians 1853
Medicine/medical care, Hispanics 74, 79, 2240
Medicine/medical care, homeless 88, 159, 177, 309, 490, 1096, 1103, 2243
Medicine/medical care, immigrants/refugees 60, 80, 213, 339, 340, 509, 906, 992, 993, 1004, 1027, 1035
Medicine/medical care, income development 486, 1332, 1530
Medicine/medical care, information services 60, 62-65, 68-74, 76, 78-81, 83-89, 107, 113, 152, 155, 159, 162, 163, 172, 177, 194, 213, 245, 249, 259, 265, 266, 271, 272, 282, 284, 309, 311, 321, 324, 329, 334, 340, 341, 346, 400, 401, 404, 428, 479, 486, 490, 509, 510, 512, 544, 594, 608, 666, 667, 702, 749, 751-753, 755, 768, 786, 851, 854, 875, 992, 1004, 1027, 1028, 1035, 1053, 1058, 1090, 1096, 1097, 1103, 1121, 1125, 1127, 1132-1135, 1142, 1144-1146, 1242, 1277, 1304, 1326, 1328, 1332, 1336, 1344, 1382, 1424, 1425, 1474, 1517, 1530, 1546, 1551, 1600, 1611, 1613, 1722, 1753, 1776, 1809, 1819, 1828, 1851, 1853, 1859, 1899, 1932, 1956, 1987, 1993, 1996, 1999, 2031, 2093, 2096, 2169, 2240, 2243, 2255, 2269, 2270, 2279, 2477, 2512, 2513, 2550, 2564, 2576, 2617, 2675, 2677, 2707, 2725, 2736
Medicine/medical care, management development 88, 249
Medicine/medical care, management/technical aid 62, 64, 73, 76, 90, 91, 259, 323, 749, 786, 992, 993, 1027, 1035, 1277, 1722, 1776, 2243, 2512
Medicine/medical care, migrant workers 79
Medicine/medical care, minorities 60, 62, 64, 65, 71, 80, 213, 339, 340, 479, 786, 851, 992, 993, 1004, 1027, 1035, 1474, 1722
Medicine/medical care, Native Americans 875, 2093, 2096, 2677
Medicine/medical care, offenders/ex-offenders 1137
Medicine/medical care, People with AIDS (PWA) 266, 284, 311, 321, 324, 329, 404, 608, 666, 1425, 1546, 1853, 1932, 1999, 2269, 2512
Medicine/medical care, physically disabled 74, 1127, 1899
Medicine/medical care, program evaluation 1336, 1530
Medicine/medical care, public education 70, 339, 851, 1133, 1753, 1777
Medicine/medical care, public policy 68, 70, 72, 86, 420, 510, 906, 1130, 1132-1135, 1143, 1326, 1328, 1332, 1336, 1428, 1491, 1745, 1915, 2031
Medicine/medical care, publication 72, 78, 213, 341, 346, 702, 1035, 1121, 1130, 1143, 1326, 1611, 2031
Medicine/medical care, reform 786, 1332, 1491
Medicine/medical care, research 78, 86, 89, 155, 339, 340, 658, 755, 906, 910, 1132, 1133, 1135, 1143, 1332, 1334-1336, 1546, 1828, 1840, 1915, 2255
Medicine/medical care, seed money 73, 79, 2512
Medicine/medical care, technical aid 64, 749, 1134, 1142
Medicine/medical care, volunteer services 71
Medicine/medical care, women 60, 65, 78, 80, 88, 113, 159, 162, 163, 177, 259, 265, 309, 346, 400, 509, 510, 667, 768, 851, 1096,

146, 1198, 1239, 1606, 1622, 1655, 1667, 2178
Museums (art), conferences/seminars 360
Museums (art), curriculum development 1731
Museums (art), electronic media/online services 140, 145, 146, 548, 1829, 2178
Museums (art), endowments 1519, 1549
Museums (art), equipment 853
Museums (art), exhibitions 1606, 1968, 2244
Museums (art), fellowships 1646
Museums (art), income development 1374
Museums (art), internships 137
Museums (art), minorities 137
Museums (art), technical aid 1198, 1239
Museums (children's), children & youth 1226, 2523, 2528
Museums (ethnic/folk arts) 739, 2734
Museums (ethnic/folk arts), Asians/Pacific Islanders 185
Museums (ethnic/folk arts), blacks 1244, 1453
Museums (ethnic/folk arts), collections management/preservation 185, 1624-1626
Museums (ethnic/folk arts), computer systems/equipment 2185
Museums (ethnic/folk arts), conferences/seminars 2160
Museums (ethnic/folk arts), electronic media/online services 1225, 1624
Museums (ethnic/folk arts), equipment 2185
Museums (ethnic/folk arts), immigrants/refugees 1225, 2160, 2185, 2215, 2235, 2282
Museums (ethnic/folk arts), income development 2185
Museums (ethnic/folk arts), minorities 1225, 2160, 2185, 2215, 2235, 2282
Museums (history) 54, 356, 437, 465, 578, 869, 870, 1220, 1702, 1896, 1901, 1949, 2086, 2149, 2218, 2258, 2273, 2286, 2425, 2526, 2534, 2571
Museums (history), building/renovation 562, 896, 921, 1380, 2192, 2193
Museums (history), capital campaigns 2300
Museums (history), children & youth 759
Museums (history), collections management/preservation 562, 911, 1235, 1687
Museums (history), computer systems/equipment 1235
Museums (history), economically disadvantaged 1887
Museums (history), electronic media/online services 279, 1235, 1481
Museums (history), endowments 454, 1673, 1887
Museums (history), exhibitions 562, 759, 896, 1114, 1687, 2536
Museums (history), fellowships 1673
Museums (history), offenders/ex-offenders 911
Museums (history), research 911, 1673
Museums (history), scholarships 802
Museums (history), technical aid 2719
Museums (natural history) 2026
Museums (natural history), building/renovation 2184
Museums (natural history), collections management/preservation 129, 143
Museums (natural history), electronic media/online services 129, 143, 2184
Museums (natural history), Native Americans 129
Museums (science & technology) 2393
Museums (science & technology), endowments 2392

Museums (specialized), building/renovation 2378
Museums (specialized), collections management/preservation 1423
Museums (specialized), electronic media/online services 1423
Museums (specialized), mentally disabled 2291
Museums (specialized), research 2291
Museums (specialized), scholarships 2291
Museums, building/renovation 2404, 2411, 2446, 2506
Museums, capital campaigns 828
Museums, collections management/preservation 1627
Museums, electronic media/online services 1925
Museums, endowments 2099
Music 2290, 2292, 2308
Music, building/renovation 2020, 2309, 2378
Music, capital campaigns 2019
Music, children & youth 1461
Music, collections management/preservation 1363, 1452, 1461
Music, electronic media/online services 188, 268, 1661, 1670, 1835
Music, endowments 1619
Music, ensembles & groups 2410
Music, equipment 49
Music, income development 2410
Music, performance/productions 190
Music, research 1835
Myanmar (Burma), arts/culture/humanities 1754
Myanmar (Burma), education 1757, 1763
Myanmar (Burma), health—general 1277
Myanmar (Burma), international affairs/development 1754, 1757, 1763

Namibia, arts/culture/humanities 1461
Native Americans, arts/culture/humanities 129, 2650
Native Americans, crime/courts/legal services 1032
Native Americans, education 129, 1002, 1184, 2640, 2650, 2662, 2670, 2672
Native Americans, environment 592
Native Americans, food/nutrition/agriculture 1010
Native Americans, health—general 875, 2093, 2096, 2105, 2677
Native Americans, human services—multipurpose 1032
Native Americans, public affairs/government 129, 2640, 2650, 2662, 2670, 2672, 2677
Native Americans, recreation/sports/athletics 2105
Natural resource conservation & protection 103, 231, 232, 247, 257, 398, 504, 506, 528, 590, 846, 970, 1086, 1123, 1291, 1375, 1444, 1744, 2017, 2256
Natural resource conservation & protection, blacks 1443
Natural resource conservation & protection, conferences/seminars 653
Natural resource conservation & protection, economically disadvantaged 517, 1443, 1740, 1742
Natural resource conservation & protection, electronic media/online services 246, 1636, 1822, 1913, 2610
Natural resource conservation & protection, endowments 1377
Natural resource conservation & protection, management development 1005

Natural resource conservation & protection, minorities 156, 1740, 1742
Natural resource conservation & protection, publication 1822, 2231
Natural resource conservation & protection, research 517, 909, 1377, 1742, 2239
Neighborhood centers 448, 2298
Neighborhood centers, aging 2186, 2463
Neighborhood centers, building/renovation 1255, 2307, 2451
Neighborhood centers, children & youth 789, 2186, 2463
Neighborhood centers, computer systems/equipment 1255
Neighborhood centers, economically disadvantaged 382, 789, 1255
Neighborhood centers, electronic media/online services 2463
Neighborhood centers, equipment 1255
Neighborhood centers, minorities 1255
Nerve/muscle/bone diseases, People with AIDS (PWA) 2458
Nerve/muscle/bone diseases, physically disabled 2458
Nerve/muscle/bone research, aging 1720
Nerve/muscle/bone research, fellowships 1720
Nerve/muscle/bone research, physically disabled 1720
Neuroscience 1026
New Zealand, education 142
Nigeria, arts/culture/humanities 1482
Nigeria, education 1482
Nigeria, food/nutrition/agriculture 1831
Nigeria, human services—multipurpose 267
Nigeria, international affairs/development 267, 1482, 1831
Nigeria, science 1831
Nonprofit management 8, 90, 101, 102, 326, 576, 878, 913, 970, 973, 1048, 1050, 1051, 1460, 2547
Nonprofit management, blacks 471
Nonprofit management, computer systems/equipment 1916
Nonprofit management, conferences/seminars 502, 962, 1418, 1724, 2457
Nonprofit management, economically disadvantaged 2584
Nonprofit management, electronic media/online services 203, 275, 503, 1129, 1486, 1724, 2284
Nonprofit management, equipment 362
Nonprofit management, faculty/staff development 962, 2538
Nonprofit management, management development 203, 1959
Nonprofit management, minorities 1486
Nonprofit management, offenders/ex-offenders 2011
Nonprofit management, program evaluation 939, 1024
Nonprofit management, publication 471, 503, 942, 1024, 1418
Nonprofit management, research 203, 755, 864, 937, 939, 1418
Nonprofit management, scholarships 2457
Nonprofit management, seed money 565, 923
Nonprofit management, technical aid 91, 1486, 1724, 1725
Nonprofit management, women 1486
Nursing care, children & youth 2617
Nursing care, economically disadvantaged 2617
Nursing care, women 2617
Nursing home/convalescent facility, aging 172, 751, 2285

Nursing home/convalescent facility, disabled 2285

Nursing home/convalescent facility, economically disadvantaged 2285

Nursing home/convalescent facility, electronic media/online services 751

Nursing school/education 605

Nutrition, People with AIDS (PWA) 2458

Nutrition, physically disabled 2458

Offenders/ex-offenders, arts/culture/humanities 911

Offenders/ex-offenders, community improvement/development 2011

Offenders/ex-offenders, crime/courts/legal services 151, 187, 261, 1137, 1756, 2011

Offenders/ex-offenders, drug/alcohol abusers 1137

Offenders/ex-offenders, education 151, 911, 2263

Offenders/ex-offenders, employment 187, 1756

Offenders/ex-offenders, health—general 1137

Offenders/ex-offenders, health—specific diseases 1137

Offenders/ex-offenders, human services—multipurpose 151, 261

Offenders/ex-offenders, international affairs/development 911

Offenders/ex-offenders, mental health/substance abuse 1137, 2263

Offenders/ex-offenders, services 151, 187, 1137

Offenders/ex-offenders, social sciences 1756

Offenders/ex-offenders, women 1137

Opera, collections management/preservation 1234

Painting, publication 1186

Pakistan, education 1296

Pakistan, health—general 265

Papua New Guinea, education 451

Papua New Guinea, religion 451

Parks/playgrounds 1385

Parks/playgrounds, children & youth 2105

Parks/playgrounds, conferences/seminars 1946

Parks/playgrounds, electronic media/online services 1946

Parks/playgrounds, Native Americans 2105

Peace 398

Peace, electronic media/online services 2610

Pediatrics research, children & youth 1546

Pediatrics research, People with AIDS (PWA) 1546

Pediatrics, children & youth 1383, 1489, 2255, 2414, 2512

Pediatrics, minorities 1489

Pediatrics, People with AIDS (PWA) 2512

Pediatrics, seed money 1489, 2512

Pediatrics, women 2512

Pensions 812

People with AIDS (PWA), arts/culture/humanities 1425

People with AIDS (PWA), civil rights 327, 328

People with AIDS (PWA), community improvement/development 1479

People with AIDS (PWA), education 324

People with AIDS (PWA), employment 2246

People with AIDS (PWA), food/nutrition/agriculture 2458

People with AIDS (PWA), health—general 22, 266, 284, 311, 321, 324, 329, 404, 608, 666, 1425, 1479, 1546, 1853, 1932, 1999, 2269, 2458, 2512

People with AIDS (PWA), health—specific diseases 22, 99, 266, 284, 311, 321, 324, 327-329, 404, 608, 666, 1425, 1479, 1853, 1932, 1976, 1999, 2269, 2458, 2512, 2557

People with AIDS (PWA), housing/shelter 2246

People with AIDS (PWA), human services—multipurpose 99, 2252, 2269, 2557

People with AIDS (PWA), international affairs/development 327, 328

People with AIDS (PWA), medical research 1546

People with AIDS (PWA), mental health/substance abuse 1853, 2246

People with AIDS (PWA), recreation/sports/athletics 324

People with AIDS (PWA), youth development 327, 328

Performing arts 1875

Performing arts (multi-media), commissioning new works 1818

Performing arts (multi-media), electronic media/online services 1818

Performing arts (multi-media), performance/productions 1818

Performing arts centers, building/renovation 2407

Performing arts, blacks 549

Performing arts, building/renovation 549, 922, 1870

Performing arts, conferences/seminars 1118

Performing arts, education 49, 1118, 1870

Performing arts, equipment 49

Performing arts, faculty/staff development 1118

Performing arts, minorities 41

Performing arts, publication 1641

Performing arts, research 1641

Peru, education 2142

Pharmacology 1026

Pharmacology, economically disadvantaged 2269

Pharmacology, People with AIDS (PWA) 2269

Pharmacology, research 1768, 2351

Pharmacology, women 768

Philanthropy/voluntarism 179, 204, 323, 554, 732, 819, 908, 935, 958, 1082, 1415, 1460, 1543, 1718, 1897, 2024, 2706

Philanthropy/voluntarism, administration/regulation 601, 877, 959, 1088, 1154, 1804

Philanthropy/voluntarism, Africa 969, 1415

Philanthropy/voluntarism, Asia 969

Philanthropy/voluntarism, Asians/Pacific Islanders 1416

Philanthropy/voluntarism, association 610, 630, 631, 639, 652, 661, 662, 681, 697, 704, 712, 716, 932, 943, 1049, 2027, 2070, 2087, 2713, 2722, 2730

Philanthropy/voluntarism, Belarus 972

Philanthropy/voluntarism, Belgium 945, 1049, 2713

Philanthropy/voluntarism, blacks 957, 1803

Philanthropy/voluntarism, Brazil 1920

Philanthropy/voluntarism, building/renovation 104, 251, 331, 332, 372, 920, 949, 1160, 1434, 1963, 2029

Philanthropy/voluntarism, Bulgaria 929, 935

Philanthropy/voluntarism, capital campaigns 501

Philanthropy/voluntarism, children & youth 784, 1488

Philanthropy/voluntarism, collections management/preservation 1337

Philanthropy/voluntarism, computer systems/equipment 32, 307, 1881, 1916

Philanthropy/voluntarism, conferences/seminars 255, 502, 906, 957, 962, 1418, 1450, 1724, 1803, 2457, 2713

Philanthropy/voluntarism, Czech Republic 943

Philanthropy/voluntarism, economically disadvantaged 784, 945, 969, 1416, 1920

Philanthropy/voluntarism, Ecuador 1920

Philanthropy/voluntarism, electronic media/online services 32, 639, 948, 953, 1129, 1195, 1237, 1435, 1486, 1528, 1566, 1637, 1724, 1821, 1879, 1910, 1911

Philanthropy/voluntarism, endowments 895, 940

Philanthropy/voluntarism, England 93, 619, 620, 867, 933-939, 1206, 1207, 1212, 1290, 1365, 1366, 1415-1418, 1552, 1553, 1709, 1787, 2140, 2687

Philanthropy/voluntarism, equipment 362

Philanthropy/voluntarism, Estonia 960

Philanthropy/voluntarism, Europe 619, 620, 867, 1206, 1207, 1212, 1417

Philanthropy/voluntarism, faculty/staff development 938, 962, 1318, 2204, 2538

Philanthropy/voluntarism, fund raising 1725

Philanthropy/voluntarism, Germany 928

Philanthropy/voluntarism, global programs 255, 953, 1290, 1430, 1709, 1758

Philanthropy/voluntarism, Hungary 961

Philanthropy/voluntarism, immigrants/refugees 906, 1430, 1488, 1758

Philanthropy/voluntarism, income development 639

Philanthropy/voluntarism, India 1416, 1418

Philanthropy/voluntarism, Indian Subcontinent & Afghanistan 1418

Philanthropy/voluntarism, information services 8, 32, 93, 102, 104, 157, 174, 179, 195, 201, 204, 218, 219, 251, 255, 301, 307, 319, 326, 331, 332, 359, 362, 372, 423, 459, 475, 501, 502, 519, 520, 555, 576, 591, 600, 601, 610, 619, 620, 630-632, 639, 652, 661, 662, 670, 681, 697, 704, 705, 712, 716, 777, 784, 818, 819, 867, 878, 895, 907, 920, 928, 932, 936, 938, 940, 943, 948, 949, 955, 956, 959-961, 964, 965, 967, 969, 972, 975, 1024, 1033, 1049, 1051, 1064, 1082, 1083, 1088, 1101, 1129, 1154, 1195, 1206, 1207, 1212, 1237, 1247, 1261, 1290, 1310, 1311, 1318, 1322, 1333, 1358, 1365, 1366, 1378, 1417, 1434, 1435, 1449, 1465, 1486, 1510, 1528, 1548, 1552, 1553, 1566, 1615, 1637, 1638, 1695, 1709, 1713, 1718, 1724, 1759, 1787, 1802-1804, 1817, 1819, 1874, 1879, 1881, 1910, 1911, 1914, 1916, 1920, 1939, 1944, 1945, 1959, 1963, 1990, 2008, 2027, 2029, 2030, 2055, 2070, 2087, 2120, 2140, 2204, 2241, 2260, 2369, 2376, 2381-2383, 2440, 2457, 2538, 2600, 2619, 2643, 2679, 2687, 2711, 2713, 2714, 2722, 2730

Philanthropy/voluntarism, Latin America 969

Philanthropy/voluntarism, Latvia 932

Philanthropy/voluntarism, management development 1804, 1959

Philanthropy/voluntarism, management/technical aid 264, 670, 784, 819, 928, 934, 948, 958, 961, 965, 969, 972, 1337, 1449, 1465, 1486, 1725, 2679, 2706, 2711

Philanthropy/voluntarism, Mexico 326, 670, 955, 1449, 1450, 1920

Philanthropy/voluntarism, minorities 784, 1486

Philanthropy/voluntarism, Moldova 956

Philanthropy/voluntarism, Poland 1465

Philanthropy/voluntarism, program evaluation 784, 939, 1024

Philanthropy/voluntarism, public education 1082, 1543

Philanthropy/voluntarism, public policy 784, 928, 937, 957, 958, 1450, 1488

Philanthropy/voluntarism, publication 219, 264, 736, 818, 953, 969, 1024, 1358, 1417, 1418, 2204, 2241, 2679

Philanthropy/voluntarism, research 255, 307, 502, 784, 906, 928, 929, 934, 937-939, 957, 1416, 1418, 1449, 1920

Philanthropy/voluntarism, Romania 937-939, 964

Philanthropy/voluntarism, Russia 933, 934, 940, 965, 967, 2140

Philanthropy/voluntarism, scholarships 2457

Philanthropy/voluntarism, seed money 895

Philanthropy/voluntarism, Serbia 936

Philanthropy/voluntarism, single organization support 93, 1365, 1366, 1552, 1553, 1709, 1787, 2687

Philanthropy/voluntarism, South Africa 962, 1460

Philanthropy/voluntarism, Sub-Saharan Africa 1821

Philanthropy/voluntarism, technical aid 1486, 1724, 1725, 2369

Philanthropy/voluntarism, United Kingdom 619, 620, 867, 1206, 1207, 1212, 1417

Philanthropy/voluntarism, volunteer services 964

Philanthropy/voluntarism, women 1486, 2679

Philanthropy/voluntarism, youth 945

Philippines, civil rights 1408

Philippines, community improvement/development 1408

Philippines, health—general 259, 266, 1809

Philippines, health—specific diseases 266

Philippines, public affairs/government 1408

Philosophy/ethics, publication 2712

Photography 1410

Photography, collections acquisition 38

Photography, collections management/preservation 1351, 1352, 1401, 1472, 1568, 1771

Photography, electronic media/online services 279, 1401

Photography, exhibitions 1832

Photography, faculty/staff development 1928

Photography, publication 1832

Photography, women 1645

Physical therapy, children & youth 2010

Physical therapy, disabled 2010

Physical therapy, economically disadvantaged 2010

Physical/earth sciences, collections management/preservation 1630

Physically disabled, education 1127, 2394

Physically disabled, food/nutrition/agriculture 2458

Physically disabled, health—general 74, 1127, 1899, 2458

Physically disabled, health—specific diseases 74, 1899, 2458

Physically disabled, human services—multipurpose 1899, 2394

Physically disabled, medical research 1720

Physically disabled, mental health/substance abuse 74

Physically disabled, public affairs/government 74

Physically disabled, social sciences 1720

Poland, philanthropy/voluntarism 1465

Poland, public affairs/government 951

Political science 625, 1411

Political science, collections management/preservation 131, 1682

Political science, computer systems/equipment 874

Political science, conferences/seminars 191

Political science, electronic media/online services 131, 1122, 1325, 1620

Political science, publication 1325

Political science, research 1273, 1325

Population studies 513, 656, 1123, 1640

Population studies, blacks 2143

Population studies, children & youth 1117, 1539

Population studies, collections management/preservation 1648

Population studies, curriculum development 1117

Population studies, economically disadvantaged 82, 2143

Population studies, electronic media/online services 1122, 1665, 1666, 2143, 2209

Population studies, Hispanics 82

Population studies, immigrants/refugees 82, 1665, 1666

Population studies, management development 1005

Population studies, minorities 2143

Population studies, research 633, 1828, 2057

Poverty studies, children & youth 947

Poverty studies, economically disadvantaged 947, 1463

Poverty studies, women 947

Professorships, education 2090, 2214, 2491

Professorships, international affairs/development 1922

Program evaluation, arts/culture/humanities 202, 1649

Program evaluation, civil rights 784

Program evaluation, community improvement/development 939, 1024

Program evaluation, education 1199, 1459, 1571, 1649, 2245

Program evaluation, health—general 1336, 1530

Program evaluation, human services—multipurpose 1165, 1336, 2252, 2596

Program evaluation, philanthropy/voluntarism 784, 939, 1024

Program evaluation, public affairs/government 939

Program evaluation, safety/disaster relief 1530

Protestant agencies & churches, capital campaigns 2019

Psychology/behavioral science, children & youth 1489

Psychology/behavioral science, collections management/preservation 1529

Psychology/behavioral science, minorities 1489

Psychology/behavioral science, research 1529

Psychology/behavioral science, seed money 1489

Psychology/behavioral science, youth 1529

Public affairs 626, 627, 637, 638

Public affairs/government, Africa 1303, 1415, 1764

Public affairs/government, Asia 1495, 1801

Public affairs/government, Belarus 668

Public affairs/government, Belgium 944

Public affairs/government, Bulgaria 926, 935

Public affairs/government, Canada 846, 848, 2630, 2657, 2665, 2671, 2682, 2683

Public affairs/government, Caribbean 1794

Public affairs/government, Chile 2633

Public affairs/government, China & Mongolia 2610

Public affairs/government, developing countries 505, 515, 588, 848, 927, 1794

Public affairs/government, Eastern Europe 946, 1764

Public affairs/government, Egypt 1405

Public affairs/government, England 935, 939, 1282, 1289, 1415, 2146

Public affairs/government, Europe 944

Public affairs/government, Finland 2646

Public affairs/government, Germany 1405

Public affairs/government, Ghana 1438

Public affairs/government, global programs 191, 504, 807, 852, 953, 971, 1238, 1260, 1262, 1282, 1325, 1391, 1451, 1594, 1595, 1780, 1827, 1835, 2685, 2717

Public affairs/government, India 1282, 1485

Public affairs/government, Japan 2610

Public affairs/government, Kenya 1455

Public affairs/government, Korea 2610

Public affairs/government, Latin America 398, 850, 1794, 1919

Public affairs/government, Mexico 506, 1440, 1450

Public affairs/government, Philippines 1408

Public affairs/government, Poland 951

Public affairs/government, Romania 939

Public affairs/government, Russia 668, 951, 1409, 1469-1471, 1481, 1925, 1930

Public affairs/government, Senegal 1760

Public affairs/government, Slovakia 950

Public affairs/government, South Africa 1483, 1674, 1689

Public affairs/government, Southeast Asia 1764

Public affairs/government, Soviet Union (Former) 713, 1481

Public affairs/government, Sub-Saharan Africa 1821

Public affairs/government, Ukraine 951

Public affairs/government, United Kingdom 1289

Public affairs/government, Vietnam 1451

Public affairs/government, Yugoslavia 946, 1764

Public affairs, administration/regulation 1801

Public affairs, alliance 910, 1596

Public affairs, blacks 2143

Public affairs, children & youth 659, 776, 1330

Public affairs, citizen participation 162, 191, 390, 398, 588, 906, 926, 935, 939, 944, 946, 950, 951, 953, 1391, 1415, 1440, 1450, 1485, 1774, 1821, 2278, 2599

Public affairs, collections management/preservation 114, 1470

Public affairs, conferences/seminars 191, 477, 653, 659, 906, 944, 1450, 1794

Public affairs, curriculum development 551

Public affairs, drug/alcohol abusers 1471

Public affairs, economically disadvantaged 82, 250, 477, 776, 1030, 1329, 1330, 1440, 1703, 1767, 1774, 2014, 2143

Public affairs, election regulation 659, 2247, 2253, 2254, 2281

Public affairs, electronic media/online services 250, 953, 971, 1325, 1391, 1409, 1455, 1469, 1481, 1813, 1821, 2143, 2601

Public affairs, ethics 850, 2253, 2254

Public affairs, film/video/radio 1813, 2601

Public affairs, finance 657, 1040, 1329, 2014

Public affairs, Hispanics 82, 1774

Public affairs, immigrants/refugees 82, 476, 477, 906, 1440, 1767, 1774

Public affairs, information services 250, 390, 551, 563, 589, 657, 659, 695, 776, 807, 926, 946, 951, 971, 1030, 1258, 1325, 1409, 1455, 1469, 1471, 1483, 1485, 1594, 1595,

Religion, Mexico 1429
Religion, minorities 966, 1429
Religion, Papua New Guinea 451
Religion, publication 736, 2303
Religion, research 2302
Religion, seed money 1778
Religion, Soviet Union (Former) 508
Religion, Ukraine 2720
Religion, United Kingdom 2700
Religion, women 1429
Reproductive rights, computer
systems/equipment 1326
Reproductive rights, electronic media/online
services 1326
Reproductive rights, publication 1326
Reproductive rights, women 162, 1326, 1424
Residential/custodial care, boys & young men
2197
Residential/custodial care, building/renovation
1090, 2197
Residential/custodial care, children & youth
1297
Residential/custodial care, computer
systems/equipment 277, 2197
Residential/custodial care, crime/abuse victims
277
Residential/custodial care, girls & young
women 277
Residential/custodial care, group home 1297
Residential/custodial care, half-way house 1090
Residential/custodial care, mentally disabled
277
Residential/custodial care, People with AIDS
(PWA) 99
Roman Catholic agencies & churches 2720
Roman Catholic agencies & churches,
building/renovation 351, 451
Roman Catholic agencies & churches, children
& youth 566
Roman Catholic agencies & churches,
computer systems/equipment 709
Roman Catholic agencies & churches,
electronic media/online services 709
Roman Catholic agencies & churches,
film/video/radio 567
Romania, community
improvement/development 937, 939
Romania, philanthropy/voluntarism 937-939,
964
Romania, public affairs/government 939
Rural development 1291, 1446
Rural development, computer
systems/equipment 2475
Rural development, economically
disadvantaged 963, 1392, 1463
Rural development, publication 1421
Rural development, research 909, 2612
Rural development, women 1392
Russia, arts/culture/humanities 668, 1401,
1406, 1411, 1414, 1423, 1452, 1466, 1472,
1481, 1925, 1927
Russia, civil rights 1477
Russia, crime/courts/legal services 672
Russia, education 668, 1273, 1276, 1401, 1406,
1411, 1412, 1414, 1423, 1452, 1466, 1467,
1470, 1472, 1481, 1925, 1930
Russia, international affairs/development 668,
672, 933, 1269, 1411, 1412, 1448, 1466,
1467, 1477, 1481, 1927, 1930
Russia, mental health/substance abuse 1471
Russia, philanthropy/voluntarism 933, 934,
940, 965, 967, 2140
Russia, public affairs/government 668, 951,
1409, 1469-1471, 1481, 1925, 1930

Russia, social sciences 672, 1269, 1273, 1276,
1406, 1409, 1411, 1412, 1469, 1470

Safety/disaster relief, Canada 1530
Safety/disasters, children & youth 2031
Safety/disasters, computer systems/equipment
2629
Safety/disasters, electronic media/online
services 2031
Safety/disasters, faculty/staff development 2031
Safety/disasters, information services 1761,
2629
Safety/disasters, public policy 2031
Safety/disasters, publication 2031
Safety, computer systems/equipment 2629
Safety, education 1530
Safety, electronic media/online services 1125
Safety, income development 1530
Safety, poisons 1125, 2629
Safety, program evaluation 1530
Scholarships/financial aid 2728
Scholarships, arts/culture/humanities 802, 2291
Scholarships, community
improvement/development 2457
Scholarships, education 802, 1298-1301, 1495,
1991, 2291, 2311
Scholarships, human services—multipurpose
2053
Scholarships, international affairs/development
1495
Scholarships, mental health/substance abuse
2291
Scholarships, philanthropy/voluntarism 2457
Scholarships, public affairs/government 1495
Scholarships, social sciences 1298
Science 1264, 2024
Science, Africa 1264, 1814, 1816
Science, boys & young men 2191
Science, building/renovation 2191, 2688
Science, Canada 846
Science, capital campaigns 416, 2191
Science, children & youth 1226
Science, China 1812
Science, collections acquisition 2688
Science, collections management/preservation
1126
Science, computer systems/equipment 1126
Science, developing countries 1820, 1824, 1825
Science, electronic media/online services 1413,
1569, 1806, 1880
Science, endowments 1569
Science, England 276, 1285, 1289, 1293, 1630,
2302
Science, equipment 2688
Science, exhibitions 1877
Science, France 1413
Science, global programs 276, 1377, 1827,
1837, 1840
Science, Honduras 1820
Science, India 2688
Science, information services 846, 1264, 1806,
1880, 1884, 1982
Science, Italy 1816
Science, Kenya 1264, 1838
Science, Mali 1413
Science, management/technical aid 1264
Science, Mexico 1824
Science, Nigeria 1831
Science, public education 1877
Science, public policy 1264
Science, publication 1569, 1884
Science, research 1413, 1569
Science, Southeast Asia 1825
Science, Spain 1285

Science, student aid 1569
Science, Turkey 1293
Science, United Kingdom 1289
Science, women 1884
Science, youth 2202
Science, Zimbabwe 1806, 1841
Scotland, civil rights 327
Scotland, health—specific diseases 327
Scotland, international affairs/development 327
Scotland, youth development 327
Sculpture, building/renovation 883
Secondary school/education, blacks 228, 1245
Secondary school/education, boys & young
men 2188, 2191
Secondary school/education,
building/renovation 1172, 1245, 2188, 2191
Secondary school/education, capital campaigns
2191
Secondary school/education, computer
systems/equipment 31, 1245
Secondary school/education, curriculum
development 1253
Secondary school/education, economically
disadvantaged 1245
Secondary school/education, electronic
media/online services 1313, 2715
Secondary school/education, endowments 2089
Secondary school/education, girls & young
women 1172, 2089
Secondary school/education, Hispanics 1245
Secondary school/education, internships 2035
Secondary school/education, seed money 2715
Secondary school/education, youth 228, 458,
582, 1245, 1253, 1313, 2035, 2202
Senegal, education 1760
Senegal, public affairs/government 1760
Senior continuing care community, aging 2285
Senior continuing care community, disabled
2285
Senior continuing care community,
economically disadvantaged 2285
Serbia, philanthropy/voluntarism 936
Single parents, crime/courts/legal services 511
Single parents, health—general 2476
Single parents, human services—multipurpose
511, 2476
Slovakia, arts/culture/humanities 1929
Slovakia, international affairs/development
1929
Slovakia, public affairs/government 950
Smoking, drug/alcohol abusers 1131
Smoking, publication 1131, 1143
Smoking, research 1143
Smoking, technical aid 1131
Social sciences, Africa 1303, 1805
Social sciences, Brazil 1920
Social sciences, building/renovation 2264
Social sciences, Chile 1457
Social sciences, China 1298, 1420, 1422, 1493,
1496, 1604
Social sciences, collections acquisition 1270
Social sciences, collections
management/preservation 1470, 1630,
1648, 1671, 1732
Social sciences, conferences/seminars 1826
Social sciences, developing countries 1640
Social sciences, Eastern Europe 1270
Social sciences, Ecuador 1920
Social sciences, electronic media/online
services 1406, 1409, 1469, 1618
Social sciences, England 1294, 1298, 1630,
1665, 1666, 1805
Social sciences, Europe 1650, 1651, 1666
Social sciences, exhibitions 39
Social sciences, faculty/staff development 1276

Wildlife, electronic media/online services 2623
Wildlife, endangered species 103, 119
Wildlife, fisheries 231, 2623
Wildlife, research 2239, 2351
Women, arts/culture/humanities 298, 310, 346, 1343, 1392, 1422, 1512, 1645, 1884, 2106, 2356
Women, centers & services 2187
Women, civil rights 162, 167, 325, 514, 931, 1280, 1281, 1326, 1393, 1422, 1424, 1429, 1442, 1445, 1483, 1487
Women, community improvement/development 1281, 1392, 1486
Women, crime/abuse victims 2187
Women, crime/courts/legal services 325, 511, 514, 1001, 1137, 1147, 1483, 2274
Women, education 148, 212, 298, 310, 598, 1343, 1512, 1645, 1669, 1884, 2106, 2230, 2356, 2617
Women, employment 57, 514, 1022, 1280, 1281, 1442
Women, food/nutrition/agriculture 1392
Women, health—general 60, 65, 75, 78, 80, 88, 113, 159, 162, 163, 177, 259, 265, 309, 346, 400, 509, 510, 667, 768, 851, 1096, 1137, 1326, 1392, 1393, 1424, 1429, 1445, 1474, 1487, 1852, 2240, 2512, 2617, 2736
Women, health—specific diseases 113, 337, 1137, 2512
Women, homeless 2187
Women, housing/shelter 1426
Women, human services—multipurpose 75, 78, 111, 176, 511, 893, 947, 1001, 1017, 1147, 2013, 2016, 2187, 2274, 2459
Women, international affairs/development 509, 931, 1281, 1282, 1284, 1393, 1426, 1445, 1487
Women, mental health/substance abuse 1137, 2016, 2187, 2459
Women, philanthropy/voluntarism 1486, 2679
Women, public affairs/government 57, 65, 113, 148, 162, 250, 776, 947, 1282, 1483, 2014, 2106
Women, recreation/sports/athletics 60
Women, religion 1429
Women, science 510, 1884
Women, social sciences 947, 1422, 1645

Women, youth development 60
Women's studies 1645
Women's studies, publication 1422

Youth development, Belgium 945
Youth development, building/renovation 2586
Youth development, centers & clubs 60, 161, 170, 178, 289, 403
Youth development, citizenship 945
Youth development, collections management/preservation 1529
Youth development, community service clubs 2035
Youth development, economically disadvantaged 60, 289, 327, 328, 577, 945, 1200, 1323, 1608, 2586
Youth development, electronic media/online services 1313
Youth development, England 327, 328
Youth development, gays/lesbians 161, 170, 178, 289, 403
Youth development, Germany 328
Youth development, immigrants/refugees 60
Youth development, information services 954, 1087, 1323, 1539
Youth development, intergenerational programs 112, 1095, 2540, 2541
Youth development, internships 2035
Youth development, management development 1323
Youth development, management/technical aid 1323
Youth development, minorities 60, 577, 1200, 1608
Youth development, People with AIDS (PWA) 327, 328
Youth development, public policy 954
Youth development, research 1529, 1608
Youth development, Scotland 327
Youth development, services 40, 327, 328, 577, 954, 1087, 1177, 1200, 1313, 1323, 1526, 1529, 1539, 1608, 2586
Youth development, technical aid 954
Youth, arts/culture/humanities 458, 582, 1253, 2234
Youth, civil rights 327, 328

Youth, community improvement/development 577
Youth, crime/abuse victims 261
Youth, economically disadvantaged 782, 791
Youth, education 228, 458, 575, 577, 582, 1245, 1253, 1307, 1313, 1320, 1529, 1714, 1791, 1793, 2035, 2202, 2350, 2586, 2732
Youth, electronic media/online services 791
Youth, employment 577, 1320, 1458, 1791, 1793
Youth, health—general 77, 81, 266, 594, 786, 1474
Youth, health—specific diseases 81, 266, 327, 328
Youth, human services—multipurpose 161, 170, 178, 289, 403, 782, 791, 2016, 2234, 2551
Youth, international affairs/development 327, 328
Youth, mental health/substance abuse 77, 2016
Youth, offenders/ex-offenders 261
Youth, philanthropy/voluntarism 945
Youth, public affairs/government 81, 1313, 1320
Youth, publication 261
Youth, science 2202
Youth, services 261, 782, 791, 2234
Youth, social sciences 1529
Youth, youth development 40, 161, 170, 178, 289, 327, 328, 403, 577, 945, 954, 1087, 1313, 1323, 1529, 2035, 2586
Yugoslavia, education 1762, 1764
Yugoslavia, international affairs/development 946, 1762, 1764
Yugoslavia, public affairs/government 946, 1764

Zambia, human services—multipurpose 1297
Zimbabwe, food/nutrition/agriculture 1806, 1841
Zimbabwe, international affairs/development 1806, 1841
Zimbabwe, science 1806, 1841

Foundations

The following is an alphabetical list of foundations appearing in this volume, including any geographic restrictions on the foundation's giving program. A full listing of geographic, program, and type of support limitations is provided with the full listing of each foundation's grants in Section 1. Please read these limitations carefully, as well as reading additional program and application information available in the foundation's report or other Foundation Center products, before applying for grant assistance. Foundations in bold face are among the 100 largest.

Abbott Laboratories Fund
Dept. 379, Bldg. Apt. 6D
100 Abbott Park Rd.
Abbott Park, IL 60064-3500
(847) 937-7075
URL: http://www.abbott.com/community/
    lab_fund.html
Limitations: Giving primarily in areas of
    company operations.

ABC, Inc. Foundation
77 W. 66th St., Rm. 16-15
New York, NY 10023
(212) 456-7498
Limitations: Giving primarily in areas where
    company properties are located.

The Abell Foundation, Inc.
111 S. Calvert St., Ste. 2300
Baltimore, MD 21202-6174
(410) 547-1300
FAX: (410) 539-6579; E-mail: abell@abell.org;
    URL: http://www.abell.org
Limitations: Giving limited to MD, with
    emphasis on Baltimore.
Publishes an annual or periodic report.

Abell-Hanger Foundation
P.O. Box 430
Midland, TX 79702
(915) 684-6655
FAX: (915) 684-4474; E-mail:
    AHF@abell-hanger.org; URL: http://
    www.abell-hanger.org/
Limitations: Giving limited to TX, with
    emphasis within the Permian Basin.
Publishes an annual or periodic report.

Louis and Anne Abrons Foundation, Inc.
c/o First Manhattan Co.
437 Madison Ave.
New York, NY 10017
(212) 756-3376
Limitations: Giving primarily in the
    metropolitan New York, NY, area.

The Achelis Foundation
767 3rd Ave., 4th Fl.
New York, NY 10017
(212) 644-0322
FAX: (212) 759-6510; E-mail:
    main@achelis-bodman-fnds.org; URL:

http://fdncenter.org/grantmaker/
    achelis-bodman/
Limitations: Giving primarily in the New York,
    NY, area.

AEGON Transamerica Foundation
c/o Tax Dept.
4333 Edgewood Rd., N.E.
Cedar Rapids, IA 52499
(319) 398-8852

Aetna Foundation, Inc.
151 Farmington Ave.
Hartford, CT 06156-3180
(860) 273-6382
URL: http://www.aetna.com/foundation/
Limitations: Giving primarily to organizations
    in the U.S.
Publishes an annual or periodic report.

The Ahmanson Foundation
9215 Wilshire Blvd.
Beverly Hills, CA 90210
(310) 278-0770
Limitations: Giving primarily in southern CA,
    with emphasis on the Los Angeles area.
Publishes an annual or periodic report.

Alabama Power Foundation, Inc.
600 N. 18th St.
Birmingham, AL 35291-0011
(205) 257-2508
FAX: (205) 257-1860
Limitations: Giving limited to AL.
Publishes an annual or periodic report.

J. A. & Kathryn Albertson Foundation, Inc.
501 Baybrook Ct.
P.O. Box 70002
Boise, ID 83707-0102
(208) 424-2621
FAX: (208) 424-2626; E-mail: fdn@jkaf.org;
    URL: http://www.jkaf.org
Limitations: Giving limited to ID.
Publishes an annual or periodic report.

Alcoa Foundation
Alcoa Corporate Ctr.
201 Isabella St.
Pittsburgh, PA 15212-5858
(412) 553-2348
URL: http://www.alcoa.com/site/community/
    foundation.asp
Limitations: Giving primarily in areas of
    company operations, national and
    international; emphasis on local
    communities: Davenport, IA, Evansville,
    IN, Massena, NY, Cleveland, OH,
    Pittsburgh, PA, Knoxville, TN, and
    Rockdale, TX.
Publishes an annual or periodic report.

The George I. Alden Trust
370 Main St., Rm. 1250
Worcester, MA 01608-1714
(508) 798-8621
FAX: (508) 791-6454
Limitations: Giving limited to the U.S.
Publishes an annual or periodic report.

Albert and Margaret Alkek Foundation
1221 McKinney, Ste. 4525
Houston, TX 77010-2011
(713) 951-0019
FAX: (713) 951-0043
Limitations: Giving limited to TX.

The Allstate Foundation
2775 Sanders Rd., Ste. F3
Northbrook, IL 60062-6127
(847) 402-5502
FAX: (847) 326-7517; URL: http://
    www.allstate.com/foundation/
Limitations: Giving limited to the U.S.

Altman Foundation
521 5th Ave., 35th Fl.
New York, NY 10175
(212) 682-0970
FAX: (212) 682-1648; URL: http://fdncenter.org/
    grantmaker/altman/
Limitations: Giving limited to NY, with
    emphasis on the boroughs of New York
    City.
Publishes an annual or periodic report.

Maurice Amado Foundation
3940 Lourel Canyon Blvd., No. 809
Studio City, CA 91604
(818) 980-9190
FAX: (818) 980-9190; E-mail:
pkaizer@mauriceamadofdn.org; URL:
http://www.mauriceamadofdn.org
Limitations: Giving on a national basis, with
some emphasis on Los Angeles, CA and
New York, NY.

Amarillo Area Foundation, Inc.
801 S. Fillmore, Ste. 700
Amarillo, TX 79101
(806) 376-4521
FAX: (806) 373-3656; E-mail: haf@aaf-hf.org;
URL: http://aaf-hf.org
Limitations: Giving limited to the 26
northernmost counties of the TX
Panhandle.
Publishes an annual or periodic report.

American Express Foundation
c/o American Express Co.
American Express Tower, World Financial Ctr.
New York, NY 10285-4803
(212) 640-5661
URL: http://www.americanexpress.com/corp/
philanthropy/
Limitations: Giving primarily in AZ, CA, FL,
GA, MA, MN, NC, NY, TX, and UT; and
internationally in Asia/Pacific, Canada,
Europe, Latin America, and Japan.

Andersen Foundation
c/o Andersen Corp.
100 4th Ave., N.
Bayport, MN 55003-1096
(651) 439-5150
Limitations: Giving on a national basis.

Hugh J. Andersen Foundation
P.O. Box 204
Bayport, MN 55003-0204
(651) 439-1557
Limitations: Giving primarily in St. Croix
Valley-Washington County, MN, and
Pierce, Polk, and St. Croix counties, WI,
with a secondary interest in St. Paul and
the greater MN area.
Publishes an annual or periodic report.

John W. Anderson Foundation
402 Wall St.
Valparaiso, IN 46383
(219) 462-4611
Limitations: Giving primarily in Lake and
Porter counties in northwest IN.

M. D. Anderson Foundation
P.O. Box 2558
Houston, TX 77252-8037
(713) 216-4513
Limitations: Giving limited to TX, primarily
the Houston area.

Anheuser-Busch Foundation
c/o Anheuser-Busch Cos., Inc.
1 Busch Pl.
St. Louis, MO 63118
(314) 577-7368
Limitations: Giving primarily in areas of major
company operations of its breweries and
theme parks: St. Louis, MO, Newark, NJ,
Los Angeles, Fairfield, and San Diego,
CA, San Antonio, TX, Columbus and
Cleveland, OH, Jacksonville, Tampa, and
Orlando, FL, Merrimack, VA,
Baldwinsville, NY, Fort Collins, CO,
Cartersville, GA, and Langhorne, PA.

The Annenberg Foundation
St. Davids Ctr.
150 Radnor-Chester Rd., Ste. A-200
St. Davids, PA 19087
(610) 341-9066
URL: http://www.whannenberg.org

Aon Foundation
123 N. Wacker Dr.
Chicago, IL 60606
(312) 701-3000
Limitations: Giving on a national basis.

Archer Daniels Midland Foundation
P.O. Box 1470
Decatur, IL 62526
(217) 424-5957

Arison Foundation, Inc.
3655 N.W. 87th Ave.
Miami, FL 33178-2428
(305) 599-2600
Limitations: Giving primarily in NY.

Arizona Community Foundation
2122 E. Highland Ave., Ste. 400
Phoenix, AZ 85016
(602) 381-1400
Limitations: Giving limited to AZ.
Publishes an annual or periodic report.

The Assisi Foundation of Memphis, Inc.
6077 Primacy Pkwy., Ste. 253
Memphis, TN 38119
Limitations: Giving primarily in Memphis and
Shelby County, TN.

AT&T Foundation
32 Ave. of the Americas, 6th Fl.
New York, NY 10013
(212) 387-4801
FAX: (212) 387-4882; E-mail:
Mcclimon@att.com; URL: http://
www.att.com/foundation
Limitations: Giving on a national and
international basis, primarily to Los
Angeles and San Francisco, CA; Denver,
CO; Washington, DC; Miami, FL;
Chicago, IL; NJ; NY; Pittsburgh and
Philadelphia, PA; and Seattle, WA.

The Atlantic Foundation of New York
125 Park Ave., 21st Fl.
New York, NY 10017-5581
Limitations: Giving on a national and
international basis.

AXA Foundation, Inc.
1290 Ave. of the Americas, 13th Fl.
New York, NY 10104
(212) 314-2566
URL: http://www.axa-financial.com/aboutus/
foundation.html
Limitations: Giving on a national basis, with
some emphasis on New York, NY.

Mary Reynolds Babcock Foundation, Inc.
2522 Reynolda Rd.
Winston-Salem, NC 27106-5123
(336) 748-9222
FAX: (336) 777-0095; E-mail: info@mrbf.org;
URL: http://www.mrbf.org/
Limitations: Giving in the southeastern U.S.,
with emphasis on eastern AR, GA, LA,
MS, NC, SC, TN, north and central FL,
and the Appalachian regions of KY and
WV.
Publishes an annual or periodic report.

Helen Bader Foundation, Inc.
233 N. Water St., 4th Fl.
Milwaukee, WI 53202
(414) 224-6464
FAX: (414) 224-1441; E-mail: info@hbf.org;
URL: http://www.hbf.org
Limitations: Giving primarily in the greater
Milwaukee, WI, area for education and
economic development; giving locally and
nationally for Alzheimer's disease and
dementia; giving in Israel for early
childhood development.
Publishes an annual or periodic report.

Pat and Jay Baker Foundation, Inc.
6350 W. Lake Dr.
Whitefish Bay, WI 53217
Limitations: Giving primarily in Milwaukee,
WI.

The George F. Baker Trust
477 Madison Ave., Ste., 1650
New York, NY 10022
(212) 755-1890
FAX: (212) 319-6316; Email:
rocio@bakernye.com
Limitations: Giving primarily in the eastern
U.S., with some emphasis on the New
York, NY, area.
Publishes an annual or periodic report.

L. G. Balfour Foundation
c/o Fleet Asset Mgmt.
100 Federal St., MADE10020B
Boston, MA 02108
(617) 434-4846
Limitations: Giving primarily in New England,
with emphasis on MA.

Ball Brothers Foundation
P.O. Box 1408
Muncie, IN 47308
(765) 741-5500
Additional address: 222 S. Mulberry St.,
Muncie, IN 47305; FAX: (765) 741-5518;
E-mail: dabakken@ecicnet.org
Limitations: Giving limited to IN.

George and Frances Ball Foundation
P.O. Box 1408
Muncie, IN 47308
(765) 741-5500
Additional address: 222 S. Mulberry St.,
    Muncie, IN 47305; FAX: (765) 741-5518
Limitations: Giving primarily in Muncie and
    Delaware County, IN.

Bank of America Foundation, Inc.
100 N. Tryon St., NC1-007-18-01
Charlotte, NC 28255-0001
URL: http://www.bankofamerica.com/
    foundation/
Limitations: Giving limited to areas of major
    company operations, including 21 states
    and Washington, DC, and other select
    areas where there is a company presence.

BANK ONE Foundation
1 BANK ONE Plz., Ste. 0308
Chicago, IL 60670
(312) 407-8052
Limitations: Giving limited to the metropolitan
    Chicago, IL, area.

Banyan Tree Foundation
1919 Pennsylvania Ave., N.W., Ste. 725
Washington, DC 20006
(202) 466-5905
FAX: (202) 466-5918; E-mail:
    foundation@banyan.org
Limitations: Giving on an international basis.

The Barker Welfare Foundation
P.O. Box 2
Glen Head, NY 11545
(516) 759-5592
FAX: (516) 759-5497
Limitations: Giving primarily in Chicago, IL,
    Michigan City, IN, and New York, NY.
Publishes an annual or periodic report.

Barr Foundation
The Pilot House
Lewis Wharf
Boston, MA 02110
(617) 854-3500
E-mail: khurley@pilothouse.com
Limitations: Giving primarily in the greater
    Boston, MA, area.

Barra Foundation, Inc.
8200 Flourtown Ave., Ste. 12
Wyndmoor, PA 19038-7976
(215) 233-5115
FAX: (215) 836-1033
Limitations: Giving primarily in the
    Philadelphia, PA, area.

Battle Creek Community Foundation
1 Riverwalk Ctr.
34 W. Jackson St.
Battle Creek, MI 49017-3505
(616) 962-2181
FAX: (616) 962-2182; E-mail:
    bccf@bccfoundation.org; URL: http://
    www.bccfoundation.org
Limitations: Giving limited to the greater Battle
    Creek, MI, area.
Publishes an annual or periodic report.

Bayport Foundation, Inc.
P.O. Box 204
Bayport, MN 55003-0204
(651) 439-1557
Limitations: Giving primarily in areas where
    Andersen Window employees live in the
    eastern Twin Cities area, MN and the St.
    Croix Valley area, WI.

Elizabeth and Stephen Bechtel, Jr. Foundation
P.O. Box 193809
San Francisco, CA 94119-3809
FAX: (415) 284-8128; E-mail:
    ldachs@fremontgroup.com
Limitations: Giving primarily in the San
    Francisco Bay Area and northern CA.

Arnold and Mabel Beckman Foundation
100 Academy Dr.
Irvine, CA 92612
(949) 721-2222
FAX: (949) 721-2225; URL: http://
    www.beckman-foundation.com
Limitations: Giving primarily in the U.S.

The J. L. Bedsole Foundation
P.O. Box 1137
Mobile, AL 36633
Limitations: Giving limited to AL, with
    emphasis on the southwestern region.

Claude Worthington Benedum Foundation
1400 Benedum-Trees Bldg.
223 4th Ave.
Pittsburgh, PA 15222
(412) 288-0360
URL: http://fdncenter.org/grantmaker/benedum/
Limitations: Giving limited to southwestern PA
    and WV.

Benwood Foundation, Inc.
SunTrust Bank Bldg.
736 Market St., Ste. 1600
Chattanooga, TN 37402
(423) 267-4311
FAX: (423) 267-9049; E-mail:
    Benwoodfnd@Benwood.org
Limitations: Giving primarily in the
    Chattanooga, TN, area.

H. N. & Frances C. Berger Foundation
P.O. Box 13390
Palm Desert, CA 92255-3390
(760) 341-5293
URL: http://www.hnberger.org
Limitations: Giving primarily in CA.

Berkshire Taconic Community Foundation
271 Main St., Ste. 3
Great Barrington, MA 01230
(800) 969-2823
Additional address: P.O. Box 569, Salisbury,
    CT 06068-0569; FAX: (413) 528-8158;
    E-mail: btcf@bcn.net
Limitations: Giving limited to northwest
    Litchfield County, CT, Berkshire County,
    MA, and northeast Dutchess and
    Columbia counties, NY.
Publishes an annual or periodic report.

Burton G. Bettingen Corporation
9777 Wilshire Blvd., Ste. 615
Beverly Hills, CA 90212
(310) 276-4115
FAX: (310) 276-4693; E-mail:
    burtonbet@aol.com
Limitations: Giving primarily in southern CA.

The Frank Stanley Beveridge Foundation, Inc.
301 Yamato Rd., Ste. 1130
Boca Raton, FL 33431
(800) 600-3723
FAX: (561) 241-8388; E-mail:
    administrator@beveridge.org; URL: http://
    www.beveridge.org
Limitations: Giving only in Orange County,
    CA, Boca Raton, FL, Kauai County, HI,
    Hampden and Hampshire counties, MA,
    NH, and RI.

The Bielfeldt Foundation
124 S.W. Adams, Ste. 340
Peoria, IL 61602
(309) 676-6003
Limitations: Giving primarily in Peoria, IL.

F. R. Bigelow Foundation
600 Norwest Ctr.
55 E. 5th St.
St. Paul, MN 55101-1797
(651) 224-5463
FAX: (651) 224-8123; E-mail:
    inbox@frbigelow.org; URL: http://
    www.frbigelow.org
Limitations: Giving limited to the greater
    metropolitan St. Paul, MN, area;
    including Ramsey, Washington, and
    Dakota counties.
Publishes an annual or periodic report.

E. K. and Lillian F. Bishop Foundation
c/o Bank of America
701 5th Ave., 47th Fl.
Seattle, WA 98104
(520) 749-2004
FAX: (520) 749-2990
Limitations: Giving limited to WA, with
    emphasis on Grays Harbor County;
    scholarship applicants must be Grays
    Harbor County residents entering their
    3rd year of college or beyond.

The Blandin Foundation
100 Pokegama Ave., N.
Grand Rapids, MN 55744
(218) 326-0523
FAX: (218) 327-1949; E-mail:
    bldnfdtn@uslink.net; URL: http://
    www.blandinfoundation.org
Limitations: Giving limited to rural areas of
    MN; scholarships limited to graduates of
    an Itasca County, Hill City, or Remer,
    MN, high school.
Publishes an annual or periodic report.

The Arthur M. Blank Family Foundation
The Forum
3290 Northside Pkwy., N.W., Ste. 600
Atlanta, GA 30327
(404) 239-0600
FAX: (404) 442-0991; URL: http://
www.blankfoundation.org
Limitations: Giving primarily in Los Angeles,
CA, Atlanta, GA, Boston, MA, and New
York City.
Publishes an annual or periodic report.

The Jacob and Hilda Blaustein Foundation, Inc.
Blaustein Bldg.
P.O. Box 238
Baltimore, MD 21203
(410) 347-7201
E-mail: info@blaufund.org
Limitations: Giving primarily in MD; no local
projects outside Baltimore, MD.

Blum-Kovler Foundation
919 N. Michigan Ave., Ste. 2800
Chicago, IL 60611
(312) 664-5050
Limitations: Giving primarily in the Chicago,
IL, area.

The Bodman Foundation
767 3rd Ave., 4th Fl.
New York, NY 10017-2023
(212) 644-0322
FAX: (212) 759-6510; E-mail:
main@achelis-bodman-fnds.org.; URL:
http://fdncenter.org/grantmaker/
achelis-bodman/
Limitations: Giving primarily in northern NJ
and New York, NY.

Boettcher Foundation
600 17th St., Ste. 2210 S.
Denver, CO 80202
(303) 534-1937
E-mail: grants@boettcherfoundation.org; URL:
http://www.boettcherfoundation.org/
Limitations: Giving limited to CO.
Publishes an annual or periodic report.

Booth Ferris Foundation
c/o J.P. Morgan Chase Company
60 Wall St., 36th Fl.
New York, NY 10260-0001
(212) 809-1630
Limitations: Giving limited to the New York,
NY, metropolitan area for social service
agencies and cultural organizations.
Publishes an annual or periodic report.

Boston Foundation, Inc.
75 Arlington St.,10th Fl.
Boston, MA 02116
(617) 338-1700
FAX: (617) 338-1604; E-mail: alk@tbf.org;
URL: http://www.tbf.org
Limitations: Giving from discretionary funds
limited to the metropolitan Boston, MA,
area.
Publishes an annual or periodic report.

The Mervin Bovaird Foundation
100 W. 5th St., Ste. 800
Tulsa, OK 74103-4291
(918) 583-1777
Limitations: Giving limited to the Tulsa, OK,
area.

BP Amoco Foundation, Inc.
200 E. Randolph Dr.
Chicago, IL 60601
(312) 856-2502
Limitations: Giving nationally in areas of
company representation to assist
communities, including the areas of
Denver, CO, Washington, DC, Atlanta,
GA, Chicago and Warrenville, IL,
northwest IN, New Orleans, LA, Towson,
MD, Minneapolis, MN, Lima, OH, Tulsa,
OK, SC, Houston and Texas City, TX,
Salt Lake City, UT, VA, and Casper, WY;
international giving in areas where BP
Amoco operates.

Helen Brach Foundation
55 W. Wacker Dr., Ste. 701
Chicago, IL 60601
(312) 372-4417
FAX: (312) 372-0290
Limitations: Giving primarily in the Midwest,
and CA, MA, OH, PA and SC, No grants
outside continental U.S.

**The Lynde and Harry Bradley Foundation,
Inc.**
P.O. Box 510860
Milwaukee, WI 53203-0153
(414) 291-9915
FAX: (414) 291-9991; URL: http://
www.bradleyfdn.org
Limitations: Giving primarily in Milwaukee,
WI; giving also on a national and
international basis.
Publishes an annual or periodic report.

Otto Bremer Foundation
445 Minnesota St., Ste. 2000
St. Paul, MN 55101-2107
(651) 227-8036
Limitations: Giving limited to cities in MN,
ND, and WI where there are Bremer Bank
affiliates, and to organizations addressing
poverty in the city of St. Paul, MN.
Publishes an annual or periodic report.

Bridgestone/Firestone Trust Fund
50 Century Blvd.
Nashville, TN 37214
(615) 872-1415
FAX: (615) 872-1414; E-mail:
bfstrustfund@bfusa.com
Limitations: Giving primarily in areas of major
company operations: AR, CO, CT, FL, IA,
IL, IN, KY, LA, MI, NC, OH, OK, PA,
SC, TN, TX, and UT.

The Bristol-Myers Squibb Foundation, Inc.
c/o Fdn. Coord.
345 Park Ave., 43rd Fl.
New York, NY 10154
URL: http://www.bms.com/aboutbms/founda/
data
Limitations: Giving primarily in Stamford and
Wallingford, CT, Evansville, IN, New

Brunswick, Princeton, and Skillman, NJ,
and Buffalo and Syracuse, NY.
Publishes an annual or periodic report.

Britton Fund
c/o Advisory Svcs., Inc.
1422 Euclid Ave., 1010 Hanna Bldg.
Cleveland, OH 44115-2078
(216) 363-6489
Limitations: Giving primarily in OH.
Publishes an annual or periodic report.

The Samuel Bronfman Foundation, Inc.
375 Park Ave.
New York, NY 10152-0192
Limitations: Giving primarily in New York,
NY, and to national U.S. programs.

The Brown Foundation, Inc.
2217 Welch Ave.
Houston, TX 77019
(713) 523-6867
Application address: P.O. Box 130646,
Houston, TX 77219-0646; FAX: (713)
523-2917; E-mail:
bfi@brownfoundation.org; URL: http://
www.brownfoundation.org
Limitations: Giving primarily in TX, with
emphasis on Houston.
Publishes an annual or periodic report.

Eva L. and Joseph M. Bruening Foundation
627 Hanna Building
1422 Euclid Ave.
Cleveland, OH 44115-1901
(216) 621-2632
FAX: (216) 621-8198
Limitations: Giving limited to the greater
Cleveland, OH, area.
Publishes an annual or periodic report.

The Buchanan Family Foundation
222 E. Wisconsin Ave.
Lake Forest, IL 60045-1701
Limitations: Giving primarily in Chicago, IL.

Temple Hoyne Buell Foundation
1666 S. University Blvd., Ste. B
Denver, CO 80210
(303) 744-1688
FAX: (303) 744-1601; E-mail:
ssteele@buellfoundation.org; URL: http://
www.buellfoundation.org
Limitations: Giving primarily in CO.
Publishes an annual or periodic report.

The Buffett Foundation
209 Kiewit Plz.
Omaha, NE 68131

The Buhl Foundation
650 Smithfield St., Ste. 2300
Pittsburgh, PA 15222
(412) 566-2711
Limitations: Giving primarily in southwestern
PA, with emphasis on the Pittsburgh area.
Publishes an annual or periodic report.

The Bullitt Foundation
1212 Minor Ave.
Seattle, WA 98101-2825
(206) 343-0807
FAX: (206) 343-0822; E-mail: info@Bullitt.org;
    URL: http://www.bullitt.org
Limitations: Giving exclusively in the Pacific
    Northwest.
Publishes an annual or periodic report.

Fritz B. Burns Foundation
4001 W. Alameda Ave., Ste. 203
Burbank, CA 91505-4338
(818) 840-8802
Limitations: Giving primarily in the Los
    Angeles, CA, area.

Burroughs Wellcome Fund
21 T. W. Alexander Dr.
P.O. Box 13901
Research Triangle Park, NC 27709-3901
(919) 991-5100
FAX: (919) 991-5160; E-mail:
    info@bwfund.org.; URL: http://
    www.bwfund.org
Limitations: Giving limited to the U.S. and
    Canada.
Publishes an annual or periodic report.

The Bush Foundation
E-900 First National Bank Bldg.
332 Minnesota St.
St. Paul, MN 55101
(651) 227-0891
FAX: (651) 297-6485; E-mail:
    info@bushfound.org; URL: http://
    www.bushfoundation.org
Limitations: Giving primarily in MN, ND, and
    SD.
Publishes an annual or periodic report.

The Robert G. Cabell III and Maude Morgan
    Cabell Foundation
P.O. Box 85678
Richmond, VA 23285-5678
(804) 780-2050
Limitations: Giving limited to VA.

The Morris and Gwendolyn Cafritz Foundation
1825 K St., N.W., 14th Fl.
Washington, DC 20006
(202) 223-3100
URL: http://www.cafritzfoundation.org
Limitations: Giving limited to the greater
    metropolitan Washington, DC, area.
Publishes an annual or periodic report.

The Louis Calder Foundation
230 Park Ave., Rm. 1525
New York, NY 10169
(212) 687-1680
URL: http://www.lcfnyc.org
Limitations: Giving primarily in the greater
    New York City metropolitan area.
Publishes an annual or periodic report.

The California Endowment
21650 Oxnard St., Ste. 1200
Woodland Hills, CA 91367
(800) 449-4149
Limitations: Giving limited to CA.
Publishes an annual or periodic report.

The California Wellness Foundation
6320 Canoga Ave., Ste. 1700
Woodland Hills, CA 91367-7111
(818) 593-6600
FAX: (818) 593-6614; URL: http://
    www.tcwf.org
Limitations: Giving limited to CA; national
    organizations providing services in CA
    are also considered.
Publishes an annual or periodic report.

Cindy and Ely Callaway Family Foundation
2285 Rutherford Rd.
Carlsbad, CA 92008-8815
(760) 931-1771
Limitations: Giving on a national basis.

Camp Younts Foundation
c/o SunTrust Bank, Atlanta
P.O. Box 4655
Atlanta, GA 30302-4655
Limitations: Giving primarily in FL, GA, NC,
    and VA.

The Cannon Foundation, Inc.
P.O. Box 548
Concord, NC 28026-0548
(704) 786-8216
Limitations: Giving primarily in NC, with
    emphasis on the Cabarrus County area.

The Capital Group Companies Charitable
    Foundation
11100 Santa Monica Blvd., Fl. 9
Los Angeles, CA 90025-3384
Limitations: Giving primarily in CA, with
    emphasis on Los Angeles.

The Carls Foundation
333 W. Fort St., Ste. 1940
Detroit, MI 48226-3134
(313) 965-0990
Limitations: Giving primarily in MI.
Publishes an annual or periodic report.

Carnegie Corporation of New York
437 Madison Ave.
New York, NY 10022
(212) 371-3200
FAX: (212) 754-4073; URL: http://
    www.carnegie.org
Limitations: Giving primarily in the U.S. Some
    grants in commonwealth Sub-Saharan
    Africa, South Africa.
Publishes an annual or periodic report.

Carolyn Foundation
4800 US Bank Pl.
Minneapolis, MN 55402
(612) 339-7101
FAX: (612) 338-2084; E-mail:
    carolyn@winternet.com
Limitations: Giving primarily in the
    metropolitan areas of New Haven, CT,
    and Minneapolis-St. Paul, MN.
Publishes an annual or periodic report.

E. Rhodes & Leona B. Carpenter Foundation
c/o Joseph A. O'Connor, Jr., Morgan, Lewis &
    Bockius
2000 1 Logan Sq.
Philadelphia, PA 19103
(215) 963-5212
Application address: P.O. Box 58880,
    Philadelphia, PA 19102-8880
Limitations: Giving primarily in areas east of
    the Mississippi River.

Amon G. Carter Foundation
201 Main St., Ste. 1945
P.O. Box 1036
Fort Worth, TX 76102
(817) 332-2783
FAX: (817) 332-2787; E-mail:
    jrobinson@agcf.org
Limitations: Giving largely restricted to Fort
    Worth and Tarrant County, TX.

The Annie E. Casey Foundation
701 St. Paul St.
Baltimore, MD 21202
(410) 547-6600
FAX: (410) 547-6624; E-mail:
    webmail@aecf.org; URL: http://
    www.aecf.org
Publishes an annual or periodic report.

Harold K. L. Castle Foundation
146 Hekili St., Ste. 203A
Kailua, HI 96734
(808) 262-9413
FAX: (808) 261-6918; E-mail:
    braden@castlefoundation.org; URL: http://
    www.castlefoundation.org
Limitations: Giving limited to HI; priority to
    Windward Oahu.
Publishes an annual or periodic report.

Samuel N. and Mary Castle Foundation
733 Bishop St., Ste. 1275
Honolulu, HI 96813
(808) 522-1101
FAX: (808) 522-1103; E-mail:
    acastle@aloha.net; URL: http://
    fdncenter.org/grantmaker/castle/
Limitations: Giving generally limited to HI.
Publishes an annual or periodic report.

Caterpillar Foundation
100 N.E. Adams St.
Peoria, IL 61629-1480
(309) 675-1000
Limitations: Giving primarily in areas of
    company operations.

The CH Foundation
P.O. Box 16458
Lubbock, TX 79490
(806) 792-0448
FAX: (806) 792-7824
Limitations: Giving primarily in Lubbock, TX
    and surrounding counties.

The Challenge Foundation
16415 Addison Rd., Ste. 157
Dallas, TX 75248
(972) 250-4573
FAX: (972) 250-4576

The Champlin Foundations
300 Centerville Rd, Ste. 300S
Warwick, RI 02886-0226
(401) 736-0370
FAX: (401) 736-7248; E-mail:
    champlinfdns@worldnet.att.net; URL:
    http://fdncenter.org/grantmaker/champlin/
Limitations: Giving primarily in RI.
Publishes an annual or periodic report.

H. A. and Mary K. Chapman Charitable Trust
1 Warren Pl., Ste. 1816
6100 S. Yale
Tulsa, OK 74136
(918) 496-7882
Limitations: Giving primarily in Tulsa, OK.

Chartwell Charitable Foundation
1999 Ave. of the Stars, Ste. 3050
Los Angeles, CA 90067
(310) 556-7600
Limitations: Giving primarily in CA and NY.

The Chatlos Foundation, Inc.
P.O. Box 915048
Longwood, FL 32791-5048
(407) 862-5077
URL: http://www.chatlos.org

Ben B. Cheney Foundation
1201 Pacific Ave., Ste. 1600
Tacoma, WA 98402
(253) 572-2442
Limitations: Giving limited to the seven
    northernmost counties in CA,
    southwestern OR, with emphasis on
    Medford, Tacoma and Pierce County, and
    southwestern WA.

The Chicago Community Trust and Affiliates
222 N. LaSalle St., Ste. 1400
Chicago, IL 60601-1009
(312) 372-3356
TDD: (312) 853-0394; FAX: (312) 580-7411;
    E-mail: sandy@cct.org; URL: http://
    www.cct.org
Limitations: Giving primarily in Cook County,
    IL.
Publishes an annual or periodic report.

Chicago Tribune Foundation
435 N. Michigan Ave., 2nd Fl.
Chicago, IL 60611-4041
(312) 222-4300
FAX: (312) 222-3751
Limitations: Giving primarily in the
    metropolitan Chicago, IL, area.

Chichester duPont Foundation, Inc.
3120 Kennett Pike
Wilmington, DE 19807-3045
(302) 658-5244
Limitations: Giving primarily in DE and MD.

China Medical Board of New York, Inc.
750 3rd Ave., 23rd Fl.
New York, NY 10017-2701
(212) 682-8000
Limitations: Giving limited to East and
    Southeast Asia, including the People's
    Republic of China, Hong Kong,
    Indonesia, Korea, Malaysia, the

Philippines, Singapore, Taiwan, and
    Thailand.
Publishes an annual or periodic report.

The Greater Cincinnati Foundation
200 W. 4th St.
Cincinnati, OH 45202-2602
(513) 241-2880
FAX: (513) 852-6886; URL: http://
    www.greatercincinnatifdn.org/
Limitations: Giving limited to southeastern IN,
    northern KY, and the greater Cincinnati,
    OH area.
Publishes an annual or periodic report.

Cisco Systems Foundation
170 W. Tasman Dr.
San Jose, CA 95134-1706
(408) 527-3040
FAX: (408) 527-6310; E-mail:
    ciscofoundation@cisco.com; URL: http://
    www.cisco.com/warp/public/750/
    fdn_home.html
Limitations: Giving primarily in CA.

Citigroup Foundation
850 Third Ave., 13th Fl
New York, NY 10022
(212) 793-8451
FAX: (212) 793-5944; E-mail:
    citigroupfoundation@citi.com; URL:
    http://www.citigroup.com/citigroup/
    corporate/fndtion/
Publishes an annual or periodic report.

Liz Claiborne & Art Ortenberg Foundation
650 5th Ave., 15th Fl.
New York, NY 10019
(212) 333-2536
FAX: (212) 956-3531; E-mail: lcaof@fcc.net
Limitations: Giving primarily in Third World
    countries in the Tropics and in the
    Northern Rocky Mountain region of the
    U.S.

Liz Claiborne Foundation
1440 Broadway
New York, NY 10018
(212) 626-5704
FAX: (212) 626-5304
Limitations: Giving only in the four areas
    where the main operating facilities of Liz
    Claiborne, Inc. are located: Montgomery,
    AL, Hudson County, NJ, New York, NY,
    and Mount Pocono, PA.

The Clark Foundation
1 Rockefeller Plz., 31st Fl.
New York, NY 10020
(212) 977-6900
Limitations: Giving primarily in upstate NY
    and New York City; scholarships
    restricted to students residing in the
    Cooperstown, NY, area.

The Edna McConnell Clark Foundation
250 Park Ave., Rm. 900
New York, NY 10177-0026
(212) 551-9100
FAX: (212) 986-4558; URL: http://
    www.emcf.org/
Limitations: Giving nationally for Children's
    Program and Student Achievement

Program; New York City preference for
    Program for New York Neighborhoods.
Publishes an annual or periodic report.

Robert Sterling Clark Foundation, Inc.
135 E. 64th St.
New York, NY 10021
(212) 288-8900
FAX: (212) 288-1033; URL: http://fdncenter.org/
    grantmaker/rsclark/
Limitations: Giving primarily in New York
    State for the Public Institutions Program
    and in New York City for the Cultural
    Program; giving nationally for
    reproductive freedom projects.
Publishes an annual or periodic report.

The Cleveland Foundation
1422 Euclid Ave., Ste. 1300
Cleveland, OH 44115-2001
(216) 861-3810
FAX: (216) 861-1729; TTY: (216) 861-3806;
    E-mail: Idunford@clevefdn.org; URL:
    http://www.clevelandfoundation.org
Limitations: Giving limited to the greater
    Cleveland, OH, area, with primary
    emphasis on Cleveland, Cuyahoga, Lake,
    and Geauga counties, unless specified by
    donor.
Publishes an annual or periodic report.

The Clorox Company Foundation
1221 Broadway, 13th Fl.
Oakland, CA 94612
(510) 271-7751
Mailing address: P.O. Box 24305, Oakland, CA
    94623-1305, tel.: (510) 271-2199; FAX:
    (510) 208-4103; URL: http://
    www.clorox.com/company/foundation/
Limitations: Giving primarily in Oakland, CA,
    and other areas of company operations.

The Clowes Fund, Inc.
320 N. Meridan St., Ste. 316
Indianapolis, IN 46204-1722
(317) 833-0144
Limitations: Giving primarily in Indianapolis,
    IN, Boston, MA, and Seattle, WA.

The Coca-Cola Foundation, Inc.
1 Coca-Cola Plz., N.W.
Atlanta, GA 30313-3009
(404) 676-2568
Application address: P.O. Drawer 1734,
    Atlanta, GA 30301; FAX: (404)
    676-8804; URL: http://
    www2.coca-cola.com/business/
    community/foundation.html
Publishes an annual or periodic report.

Naomi and Nehemiah Cohen Foundation
P.O. Box 73708
Washington, DC 20056
(202) 363-5195
FAX: (202) 363-5209; E-mail:
    NNCF@erols.com
Limitations: Giving primarily in Washington,
    DC and Israel.

The Collins Foundation
1618 S.W. 1st Ave., Ste. 505
Portland, OR 97201-5708
(503) 227-7171
FAX: (503) 295-3794; URL: http://
www.collinsfoundation.org/
Limitations: Giving limited to OR, with
emphasis on Portland.
Publishes an annual or periodic report.

Columbia Foundation
1 Lombard St., Ste. 305
San Francisco, CA 94111
(415) 986-5179
FAX: (415) 986-1732; URL: http://
www.columbia.org
Limitations: Giving primarily in the San
Francisco Bay Area, CA and London,
England for arts.
Publishes an annual or periodic report.

**The Columbus Foundation and Affiliated
Organizations**
1234 E. Broad St.
Columbus, OH 43205-1453
(614) 251-4000
FAX: (614) 251-4009; E-mail:
info@columbusfoundation.org; URL:
http://www.columbusfoundation.org
Limitations: Giving limited to Franklin County,
OH, from unrestricted and other
discretionary funds.
Publishes an annual or periodic report.

The Comer Foundation
c/o Neal Gerber & Eisenberg
2 N. LaSalle St.
Chicago, IL 60602
Limitations: Giving primarily in Chicago, IL.

The Commonwealth Fund
1 E. 75th St.
New York, NY 10021-2692
(212) 606-3844
FAX: (212) 606-3500; E-mail:
cmwf@cmwf.org; URL: http://
www.cmwf.org
Publishes an annual or periodic report.

Communities Foundation of Texas, Inc.
4605 Live Oak St.
Dallas, TX 75204
(214) 826-5231
FAX: (214) 823-7737; URL: http://
www.cftexas.org
Limitations: Giving primarily in the Dallas,
TX, area (for grants from unrestricted
funds).
Publishes an annual or periodic report.

The Community Foundation
121 W. Forsyth St., Ste. 900
Jacksonville, FL 32202
(904) 356-4483
FAX: (904) 356-7910; URL: http://
www.jaxcf.org
Limitations: Giving primarily in northeastern
FL, including Baker, Clay, Duval, Nassau
and St. Johns counties; and southeastern
GA.
Publishes an annual or periodic report.

Community Foundation for Greater Atlanta
The Hurt Bldg., Ste. 449
Atlanta, GA 30303
(404) 688-5525
FAX: (404) 688-3060; URL: http://
www.atlcf.org
Limitations: Giving limited to the 22-county
metropolitan area of Atlanta, GA.
Publishes an annual or periodic report.

Community Foundation for Greater Buffalo
712 Main St.
Buffalo, NY 14202-1720
(716) 852-2857
FAX: (716) 852-2861; E-mail: mail@cfgb.org;
URL: http://www.cfgb.org
Limitations: Giving limited to western NY;
scholarships awarded to students
primarily from Erie County.
Publishes an annual or periodic report.

Community Foundation for Southeastern
Michigan
333 W. Fort St., Ste. 2010
Detroit, MI 48226
(313) 961-6675
FAX: (313) 961-2886; E-mail:
cfsm@voyager.net; URL: http://
comnet.org/comfound/
Limitations: Giving limited to southeastern MI.
Publishes an annual or periodic report.

**The Community Foundation for the National
Capital Region**
1112 16th St. N.W., Ste. 340
Washington, DC 20036
(202) 955-5890
FAX: (202) 955-8084; E-mail: cfncr@aol.com;
URL: http://www.cfncr.org/
Limitations: Giving limited to the metropolitan
Washington, DC, area.
Publishes an annual or periodic report.

The Community Foundation of Greater
Birmingham
2027 1st Ave., N., Ste. 410
Birmingham, AL 35203
(205) 328-8641
FAX: (205) 328-6576; E-mail:
cfgb@bellsouth.net
Limitations: Giving limited to the Birmingham,
AL, area, including five counties:
Jefferson, Shelby, Blount, St. Clair and
Walker.
Publishes an annual or periodic report.

The Community Foundation of Greater Lorain
County
1865 N. Ridge Rd. E., Ste. A
Lorain, OH 44055
(440) 277-0142
Limitations: Giving limited to Lorain County,
OH, and immediate vicinity.
Publishes an annual or periodic report.

Community Foundation of Greater Memphis
1900 Union Ave.
Memphis, TN 38104
(901) 728-4600
FAX: (901) 722-0010; URL: http://
www.cfgm.org
Limitations: Giving limited to Crittenden
County, AR, DeSoto County, MS, and

metropolitan Memphis, including Fayette,
Shelby, and Tipton counties, TN.
Publishes an annual or periodic report.

The Community Foundation of South Alabama
154 St. Louis St.
Mobile, AL 36602
(334) 438-5591
Application address: P.O. Box 990, Mobile, AL
36601-0990; FAX: (334) 438-5592;
E-mail: cfsa990@bellsouth.net
Limitations: Giving primarily in southern AL,
south of Montgomery County (Mobile
and Baldwin counties).
Publishes an annual or periodic report.

Community Foundation of Western
Massachusetts
1500 Main St., Ste. 622
P.O. Box 15769
Springfield, MA 01115
(413) 732-2858
FAX: (413) 733-8565; E-mail:
wmass@communityfoundation.org
Limitations: Giving limited to western MA,
including on Hampden County,
Hampshire County, and Franklin County.
Publishes an annual or periodic report.

The Community Foundation Serving Richmond
& Central Virginia
7325 Beaufant Springs Dr., Ste. 210
Richmond, VA 23225
(804) 330-7400
FAX: (804) 330-5992; URL: http://
www.tcfrichmond.org
Limitations: Giving limited to residents of
metropolitan Richmond, the tri-cities area,
including Hopewell, Colonial Heights,
and Petersburg, and Chesterfield,
Hanover, and Henrico counties, VA.
Publishes an annual or periodic report.

Compton Foundation, Inc.
545 Middlefield Rd., Ste. 178
Menlo Park, CA 94025
(650) 328-0101
FAX: (650) 328-0171; URL: http://
www.comptonfoundation.org
Limitations: Giving on an international basis to
U.S.-based organizations for projects in
Mexico, Central America, and
Sub-Saharan Africa and on a national
basis for programs in peace and
population and the environment. Other
funding limited to areas where board
members reside: primarily San Francisco,
Marin, and Santa Clara counties, CA.

Connelly Foundation
1 Tower Bridge, Ste. 1450
West Conshohocken, PA 19428
(610) 834-3222
FAX: (610) 834-0866; E-mail:
info@connellyfdn.org; URL: http://
www.connellyfdn.org
Limitations: Giving primarily in the
Philadelphia, PA, and Delaware Valley
areas.

Adolph Coors Foundation
4100 E. Mississippi Ave., Ste. 1850
Denver, CO 80246
(303) 388-1636
Limitations: Giving primarily in CO.
Publishes an annual or periodic report.

The Cord Foundation
1 E. 1st St.
Reno, NV 89501
(775) 323-0373
Limitations: Giving primarily in northern NV.

Corning Incorporated Foundation
MP-LB-02-1
Corning, NY 14831
(607) 974-8746
URL: http://www.corning.com/employment/
quality_of_life/foundation.html
Limitations: Giving primarily in communities
where Corning Incorporated has
operations.
Publishes an annual or periodic report.

S. H. Cowell Foundation
120 Montgomery St., Ste. 2570
San Francisco, CA 94104
(415) 397-0285
URL: http://www.shcowell.org/
Limitations: Giving limited to CA, excluding
southern CA.
Publishes an annual or periodic report.

Gardner and Florence Call Cowles Foundation,
Inc.
715 Locust St.
Des Moines, IA 50309
(515) 284-8116
Limitations: Giving limited to IA, with
emphasis on Des Moines.
Publishes an annual or periodic report.

Henry P. Crowell and Susan C. Crowell Trust
620 Southpoint Ct., Ste. 205
Colorado Springs, CO 80906
(719) 540-0203
E-mail: crowellhp@aol.com

Arie and Ida Crown Memorial
222 N. LaSalle St., Ste. 2000
Chicago, IL 60601
(312) 236-6300
Limitations: Giving primarily in metropolitan
Chicago, IL.

Crystal Trust
1088 DuPont Bldg.
Wilmington, DE 19898
(302) 774-8421
Limitations: Giving primarily in DE, with
emphasis on Wilmington.

Lewis B. & Dorothy Cullman Foundation, Inc.
c/o Lewis B. Cullman
767 3rd Ave., 36th Fl.
New York, NY 10017
(212) 751-6655
Limitations: Giving primarily in NY.

The Nathan Cummings Foundation, Inc.
475 10th Ave., 14th Fl.
New York, NY 10018
(212) 787-7300
FAX: (212) 787-7377; E-mail:
info@cummings.ncf.org; URL: http://
www.ncf.org
Limitations: Giving primarily in the U.S. and
Israel.
Publishes an annual or periodic report.

Dade Community Foundation, Inc.
200 S. Biscayne Blvd., Ste. 505
Miami, FL 33131-2343
(305) 371-2711
FAX: (305) 371-5342; E-mail:
dadecomfnd@aol.com
Limitations: Giving limited to Dade County, FL.
Publishes an annual or periodic report.

DaimlerChrysler Corporation Fund
1000 Chrysler Dr.
Auburn Hills, MI 48326-2766
(248) 512-2501
E-mail: mek@dcx.com; URL: http://
www.fund.daimlerchrysler.com
Limitations: Giving primarily in areas where
company employees live and work,
including AL, AZ, DE, IL, IN, MI, MO,
NY, OH, and WI.
Publishes an annual or periodic report.

The Dallas Foundation
900 Jackson St., Ste. 150
Dallas, TX 75202
(214) 741-9898
FAX: (214) 741-9848; E-mail:
mjalonick@dallasfoundation.org; URL:
http://www.dallasfoundation.org
Limitations: Giving limited to the City and
County of Dallas, TX.
Publishes an annual or periodic report.

Eleanor Naylor Dana Charitable Trust
375 Park Ave., 38th Fl., Ste. 3807
New York, NY 10152
(212) 754-2890
Limitations: Giving primarily in areas east of
the Mississippi River.

The Danforth Foundation
211 N. Broadway, Ste. 2390
St. Louis, MO 63102
(314) 588-1900
FAX: (314) 588-0035
Limitations: Giving limited to the metropolitan
St. Louis, MO, area.
Publishes an annual or periodic report.

The Daniel Foundation of Alabama
820 Shades Creek Pkwy., Ste. 1200
Birmingham, AL 35209
(205) 879-0902
Limitations: Giving primarily in the
southeastern U.S., with emphasis on AL.

Charles H. Dater Foundation, Inc.
302 Gwynne Bldg.
602 Main St., Ste. 302
Cincinnati, OH 45202
(513) 241-1234
E-mail: BruceA.Krone@Dater.org
Limitations: Giving primarily in the greater
Cincinnati, OH, area.

Irene E. and George A. Davis Foundation
1 Monarch Pl., Ste. 1450
Springfield, MA 01144-1450
(413) 734-8336
FAX: (413) 734-7845; E-mail:
davisfoun@aol.com
Limitations: Giving primarily in Hampden
County, MA.

Joe C. Davis Foundation
28 White Bridge Rd., Ste. 210
Nashville, TN 37205
Application address: 908 Audubon Rd.,
Nashville, TN 37204
Limitations: Giving primarily in the Nashville,
TN, area.

The Arthur Vining Davis Foundations
111 Riverside Ave., Ste. 130
Jacksonville, FL 32202-4921
(904) 359-0670
FAX: (904) 359-0675; E-mail:
arthurvining@bellsouth.net.com; URL:
http://www.jvm.com/davis
Limitations: Giving limited to the U.S. and its
possessions and territories.
Publishes an annual or periodic report.

The Ira W. DeCamp Foundation
c/o J.P. Morgan Chase
60 Wall St., 36th Fl.
New York, NY 10260
(212) 648-9673
FAX: (212) 648-5082
Limitations: Giving primarily in NY including
the metropolitan area and NJ and CT.

John Deere Foundation
1 John Deere Pl.
Moline, IL 61265
(309) 765-4137
FAX: (309) 765-9855; E-mail:
dp51104@deere.com
Limitations: Giving limited to areas where
company employees live and work.

Dekko Foundation, Inc.
P.O. Box 548
Kendallville, IN 46755-0548
(219) 347-1278
FAX: (219) 347-7103; E-mail:
dekko@dekkofoundation.org; URL: http://
www.dekkofoundation.org
Limitations: Giving primarily in Limestone
County, AL; Clarke, Decatur, Lucas,
Ringgold, and Union counties, IA; Noble,
DeKalb, Whitley, Steuben, LaGrange, and
Kosciousko counties, IN; and Lincoln and
Giles counties, TN.

Beatrice P. Delany Charitable Trust
c/o The Chase Manhattan Bank, N.A.
1211 Avenue of the Americas, 34th FL.
New York, NY 10036
Limitations: Giving primarily in the
metropolitan Chicago, IL, area.

The Gladys Krieble Delmas Foundation
521 5th Ave., Ste. 1612
New York, NY 10175-1699
(212) 687-0011
FAX: (212) 687-8877; E-mail:
info@Delmas.org; URL: http://
www.delmas.org
Limitations: Giving on a national basis to
organizations, but only in New York, NY,
for performing arts grants; giving for
individual research projects conducted in
Venice or the Veneto, Italy.

The Denver Foundation
950 S. Cherry St., Ste. 200
Denver, CO 80246
(303) 300-1790
FAX: (303) 300-6547; URL: http://
www.denverfoundation.org
Limitations: Giving limited to Adams,
Arapahoe, Boulder, Denver, Douglas, and
Jefferson counties, CO.
Publishes an annual or periodic report.

Deutsche Bank Americas Foundation
130 Liberty St., 10th Fl., NYC 02-1007
New York, NY 10006
(212) 250-7065
URL: http://www.db.com/community
Limitations: Giving primarily in areas of
company operations in the U.S., Canada
and Latin America.
Publishes an annual or periodic report.

Irene Diamond Fund
375 Park Ave., Ste. 3303
New York, NY 10152-3399
(212) 838-9525
Limitations: Giving primarily in NY.

The Dibner Fund, Inc.
44 Old Ridgefield Rd.
P.O. Box 7575
Wilton, CT 06897
(203) 761-9904
FAX: (203) 761-9989; E-mail:
dibnerfund@worldnet.att.net
Limitations: Giving primarily in CT, MA, and
NY.

Harriet Ford Dickenson Foundation
c/o Morgan Guaranty Trust Co.
345 Park Ave.
New York, NY 10154
(212) 464-1937
Limitations: Giving limited to Broome County,
NY.

Dillon Foundation
P.O. Box 537
Sterling, IL 61081
(815) 626-9000
FAX: (815) 626-4000
Limitations: Giving primarily in the Sterling,
IL, area.

The Dillon Fund
1330 Ave. of the Americas, 27th Fl.
New York, NY 10019

The Walt Disney Company Foundation
500 S. Buena Vista St.
Burbank, CA 91521-9640
Limitations: Giving primarily in areas of
company operations, including Los
Angeles and Orange County, CA, and
Orange and Osceola counties, FL.

Geraldine R. Dodge Foundation, Inc.
163 Madison Ave., 6th Fl.
P.O. Box 1239
Morristown, NJ 07962-1239
(973) 540-8442
E-mail: info@grdodge.org; URL: http://
www.grdodge.org
Limitations: Giving primarily in NJ, with
support for the arts and local humane
groups limited to NJ, and support for
other local projects limited to the
Morristown-Madison area; some giving in
the other Middle Atlantic states and New
England, and to national organizations.
Publishes an annual or periodic report.

Dodge Jones Foundation
P.O. Box 176
Abilene, TX 79604
(915) 673-6429
Limitations: Giving primarily in Abilene, TX.

Carrie Estelle Doheny Foundation
707 Wilshire Blvd., Ste. 4960
Los Angeles, CA 90017-9843
(213) 488-1122
FAX: (213) 488-1544; E-mail:
shirley@dohenyfoundation.org,
peggy@dohenyfoundation.org; URL:
http://www.dohenyfoundation.org
Limitations: Giving primarily in the Los
Angeles, CA, area.
Publishes an annual or periodic report.

The William H. Donner Foundation, Inc.
500 5th Ave., Ste. 1230
New York, NY 10110-0180
FAX: (212) 302-8734; E-mail:
whdf@donner.org; URL: http://
www.donner.org

Dorot Foundation
439 Benefit St.
Providence, RI 02903
(401) 351-8866
E-mail: info@dorot.org; URL: http://
www.dorot.org/
Limitations: Giving primarily in the U.S.; some
giving also in Israel.

Dow Chemical Company Foundation
2030 Dow Ctr.
Midland, MI 48674
(517) 636-6891
URL: http://www.dow.com/about/corp/social/
social.htm

The Herbert H. and Grace A. Dow Foundation
1018 W. Main St.
Midland, MI 48640-4292
(989) 631-3699
FAX: (989) 631-0675; E-mail:
info@hhdowfdn.org
Limitations: Giving limited to MI, with
emphasis on Midland County.
Publishes an annual or periodic report.

Joseph Drown Foundation
1999 Ave. of the Stars, Ste. 1930
Los Angeles, CA 90067
(310) 277-4488
URL: http://www.jdrown.org
Limitations: Giving primarily in CA.

Doris Duke Charitable Foundation
650 5th Ave., 19th Fl.
New York, NY 10019
(212) 974-7000
Limitations: Giving on a national basis.

The Duke Endowment
100 N. Tryon St., Ste. 3500
Charlotte, NC 28202-4012
(704) 376-0291
FAX: (704) 376-9336 (Charlotte); Rural Church
Div. address: 3329 Chapel Hill Blvd., P.O.
Box 51307, Durham, NC 27717-1307,
tel.: (919) 489-3359; E-mail:
droberson@tde.org; URL: http://
www.dukeendowment.org
Limitations: Giving limited to NC and SC.
Publishes an annual or periodic report.

Duke Energy Foundation
526 S. Church St., M.C. ECO6G
P.O. Box 1009
Charlotte, NC 28201-1009
(704) 373-7930
FAX: (704) 382-7600; URL: http://
www.duke-energy.com/internet/
stewardship/community/foundation.asp
Limitations: Giving primarily in the company's
headquarters and service areas in NC and
SC.

Durham Foundation
c/o Charles W. Durham
8401 W. Dodge Rd., Ste. 100
Omaha, NE 68114
(402) 390-2450
Limitations: Giving primarily in Omaha, NE.

Dyson Foundation
25 Halcyon Rd.
Millbrook, NY 12545-9611
(845) 677-0644
FAX: (845) 677-0650; E-mail: info@dyson.org;
URL: http://www.dysonfoundation.org
Limitations: Giving primarily in Dutchess
County, NY, and organizations providing
services in Dutchess County, NY.
National and other grants on a solicited
basis.
Publishes an annual or periodic report.

Earhart Foundation
2200 Green Rd., Ste. H
Ann Arbor, MI 48105
Publishes an annual or periodic report.

Eastman Kodak Charitable Trust
c/o The Chase Manhattan Bank
P.O. Box 1412
Rochester, NY 14603
(716) 724-2434
Limitations: Giving primarily in high
   employment locations, including Windsor,
   CO, Rochester, NY, and Kingsport, TN;
   giving nationally only for higher
   education.

The Eberly Foundation
2 W. Main St., Ste. 600
Uniontown, PA 15401-3448
(724) 438-3789
FAX: (724) 438-3856
Limitations: Giving primarily in OK, PA, and
   WV.
Publishes an annual or periodic report.

**The George S. and Dolores Dore Eccles
   Foundation**
Deseret Bldg.
79 S. Main St., 12th Fl.
Salt Lake City, UT 84111
(801) 246-5336
Limitations: Giving primarily in the
   intermountain area, particularly UT.

Eden Hall Foundation
600 Grant St., Ste. 3232
Pittsburgh, PA 15219
(412) 642-6697
Limitations: Giving limited to western PA.

The Educational Foundation of America
35 Church Ln.
Westport, CT 06880-3515
(203) 226-6498
E-mail: efa@efaw.org; URL: http://
   www.efaw.org
Limitations: Giving limited to the U.S.
Publishes an annual or periodic report.

El Pomar Foundation
10 Lake Cir.
Colorado Springs, CO 80906
(719) 633-7733
Limitations: Giving limited to CO.
Publishes an annual or periodic report.

Emerson Charitable Trust
c/o Emerson Electric Co.
8000 W. Florissant Ave., P.O. Box 4100
St. Louis, MO 63136
(314) 553-2000
FAX: (314) 553-1605
Limitations: Giving primarily in areas of
   company operations.

Fred L. Emerson Foundation, Inc.
P.O. Box 276
Auburn, NY 13021
(315) 253-9621
Limitations: Giving primarily in Auburn,
   Cayuga County, and upstate NY.

Energy Foundation
Presido Bldg. 1012, 2nd Fl.
Torney Ave., P.O. Box 29905
San Francisco, CA 94129-0905
(415) 561-6700
FAX: (415) 561-6709; E-mail:
   energyfund@ef.org; URL: http://
   www.energyfoundation.org
Limitations: Giving limited to the U.S. and
   China.
Publishes an annual or periodic report.

The Charles Engelhard Foundation
645 5th Ave., Ste. 712
New York, NY 10022
(212) 935-2433
Limitations: Giving on a national basis.

English-Bonter-Mitchell Foundation
900 Fort Wayne National Bank Bldg.
Fort Wayne, IN 46802
Limitations: Giving primarily in Fort Wayne,
   IN.

ExxonMobil Foundation
5959 Las Colinas Blvd.
Irving, TX 75039-2298
(972) 444-1104
FAX: (972) 444-1405; URL: http://
   www.exxonmobil.com/contributions/
   index.html
Publishes an annual or periodic report.

The Sherman Fairchild Foundation, Inc.
5454 Wisconsin Ave., Ste. 1205
Chevy Chase, MD 20815-6901
(301) 913-5990

Fannie Mae Foundation
N. Tower, Ste. 1
4000 Wisconsin Ave., N.W.
Washington, DC 20016-2800
(202) 274-8057
FAX: (202) 274-8100; URL: http://
   www.fanniemaefoundation.org
Limitations: Giving within the United States
   only.
Publishes an annual or periodic report.

Fidelity Foundation
82 Devonshire St., S3
Boston, MA 02109-3614
(617) 563-6806
Limitations: Giving primarily in KY, MA, NH,
   NY, OH, RI, TX, UT, Toronto, Canada,
   and in other communities where FMR
   employees live and work.

Leland Fikes Foundation, Inc.
3050 Lincoln Plz.
500 N. Akard
Dallas, TX 75201
(214) 754-0144
Limitations: Giving primarily in the Dallas,
   TX, area.

The First Union Foundation
c/o First Union Corp.
301 S. College St.
Charlotte, NC 28288-0143
(704) 374-4689
FAX: (704) 374-2484; Local bank addresses:
   CT, NJ, NY: Fran Durst, 370 Scotch Rd.,

Trenton, NJ 08628, tel.: (609) 530-7357,
   FL: Debbie Clark, P.O. Box 4425,
   Jacksonville, FL 32231, tel.: (904)
   361-3147, GA: Gwen Adams, 999
   Peachtree St., N.E., Atlanta, GA 30309,
   tel.: (404) 827-7566, PA, DE: Bronal
   Harris, P.O. Box 7618, Philadelphia, PA
   19101, tel.: (215) 973-4181, TN: Chris
   McComish, 150 N. 4th Ave., 23rd Fl.,
   Nashville, TN 37219, tel.: (615)
   251-0746, DC, MD, VA: Carol Jarratt, 7
   N. 8th St., Richmond, VA 23219, tel.:
   (804) 771-7847, First Union Securities,
   Inc.: Robin Schilling, 10750 Wheat 1st
   Dr., Glen Allen, VA 23060, tel.: (804)
   965-2415
Limitations: Giving limited to CT, Washington,
   DC, DE, FL, GA, MD, NC, NJ, NY, PA,
   SC, TN, and VA.

Firstar Foundation, Inc.
c/o Firstar Bank, N.A.
P.O. Box 1118, Trust Tax ML CN-WN-06TX
Cincinnati, OH 45201
(513) 632-4426
Application address: c/o US Bank Pl., ML
   MPFP2714, 601 2nd Ave. Minneapolis,
   MN 55402-4302
Limitations: Giving primarily in the areas
   where Firstar Bank does business.
Publishes an annual or periodic report.

FirstEnergy Foundation
76 S. Main St.
Akron, OH 44308
(330) 761-4246
URL: http://www.firstenergycorp.com/
   communitysupport
Limitations: Giving limited to areas served in
   OH and western PA.

Fleck Foundation
2525 N. 124th St., Ste. 200
Brookfield, WI 53005
(262) 860-1680
FAX: (262) 860-1683
Limitations: Giving primarily in Milwaukee,
   WI.
Publishes an annual or periodic report.

FleetBoston Financial Foundation
100 Federal St., MA DE 10028E
Boston, MA 02110
(617) 434-2804
FAX: (617) 434-6072; URL: http://
   www.fleet.com/
   about_inthecommunity_fleetbostonfinancia
   lfoundation.asp
Limitations: Giving limited to states where the
   company subsidiaries do business: CT,
   MA, ME, NH, NJ, NY, PA, and RI.

The Fluor Foundation
1 Enterprise Dr.
Aliso Viejo, CA 92656-2606
(949) 349-6797
FAX: (949) 349-7175; E-mail:
   community.relations@fluor.com; URL:
   http://www.fluor.com/community/
   involvement.asp
Limitations: Giving primarily in areas where
   the corporation has permanent offices,
   with some emphasis on Orange County,

CA, Greenville, SC, and Fort Bend and Harris County, TX.

The Fondren Foundation
7 TCT 37
P.O. Box 2558
Houston, TX 77252-8037
(713) 216-4513
Limitations: Giving primarily in TX, with emphasis on Houston.

The Ford Family Foundation
1600 N.W. Stewart Parkway
Roseburg, OR 97470
(541) 957-5574
FAX: (541) 957-5720; URL: http://www.tfff.org/
Limitations: Giving primarily in rural OR, with special interest in Douglas and Coos counties and in Siskiyou County, CA.
Publishes an annual or periodic report.

The Ford Foundation
320 E. 43rd St.
New York, NY 10017
(212) 573-5000
E-mail: office-secretary@fordfoundation.org; URL: http://www.fordfound.org
Limitations: Giving on an international basis, including the U.S., Eastern Europe, Africa and the Middle East, Asia, Russia, Latin America and the Caribbean.
Publishes an annual or periodic report.

Ford Motor Company Fund
The American Rd.
P.O. Box 1899
Dearborn, MI 48121-1899
(313) 248-4745
Limitations: Giving primarily in areas where plants and offices are located and members of the community are employed, with special emphasis on Detroit, MI.
Publishes an annual or periodic report.

Foundation for Child Development
145 E. 32nd St., 14th Fl.
New York, NY 10016-6055
(212) 213-8337
FAX: (212) 213-5897; E-mail: claudia@ffcd.org; URL: http://www.ffcd.org
Limitations: Giving limited to research and policy grants related to foundation focus and restricted to the U.S.; program development grants in New York City only.
Publishes an annual or periodic report.

Foundation for Deep Ecology
Bldg. 1062 Fort Cronkhite
Sausalito, CA 94965
(415) 229-9339
FAX: (415) 229-9340; E-mail: info@deepecology.org; URL: http://www.deepecology.org
Limitations: Giving on a national and international basis.

Foundation For The Carolinas
P.O. Box 34769
Charlotte, NC 28234-4769
(704) 376-9541
FAX: (704) 376-1243; URL: http://www.fftc.org
Limitations: Giving primarily to organizations serving the citizens of NC and SC, with emphasis on the greater Charlotte, NC region.
Publishes an annual or periodic report.

France-Merrick Foundation
The Exchange
1122 Kenilworth Dr., Ste. 118
Baltimore, MD 21204
(410) 832-5700
FAX: (410) 832-5704
Limitations: Giving primarily in the metropolitan Baltimore, MD, area.

Freddie Mac Foundation
M.S. A-40
8250 Jones Branch Dr.
McLean, VA 22102
(703) 918-8888
FAX: (703) 918-8895; URL: http://www.freddiemacfoundation.org
Limitations: Giving primarily in the metropolitan Washington, DC, area, as well as statewide initiatives in MD and VA. Funding also for groups providing services on a national scope and to organizations located in areas of the corporation's regional offices.
Publishes an annual or periodic report.

Freedom Forum, Inc.
1101 Wilson Blvd.
Arlington, VA 22209
FAX: (703) 284-3770; E-mail: news@freedomforum.org; URL: http://www.freedomforum.org
Limitations: Giving on a national and international basis.
Publishes an annual or periodic report.

The Freeman Foundation
c/o J.P. Morgan & Co. Incorporated
60 Wall St., 36th Fl.
New York, NY 10260-0060
(212) 648-9673
Limitations: Giving primarily in VT for environment and special interest grants; Asian studies grants awarded nationally.
Publishes an annual or periodic report.

The Fremont Area Community Foundation
4424 W. 48th St.
P.O. Box B
Fremont, MI 49412
(231) 924-5350
FAX: (231) 924-5391; E-mail: gzerlaut@tfaf.org; URL: http://www.tfaf.org
Limitations: Giving primarily in Newaygo County, MI.
Publishes an annual or periodic report.

Frey Foundation
40 Pearl St., N.W., Ste. 1100
Grand Rapids, MI 49503-3028
(616) 451-0303
FAX: (616) 451-8481; E-mail: rohwer@freyfdn.org (general), or rohwer@freyfdn.org (M. Rohwer); URL: http://www.freyfdn.org
Limitations: Giving primarily in Emmet, Charlevoix, and Kent counties, MI.
Publishes an annual or periodic report.

The Frist Foundation
3319 West End Ave., Ste. 900
Nashville, TN 37203-1076
(615) 292-3868
FAX: (615) 292-5843; E-mail: info@fristfoundation.org; URL: http://www.fristfoundation.org
Limitations: Giving primarily in Nashville, TN.
Publishes an annual or periodic report.

Charles A. Frueauff Foundation, Inc.
3 Financial Ctr.
900 S. Shackleford, Ste. 300
Little Rock, AR 72211
(501) 219-1410
FAX: (501) 219-1416; URL: http://www.frueafffoundation.com
Limitations: Giving limited to the U.S. with emphasis on east of the Rockies, the South, and Northeast.

Lloyd A. Fry Foundation
120 S. LaSalle St., Ste. 1950
Chicago, IL 60603
(312) 580-0310
FAX: (312) 580-0980; E-mail: jdarrow@fryfoundation.org; URL: http://www.fryfoundation.org
Limitations: Giving primarily in Chicago, IL.
Publishes an annual or periodic report.

George F. and Sybil H. Fuller Foundation
730 Main St.
1-B Central St.
Boylston, MA 01505
(508) 869-6723
Limitations: Giving primarily in MA, with emphasis on Worcester.

The Fund for New Jersey
94 Church St., Ste. 303
New Brunswick, NJ 08901
(732) 220-8656
FAX: (732) 220-8654
Limitations: Giving primarily in NJ or to regional programs that benefit NJ.
Publishes an annual or periodic report.

Gannett Foundation, Inc.
1100 Wilson Blvd., 30th Fl.
Arlington, VA 22234
(703) 284-6069
FAX: (703) 558-3819; E-mail: isimpson@gcil.gannett.com; URL: http://www.gannettfoundation.org/
Limitations: Giving limited to organizations in Gannett-served communities, including the U.S., Canada, and the U.S. territory of Guam.
Publishes an annual or periodic report.

John Jewett & H. Chandler Garland Foundation
P.O. Box 550
Pasadena, CA 91102-0550
Limitations: Giving primarily in CA, with
    emphasis on southern CA.

Gates Family Foundation
3200 Cherry Creek S. Dr., Ste. 630
Denver, CO 80209-3247
(303) 722-1881
FAX: (303) 698-9031; E-mail:
    info@GatesFamilyFdn.org; URL: http://
    www.gatesFamilyFdn.org
Limitations: Giving limited to CO, with
    emphasis on the Denver area, except for
    foundation-initiated grants.
Publishes an annual or periodic report.

Bill & Melinda Gates Foundation
P.O. Box 23350
Seattle, WA 98102
(206) 709-3100
FAX: (206) 709-3180; E-mail:
    info@gatesfoundation.org; URL: http://
    www.gatesfoundation.org
Limitations: Giving on a national and
    international basis to support initiatives in
    health and learning; the foundation also
    supports community giving in the Pacific
    Northwest.
Publishes an annual or periodic report.

GE Fund
3135 Easton Tpke.
Fairfield, CT 06431
(203) 373-3216
FAX: (203) 373-3029; E-mail:
    gefund@corporate.ge.com; URL: http://
    www.gefund.org
Limitations: Giving on a national and
    international basis; grants mainly to areas
    where the company has a significant
    presence.
Publishes an annual or periodic report.

Gebbie Foundation, Inc.
Hotel Jamestown Bldg., Rm. 308
110 W. 3rd St.
Jamestown, NY 14701
(716) 487-1062
FAX: (716) 484-6401; E-mail:
    gebfnd@netsync.net
Limitations: Giving primarily in Chautauqua
    County and, secondarily, in neighboring
    areas of western NY.

The David Geffen Foundation
10 Universal City Plz., 27th Fl.
Universal City, CA 91608
(818) 733-6333
FAX: (818) 733-6129
Limitations: Giving primarily in Los Angeles,
    CA, and New York, NY.

General Mills Foundation
P.O. Box 1113
Minneapolis, MN 55440
(612) 540-7891
FAX: (612) 540-4114; E-mail:
    mills999@mail.genmills.com; URL: http://

www.generalmills.com/explore/
    community/foundation/
Limitations: Giving primarily in areas of major
    parent company operations.
Publishes an annual or periodic report.

General Service Foundation
557 N. Mill St., Ste. 201
Aspen, CO 81611-1513
(970) 920-6834
FAX: (970) 920-4578; E-mail:
    info@generalservice.org; URL: http://
    www.generalservice.org
Limitations: Giving limited to the U.S.,
    Mexico, Central America and the
    Caribbean.

The Ann and Gordon Getty Foundation
1 Embarcadero Ctr., Ste. 1050
San Francisco, CA 94111-3600
Limitations: Giving primarily in CA, with
    emphasis on the San Francisco Bay Area.

J. Paul Getty Trust
1200 Getty Ctr. Dr., Ste. 800
Los Angeles, CA 90049-1685
(310) 440-7320
FAX: (310) 440-7703; URL: http://
    www.getty.edu
Limitations: Giving on an international basis.
Publishes an annual or periodic report.

The Gheens Foundation, Inc.
1 Riverfront Plz., Ste. 705
Louisville, KY 40202
(502) 584-4650
FAX: (502) 584-4652; E-mail: lindahw@aye.net
Limitations: Giving primarily in KY, with
    emphasis on Louisville.

Gilder Foundation, Inc.
c/o Anchin, Block & Anchin, LLP
1375 Broadway
New York, NY 10018
(212) 765-2500
Limitations: Giving primarily in NY.

The Gill Foundation
2215 Market St., Ste. 205
Denver, CO 80205
(303) 292-4455
FAX: (303) 292-2155; Additional address: 8 S.
    Nevada Ave., Ste. 303, Colorado Springs,
    CO 80903, tel.: (719) 473-4455, FAX:
    (719) 473-2254; E-mail:
    info@gillfoundation.org; URL: http://
    www.gillfoundation.org
Limitations: Giving primarily in
    non-metropolitan areas with populations
    of 1.5 million or less.
Publishes an annual or periodic report.

Irving S. Gilmore Foundation
136 E. Michigan Ave., Ste. 615
Kalamazoo, MI 49007
(616) 342-6411
URL: http://www.isgilmorefoundation.org
Limitations: Giving primarily in the greater
    Kalamazoo, MI, area.
Publishes an annual or periodic report.

The Goergen Foundation, Inc.
c/o Thomas E. Finn
35 Mason St.
Greenwich, CT 06830-5420
Limitations: Giving primarily in CT, NY, and
    PA.

Richard & Rhoda Goldman Fund
1 Lombard St., Ste. 303
San Francisco, CA 94111
(415) 788-1090
FAX: (415) 788-7890; E-mail:
    info@goldmanfund.org; URL: http://
    www.goldmanfund.org
Limitations: Giving primarily in the San
    Francisco Bay Area, CA.
Publishes an annual or periodic report.

Morris Goldseker Foundation of Maryland, Inc.
The Latrobe Bldg.
2 E. Read St., 9th Fl.
Baltimore, MD 21202
(410) 837-5100
FAX: (410) 837-4701; E-mail:
    mgoldseker@aol.com; URL: http://
    www.goldsekerfoundation.org
Limitations: Giving limited to the Baltimore,
    MD, area.
Publishes an annual or periodic report.

Horace W. Goldsmith Foundation
375 Park Ave., Ste. 1602
New York, NY 10152
(212) 319-8700
Limitations: Giving primarily in AZ, MA, and
    New York, NY.

The Gottesman Fund
1818 N St., N.W., Ste. 700
Washington, DC 20036
(202) 785-2727
Limitations: Giving primarily in NY.

The Florence Gould Foundation
c/o Cahill Gordon and Reindel
80 Pine St., Ste. 1701
New York, NY 10005-1702
(212) 701-3400
Limitations: Giving primarily in the U.S. and
    France.

Grable Foundation
650 Smithfield St., Ste. 240
Pittsburgh, PA 15222
(412) 471-4550
FAX: (412) 471-2267; E-mail:
    grable@grablefdn.org; URL: http://
    www.grablefdn.org/
Limitations: Giving primarily in southwestern
    PA.
Publishes an annual or periodic report.

Philip L. Graham Fund
c/o The Washington Post Co.
1150 15th St., N.W.
Washington, DC 20071
(202) 334-6640
FAX: (202) 334-4498; E-mail:
    plgfund@washpost.com
Limitations: Giving primarily in the
    metropolitan Washington, DC, area.

Grand Rapids Community Foundation
209-C Waters Bldg.
161 Ottawa Ave. N.W.
Grand Rapids, MI 49503-2757
(616) 454-1751
FAX: (616) 454-6455; E-mail:
    grfound@grfoundation.org; URL: http://
    www.grfoundation.org
Limitations: Giving limited to Grand Rapids,
    MI, and surrounding communities.
Publishes an annual or periodic report.

William T. Grant Foundation
570 Lexington Ave., 18th Fl.
New York, NY 10022-6837
(212) 752-0071
E-mail: info@wtgrantfdn.org; URL: http://
    www.wtgrantfoundation.org/
Limitations: Giving internationally for research
    grants and faculty scholars; giving limited
    to NY, NJ, and CT for youth service
    grants.
Publishes an annual or periodic report.

William Caspar Graustein Memorial Fund
One Hamden Ctr.
2319 Whitney Ave., Ste. 2B
Hamden, CT 06518
(203) 230-3330
FAX: (203) 230-3331; E-mail:
    GMFmail@wcgmf.org; URL: http://
    www.wcgmf.org
Limitations: Giving primarily in CT.
Publishes an annual or periodic report.

The Green Fund, Inc.
14 E. 60th St., Ste. 702
New York, NY 10022
(212) 755-2445
Limitations: Giving primarily in the
    metropolitan New York, NY, area.

The Greenwall Foundation
2 Park Ave., 24th Fl.
New York, NY 10016-5603
(212) 679-7266
FAX: (212) 679-7269; URL: http://
    www.greenwall.org
Limitations: Giving primarily in New York,
    NY, for arts and humanities; giving
    nationally for bioethics.
Publishes an annual or periodic report.

The Grousbeck Family Foundation
c/o Stanford University
Graduate School of Business, Rm. L-336
Stanford, CA 94305-5015

Henry L. Guenther Foundation
2029 Century Park E., Ste. 4392
Los Angeles, CA 90067
(310) 785-0658
Limitations: Giving primarily in Los Angeles,
    CA.

The Agnes Gund Foundation
c/o Agnes Gund
517 Broadway, 3rd Fl.
East Liverpool, OH 43920
(330) 385-3400
Limitations: Giving primarily in New York, NY.

The George Gund Foundation
1845 Guildhall Bldg.
45 Prospect Ave., W.
Cleveland, OH 44115-1018
(216) 241-3114
FAX: (216) 241-6560; URL: http://
    www.gundfdn.org
Limitations: Giving primarily in northeastern
    OH and the greater Cleveland, OH, area.
Publishes an annual or periodic report.

The H & R Block Foundation
1 Main Plz.
4435 Main St., Ste. 500
Kansas City, MO 64111
(816) 932-8324
FAX: (816) 753-1585; URL: http://
    www.hrblock.com/about/community
Limitations: Giving primarily in the
    metropolitan bi-state Kansas City, MO,
    area.
Publishes an annual or periodic report.

Walter and Elise Haas Fund
1 Lombard St., Ste. 305
San Francisco, CA 94111
(415) 398-4474
URL: http://www.haassr.org
Limitations: Giving primarily in San Francisco,
    CA; activities of unusual merit in the
    counties of Alameda, Marin and San
    Mateo, CA, are also supported.
    Professional ethics grants are awarded
    nationally.
Publishes an annual or periodic report.

Evelyn and Walter Haas, Jr. Fund
1 Market, Landmark, Ste. 400
San Francisco, CA 94105
(415) 856-1400
FAX: (415) 856-1500; E-mail:
    guidelines@haasjr.org; URL: http://
    www.haasjr.org
Limitations: Giving primarily in San Francisco
    and Alameda counties, CA.
Publishes an annual or periodic report.

Hagedorn Fund
c/o J.P. Morgan Chase
60 Wall St., 36th Fl.
New York, NY 10260
(212) 648-9673
Limitations: Giving primarily in New York, NY.

Hall Family Foundation
c/o Charitable & Crown Investment-323
P.O. Box 419580
Kansas City, MO 64141-6580
(816) 274-8516
Limitations: Giving limited to Kansas City, MO.
Publishes an annual or periodic report.

Hallmark Corporate Foundation
P.O. Box 419580, M.D. 323
Kansas City, MO 64141-6580
(816) 545-6906
Limitations: Giving limited to the Kansas City,
    MO, area, and communities where major
    Hallmark facilities are located, including
    Enfield, CT, Columbus, GA, Metamora,
    IL, Lawrence, Leavenworth, and Topeka,
    KS, Liberty, MO, and Center, TX.

The Ewing Halsell Foundation
711 Navarro St., Ste. 537
San Antonio, TX 78205
(210) 223-2640
Limitations: Giving limited to TX, with
    emphasis on southwestern TX,
    particularly San Antonio.

Harden Foundation
P.O. Box 779
Salinas, CA 93902-0779
(831) 442-3005
FAX: (831) 443-1429
Limitations: Giving limited to Monterey
    County, with emphasis on the Salinas
    Valley, CA, area.
Publishes an annual or periodic report.

John H. and Wilhelmina D. Harland Charitable
    Foundation, Inc.
2 Piedmont Ctr., Ste. 106
Atlanta, GA 30305
(404) 264-9912
E-mail: harland@randomc.com
Limitations: Giving limited to GA, with
    emphasis on metropolitan Atlanta.
Publishes an annual or periodic report.

Gladys and Roland Harriman Foundation
c/o Brown Brothers Harriman Trust Co.
63 Wall St., Ste. 3101
New York, NY 10005
(212) 493-8182

The John A. Hartford Foundation, Inc.
55 E. 59th St., 16th Fl.
New York, NY 10022
(212) 832-7788
FAX: (212) 593-4913; E-mail:
    mail@jhartfound.org; URL: http://
    www.jhartfound.org
Limitations: Giving primarily on a national
    basis.
Publishes an annual or periodic report.

Hartford Foundation for Public Giving
85 Gillett St.
Hartford, CT 06105
(860) 548-1888
FAX: (860) 524-8346; E-mail: chall@hfpg.org;
    URL: http://www.hfpg.org
Limitations: Giving limited to the greater
    Hartford, CT, area.
Publishes an annual or periodic report.

Charles Hayden Foundation
900 3rd Ave., Ste. 1203
New York, NY 10022
(212) 319-6450
URL: http://fdncenter.org/grantmaker/hayden/
Limitations: Giving limited to the metropolitan
    Boston, MA, and the metropolitan New
    York, NY (including northern NJ), areas.
Publishes an annual or periodic report.

The John Randolph Haynes and Dora Haynes
   Foundation
888 W. 6th St., Ste. 1150
Los Angeles, CA 90017-2737
(213) 623-9151
FAX: (213) 623-3951; E-mail:
   info@haynesfoundation.org; URL: http://
   www.haynesfoundation.org
Limitations: Giving limited to the greater Los
   Angeles, CA, area.

The Healthcare Foundation of New Jersey
75 Livingston Ave.
Roseland, NJ 07068
(973) 535-8200
FAX: (973) 535-8393; E-mail: info@hfnj.org;
   URL: http://www.hfnj.org/
Limitations: Giving primarily in NJ, with
   emphasis on Newark and Essex, Morris,
   and Union counties. Limited giving for
   regional and national programs.
Publishes an annual or periodic report.

The Hearst Foundation, Inc.
888 7th Ave., 45th Fl.
New York, NY 10106-0057
(212) 586-5404
*Address for applicants from west of the
   Mississippi River:* c/o Thomas Eastham,
   V.P. and Western Dir., 90 New
   Montgomery St., Ste. 1212, San
   Francisco, CA 94105; tel.: (415)
   543-0400; URL: http://www.hearstfdn.org/
Limitations: Giving limited to the U.S. and its
   territories.

William Randolph Hearst Foundation
888 7th Ave., 45th Fl.
New York, NY 10106-0057
(212) 586-5404
*Address for applicants from west of the
   Mississippi River:* c/o Thomas Eastham,
   V.P. and Western Dir., 90 New
   Montgomery St., Ste. 1212, San
   Francisco, CA 94105; tel.: (415)
   543-0400; URL: http://www.hearstfdn.org/
Limitations: Giving limited to the U.S. and its
   territories.

Hedco Foundation
c/o Fitzgerald, Abbott & Beardsley
1221 Broadway, 21st Fl.
Oakland, CA 94612-1837
(510) 451-3300
Application address: P.O. Box 1273, Lafayette,
   CA 94549; Tel: (925) 283-3442; FAX:
   (925) 283-1611
Limitations: Giving primarily in CA.

Howard Heinz Endowment
30 CNG Tower
625 Liberty Ave.
Pittsburgh, PA 15222-3115
(412) 281-5777
E-mail: info@heinz.org; URL: http://
   www.heinz.org
Limitations: Giving limited to activities which
   directly benefit the citizens of PA, with
   emphasis on Pittsburgh and western PA.
Publishes an annual or periodic report.

Vira I. Heinz Endowment
30 CNG Tower
625 Liberty Ave.
Pittsburgh, PA 15222-3115
(412) 281-5777
E-mail: info@heinz.org; URL: http://
   www.heinz.org
Limitations: Giving primarily directed to
   Pittsburgh and western PA, although in
   certain cases support may be considered
   on a national or international basis.
Publishes an annual or periodic report.

Heinz Family Foundation
3200 CNG Twr.
625 Liberty Ave.
Pittsburgh, PA 15222
(412) 497-5775
FAX: (412) 497-5790

Drue Heinz Trust
FDR Station
P.O. Box 68
New York, NY 10150
(412) 281-5737
Limitations: Giving primarily in NY and PA.

The Helmerich Foundation
1579 E. 21st St.
Tulsa, OK 74114
Limitations: Giving limited to the Tulsa, OK,
   area.

The F. B. Heron Foundation
c/o Rockefeller & Co., Inc.
100 Broadway, 17th Fl.
New York, NY 10005
(212) 404-1800
FAX: (212) 404-1805; URL: http://fdncenter.org/
   grantmaker/fbheron/
Limitations: Giving on a national basis in both
   urban and rural areas.
Publishes an annual or periodic report.

Herrick Foundation
840 W. Long Lake Rd., Ste. 200
Troy, MI 48098
(248) 267-3321
FAX: (248) 879-2001
Limitations: Giving primarily in MI; support
   also in Washington, DC, IN, MS, NY, OH,
   TN, and WI.

The William and Flora Hewlett Foundation
525 Middlefield Rd., Ste. 200
Menlo Park, CA 94025
(650) 329-1070
FAX: (650) 329-9342; URL: http://
   www.hewlett.org
Limitations: Giving limited to the San
   Francisco Bay Area, CA, for family and
   community development program;
   performing arts primarily limited to the
   Bay Area; environment programs limited
   to North American West.
Publishes an annual or periodic report.

The Highland Street Connection
P.O. Box 5209
Framingham, MA 01701
Limitations: Giving primarily in MA.

Hillcrest Foundation
c/o Bank of America
P.O. Box 830241
Dallas, TX 75283-0241
(214) 209-1965
Limitations: Giving limited to TX, with
   emphasis on Dallas County.

The Hillman Foundation, Inc.
2000 Grant Bldg.
Pittsburgh, PA 15219
(412) 338-3466
FAX: (412): 338-3463; E-mail:
   foundation@hillmanfo.com
Limitations: Giving primarily in Pittsburgh and
   southwestern PA.
Publishes an annual or periodic report.

Hobby Family Foundation
2131 San Felipe
Houston, TX 77019-5620
(713) 521-1163
Limitations: Giving primarily in TX.

Hoblitzelle Foundation
5956 Sherry Ln., Ste. 901
Dallas, TX 75225-6522
(214) 373-0462
URL: http://home.att.net/~hoblitzelle/
Limitations: Giving limited to TX, primarily
   Dallas.
Publishes an annual or periodic report.

William M. & Nina B. Hollis Foundation, Inc.
P.O. Box 8847
Lakeland, FL 33806-8847
(863) 648-4171
Limitations: Giving primarily in Lakeland, FL.

Honeywell Foundation
P.O. Box 524
Minneapolis, MN 55440-0524
(612) 951-2368
FAX: (612) 951-0433; URL: http://
   www.honeywell.com/merger/
   page_3_2.html
Limitations: Giving limited to cities where the
   company has major facilities, with
   emphasis on Minneapolis, MN; support
   also in AZ, FL, IL, and NM.

Honeywell International Foundation
101 Columbia Rd.
Morristown, NJ 07962-2245
(973) 455-5876
Application address: P.O. Box 2245,
   Morristown, NJ 07962-2245; FAX: (973)
   455-3632
Limitations: Giving primarily in areas of
   company operations.

The Hoover Foundation
101 E. Maple St.
North Canton, OH 44720
(330) 499-9200
Limitations: Giving primarily in Stark County,
   OH.

Houston Endowment Inc.
600 Travis, Ste. 6400
Houston, TX 77002-3007
(713) 238-8100
FAX: (713) 238-8101; URL: http://
www.houstonendowment.org
Limitations: Giving primarily in Houston, TX;
no grants outside the continental U.S.
Publishes an annual or periodic report.

HRK Foundation
345 St. Peter St., Ste. 1200
St. Paul, MN 55102
(651) 293-9001
FAX: (651) 298-0551; E-mail:
HRKFoundation@HRKGroup.com
Limitations: Giving primarily in MN, with
emphasis on the metropolitan Twin Cities
and St. Croix Valley areas, and in Ashland
and Bayfield counties, WI.

The Hubbard Foundation
3415 University Ave., S.E.
St. Paul, MN 55114
(651) 642-4305
Limitations: Giving primarily in MN.

Hudson-Webber Foundation
333 W. Fort St., Ste. 1310
Detroit, MI 48226-3134
(313) 963-7777
Limitations: Giving primarily in the city of
Detroit, and the tri-county Wayne,
Oakland, and Macomb area of
southeastern MI.

The Humana Foundation, Inc.
The Humana Bldg., 500 W. Main St.
P.O. Box 1438
Louisville, KY 40201
(502) 580-3041
URL: http://www.humanafoundation.org

Jaquelin Hume Foundation
600 Montgomery St., Ste. 2800
San Francisco, CA 94111
(415) 705-5115
Limitations: Giving primarily in the San
Francisco Bay Area, CA, and to
organizations with a national impact.

The Jon and Karen Huntsman Foundation
c/o Huntsman, Inc.
500 Huntsman Way
Salt Lake City, UT 84108-1235
Limitations: Giving on a national basis.

The Hyams Foundation, Inc.
175 Federal St., 14th Fl.
Boston, MA 02110
(617) 426-5600
FAX: (617) 426-5696; E-mail:
info@hyamsfoundation.org
Limitations: Giving primarily in Boston and
Chelsea, MA.
Publishes an annual or periodic report.

The Hyde and Watson Foundation
437 Southern Blvd.
Chatham, NJ 07928
(973) 966-6024
FAX: (973) 966-6404; E-mail:
Hcorbin@HydeandWatson.org; URL:

http://fdncenter.org/grantmaker/
hydeandwatson/
Limitations: Giving includes the metropolitan
New York, NY, region, and primarily
Essex, Union and Morris counties in NJ.
No giving outside the U.S.
Publishes an annual or periodic report.

Illinois Tool Works Foundation
3600 W. Lake Ave.
Glenview, IL 60025-5811
(847) 724-7500
FAX: (847) 657-4505; E-mail:
mmallahan@itw.com
Limitations: Giving primarily in areas of
company operations, with emphasis on
Chicago, IL.

Independence Foundation
200 S. Broad St., Ste. 1101
Philadelphia, PA 19102
(215) 985-4009
FAX: (215) 985-3989
Limitations: Giving primarily in Philadelphia,
PA, and Bucks, Chester, Delaware, and
Montgomery counties.
Publishes an annual or periodic report.

The Institute for Aegean Prehistory
c/o The Millburn Corp.
1270 Ave. of the Americas
New York, NY 10020
E-mail: all@styx.ios.com
Limitations: Giving on a national and
international basis, with emphasis on
Greece.

Intel Foundation
c/o Prog. Off.
5200 N.E. Elam Young Pkwy., AG6-601
Hillsboro, OR 97124-6497
(503) 456-1515
FAX: (503) 456-1539; URL: http://
www.intel.com/education/grants/index.htm
Limitations: Giving primarily in major
operating areas in Phoenix, AZ, Santa
Clara and Folsom, CA, Colorado Springs,
CO, Albuquerque, NM, Hudson, MA,
Portland, OR, Fort Worth, TX, Provo, UT,
and Tacoma, WA.
Publishes an annual or periodic report.

International Paper Company Foundation
2 Manhattanville Rd.
Purchase, NY 10577
(914) 397-1500
FAX: (914) 397-1505; URL: http://
www.internationalpaper.com/our_world/
outreach_frame.html
Limitations: Giving primarily in communities
where there are company plants and mills,
and in Memphis, TN.
Publishes an annual or periodic report.

Iowa West Foundation
500 W. Broadway, Ste. 100
Council Bluffs, IA 51503
(712) 325-3132
Limitations: Giving primarily in southwest IA
and the Council Bluffs, Omaha, NE, area.

The James Irvine Foundation
1 Market St.
Steuart Tower, Ste. 2500
San Francisco, CA 94105
(415) 777-2244
FAX: (415) 777-0869; Southern CA office: 777
S. Figueroa St., Ste. 740, Los Angeles,
CA 90017-5430; tel.: (213) 236-0552;
FAX: (213) 236-0537; URL: http://
www.irvine.org
Limitations: Giving limited to CA.
Publishes an annual or periodic report.

Janirve Foundation
1 N. Pack Sq., Ste. 416
Asheville, NC 28801
(828) 258-1877
FAX: (828) 258-1837
Limitations: Giving primarily in western NC.
Publishes an annual or periodic report.

The Jeld-Wen Foundation
P.O. Box 1329
Klamath Falls, OR 97601
(541) 882-3451
Limitations: Giving primarily in areas of
company operations in AZ, FL, IA, KY,
NC, OH, OR, SD, and WA for projects
serving communities in which company
plants exist; projects in adjacent
communities may be accepted if sufficient
numbers of employees reside in the area
and would benefit.

The Mary Hillman Jennings Foundation
625 Stanwix St., Ste. 2203
Pittsburgh, PA 15222
(412) 434-5606
FAX: (412) 434-5907
Limitations: Giving primarily in the Pittsburgh,
PA, area.

Jerome Foundation
125 Park Square Ct.
400 Sibley St.
St. Paul, MN 55101-1928
(651) 224-9431
Limitations: Giving limited to MN and New
York, NY.

Jesselson Foundation
450 Park Ave
New York, NY 10022
(212) 751-3666
Limitations: Giving on a national basis, with
emphasis on NY.

The JM Foundation
60 E. 42nd St., Rm. 1651
New York, NY 10165
(212) 687-7735
FAX: (212) 697-5495
Publishes an annual or periodic report.

Johnson Controls Foundation
5757 N. Green Bay Ave.
P.O. Box 591, M.S. X-46
Milwaukee, WI 53201
(414) 524-2296
URL: http://www.johnsoncontrols.com/
corpvalues/foundation.htm

Christian A. Johnson Endeavor Foundation
1060 Park Ave.
New York, NY 10128-1033
(212) 534-6620
FAX: (212) 410-5909
Limitations: Giving limited to the eastern U.S.

Helen K. and Arthur E. Johnson Foundation
1700 Broadway, Ste 1100
Denver, CO 80290-1718
(303) 861-4127
Limitations: Giving limited to CO.
Publishes an annual or periodic report.

The Robert Wood Johnson Foundation
Rte. 1 and College Rd. E.
P.O. Box 2316
Princeton, NJ 08543-2316
(609) 452-8701
E-mail: mail@rwjf.org; URL: http://
www.rwjf.org
Limitations: Giving limited to the U.S.
Publishes an annual or periodic report.

The James M. Johnston Trust for Charitable
and Educational Purposes
2 Wisconsin Cir., Ste. 600
Chevy Chase, MD 20815
(301) 907-0135
Limitations: Giving primarily in Washington,
DC, and NC.

The Fletcher Jones Foundation
1 Wilshire Bldg., Ste. 2920
624 S. Grand Ave.
Los Angeles, CA 90017-3335
FAX: (213) 426-6555
Limitations: Giving primarily in CA.
Publishes an annual or periodic report.

W. Alton Jones Foundation, Inc.
232 E. High St.
Charlottesville, VA 22902-5178
(804) 295-2134
FAX: (804) 295-1648; E-mail:
earth@wajones.org; URL: http://
www.wajones.org
Publishes an annual or periodic report.

Joukowsky Family Foundation
410 Park Ave., Ste. 1610
New York, NY 10022
E-mail: info@joukowsky.org; URL: http://
www.joukowsky.org
Limitations: Giving primarily in the
northeastern U.S.

The Joyce Foundation
3 First National Plz.
70 W. Madison St., Ste. 2750
Chicago, IL 60602
(312) 782-2464
FAX: (312) 782-4160; E-mail:
info@joycefdn.org; URL: http://
www.joycefdn.org
Limitations: Giving primarily in the Great
Lakes region, including IA, IL, IN, MI,
MN, OH, and WI; limited number of
environment grants made in Canada;
culture grants restricted to the
metropolitan Chicago, IL, area.
Publishes an annual or periodic report.

The Henry J. Kaiser Family Foundation
2400 Sand Hill Rd.
Menlo Park, CA 94025
(650) 854-9400
Tel. for application guidelines: (800) 656-4533;
FAX: (650) 854-4800; E-mail:
rwells@kff.org; URL: http://www.kff.org
Limitations: Giving limited to CA for the
California Grants Program only; and
South Africa for the international grants
program; other grants nationwide.
Publishes an annual or periodic report.

**The Greater Kansas City Community
Foundation and Affiliated Trusts**
1055 Broadway, Ste. 130
Kansas City, MO 64105-1595
(816) 842-0944
FAX: (816) 842-8079; URL: http://
www.gkccf.org
Limitations: Giving primarily in the bi-state
Kansas City area.
Publishes an annual or periodic report.

Kansas Health Foundation
309 E. Douglas
Wichita, KS 67202-3405
(316) 262-7676
Limitations: Giving limited to KS.
Publishes an annual or periodic report.

The J. M. Kaplan Fund, Inc.
261 Madison Ave., 19th Fl.
New York, NY 10016
(212) 767-0630
FAX: (212) 767-0639; Application address for
publication program: Furthermore, P.O.
Box 667, Hudson, NY 12534; tel.: (518)
828-8900
Limitations: Giving primarily in NY, with
emphasis on New York City.
Publishes an annual or periodic report.

Ewing Marion Kauffman Foundation
4801 Rockhill Rd.
Kansas City, MO 64110-2046
(816) 932-1000
FAX: (816) 932-1100; E-mail: info@emkf.org;
URL: http://www.emkf.org or http://
www.entreworld.org
Limitations: Giving limited to the U.S., with
emphasis on the metropolitan Kansas
City, MO, area for youth development.
Publishes an annual or periodic report.

Muriel McBrien Kauffman Foundation
4801 Rockhill Rd.
Kansas City, MO 64110
FAX: (913) 649-9438
Limitations: Giving primarily in Kansas City,
MO, and New York, NY.

W. K. Kellogg Foundation
1 Michigan Ave. E.
Battle Creek, MI 49017-4058
(616) 968-1611
FAX: (616) 968-0413; URL: http://
www.wkkf.org
Limitations: Giving primarily in the U.S., Latin
America and the Caribbean, and the south
African countries of Botswana, Lesotho,

South Africa, Swaziland, Zimbabwe and
Mozambique.
Publishes an annual or periodic report.

Kellogg's Corporate Citizenship Fund
1 Kellogg Sq.
P.O. Box 3599
Battle Creek, MI 49016-3599
(616) 961-2837
FAX: (616) 961-3494
Limitations: Giving primarily in areas of
company operations.

William T. Kemper Foundation
P.O. Box 13095
Kansas City, MO 64199-3095
(816) 234-2985
Limitations: Giving primarily in the Midwest
with emphasis on MO and surrounding
areas.

William R. Kenan, Jr. Charitable Trust
Kenan Ctr.
P.O. Box 3858, Bowles Dr.
Chapel Hill, NC 27515-3858
(919) 962-8150
Limitations: Giving for secondary schools
limited to Eastern Seaboard states.
Publishes an annual or periodic report.

The Henry P. Kendall Foundation
176 Federal St.
Boston, MA 02110
(617) 951-2525
FAX: (617) 443-1977; URL: http://
www.kendall.org/
Limitations: Giving primarily in northeastern
and northwestern North America (U.S.
and Canada) for environmental and
natural resource programs.
Publishes an annual or periodic report.

Peter Kiewit Foundation
Guarantee Centre II
8805 Indian Hills Dr., Ste. 225
Omaha, NE 68114
(402) 344-7890
FAX: (402) 344-8099
Limitations: Giving limited to Rancho Mirage,
CA, western IA, NE, and Sheridan, WY;
college scholarships available to high
school students in the Omaha,
NE-Council Bluffs, IA, area only.
Publishes an annual or periodic report.

The Sidney Kimmel Foundation
c/o R. Jaffe
1600 Market St.
Philadelphia, PA 19103-7286
(215) 751-2500
URL: http://www.kimmel.org/
Limitations: Giving primarily in NY and PA.

Stephen and Tabitha King Foundation, Inc.
101 Park Ave.
New York, NY 10178
(212) 661-8200
URL: http://www.stkfoundation.org
Limitations: Giving primarily in ME.

F. M. Kirby Foundation, Inc.
17 DeHart St.
P.O. Box 151
Morristown, NJ 07963-0151
(973) 538-4800
URL: http://fdncenter.org/grantmaker/kirby/
Limitations: Giving primarily in NC, NJ, and
PA.

The Esther A. & Joseph Klingenstein Fund, Inc.
787 7th Ave., 6th Fl.
New York, NY 10019-6016
(212) 492-6181
FAX: (212) 492-7007

The John W. Kluge Foundation
c/o Edward A. Hopkins
15004 Sunflower Ct.
Rockville, MD 20853-1748
(301) 929-9340

John S. and James L. Knight Foundation
1 Biscayne Tower, Ste. 3800
2 S. Biscayne Blvd.
Miami, FL 33131-1803
(305) 908-2600
Limitations: Giving limited to projects serving
the 26 communities where the Knight
brothers published newspapers for
Community Initiatives Program and local
grants: Long Beach and San Jose, CA,
Boulder, CO, Boca Raton, Bradenton,
Miami, and Tallahassee, FL, Columbus,
Macon, and Milledgeville, GA, Fort
Wayne and Gary, IN, Wichita, KS,
Lexington, KY, Detroit, MI, Duluth and
St. Paul, MN, Biloxi, MS, Charlotte, NC,
Grand Forks, ND, Akron, OH,
Philadelphia and State College, PA,
Columbia and Myrtle Beach, SC, and
Aberdeen, SD;international for
Journalism.
Publishes an annual or periodic report.

David H. Koch Charitable Foundation
4111 E. 37th St., N.
Wichita, KS 67220
(316) 828-5552
Additional address: P.O. Box 2256, Wichita,
KS 67201
Limitations: Giving on a national basis, with
emphasis on KS for education, social
science, and public affairs; New York,
NY, for arts and culture.

Koch Foundation, Inc.
2830 N.W. 41st St., Ste. H
Gainesville, FL 32606
(352) 373-7491
Publishes an annual or periodic report.

Koret Foundation
33 New Montgomery St., Ste. 1090
San Francisco, CA 94105-4526
(415) 882-7740
FAX: (415) 882-7775; E-mail:
koret@koretfoundation.org; URL: http://
www.koretfoundation.org
Limitations: Giving limited to the Bay Area
counties of San Francisco, Alameda,
Contra Costa, Marin, Santa Clara, and
San Mateo, CA; giving also in Israel.

The Kresge Foundation
3215 W. Big Beaver Rd.
P.O. Box 3151
Troy, MI 48007-3151
(248) 643-9630
FAX: (248) 643-0588; URL: http://
www.kresge.org
Publishes an annual or periodic report.

Samuel H. Kress Foundation
174 E. 80th St.
New York, NY 10021
(212) 861-4993
URL: http://www.kressfoundation.org/kress/
index.html
Limitations: Giving primarily in the U.S. and
Europe.
Publishes an annual or periodic report.

Albert & Bessie Mae Kronkosky Charitable
Foundation
112 E. Pecan, Ste. 830
San Antonio, TX 78205
(210) 475-9000
Limitations: Giving limited to Bandera, Bexar,
Comal, and Kendall counties, TX.

Lannan Foundation
313 Read St.
Santa Fe, NM 87501
(505) 986-8160
FAX: (505) 986-8195; FAX: (505) 954-5143;
URL: http://www.lannan.org/

Forrest C. Lattner Foundation, Inc.
777 E. Atlantic Ave., Ste. 317
Delray Beach, FL 33483-5352
(561) 278-3781
Limitations: Giving primarily in Palm Beach
County, FL, Wichita, KS, St. Louis, MO,
and Westerly, RI.

Laurel Foundation
2 Gateway Ctr., Ste. 1800
Pittsburgh, PA 15222
(412) 765-2400
FAX: (412) 765-2407
Limitations: Giving primarily in southwestern
PA.
Publishes an annual or periodic report.

The Lebensfeld Foundation
c/o VIS, Inc.
15 Exchange Pl.
Jersey City, NJ 07302-3912
Limitations: Giving primarily in NY and PA.

Sara Lee Foundation
3 First National Plz.
Chicago, IL 60602-4260
(312) 558-8448
URL: http://www.saraleefoundation.org
Limitations: Giving primarily in the Chicago,
IL, area.
Publishes an annual or periodic report.

Libra Foundation
3 Canal Plz.
P.O. Box 17516
Portland, ME 04112-8516
(207) 879-6280
FAX: (207) 879-6281; URL: http://
www.librafoundation.org
Limitations: Giving limited to ME.
Publishes an annual or periodic report.

Lied Foundation Trust
3907 W. Charleston Blvd.
Las Vegas, NV 89102
(702) 878-1559
Limitations: Giving primarily in NE and Las
Vegas, NV.

Lilly Endowment Inc.
2801 N. Meridian St.
Indianapolis, IN 46208-0068
(317) 924-5471
Mailing address: P.O. Box 88068, Indianapolis,
IN 46208; FAX: (317) 926-4431
Limitations: Giving limited to IN, with
emphasis on Indianapolis, for community
development projects (including the arts,
preservation, capital building funds,
operating funds, and social services).
Education funding focused principally on
Indiana under invitational grant programs.
National giving in religion, philanthropic
studies, leadership education, and selected
higher education initiatives.
Publishes an annual or periodic report.

The Lincy Foundation
150 S. Rodeo Dr., Ste. 250
Beverly Hills, CA 90212
Limitations: Giving primarily in CA.

George Link, Jr. Foundation, Inc.
c/o The Bank of New York
1290 Ave. of The Americas, 5th Fl.
New York, NY 10104
(212) 238-3000
Limitations: Giving primarily in MA, NJ, and
NY.

Albert A. List Foundation, Inc.
The Chesterfield Suites
180 W. 80th St., Ste. 213
New York, NY 10024-6301
(212) 799-1090
FAX: (212) 799-1160; URL: http://fdncenter.org/
grantmaker/listfdn/

The Lucius N. Littauer Foundation, Inc.
60 E. 42nd St., Ste. 2910
New York, NY 10165
(212) 697-2677
Limitations: Giving primarily in NY for
medical ethics and environmental projects.

Lockheed Martin Corporation Foundation
6801 Rockledge Dr.
Bethesda, MD 20817
(301) 897-6292
Limitations: Giving primarily in areas of
company operations.

Longwood Foundation, Inc.
100 W. 10th St., Ste. 1109
Wilmington, DE 19801
(302) 654-2477
Limitations: Giving limited to DE, with
emphasis on the greater Wilmington area.

Richard Lounsbery Foundation, Inc.
51 E. 63rd St.
New York, NY 10021
Limitations: Giving limited to the U.S., France
and Canada.

Leon Lowenstein Foundation, Inc.
126 E. 56th St., 28th Fl.
New York, NY 10022
(212) 319-0670
FAX: (212) 688-0134
Limitations: Giving primarily in the
metropolitan New York, NY, area.

The Henry Luce Foundation, Inc.
111 W. 50th St., Rm. 4601
New York, NY 10020
(212) 489-7700
FAX: (212) 581-9541; E-mail: hlf@hluce.org;
URL: http://www.hluce.org
Limitations: Giving on a national and
international basis; international activities
limited to East and Southeast Asia.

Lucent Technologies Foundation
535 Mountain Ave.
Murray Hill, NJ 07974
(908) 582-7909
E-mail: foundation@lucent.com; URL: http://
www.lucent.com/news/about/community/
foundation.html
Limitations: Giving on a national basis.

Lyndhurst Foundation
517 E. 5th St.
Chattanooga, TN 37403-1826
(423) 756-0767
FAX: (423) 756-0770; URL: http://
www.lyndhurstfoundation.org
Limitations: Giving limited to the southeastern
U.S., with emphasis on Chattanooga, TN.
Education grants are limited to two
clusters of public schools, one in AL and
one in Chattanooga, TN.
Publishes an annual or periodic report.

**John D. and Catherine T. MacArthur
Foundation**
140 S. Dearborn St., Ste. 1100
Chicago, IL 60603-5285
(312) 726-8000
FAX: (312) 920-6258; TDD: (312) 920-6285;
E-mail: 4answers@macfdn.org; URL:
http://www.macfdn.org
Limitations: Giving on a national and
international basis, with emphasis on
Palm Beach County, FL, and Chicago, IL.
Publishes an annual or periodic report.

Josiah Macy, Jr. Foundation
44 E. 64th St.
New York, NY 10021
(212) 486-2424
FAX: (212) 644-0765; URL: http://
www.josiahmacyfoundation.org
Publishes an annual or periodic report.

M&T Charitable Foundation
1 M & T Plz., 6th Fl.
Buffalo, NY 14203
(716) 848-3804
FAX: (716) 848-7318
Limitations: Giving primarily in NY.

Mardag Foundation
55 5th St. E. 600 Norwest Ctr.
St. Paul, MN 55101-1797
(651) 224-5463
FAX: (651) 224-8123; E-mail:
inbox@mardag.org; URL: http://
www.mardag.org
Limitations: Giving primarily in the east
metropolitan area of Ramsey, Washington,
and Dakota counties, MN, and greater
MN. No support for programs serving
Minneapolis, MN, and the surrounding
west metropolitan area.
Publishes an annual or periodic report.

Marin Community Foundation
17 E. Sir Francis Drake Blvd., Ste. 200
Larkspur, CA 94939
(415) 461-3333
FAX: (415) 464-2555; E-mail:
mcf@marincf.org; URL: http://
www.marincf.org
Limitations: Giving from Buck Trust limited to
Marin County, CA; other giving on a
national and international basis with
emphasis on the San Francisco Bay Area.
Publishes an annual or periodic report.

The John and Mary R. Markle Foundation
10 Rockefeller Plz., 16th Fl.
New York, NY 10020-1903
(212) 489-6655
FAX: (212) 765-9690; E-mail:
info@markle.org; URL: http://
www.markle.org/index.html
Publishes an annual or periodic report.

G. Harold & Leila Y. Mathers Charitable
Foundation
103 S. Bedford Rd., Ste. 101
Mount Kisco, NY 10549-3440
(914) 242-0465

Mattel Children's Foundation
c/o Mattel, Inc.
333 Continental Blvd.
El Segundo, CA 90245-5012
(310) 252-3802
FAX: (310) 252-4443; URL: http://
www.mattel.com/about_us/
Comm_Involvement/ci_mcf_over.asp
Limitations: Giving on a national and
international basis, with emphasis in Los
Angeles, CA, Mount Laurel, NJ, Buffalo,
NY, and Madison, WI.
Publishes an annual or periodic report.

The May Department Stores Company
Foundation, Inc.
611 Olive St., Ste. 1350
St. Louis, MO 63101-1799
(314) 342-6299
FAX: (314) 342-4461
Limitations: Giving primarily in areas of
company operations.

Maytag Corporation Foundation
P.O. Box 39
403 W. 4th St., N.
Newton, IA 50208-0039
(641) 787-8357
Limitations: Giving limited to areas of
company operations, particularly Searcy,
AR, Anana and Newton, IA, Galesburg
and Herrin, IL, North Canton, OH,
Florence and Williston, SC, Cleveland
and Jackson, TN.
Publishes an annual or periodic report.

Faye McBeath Foundation
1020 N. Broadway
Milwaukee, WI 53202
(414) 272-2626
FAX: (414) 272-6235; E-mail:
info@fayemcbeath.org; URL: http://
www.fayemcbeath.org
Limitations: Giving limited to WI, with
emphasis on the greater Milwaukee area.
Publishes an annual or periodic report.

B. C. McCabe Foundation
8152 Painter Ave., Ste. 201
Whittier, CA 90602
(562) 696-1433
FAX: (562) 698-5508
Limitations: Giving primarily in CA.

McCasland Foundation
McCasland Bldg.
P.O. Box 400
Duncan, OK 73534
(580) 252-5580
Limitations: Giving primarily in OK.

Robert R. McCormick Tribune Foundation
435 N. Michigan Ave., Ste. 770
Chicago, IL 60611
(312) 222-3512
FAX: (312) 222-3523; E-mail:
rrmtf@tribune.com; URL: http://
www.rrmtf.org
Limitations: Giving primarily in the
metropolitan Chicago, IL, area; except for
Journalism Program which gives on a
national basis and in Latin America; and
communities program which operates in:
Phoenix, AZ, Anaheim, Escondido, Los
Angeles, Sacramento and San Diego, CA,
Denver, CO, Fort Lauderdale and
Orlando, FL, Atlanta, GA, Chicago, IL,
Indianapolis, IN, Manhattan, KS, New
Orleans, LA, Boston and Lowell, MA,
New York, NY, Cleveland, OH,
Philadelphia and York, PA, Dallas,
Houston, and El Paso, TX, and Newport
News, VA.
Publishes an annual or periodic report.

McCune Charitable Foundation
345 E. Alameda St.
Santa Fe, NM 87501-2229
(505) 983-8300
FAX: (505) 983-7887; E-mail:
fsowers@trail.com; URL: http://
www.nmmccune.org
Limitations: Giving limited to NM.

John R. McCune Charitable Trust
6 PPG Pl. Ste. 750
Pittsburgh, PA 15222
(412) 644-7796
FAX: (412) 644-8059
Limitations: Giving primarily in southwestern
PA.

McCune Foundation
750 6 PPG Pl.
Pittsburgh, PA 15222
(412) 644-8779
FAX: (412) 644-8059; URL: http://
www.mccune.org
Limitations: Giving primarily in southwestern
PA, with emphasis on the Pittsburgh area.
Publishes an annual or periodic report.

The Eugene McDermott Foundation
3808 Euclid Ave.
Dallas, TX 75205
Limitations: Giving primarily in Dallas, TX.

R. J. McElroy Trust
KWWL Bldg., Ste. 318
500 E. 4th St.
Waterloo, IA 50703
(319) 287-9102
FAX: (319) 287-9105; E-mail:
mcelroy@cedarnet.org; URL: http://
www.cedarnet.org/mcelroy/index.html
Limitations: Giving primarily in the KWWL
viewing area, 22 counties in northeast IA.

John P. McGovern Foundation
2211 Norfolk St., Ste. 900
Houston, TX 77098-4044
(713) 661-4808
FAX: (713) 661-3031
Limitations: Giving primarily in TX, with
emphasis on Houston; giving also in the
Southwest.

McGovern Fund
2211 Norfolk, Ste. 900
Houston, TX 77098-4044
(713) 661-4808
FAX: (713) 661-3031
Limitations: Giving primarily in TX, with
emphasis on Houston; giving also in the
Southwest.

William G. McGowan Charitable Fund
P.O. Box 40515
Washington, DC 20016-0515
(202) 364-5030
FAX: (202) 364-3382; E-mail:
goodric@aol.com; URL: http://
www.mcgowanfund.com
Limitations: Giving limited to northern CA, the
Washington, DC, area, IL, the
metropolitan Kansas City, KS, area,

western NY, northeastern PA, central TX,
and northern VA.

McGregor Fund
333 W. Fort St., Ste. 2090
Detroit, MI 48226-3134
(313) 963-3495
FAX: (313) 963-3512; E-mail:
info@mcgregorfund.org; URL: http://
www.mcgregorfund.org
Limitations: Giving primarily in the
metropolitan Detroit, MI, area, including
Wayne, Oakland, and Macomb counties;
grants to private colleges and universities
under special program limited to MI and
OH.
Publishes an annual or periodic report.

The McKnight Foundation
600 TCF Tower
121 S. 8th St.
Minneapolis, MN 55402
(612) 333-4220
FAX: (612) 332-3833; E-mail:
info@mcknight.org; URL: http://
www.mcknight.org
Limitations: Giving limited to organizations in
MN, especially the seven-county Twin
Cities, MN, area, except for programs in
the environment, international aid, and
research.
Publishes an annual or periodic report.

The Robert and Janice McNair Foundation
711 Louisiana St., 33rd Fl.
Houston, TX 77002-2734
Limitations: Giving primarily in Houston, TX.

The Meadows Foundation, Inc.
Wilson Historic District
3003 Swiss Ave.
Dallas, TX 75204-6090
(214) 826-9431
FAX: (214) 827-7042; E-mail: grants@mfi.org;
URL: http://www.mfi.org
Limitations: Giving limited to TX.
Publishes an annual or periodic report.

The Medtronic Foundation
710 Medtronic Pkwy.
Minneapolis, MN 55432-5604
(763) 505-2639
FAX: (763) 505-2698; URL: http://
www.medtronic.com/foundation
Limitations: Giving primarily in areas of
company operations, including Phoenix
and Tempe, AZ, Goleta, Santa Ana, and
Santa Rosa, CA, Louisville and Parker,
CO, Warsaw, IN, Danvers, MA, Grand
Rapids, MI, Milaca and the Twin
Cities-Seven County metro, MN, area,
Humacao and Villalba, PR, Memphis, TN,
and Redmond, WA, or to national
organizations having an effect on these
areas; international giving in Medtronic
communities.
Publishes an annual or periodic report.

The Andrew W. Mellon Foundation
140 E. 62nd St.
New York, NY 10021
(212) 838-8400
URL: http://www.mellon.org
Publishes an annual or periodic report.

Richard King Mellon Foundation
1 Mellon Bank Ctr.
500 Grant St., 41st Fl., Ste. 4106
Pittsburgh, PA 15219-2502
(412) 392-2800
FAX: (412) 392-2837; URL: http://fdncenter.org/
grantmaker/rkmellon/
Limitations: Giving primarily in Pittsburgh and
southwestern PA, except for nationwide
conservation programs. No grants outside
the U.S.
Publishes an annual or periodic report.

The Merck Company Foundation
1 Merck Dr.
P.O. Box 100
Whitehouse Station, NJ 08889-0100
(908) 423-2042
FAX: (908) 423-1987
Limitations: Giving primarily in areas of
company operations, including CA, GA,
NJ, PA, and VA.

The John Merck Fund
11 Beacon St., Ste. 1230
Boston, MA 02108
(617) 723-2932
FAX: (617) 523-6029; E-mail: info@jmfund.org

Merrill Lynch & Co. Foundation, Inc.
100 Union Ave.
Cresskill, NJ 07626
(201) 871-0350
Application address: c/o Community Rels., 2
World Financial Ctr., 6th Fl. New York,
NY 10281; FAX: (212) 236-3821; E-mail:
philant7@exchange.ml.com; URL: http://
philanthropy.ml.com

Joyce Mertz-Gilmore Foundation
218 E. 18th St.
New York, NY 10003-3694
(212) 475-1137
FAX: (212) 777-5226; E-mail: jmgf@jmgf.org;
URL: http://www.jmgf.org
Limitations: Giving on a national and
international basis, with the exception of
the New York City Program.

Metropolitan Life Foundation
1 Madison Ave.
New York, NY 10010-3690
(212) 578-6272
FAX: (212) 685-1435; URL: http://
www.metlife.com/Companyinfo/
Community/Found/index.html
Publishes an annual or periodic report.

Eugene and Agnes E. Meyer Foundation
1400 16th St., N.W., Ste. 360
Washington, DC 20036
(202) 483-8294
FAX: (202) 328-6850; E-mail:
meyer@meyerfdn.org; URL: http://
www.meyerfoundation.org
Limitations: Giving limited to the metropolitan
Washington, DC, area, including suburban
MD and northern VA.
Publishes an annual or periodic report.

Meyer Memorial Trust
1515 S.W. 5th Ave., Ste. 500
Portland, OR 97201
(503) 228-5512
E-mail: mmt@mmt.org; URL: http://
www.mmt.org
Limitations: Giving primarily in OR and Clark
County, WA.
Publishes an annual or periodic report.

Paul and Irma Milstein Foundation
1271 Ave. of the Americas, Ste. 4200
New York, NY 10020
Limitations: Giving primarily in New York, NY.

Greater Milwaukee Foundation
1020 N. Broadway
Milwaukee, WI 53202
(414) 272-5805
FAX: (414) 272-6235;
E-mail:info@mkefdn.org; URL: http://
www.greatermilwaukeefoundation.org
Limitations: Giving primarily in the greater
Milwaukee, WI, area.
Publishes an annual or periodic report.

The Minneapolis Foundation
A200 Foshay Tower
821 Marquette Ave., S.
Minneapolis, MN 55402
(612) 339-7343
*Application address for the Minnesota
Nonprofits Assistance Fund:* c/o Susan
Kenny Stevens, Admin., Loan Tech,
World Trade Center, Ste. 950, 30 E. 7th
St., St. Paul, MN 55101-4910; FAX: (612)
672-3870; URL: http://
www.mplsfoundation.org
Limitations: Giving limited to MN, with
emphasis on organizations from the City
of Minneapolis.
Publishes an annual or periodic report.

The Ambrose Monell Foundation
c/o Fulton, Rowe, Hart & Coon
1 Rockefeller Plz., Ste. 301
New York, NY 10020-2002
(212) 586-0700
URL: http://www.monellvetlesen.org/

Moore Family Foundation
P.O. Box 3099
Los Altos, CA 94024-0099
Limitations: Giving primarily in CA.

The J. P. Morgan Chase Foundation
1 Chase Manhattan Plz., 5th Fl.
New York, NY 10081
(212) 552-1112
Limitations: Giving in the tri-state region of
NY, NJ, and CT; the states of AZ, CA,

DE, FL, IL, LA, MA, and OH; some
national programs; and approximately 50
countries where J.P. Morgan Chase has a
business presence.
Publishes an annual or periodic report.

Moriah Fund
1 Farragut Sq. S.
1634 I St., N.W., Ste. 1000
Washington, DC 20006
(202) 783-8488
FAX: (202) 783-8499; Request in Israel: Susan
Feit, P.O.Box 2788, Neve Monosson,
Israel 60190
Limitations: Giving nationally and
internationally, including Israel and Latin
America; giving primarily in Washington,
DC for poverty program.
Publishes an annual or periodic report.

Motorola Foundation
1303 E. Algonquin Rd.
Schaumburg, IL 60196
(847) 576-6200
URL: http://www.motorola.com/GSS/SSTG/
MOTinAZ/giving.html
Limitations: Giving primarily in communities
where the company has major facilities,
with emphasis on Huntsville, AL,
Phoenix, AZ, Boyton Beach and Fort
Lauderdale, FL, IL, Austin and Sequin,
TX; and internationally, where company
has a significant presence.

Charles Stewart Mott Foundation
Mott Foundation Building
503 S. Saginaw St., Ste. 1200
Flint, MI 48502-1851
(810) 238-5651
Publication Hotline: (800) 645-1766; FAX:
(810) 766-1753; E-mail:
infocenter@mott.org; URL: http://
www.mott.org
Limitations: Giving nationally and to emerging
countries in Central and Eastern Europe,
Russia, and South Africa.
Publishes an annual or periodic report.

M. J. Murdock Charitable Trust
703 Broadway, Ste. 710
Vancouver, WA 98660
(360) 694-8415
Mailing address: P.O. Box 1618, Vancouver,
WA 98668; tel.: (503) 285-4086; FAX:
(360) 694-1819; URL: http://
www.murdock-trust.org
Limitations: Giving primarily in the Pacific
Northwest (AK, ID, MT, OR, and WA).
Publishes an annual or periodic report.

John P. Murphy Foundation
c/o Terminal Tower
50 Public Sq., Ste. 924
Cleveland, OH 44113-2203
(216) 623-4770
FAX: (216) 623-4773; URL: http://fdncenter.org/
grantmaker/jpmurphy/
Limitations: Giving primarily in the greater
Cleveland, OH, area.

Katherine John Murphy Foundation
50 Hurt Plz., Ste. 745
Atlanta, GA 30303
(404) 589-8090
E-mail: info@kjmurphyfoundation.org
Limitations: Giving primarily in Atlanta, GA.

Nationwide Foundation
1 Nationwide Plz.
Columbus, OH 43215-2220
(614) 249-5095
Additonal tel.: (614) 249-4310; URL: http://
www.nationwide.com/about_us/involve/
fndatn.htm
Limitations: Giving primarily in OH, with
emphasis on Columbus, and other
communities where the company
maintains offices.

NCC Charitable Foundation II
c/o National City Bank
P.O. Box 5756, LOC 2205
Cleveland, OH 44101
(216) 575-2994
Limitations: Giving primarily in the
northeastern U.S., with emphasis on OH.

The New York Community Trust
2 Park Ave., 24th Fl.
New York, NY 10016-9385
(212) 686-0010
FAX: (212) 532-8528; URL: http://
www.nycommunitytrust.org; Alternate
URL: http://www.nyct-cfi.org
Limitations: Giving limited to the metropolitan
New York, NY, area.
Publishes an annual or periodic report.

New York Foundation
350 5th Ave., No. 2901
New York, NY 10118
(212) 594-8009
URL: http://www.nyf.org/
Limitations: Giving limited to local programs
in the New York, NY, metropolitan area.
Publishes an annual or periodic report.

The New York Times Company Foundation, Inc.
229 W. 43rd St.
New York, NY 10036-3959
(212) 556-1091
FAX: (212) 556-4450
Limitations: Giving primarily in the New York,
NY, metropolitan area and in localities
served by affiliates of the company.
Publishes an annual or periodic report.

Samuel I. Newhouse Foundation, Inc.
c/o Paul Scherer & Co. LLP
335 Madison Ave., 15th Fl.
New York, NY 10017

The Samuel Roberts Noble Foundation, Inc.
2510 Sam Noble Pkwy.
P.O. Box 2180
Ardmore, OK 73402
(580) 223-5810
URL: http://www.noble.org
Limitations: Giving primarily in the Southwest,
with emphasis on OK.
Publishes an annual or periodic report.

The Nord Family Foundation
347 Midway Blvd., Ste. 312
Elyria, OH 44035
(440) 324-2822
Limitations: Giving primarily in the Lorain and
Cuyahoga County, OH, areas; also gives
secondarily in Denver, CO, Boston, MA,
and Columbia, SC.
Publishes an annual or periodic report.

The Nordson Corporation Foundation
28601 Clemens Rd.
Westlake, OH 44145-1119
(440) 892-1580
Limitations: Giving limited to the Monterey
Peninsula and San Diego County, CA,
Atlanta, GA, and northern OH areas.
Publishes an annual or periodic report.

The Norfolk Foundation
1 Commercial Pl., Ste 1410
Norfolk, VA 23510-2113
(757) 622-7951
FAX: (757) 622-1751; E-mail:
info@norfolkfoundation.org; URL: http://
www.norfolkfoundation.org
Limitations: Giving limited to Norfolk, VA, and
a 50-mile area from its boundaries.
Publishes an annual or periodic report.

The Kenneth T. and Eileen L. Norris Foundation
11 Golden Shore, Ste. 450
Long Beach, CA 90802
(562) 435-8444
FAX: (562) 436-0584; E-mail: boyer@ktn.org;
URL: http://www.norrisfoundation.org
Limitations: Giving limited to southern CA.
Publishes an annual or periodic report.

The Northern Trust Company Charitable Trust
c/o The Northern Trust Co., Community Affairs
Div.
50 S. LaSalle St.
Chicago, IL 60675
(312) 444-4059
Limitations: Giving limited to Cook County,
IL, with focus on the Chicago area.
Publishes an annual or periodic report.

Northwest Area Foundation
332 Minnesota St., Ste. E-1201
St. Paul, MN 55101-1373
(651) 224-9635
FAX: (651) 225-3881; E-mail: info@nwaf.org;
URL: http://www.nwaf.org
Limitations: Giving limited to IA, ID, MN, MT,
ND, OR, SD, and WA.

Northwestern Mutual Foundation
720 E. Wisconsin Ave.
Milwaukee, WI 53202
(414) 665-2200
Limitations: Giving primarily in the greater
Milwaukee, WI, area.

Jessie Smith Noyes Foundation, Inc.
6 E. 39th St., 12th Fl.
New York, NY 10016-0112
(212) 684-6577
FAX: (212) 689-6549; E-mail:
noyes@noyes.org; URL: http://
www.noyes.org
Limitations: Giving primarily in the southeast,
south central, and southwest regions of
the U.S.
Publishes an annual or periodic report.

Oakleaf Foundation
5140 Norwest Ctr.
90 S. 7th St.
Minneapolis, MN 55402
Limitations: Giving primarily in the
Minneapolis-St. Paul, MN, area.

The Offield Family Foundation
400 N. Michigan Ave., Rm. 407
Chicago, IL 60611
Limitations: Giving primarily in AZ, CA, the
Chicago, IL, area and MI.

The Ohrstrom Foundation, Inc.
c/o Curtis Mallet
101 Park Ave., 35th Fl.
New York, NY 10178-0061
Limitations: Giving primarily in NY and VA.

F. W. Olin Foundation, Inc.
780 3rd Ave.
New York, NY 10017-2024
(212) 832-0508
FAX: (212) 935-9083; MN address: c/o William
B. Horn, 1500 Foshay Tower,
Minneapolis, MN 55402; tel.: (612)
341-2581; FAX: (612) 341-3801

John M. Olin Foundation, Inc.
330 Madison Ave., 22nd Fl.
New York, NY 10017
(212) 661-2670
URL: http://www.jmof.org
Publishes an annual or periodic report.

Olive Bridge Fund, Inc.
500 5th Ave., 50th Fl.
New York, NY 10110
(212) 391-8960
Limitations: Giving primarily in MA and NY.

Omaha Community Foundation
1623 Farnam St., Ste. 600
Omaha, NE 68102
(402) 342-3458
FAX: (402) 342-3582; URL: http://
www.omahacf.org
Limitations: Giving primarily in the
metropolitan Omaha, NE, area including
southwest IA.
Publishes an annual or periodic report.

The ONDEO Nalco Foundation
ONDEO Nalco Ctr.
1601 W. Diehl Rd.
Naperville, IL 60563-1198
(630) 305-1566
FAX: (630) 305-2896; E-mail:
foundation@ondeo-nalco.com; URL:
http://www.ondeo-nalco.com/

About_Nalco/AN-Foundation/
an-foundation.html
Limitations: Giving primarily in areas where
company has major offices, labs, or
manufacturing operations: metropolitan
and the western suburbs of Chicago, IL,
Carson, CA, Garyville, LA, Paulsboro,
NJ, Chagrin Falls, OH, and Sugar Land
and Freeport, TX.

Open Society Institute
400 W. 59th St., 4th Fl.
New York, NY 10019
(212) 548-0600
FAX: (212) 548-4679; URL: http://
www.soros.org
Limitations: Giving on a national and
international basis.

The Oregon Community Foundation
1221 S.W. Yamhill, No. 100
Portland, OR 97205
(503) 227-6846
FAX: (503) 274-7771; E-mail: info@ocf1.org;
URL: http://
www.oregoncommunityfound.org
Limitations: Giving limited to OR.
Publishes an annual or periodic report.

Bernard Osher Foundation
909 Montgomery St., 300
San Francisco, CA 94133
(415) 861-5587
FAX: (415) 677-5868; E-mail:
nagle@osherfoundation.com
Limitations: Giving limited to Alameda and
San Francisco counties, CA.

The Overbrook Foundation
122 East 42nd St., Ste. 2500
New York, NY 10168-2500
(212) 661-8710
FAX: (212) 661-8664
Limitations: Giving primarily in New York, NY.

The David and Lucile Packard Foundation
300 2nd St., Ste. 200
Los Altos, CA 94022
(650) 948-7658
URL: http://www.packfound.org
Limitations: Giving for the arts and community
development primarily in Santa Clara,
San Mateo, Santa Cruz, and Monterey
counties, CA, with some support also in
the Pueblo, CO, area; national giving for
child health and development; national
and international giving for population
and the environment.
Publishes an annual or periodic report.

Park Foundation, Inc.
P.O. Box 550
Ithaca, NY 14851
(607) 272-9124
FAX: (607) 272-6057
Limitations: Giving limited to the East Coast
(primarily in central NY) and the
southeastern U.S.

The Mary Morton Parsons Foundation
P.O. Box 85678
Richmond, VA 23285-5678
Limitations: Giving primarily in Richmond, VA.

The Ralph M. Parsons Foundation
1055 Wilshire Blvd., Ste. 1701
Los Angeles, CA 90017
(213) 482-3185
FAX: (213) 482-8878
Limitations: Giving limited to Los Angeles
County, CA, with the exception of some
grants for higher education.
Publishes an annual or periodic report.

Pasadena Foundation
16 N. Marengo Ave., Ste. 300
Pasadena, CA 91101
(626) 796-2097
FAX: (626) 583-4738; E-mail:
pfstaff@pasadenafoundation.org; URL:
http://www.PasadenaFoundation.org
Limitations: Giving limited to the Pasadena,
CA, area.
Publishes an annual or periodic report.

Frank E. Payne and Seba B. Payne Foundation
c/o Bank of America
231 S. LaSalle St.
Chicago, IL 60697
(312) 828-1785
Limitations: Giving primarily in the
metropolitan Chicago, IL, area and PA.

Amelia Peabody Charitable Fund
10 P.O. Sq., North Ste. 995
Boston, MA 02109-4603
(617) 451-6178
Limitations: Giving primarily in New England
with emphasis on MA.

Amelia Peabody Foundation
1 Hollis St.
Wellesley, MA 02482
(781) 237-6468
FAX: (781) 237-5014
Limitations: Giving limited to MA.

Peninsula Community Foundation
1700 S. El Camino Real, Ste. 300
San Mateo, CA 94402-3049
(650) 358-9369
FAX: (650) 358-9817; E-mail: inquiry@pcf.org;
URL: http://www.pcf.org
Limitations: Giving limited to San Mateo
County and northern Santa Clara County,
CA.
Publishes an annual or periodic report.

The William Penn Foundation
2 Logan Sq., 11th Fl.
100 N. 18th St.
Philadelphia, PA 19103-2757
(215) 988-1830
FAX: (215) 988-1823; E-mail:
moreinfo@wpennfdn.org; URL: http://
www.wpennfdn.org/
Limitations: Giving limited to Camden, NJ and
Philadelphia, Bucks, Chester, Delaware,
and Montgomery counties, PA;
environmental giving in northern DE,
small portion of northeastern MD,
southern NJ, and larger area of

southeastern PA; no national or
international giving (except at
foundation's initiative).
Publishes an annual or periodic report.

The PepsiCo Foundation, Inc.
700 Anderson Hill Rd.
Purchase, NY 10577
(914) 253-3153
Limitations: Giving primarily in communities
where operating divisions are located,
including Irvine, CA, Wichita, KS,
Louisville, KY, Somers, NY, and Plano,
TX.

Hal & Charlie Peterson Foundation
515 Jefferson St.
P.O. Box 293870
Kerrville, TX 78029-3870
(830) 896-2262
FAX: (830) 896-2283; E-mail: hcpfdn@ktc.com
Limitations: Giving primarily in Kerr County,
TX, and adjacent counties, and to state or
national organizations with a local chapter
in this area.

Jane Bradley Pettit Foundation
660 E. Mason St.
Milwaukee, WI 53202
(414) 227-1266
Limitations: Giving primarily in the greater
Milwaukee, WI, area.

The Pew Charitable Trusts
1 Commerce Sq.
2005 Market St., Ste. 1700
Philadelphia, PA 19103-7077
(215) 575-9050
FAX: (215) 575-4939; E-mail:
info@pewtrusts.com; URL: http://
www.pewtrusts.com
Limitations: Giving on a national basis, with a
special commitment to the Philadelphia,
PA, region.

The Carl and Lily Pforzheimer Foundation, Inc.
650 Madison Ave., 23rd Fl.
New York, NY 10022
(212) 223-6500

Pharmacia Foundation, Inc.
100 Route 206 N.
Peapack, NJ 07977
(908) 901-8766
FAX: (908) 901-1839; E-mail:
erica.ferry@pharmacia.com
Limitations: Giving primarily in areas where
employees and their families live and
work.

The Philadelphia Foundation
1234 Market St., Ste. 1800
Philadelphia, PA 19107-3794
(215) 563-6417
FAX: (215) 563-6882; URL: http://
www.philafound.org
Limitations: Giving limited to Bucks, Chester,
Delaware, Montgomery, and Philadelphia
counties in southeastern PA, except for
designated funds.
Publishes an annual or periodic report.

The Jay and Rose Phillips Family Foundation
10 2nd St., N.E., Ste. 200
Minneapolis, MN 55413
(612) 623-1654
FAX: (612) 623-1653; E-mail:
phillipsfnd@phillipsfnd.org
Limitations: Giving primarily in the Twin Cities
metropolitan, MN, area.
Publishes an annual or periodic report.

Howard Phipps Foundation
c/o Bessemer Trust Co., N.A.
100 Woodbridge Ctr. Dr.
Woodbridge, NJ 07095-0983
Application address: c/o Bessemer Trust Co.,
N.A., 630 5th Ave., New York, NY 10111,
tel.: (212) 708-9242
Limitations: Giving primarily in New York, NY.

The Picower Foundation
1410 S. Ocean Blvd.
Palm Beach, FL 33480
FAX: (212) 752-5082
Limitations: Giving primarily in southeast FL
and the Northeast.

The Pincus Family Fund
466 Lexington Ave.
New York, NY 10017
(212) 878-9291
Limitations: Giving primarily in NY.

The Pinkerton Foundation
630 5th Ave., Ste. 1755
New York, NY 10111
(212) 332-3385
FAX: (212) 332-3399; E-mail:
pinkfdn@mindspring.com; URL: http://
fdncenter.org/grantmaker/pinkerton/
Limitations: Giving primarily in New York, NY.

The Pittsburgh Foundation
1 PPG Pl., 30th Fl.
Pittsburgh, PA 15222-5401
(412) 391-5122
FAX: (421) 391-7259; E-mail:
email@pghfdn.org; URL: http://
www.pittsburghfoundation.org/
Limitations: Giving from unrestricted funds
limited to Pittsburgh and Allegheny
County, PA.
Publishes an annual or periodic report.

Plough Foundation
6410 Poplar Ave., Ste. 710
Memphis, TN 38119
(901) 761-9180
FAX: (901) 761-6186; E-mail:
Haynes@plough.org
Limitations: Giving primarily in Shelby
County, TN, with an emphasis on
Memphis.

The PNC Foundation
c/o PNC Financial Services Group, Inc.
2 PNC Plz., 34th Fl., 620 Liberty Ave.
Pittsburgh, PA 15222-2719
(412) 762-7076
FAX: (412) 705-1062
Limitations: Giving primarily in headquarters
     and company locations: DE, IN, KY, NJ,
     OH, and PA.
Publishes an annual or periodic report.

Polk Bros. Foundation, Inc.
420 N. Wabash Ave., No. 204
Chicago, IL 60611
(312) 527-4684
FAX: (312) 527-4681; E-mail:
     info@polkbrosfdn.org; URL: http://
     www.polkbrosfdn.org/
Limitations: Giving primarily in Chicago, IL.
Publishes an annual or periodic report.

PPG Industries Foundation
1 PPG Pl.
Pittsburgh, PA 15272
(412) 434-2453
Limitations: Giving primarily in areas of
     company operations, with emphasis on
     the Pittsburgh, PA, region.
Publishes an annual or periodic report.

Pritzker Foundation
200 W. Madison St., 25th Fl.
Chicago, IL 60606
(312) 750-8400
Limitations: Giving on a national basis, with
     some emphasis on Chicago, IL.

The Procter & Gamble Fund
P.O. Box 599
Cincinnati, OH 45201
(513) 945-8454
Information line: (513) 945-8454; FAX: (513)
     945-8979; E-mail: ratliff.bl@pg.com
Limitations: Giving primarily in areas in the
     U.S. where the company and its
     subsidiaries have large concentrations of
     employees; national giving for higher
     education and economic and public affairs.

The Prospect Hill Foundation, Inc.
99 Park Ave., Ste. 2220
New York, NY 10016-1601
(212) 370-1165
FAX: (212) 599-6282; URL: http://fdncenter.org/
     grantmaker/prospecthill/
Limitations: Giving primarily in the
     northeastern U.S., including NY and RI.

The Prudential Foundation
Prudential Plz.
751 Broad St., 15th Fl.
Newark, NJ 07102-3777
(973) 802-4791
URL: http://www.prudential.com/community/
     foundation/cmfzz1000.html
Limitations: Giving primarily in areas of
     company operations, with emphasis on
     Phoenix, AZ, Los Angeles, CA,
     Jacksonville, FL, Atlanta, GA,
     Minneapolis, MN, Newark, NJ,
     Philadelphia, PA, and Houston, TX.
Publishes an annual or periodic report.

Public Welfare Foundation, Inc.
1200 U. St., N.W.
Washington, DC 20009-4443
(202) 965-1800
E-mail: general@publicwelfare.org; URL:
     http://www.publicwelfare.org
Limitations: Giving is generally limited to the
     U.S. (more than 90 percent).
Publishes an annual or periodic report.

Publix Super Markets Charities
1936 George Jenkins Blvd.
Lakeland, FL 33815
(863) 688-1188
Application address: P.O. Box 407, Lakeland,
     FL 33802-0407
Limitations: Giving primarily in FL.

Qwest Foundation
1801 California St., 50th Fl.
Denver, CO 80202
(303) 896-1266
Limitations: Giving limited to the states served
     by Qwest, including AZ, CO, IA, ID, MN,
     MT, ND, NE, NM, OR, SD, UT, WA, and
     WY.

The Ralphs-Food 4 Less Foundation
1100 W. Artesia Blvd.
Compton, CA 90220
(310) 884-6250
Application address: P.O. Box 54143, Los
     Angeles, CA 90054
Limitations: Giving primarily in southern CA.

Bernard and Audre Rapoport Foundation
5400 Bosque Blvd., 245
Waco, TX 76710
(254) 741-0510
FAX: (254) 756-0510; E-mail:
     rapoport@texnet.net
Limitations: Giving on a national basis, with
     major emphasis on Waco, TX, including
     McKennan and surrounding counties;
     some support also in Israel.
Publishes an annual or periodic report.

Raskob Foundation for Catholic Activities, Inc.
P.O. Box 4019
Wilmington, DE 19807-0019
(302) 655-4440
FAX: (302) 655-3223; URL: http://www.rfca.org
Limitations: Giving to domestic and
     international programs affiliated with the
     Catholic church.

Reader's Digest Foundation
Reader's Digest Rd.
Pleasantville, NY 10570-7000
(914) 244-5370
FAX: (914) 238-7642; URL: http://
     www.readersdigest.com/corporate/
     rd_foundation.html
Limitations: Giving primarily in Westchester
     County, NY.
Publishes an annual or periodic report.

Reiman Charitable Foundation, Inc.
115 S. 84th St., No. 221
Milwaukee, WI 53214

Reliant Energy Foundation
P.O. Box 4567
Houston, TX 77210
(713) 207-5155

The Retirement Research Foundation
8765 W. Higgins Rd., Ste. 430
Chicago, IL 60631-4170
(773) 714-8080
FAX: (773) 714-8089; E-mail: info@rrf.org,
     hennessy@rrf.org; URL: http://
     www.rrf.org/
Limitations: Giving limited to the Midwest (IA,
     IL, IN, KY, MI, MO, WI) and FL for
     direct service projects not having the
     potential of national impact.

Kate B. Reynolds Charitable Trust
128 Reynolda Village
Winston-Salem, NC 27106-5123
(336) 723-1456
FAX: (336) 723-7765; URL: http://www.kbr.org
Limitations: Giving limited to NC; social
     welfare grants limited to Winston-Salem
     and Forsyth County; health care giving,
     statewide.
Publishes an annual or periodic report.

Donald W. Reynolds Foundation
1701 Village Center Cir.
Las Vegas, NV 89134
(702) 804-6000
FAX: (702) 804-6099; URL: http://
     www.dwreynolds.org
Limitations: Giving primarily in AR, NV, and
     OK for Capital Grants and Community
     Services Center grants. Giving nationally
     for cardiovascular clinic research and
     geriatrics training of physicians.
Publishes an annual or periodic report.

Z. Smith Reynolds Foundation, Inc.
101 Reynolda Village
Winston-Salem, NC 27106-5199
(336) 725-7541
Limitations: Giving limited to NC.
Publishes an annual or periodic report.

The Rhode Island Foundation
1 Union Sta.
Providence, RI 02903
(401) 274-4564
FAX: (401) 331-8085; URL: http://
     www.rifoundation.org
Limitations: Giving limited to RI.
Publishes an annual or periodic report.

Sid W. Richardson Foundation
309 Main St.
Fort Worth, TX 76102
(817) 336-0494
URL: http://www.sidrichardson.org
Limitations: Giving limited to TX, with
     emphasis on Fort Worth for the arts and
     human services, and statewide for health
     and education.
Publishes an annual or periodic report.

Smith Richardson Foundation, Inc.
60 Jesup Rd.
Westport, CT 06880
(203) 222-6222
FAX: (203) 222-6282; URL: http://www.srf.org
Limitations: Giving limited to U.S.-based
    organizations only.
Publishes an annual or periodic report.

Righteous Persons Foundation
1460 4th St., Ste. 212
Santa Monica, CA 90401
(310) 395-3599
Limitations: Giving on a national basis.

Fannie E. Rippel Foundation
180 Mount Airy Rd., Ste. 200
Basking Ridge, NJ 07920-2021
(908) 766-0404
E-mail: rippel@gti.net; URL: http://
    fdncenter.org/grantmaker/rippel/
Limitations: Giving primarily in the Eastern
    Seaboard states, with emphasis on NJ and
    the metropolitan New York, NY, area.
Publishes an annual or periodic report.

Robins Foundation
1021 E. Cary St., 4th Fl.
Richmond, VA 23219
(804) 697-6917
Application address: P.O. Box 1124,
    Richmond, VA 23218; URL: http://
    www.robins-foundation.org
Limitations: Giving primarily in Richmond, VA.
Publishes an annual or periodic report.

Rockefeller Brothers Fund, Inc.
437 Madison Ave., 37th Fl.
New York, NY 10022-7001
(212) 812-4200
FAX: (212) 812-4299; General E-mail:
    rock@rbf.org; E-mail for annual report:
    anreport@rbf.org; URL: http://
    www.rbf.org
Limitations: Giving on a national basis, and in
    Central and Eastern Europe, East and
    Southeast Asia, and South Africa.
Publishes an annual or periodic report.

The Rockefeller Foundation
420 5th Ave.
New York, NY 10018-2702
(212) 869-8500
URL: http://www.rockfound.org
Limitations: Giving on a national and
    international basis.
Publishes an annual or periodic report.

The Winthrop Rockefeller Foundation
308 E. 8th St.
Little Rock, AR 72202-3999
(501) 376-6854
FAX: (501) 374-4797; E-mail:
    program_manager@wrfoundation.org;
    URL: http://
    www.wrockefellerfoundation.org
Limitations: Giving limited to AR, or for
    projects that benefit AR.
Publishes an annual or periodic report.

Rockwell Fund, Inc.
1330 Post Oak Blvd., Ste. 1825
Houston, TX 77056
(713) 629-9022
FAX: (713) 629-7702; URL: http://
    www.rockfund.org
Limitations: Giving primarily in TX, with
    emphasis on Houston.
Publishes an annual or periodic report.

Rockwell International Corporation Trust
c/o Firstar Bank
777 E. Wisconsin Ave., Ste. 1400
Milwaukee, WI 53202
(414) 212-5274
FAX: (414) 212-5279; E-mail:
    emwalter@corp.rockwell.com
Limitations: Giving nationally in areas of
    corporate operations, except for selected
    national organizations and universities
    which are sources of recruits or whose
    research is of interest; giving
    internationally where the company has
    formal programs.
Publishes an annual or periodic report.

Mary Stuart Rogers Foundation
c/o Stockton & Sadler
P.O. Box 3153
Modesto, CA 95353
(209) 572-6088
Limitations: Giving primarily in CA.

Frederick P. & Sandra P. Rose Foundation
200 Madison Ave., 5th Fl.
New York, NY 10016
Limitations: Giving primarily in New York, NY.

Daniel and Joanna S. Rose Fund, Inc.
c/o Rose Assocs.
200 Madison Ave., 5th Fl.
New York, NY 10016
Limitations: Giving primarily in NY.

Rosenberg Foundation
47 Kearny St., Ste. 804
San Francisco, CA 94108-5528
(415) 421-6105
FAX: (415) 421-0141; E-mail:
    rosenfdn@rosenbergfdn.org; URL: http://
    www.rosenbergfdn.org
Limitations: Giving limited to CA, except for
    national grants related to the promotion of
    philanthropy and for projects likely to
    benefit CA.
Publishes an annual or periodic report.

Ross Family Charitable Foundation
c/o Starr & Co., LLC
350 Park Ave., Ste. 9
New York, NY 10022-6022
(212) 759-6556
Limitations: Giving primarily in the greater
    metropolitan New York, NY, area,
    including Long Island.

Helena Rubinstein Foundation, Inc.
477 Madison Ave., 7th Fl.
New York, NY 10022-5802
(212) 750-7310
Limitations: Giving primarily in New York, NY.

May and Samuel Rudin Family Foundation, Inc.
c/o Rudin
345 Park Ave.
New York, NY 10154
(212) 407-2512
Limitations: Giving primarily in New York City.

The Saint Paul Foundation, Inc.
600 Norwest Ctr.
55 Fifth St., E.
St. Paul, MN 55101-1797
(651) 224-5463
FAX: (651) 224-8123; E-mail: inbox@tspf.org;
    URL: http://www.tspf.org
Limitations: Giving from restricted and
    unrestricted funds limited to nonprofit
    organizations and public entities primarily
    serving residents of the East Metro area of
    Ramsey, Washington, and Dakota counties
    in the metropolitan Saint Paul, MN, area.
Publishes an annual or periodic report.

The Fan Fox and Leslie R. Samuels
    Foundation, Inc.
350 5th Ave., Ste. 4301
New York, NY 10118
(212) 239-3030
FAX: (212) 239-3039; E-mail:
    info@samuels.org; URL: http://
    www.samuels.org
Limitations: Giving limited to New York, NY.

The San Diego Foundation
1420 Kettner Blvd., Ste. 500
San Diego, CA 92101-9693
(619) 235-2300
FAX: (619) 239-1710; URL: http://
    www.sdfoundation.org
Limitations: Giving primarily in the greater San
    Diego, CA, region.
Publishes an annual or periodic report.

The San Francisco Foundation
225 Bush St., 5th Fl.
San Francisco, CA 94104-4224
(415) 733-8500
FAX: (415) 477-2783; E-mail: SRH@sff.org;
    URL: http://www.sff.org
Limitations: Giving limited to the San
    Francisco Bay Area, CA, counties of
    Alameda, Contra Costa, Marin, San
    Francisco, and San Mateo.
Publishes an annual or periodic report.

Santa Barbara Foundation
15 E. Carrillo St.
Santa Barbara, CA 93101
(805) 963-1873
FAX: (805) 966-2345; E-mail:
    mday@sbfoundation.org,
    rstebbins@sbfoundation.org,
    amy6@sbfoundation.org, or
    cslosser@sbfoundation.org; URL: http://
    www.sbfoundation.org
Limitations: Giving limited to Santa Barbara
    County, CA.
Publishes an annual or periodic report.

Sarkeys Foundation
530 E. Main
Norman, OK 73071
(405) 364-3703
FAX: (405) 364-8191; E-mail:
    Sarkeys@telepath.com; URL: http://
    www.sarkeys.org/
Limitations: Giving limited to OK.
Publishes an annual or periodic report.

SBC Foundation
130 E. Travis, Ste. 350
San Antonio, TX 78205
(210) 351-2218
Limitations: Giving primarily in AR, CA, CT,
    IL, IN, KS, MI, MO, NV, OH, OK, TX,
    and WI.

Sarah Scaife Foundation, Inc.
1 Oxford Ctr.
301 Grant St., Ste. 3900
Pittsburgh, PA 15219-6401
(412) 392-2900
URL: http://www.scaife.com
Publishes an annual or periodic report.

The Scherman Foundation, Inc.
16 E. 52nd St., Ste. 601
New York, NY 10022-5306
(212) 832-3086
FAX: (212) 838-0154
Limitations: Giving primarily in New York, NY
    for arts and social welfare.
Publishes an annual or periodic report.

S. H. and Helen R. Scheuer Family Foundation,
    Inc.
350 5th Ave., Ste. 1413
New York, NY 10118
(212) 947-9009
Limitations: Giving primarily in New York, NY.

Jacob G. Schmidlapp Trust No. 1 and No. 2
c/o Fifth Third Bank
Fifth Third Ctr., MD 1090C7
Cincinnati, OH 45263
(513) 579-6034
Limitations: Giving primarily in the greater
    Cincinnati, OH, area.
Publishes an annual or periodic report.

Schmidt Family Foundation
399 N.W. Boca Raton Blvd.
Boca Raton, FL 33432
Limitations: Giving primarily in southern FL.

Dr. Scholl Foundation
11 S. LaSalle St., Ste. 2100
Chicago, IL 60603-1302
(312) 782-5210
Limitations: Giving in the U.S., with emphasis
    on IL.

The Schumann Fund for New Jersey, Inc.
21 Van Vleck St.
Montclair, NJ 07042
(973) 509-9883
URL: http://fdncenter.org/grantmaker/schumann/
Limitations: Giving limited to NJ, with
    emphasis on Essex County.
Publishes an annual or periodic report.

Charles and Lynn Schusterman Family
    Foundation
2 W. 2nd St., 20th Fl.
Tulsa, OK 74103-3101
(918) 591-1090
Mailing address: P.O. Box 51, Tulsa, OK
    74101-0051; FAX: (918) 591-1758;
    E-mail: ahughes@schusterman.org; URL:
    http://www.schusterman.org
Limitations: Giving primarily to nonsectarian
    organizations in OK; giving on a local,
    national, and international basis for
    Jewish organizations.

The Charles Schwab Corporation Foundation
c/o Direct Grants Prog.
101 Montgomery St., 28th Fl.
San Francisco, CA 94104
(877) 408-5438
Limitations: Giving primarily in the San
    Francisco Bay Area, CA; limited giving
    where company has branch locations (350
    cities nationwide); state or national
    organizations are considered only if they
    serve branch communities; grants are
    mostly to local organizations.
Publishes an annual or periodic report.

Charles and Helen Schwab Foundation
1650 S. Amphlett Blvd., Ste. 300
San Mateo, CA 94402-2516
(650) 655-2412
FAX: (650) 655-2411; E-mail:
    info@schwabfamilyfdn.org; URL: http://
    www.schwabfamilyfdn.org
Limitations: Giving limited to San Francisco
    and San Mateo counties, CA.

Scripps Howard Foundation
P.O. Box 5380
312 Walnut St., 28th Fl.
Cincinnati, OH 45202
(513) 977-3035
FAX: (513) 977-3800; E-mail:
    clabes@scripps.com or
    cottingham@scripps.com; URL: http://
    www.scripps.com/foundation
Limitations: Giving primarily in areas of
    company operations for scholarships,
    internships and literary grants, and
    nationally for special grants and awards.
Publishes an annual or periodic report.

The Seattle Foundation
425 Pike St., Ste. 510
Seattle, WA 98101
(206) 622-2294
FAX: (206) 622-7673; E-mail:
    info@seafound.org; URL: http://
    www.seafound.org
Limitations: Giving limited to the greater Puget
    Sound region, WA.
Publishes an annual or periodic report.

William G. Selby and Marie Selby Foundation
1800 2nd St., Ste. 750
Sarasota, FL 34236
(941) 957-0442
Limitations: Giving limited to Charlotte,
    DeSoto, Manatee, and Sarasota counties,
    FL.

The Self Family Foundation
P.O. Drawer 1017
Greenwood, SC 29648
(864) 941-4011
FAX: (864) 941-4091; E-mail:
    SelfFound@greenwood.net,
    fwideman@greenwood.net,
    mamienic@greenwood.net; URL: http://
    www.selffoundation.org
Limitations: Giving limited to SC, with primary
    emphasis on Greenwood.
Publishes an annual or periodic report.

The Peter Jay Sharp Foundation
545 Madison Ave., 11th Fl.
New York, NY 10022
(212) 397-6060
Limitations: Giving primarily in New York, NY.

Ralph C. Sheldon Foundation, Inc.
P.O. Box 417
Jamestown, NY 14702-0417
(716) 664-9890
Application address: 7 E. 3rd St., Jamestown,
    NY 14701; FAX: (716) 483-6116
Limitations: Giving limited to southern
    Chautauqua County, NY.

Shell Oil Company Foundation
910 Louisiana, Ste. 4137
P.O. Box 2099
Houston, TX 77252
(713) 241-3616
FAX: (713) 241-3329; E-mail:
    socfoundation@shellus.com; URL: http://
    www.countonshell.com/community/
    involvement/shell_foundation.html
Limitations: Giving primarily in areas of
    company operations in the U.S.

The Shubert Foundation, Inc.
234 W. 44th St.
New York, NY 10036
(212) 944-3777
FAX: (212) 944-3767
Publishes an annual or periodic report.

Siebert Lutheran Foundation, Inc.
2600 N. Mayfair Rd., Ste. 390
Wauwatosa, WI 53226
(414) 257-2656
FAX: (414) 257-1387; E-mail:
    siebertf@execpc.com; URL: http://
    www.siebertfoundation.org/
Limitations: Giving primarily in WI.

Sierra Health Foundation
1321 Garden Hwy.
Sacramento, CA 95833
(916) 922-4755
FAX: (916) 922-4024; URL: http://
    www.sierrahealth.org
Limitations: Giving limited to the following CA
    counties: Alpine, Amador, Butte,
    Calaveras, Colusa, El Dorado, Glenn,
    Lassen, Modoc, Mono, Nevada, Placer,
    Plumas, Sacramento, San Joaquin, Shasta,
    Sierra, Siskiyou, Solano (eastern),
    Stanislaus, Sutter, Tehama, Trinity,
    Tuolumne, Yolo, and Yuba.

R. P. Simmons Family Foundation
Birchmere Quaker Hollow Rd.
Sewickley, PA 15143
Limitations: Giving primarily in PA, with
    emphasis on Pittsburgh.

The Skillman Foundation
600 Renaissance Ctr., Ste. 1700
Detroit, MI 48243
(313) 393-1185
FAX: (313) 393-1187; URL: http://
    www.skillman.org
Limitations: Giving primarily in southeastern
    MI, with emphasis on metropolitan
    Detroit, and Macomb, Oakland, and
    Wayne counties.
Publishes an annual or periodic report.

Skirball Foundation
767 5th Ave., 43rd Fl.
New York, NY 10153
(212) 832-8500
Limitations: Giving primarily in CA.

Alfred P. Sloan Foundation
630 5th Ave., Ste. 2550
New York, NY 10111-0242
(212) 649-1649
FAX: (212) 757-5117; URL: http://
    www.sloan.org

Smart Family Foundation
74 Pin Oak Ln.
Wilton, CT 06897-1329

The Kelvin and Eleanor Smith Foundation
26380 Curtiss Wright Pkwy., Ste. 105
Cleveland, OH 44143
(216) 289-5789
FAX: (216) 289-5948
Limitations: Giving primarily in the greater
    Cleveland, OH, area.

C. D. Spangler Foundation, Inc.
P.O. Box 36007
Charlotte, NC 28236-6007
(704) 372-4500
Limitations: Giving primarily in NC.

The Spencer Foundation
875 N. Michigan Ave., Ste. 3930
Chicago, IL 60611-1803
(312) 337-7000
FAX: (312) 337-0282; URL: http://
    www.spencer.org
Limitations: Giving on a national and
    international basis.
Publishes an annual or periodic report.

The St. Paul Companies, Inc. Foundation
385 Washington St., MC 514D
St. Paul, MN 55102
(651) 310-7757
URL: http://www.stpaul.com/wwwcorporate/
    content/communities/programs.asp
Limitations: Giving limited to the Twin Cities,
    MN, the Baltimore, MD, area, the United
    Kingdom, and selected locations where
    the company has a significant presence.

Theodore & Vada Stanley Foundation
47 Richards Ave.
Norwalk, CT 06857-1915

Stark Community Foundation, Inc.
The Saxton House
331 Market Ave., S.
Canton, OH 44702-2107
(330) 454-3426
FAX: (330) 454-5855; E-mail:
    starkcf@cannet.com
Limitations: Giving limited to Stark County,
    OH.
Publishes an annual or periodic report.

The Starr Foundation
70 Pine St.
New York, NY 10270
(212) 770-6881
FAX: (212) 425-6261; E-mail:
    florence.davis@starrfdn.org; URL: http://
    fdncenter.org/grantmaker/starr/

State Farm Companies Foundation
1 State Farm Plz., B-4
Bloomington, IL 61710
(309) 766-2161
FAX: (309) 766-2314; E-mail:
    Lori.Manning.gsu2@statefarm.com;
    URL: http://www.statefarm.com/foundati/
    foundati.htm
Limitations: Giving in Bloomington, IL, and 27
    U.S. regional office sites.

State Street Foundation
c/o State Street Corp.
P.O. Box 351, M-10
Boston, MA 02101
(617) 664-3381
Application address: State Street Corp., c/o
    Public Affairs Div., 225 Franklin St.,
    Boston, MA 02101; URL: http://
    www.statestreet.com/stst/statestreet.nsf/
    Framesets/communityAffairs
Limitations: Giving primarily in the greater
    Boston, MA, area.

Steelcase Foundation
P.O. Box 1967, CH-4E
Grand Rapids, MI 49501-1967
(616) 246-4695
FAX: (616) 475-2200; E-mail:
    sbroman@steelcase.com
Limitations: Giving limited to areas of
    company operations, including Athens,
    AL, Orange County, CA, Grand Rapids,
    MI, Asheville, NC, and Markham, Canada.
Publishes an annual or periodic report.

The Steele Foundation, Inc.
702 E. Osborn Rd.
Phoenix, AZ 85014-5215
(602) 230-2038
Additional address: P.O. Box 1112, Phoenix,
    AZ 85001
Limitations: Giving only in AZ.

The Harold & Mimi Steinberg Charitable Trust
c/o Schulte Roth & Zabel
900 3rd Ave.
New York, NY 10022
Limitations: Giving primarily in New York, NY.

The Judy and Michael Steinhardt Foundation
650 Madison Ave., 17th Fl
New York, NY 10022

The Stewardship Foundation
Tacoma Financial Ctr., Ste. 1500
1145 Broadway Plz.
Tacoma, WA 98402
(253) 620-1340
Application address: P.O. Box 1278, Tacoma,
    WA 98401; FAX: (253) 572-2721; E-mail:
    info@stewardshipfdn.org; URL: http://
    www.stewardshipfdn.org
Limitations: Giving internationally, nationally
    and in western WA, especially in Tacoma
    and Pierce County and the Puget Sound
    Region.

Stewart Education Foundation
c/o First Security Bank of Utah, N.A.
P.O. Box 9936
Ogden, UT 84409
(801) 626-9531
Additional address: 802 Whispering Oaks Rd.,
    Ogden, UT 84403
Limitations: Giving primarily in Ogden, UT.

Silva Casa Stiftung Trust
c/o Ropes & Gray
1 International Plz.
Boston, MA 02110-2624
Limitations: Giving on an international basis,
    with emphasis on Switzerland.

The Philip A. and Lynn Straus Foundation, Inc.
1037 Constable Dr. S.
Mamaroneck, NY 10543
Limitations: Giving primarily in NY.

Levi Strauss Foundation
1155 Battery St., 7th Fl.
San Francisco, CA 94111
(415) 501-6579
URL: http://www.levistrauss.com/responsibility/
    foundation/index.htm
Limitations: Giving generally limited to areas
    of company operations in AR, CA, FL,
    GA, KY, NV, TN, and TX.

Stuart Foundation
50 California St., Ste. 3350
San Francisco, CA 94111-4735
(415) 393-1551
FAX: (415) 393-1552; URL: http://
    www.stuartfoundation.org
Limitations: Giving primarily in CA and WA.

Roy and Christine Sturgis Charitable and
    Educational Trust
c/o Bank of America
P.O. Box 830241
Dallas, TX 75283-0241
(214) 209-1965
Limitations: Giving primarily in AR and the
    Dallas, TX, area.

Surdna Foundation, Inc.
330 Madison Ave., 30th Fl.
New York, NY 10017-5001
(212) 557-0010
FAX: (212) 557-0003; E-mail:
    request@surdna.org; URL: http://
    www.surdna.org
Publishes an annual or periodic report.

S. Mark Taper Foundation
12011 San Vicente Blvd., Ste. 400
Los Angeles, CA 90049
(310) 476-5413
FAX: (310) 471-4993; E-mail:
    rreisler@smtfoundation.org
Limitations: Giving primarily in CA.

Target Foundation
33 S. 6th St., CC-28Y
Minneapolis, MN 55402
(612) 304-8457
FAX: (612) 304-9666; E-mail:
    guidelines@Target.com; URL: http://
    www.targetfoundation.org
Limitations: Giving primarily in the
    Minneapolis/St. Paul, MN, metropolitan
    area.

The Teagle Foundation, Inc.
10 Rockefeller Plz., Rm. 920
New York, NY 10020-1903
(212) 373-1970
Limitations: Giving limited to the U.S. No
    grants to community organizations
    outside New York City. No grants to U.S.
    organizations for foreign programmatic
    activities.
Publishes an annual or periodic report.

T. L. L. Temple Foundation
109 Temple Blvd., Ste. 300
Lufkin, TX 75901
(409) 639-5197
E-mail: tlltf@lcc.net
Limitations: Giving primarily in counties in TX
    constituting the East Texas Pine Timber
    Belt.

Temple-Inland Foundation
303 S. Temple Dr.
P.O. Drawer 338
Diboll, TX 75941
(409) 829-1721
Limitations: Giving primarily in areas of
    company operations.

John Templeton Foundation
P.O. Box 8322
Radnor, PA 19087-8322
FAX: (610) 687-8961; URL: http://
    www.templeton.org
Limitations: Giving on a national and
    international basis.
Publishes an annual or periodic report.

Tenet Healthcare Foundation
c/o Barbara B. Luton
3820 State St.
Santa Barbara, CA 93105-3112
(805) 563-6865
Application address: P.O. Box 31907, Santa
    Barbara, CA 93130; FAX: (805)
    898-9104; E-mail:

foundation@tenethealth.com; URL: http://
    www.tenethealth.com/Foundation/
    Foundation.cfm
Limitations: Giving on a nationwide basis, with
    emphasis on communities where Tenet
    employees live and work.

Eugene V. & Clare E. Thaw Charitable Trust
P.O. Box 2422
Santa Fe, NM 87504-2422
(505) 982-7023
FAX: (505) 982-7027; E-mail:
    thawtrust@cybenmesa.com
Limitations: Giving on a national basis.

The Times Mirror Foundation
Times Mirror Sq.
Los Angeles, CA 90053
(213) 237-3945
FAX: (213) 237-4782; URL: http://
    www.timesmirrorfoundation.org/
Limitations: Giving primarily in communities
    served by the company's subsidiaries,
    with emphasis on southern CA.

Timken Foundation of Canton
236 3rd St., S.W.
Canton, OH 44702
Limitations: Giving primarily in local areas of
    Timken Co. domestic operations in
    Ashland, Bucyrus, Canton, Columbus,
    Eaton, New Philadelphia, Wauseon, and
    Wooster, OH; Ashboro, Columbus, and
    Lincolnton, NC; Concord, Keene, and
    Lebanon, NH; Latrobe, PA; Gaffney, SC;
    and Altavista, VA. Giving also in local
    areas in Australia, Brazil, Canada, France,
    Great Britain, Italy, Poland, Romania, and
    South Africa where Timken Co. has
    manufacturing facilities.

The Tinker Foundation Inc.
55 E. 59th St., 21st Fl.
New York, NY 10022
(212) 421-6858
FAX: (212) 223-3326; E-mail:
    tinker@tinker.org; URL: http://
    fdncenter.org/grantmaker/tinker/
Limitations: Giving limited to projects related
    to Latin America, Spain, Portugal, and
    Antarctica.
Publishes an annual or periodic report.

Tisch Foundation, Inc.
655 Madison Ave., 8th Fl.
New York, NY 10021-8087
(212) 521-2930
Limitations: Giving primarily in NY.

Town Creek Foundation, Inc.
P.O. Box 159
Oxford, MD 21654
(410) 226-5315
Additional address: 221 South St., Oxford, MD
    21654; FAX: (410) 226-5468; E-mail:
    info@towncreekfdn.org; URL: http://
    www.towncreekfdn.org
Limitations: Giving nationally for major
    programs; support limited to Talbot
    County, MD, for social services.

Emily Hall Tremaine Foundation, Inc.
290 Pratt St.
Meriden, CT 06450
(203) 639-5544
FAX: (203) 639-5545; URL: http://
    www.tremainefoundation.org/

Harry C. Trexler Trust
33 S. 7th St., Ste. 205
Allentown, PA 18101
(610) 434-9645
FAX: (610) 437-5721
Limitations: Giving limited to Lehigh County,
    PA.

The Trust for Mutual Understanding
30 Rockefeller Plz., Rm. 5600
New York, NY 10112
(212) 632-3405
FAX: (212) 632-3409; E-mail: tmu@tmuny.org;
    URL: http://www.tmuny.org
Limitations: Giving for exchanges between the
    U.S., the former Soviet Union, and the
    countries of Central and Eastern Europe,
    primarily the Czech Republic, Hungary,
    Poland, Russia, Slovakia, and Ukraine.

TRW Foundation
1900 Richmond Rd.
Cleveland, OH 44124
URL: http://www.trw.com/foundation
Limitations: Giving primarily in TRW plant
    communities, particularly AL, AZ, CA,
    CO, Washington, DC, IL, IN, MA, MD,
    MI, MN, MT, NM, NY, NV, OH, PA, TN,
    TX, UT, and VA.
Publishes an annual or periodic report.

Turner Foundation, Inc.
1 CNN Ctr., Ste. 1090, S. Tower
Atlanta, GA 30303
(404) 681-9900
FAX: (404) 681-0172; E-mail:
    turnerfi@mindspring.com; URL: http://
    www.turnerfoundation.org
Limitations: Giving primarily in AK, CO, FL,
    GA, MT, NE, NM, SC, Argentina,
    Mexico, and Russia.
Publishes an annual or periodic report.

Turrell Fund
21 Van Vleck St.
Montclair, NJ 07042-2358
(973) 783-9358
FAX: (973) 783-9283; E-mail:
    Turrell@bellatlantic.net; URL: http://
    fdncenter.org/grantmaker/turrell/
Limitations: Giving limited to Essex, Union,
    Hudson and Passaic counties, NJ, and VT.
Publishes an annual or periodic report.

Union Pacific Foundation
1416 Dodge St., Rm. 802
Omaha, NE 68179
(402) 271-5600
FAX: (402) 271-5477; E-mail: upf@up.com;
    URL: http://www.up.com/found
Limitations: Giving primarily in areas of
    company operations, with emphasis on
    the midwestern and western U.S.: AR,
    AZ, CA, CO, IA, ID, IL, KS, LA, MN,

MO, MT, NE, NM, NV, OK, OR, TX, UT, WA, WI, and WY.

United States-Japan Foundation
145 E. 32nd St., 12th Fl.
New York, NY 10016
(212) 481-8753
FAX: (212) 481-8762; E-mail: info@US-JF.org; Tokyo, Japan office address: Reinanzaka Bldg. 1F, 1-14-2 Akasaka, Minato-ku, Tokyo 107-0052, Japan, tel.: (03) 3586-0541; FAX: (03) 3586-1128; E-mail: JDU05456@nifty.ne.jp; URL: http://www.us-jf.org
Limitations: Giving primarily in the U.S. and Japan.
Publishes an annual or periodic report.

The UPS Foundation
55 Glenlake Pkwy., N.E.
Atlanta, GA 30328
(404) 828-6374
FAX: (404) 828-7435; URL: http://www.community.ups.com/community/resources/foundation/index.html
Limitations: Giving limited to the U.S., Mexico, and Canada.

USAA Foundation, A Charitable Trust
USAA Bldg.
9800 Fredericksburg Rd., D-3-E
San Antonio, TX 78288-3500
(210) 498-1225
Limitations: Giving primarily in AZ, CA, CO, Washington, DC, FL, TX, and VA.

USX Foundation, Inc.
600 Grant St., Rm. 685
Pittsburgh, PA 15219-4776
(412) 433-5237
FAX: (412) 433-6847; URL: http://www.usx.com/corp/usxfoundation/usxfound.htm
Limitations: Giving primarily in areas of company operations in the U.S., including AK, AL, CO, IL, IN, LA, MI, MN, OH, OK, western PA, and TX.
Publishes an annual or periodic report.

The Valley Foundation
16450 Los Gatos Blvd., Ste. 210
Los Gatos, CA 95032
(408) 358-4545
FAX: (408) 358-4548; E-mail: ervie@valley.org; URL: http://www.valley.org
Limitations: Giving limited to Santa Clara County, CA.
Publishes an annual or periodic report.

Wayne & Gladys Valley Foundation
1939 Harrison St., Ste. 510
Oakland, CA 94612-3532
(510) 466-6060
FAX: (510) 466-6067
Limitations: Giving primarily in Alameda and Contra Costa counties, CA.
Publishes an annual or periodic report.

H. van Ameringen Foundation
509 Madison Ave.
New York, NY 10022-5501
(212) 758-6221
Limitations: Giving primarily in NY.

Verizon Foundation
1095 Ave. of the Americas, Rm. 3200
New York, NY 10036
(800) 360-7955
FAX: (212) 398-0951; E-mail: suzanne.dubose@verizon.com; URL: http://foundation.verizon.com/
Limitations: Giving primarily in areas of corporate sponsor's operations concentrated in New England, DE, NJ, NY, PA, WV, and the greater metropolitan Washington, DC, area.
Publishes an annual or periodic report.

Victoria Foundation, Inc.
40 S. Fullerton Ave.
Montclair, NJ 07042
(973) 783-4450
FAX: (973) 783-6664; E-mail: CMCFarvic@aol.com
Limitations: Giving limited to greater Newark, NJ; environmental grants limited to NJ.
Publishes an annual or periodic report.

The Wachovia Foundation, Inc.
c/o Wachovia Bank of North Carolina, N.A.
P.O. Box 3099
Winston-Salem, NC 27150-7131
Application addresses: for NC and SC: contact local bank office; for GA: Ben Boswell, P.O. Box 4148, M.C.-1102, Atlanta, GA 30302; for VA: Kenneth L. Flemins, 1021 E. Cary St., Richmond, VA 23219; and for FL: Teresa Weaver, 100 N. Tampa St., Ste. 4100, Tampa, FL 33609
Limitations: Giving primarily in FL, GA, NC, SC, and VA.

Wal-Mart Foundation
702 S.W. 8th St.
Bentonville, AR 72716-8071
URL: http://www.walmartfoundation.org
Limitations: Giving primarily in areas of company operations.

Wallace Genetic Foundation, Inc.
4900 Massachusetts Ave., N.W., Ste. 220
Washington, DC 20016
(202) 966-2932
FAX: (202) 966-3370; E-mail: WGFDN@aol.com

Wallace-Readers Digest Funds
2 Park Ave., 23rd Fl.
New York, NY 10016
(212) 251-9700
E-mail: wrdf@wallacefunds.org; URL: http://www.wallacefunds.org
Limitations: Giving on a national basis.
Publishes an annual or periodic report.

Wallis Foundation
4100 W. Alameda, Ste. 204
Burbank, CA 91505
Limitations: Giving primarily in CA.

Washington Mutual Foundation
1201 3rd Ave., WMT1613
Seattle, WA 98101
(800) 258-0543
Limitations: Giving primarily in areas of company operations in CA, FL, ID, IL, MA, NY, NV, OR, TX, UT, and WA.
Publishes an annual or periodic report.

Wasserman Foundation
1 Wilshire Blvd., Ste. 2000
Los Angeles, CA 90017-3383
Limitations: Giving primarily in CA.

The Thomas J. Watson Foundation
293 S. Main St.
Providence, RI 02903-2910
(401) 274-1952
FAX: (401) 274-1954; URL: http://www.watsonfellowship.org

The Raymond John Wean Foundation
P.O. Box 760
Warren, OH 44482-0760
(330) 394-5600
Additional address: 108 Main Ave. SW, Ste. 1005, Warren, OH, 44481; FAX: (330) 394-5601; E-mail: rjweanfdn@aol.com
Limitations: Giving primarily in Allegheny County, PA, and northeast OH, with emphasis on Cuyahoga, Mahoning, and Trumbull counties.

The Harry and Jeanette Weinberg Foundation, Inc.
7 Park Center Ct.
Owings Mills, MD 21117

Weingart Foundation
1055 W. 7th St., Ste. 3050
Los Angeles, CA 90017-2305
(213) 688-7799
FAX: (213) 688-1515; E-mail: info@weingartfund; URL: http://www.weingartfnd.org
Limitations: Giving limited to 7 southern CA counties; Los Angeles, Kern, Orange, Santa Barbara, Riverside, San Bernadino, and Ventura.
Publishes an annual or periodic report.

Welfare Foundation, Inc.
100 W. 10th St. Ste 1109
Wilmington, DE 19801
(302) 654-2477
Limitations: Giving limited to DE, with emphasis on the greater Wilmington area.

The Wells Fargo Foundation
550 California St., 7th Fl.
San Francisco, CA 94104
(415) 396-3567
Limitations: Giving primarily in areas of company operations, including AZ, CO, IA, IL, IN, MN, MT, ND, NE, NM, NV, OH, SD, TX, WI, and WY.

WEM Foundation
P.O. Box 9300, Dept. 28
Minneapolis, MN 55440-9300
(612) 742-7544
Limitations: Giving primarily in MN.

The Margaret L. Wendt Foundation
40 Fountain Plz., Ste. 277
Buffalo, NY 14202-2220
(716) 855-2146
Limitations: Giving primarily in Buffalo and
western NY.

Weyerhaeuser Company Foundation
EC2-2A8
P.O. Box 9777
Federal Way, WA 98063-9777
(253) 924-3159
FAX: (253) 924-3660; E-mail:
foundation@weyerhaeuser.com; URL:
http://www.weyerhaeuser.com/citizenship/
philanthropy/weyerfoundation.asp
Limitations: Giving limited to areas of
company operations, especially AL, AR,
MS, NC, southeastern OK, western OR,
and western WA (including Tacoma,
Seattle, and Federal Way); giving to
national organizations in fields related to
the forest products industry.

Whirlpool Foundation
2000 N. M-63
Benton Harbor, MI 49022-2692
(616) 923-5580
FAX: (616) 925-0154; URL: http://
whirlpoolcorp.com/whr/foundation/
foundation.html
Limitations: Giving limited to communities
where major company units are located:
Fort Smith, AR, Evansville and La Porte,
IN, Benton Harbor, MI, Oxford, MS,
Clyde, Findlay, Greenville, and Marion,
OH, and Lavergne and Knoxville, TN.
Publishes an annual or periodic report.

The Whitaker Foundation
1700 N. Moore St., Ste. 2200
Rosslyn, VA 22209
(703) 528-2430
E-mail: info@whitaker.org; URL: http://
www.whitaker.org
Limitations: Giving limited to the U.S. and
Canada for Biomedical Engineering

Research and Special Opportunity Awards
Programs; Regional Program limited to
Collier County, FL; other programs are
limited to the U.S.
Publishes an annual or periodic report.

The Helen F. Whitaker Fund
4718 Old Gettysburg Rd., Ste. 209
Mechanicsburg, PA 17055-8411
(717) 763-1600
Limitations: Giving on a national basis,
additional regional programs for the
Naples, FL, area and the Harrisburg and
Philadelphia, PA, areas.

The Whitehead Foundation
65 E. 55th St.
New York, NY 10022
(212) 755-3131
Limitations: Giving primarily in NY.

E. L. Wiegand Foundation
Wiegand Ctr.
165 W. Liberty St., Ste. 200
Reno, NV 89501
(775) 333-0310
Limitations: Giving primarily in NV and
adjoining western states, including AZ,
ID, OR, UT and WA; public affairs grants
given primarily in CA, Washington, DC,
and New York, NY.

Matilda R. Wilson Fund
100 Renaissance Ctr., 34th Fl.
Detroit, MI 48243
(313) 259-7777
Limitations: Giving primarily in southeast MI.

The Norman and Rosita Winston Foundation,
Inc.
c/o Paul Weiss, Rifkind, et al.
1285 Ave. of the Americas
New York, NY 10019-6064
(212) 373-3000
Limitations: Giving primarily in NY.

Wisconsin Energy Corporation Foundation, Inc.
231 W. Michigan St.
Milwaukee, WI 53290
(414) 221-2106
Limitations: Giving primarily in service
territories in the Upper Peninsula, MI,

area and the southeastern and Fox Valley,
WI, areas.

Wolfe Associates, Inc.
34 S. 3rd St.
Columbus, OH 43215
(614) 461-5211
Limitations: Giving primarily in central OH.

Wood-Claeyssens Foundation
P.O. Box 30586
Santa Barbara, CA 93130-0586
(805) 966-0543
FAX: (805) 966-1415
Limitations: Giving limited to Santa Barbara
and Ventura counties, CA.

Robert W. Woodruff Foundation, Inc.
50 Hurt Plz., Ste. 1200
Atlanta, GA 30303
(404) 522-6755
FAX: (404) 522-7026; E-mail:
fdns@woodruff.org; URL: http://
www.woodruff.org
Limitations: Giving primarily in GA.

WPWR-TV Channel 50 Foundation
2151 N. Elston
Chicago, IL 60614
(773) 292-5016
E-mail: wpwr50fund@aol.com
Limitations: Giving primarily in the
metropolitan Chicago, IL, area and
northwestern IN.

The Zellerbach Family Fund
120 Montgomery St., Ste. 1550
San Francisco, CA 94104
(415) 421-2629
FAX: (415) 421-6713
Limitations: Giving primarily in the San
Francisco Bay Area, CA.
Publishes an annual or periodic report.